DIFFERENTIAL EQUATIONS

This new edition is dedicated to the memory of

FOREST RAY MOULTON

1872 - 1952

Contributor to American teaching and American science.

DIFFERENTIAL EQUATIONS

BY

FOREST RAY MOULTON, Ph.D., Sc.D

DOVER PUBLICATIONS, INC.
NEW YORK · NEW YORK

Dover Publications, Inc., 920 Broadway
New York 10, N. Y.

PREFACE

It is evident that only a part of a subject so vast as that of differential equations can be adequately developed within a single volume. The portion of it covered by this book does not include elementary differential equations, which have been well treated by several writers; nor does it include partial differential equations, which in reality constitute a distinct branch of analysis. Its domain is, rather, that of general classes of ordinary differential equations, both from the theoretical and also from the practical point of view. Even in this domain, it has not been possible to include a discussion of the existence and the properties of solutions at, and in the neighborhood of, singular points of differential equations; nor has it been possible to include solutions subject to general boundary conditions rather than to initial conditions. These theories are special in character, and they have given rise, particularly in the case of linear differential equations, to an extensive literature.

Within the limits set, however, this volume presents a complete treatment of all the processes for solving differential equations that have wide applicability. Its contents are a part of the lectures on differential equations given by the author at The University of Chicago for more than twenty years. These lectures from time to time included, besides the subjects treated here, also partial differential equations, and the solutions of ordinary linear and non-linear differential equations in the neighborhood of their singular points.

In writing on a subject, one naturally is influenced by the history of its origin and development. From the practical point of view, the subject of differential equations had its birth, about 1687, in the work of Newton on the motions of the planets and of the moon. It was extensively developed on its formal side by the successors of Newton, who applied it with remarkable success to every branch of celestial mechanics, dynamics, and physics.

The application of differential equations to the explanation and interpretation of natural phenomena constitutes one of the finest chapters in physical science.

From the general logical point of view, the subject of differential equations originated about one hundred and fifty years after the time of Newton with the investigations of Cauchy, in 1842. Since the work of Cauchy, its literature has been enriched by the writings of many of the greatest mathematicians, and it is now one of the most extensively developed and highly perfected branches of analysis.

It would be inexcusable to discuss general theories of differential equations and not to treat them with the rigor and completeness of reasoning that are characteristic of analysis of the present day. The aim in this book has been to meet current standards of rigor in the discussion of every subject treated. This aim has been inspired, in part, by the beauty and perfection of the theories themselves as logical structures, and, in part, by the firm conviction that the time is at hand for insisting on equally high standards in the applications of differential equations to the physical world. Only by logically complete reasoning can there be any assurance that conclusions reached are actually consequences of original premises, or that they are not contradictory to observational data or accepted theories. For an astronomer or a physicist to regard mathematics simply as a tool whose refinements of reasoning are not of vital importance is as absurd, and as dangerous for sound conclusions, as it would be for a chemist to start with pure reagents and then neglect to make sure that they are not contaminated in the course of his experiment. It is essential for progress in interpreting the world about us that the methods of applied mathematics should be improved as much as the experimental results have been, for the remarkable recent discoveries in every domain of physical science have given rise to numerous intricate theories whose consistency with one another and with observed phenomena can be assured only by the use of sound logical tools.

Several chapters of this book are devoted to the treatment of practical problems, mostly of a physical nature, which, in respect to difficulty, are far beyond the type of those usually used for illustrations. There is no disposition to apologize for devoting so much space to this purpose, even from the theoretical point of view, for these problems help to bring out the richness of the logical results contained in the general theorems, a richness which would not be suspected by a beginner in this field. The problems chosen illustrate a considerable number of the most important methods in differential equations and in implicit functions; and they all have been treated fully both from the logical and also from the practical point of view.

In going over an extensive mathematical field, however long it may have been cultivated, one will naturally add more or less that is essentially new. Among the things in this book that may fairly be classed as new is the placing of the method of numerical solution of differential equations on a complete logical basis, in Chapter XII. This work has not heretofore been published except in the author's *New Methods in Exterior Ballistics*, Chapter III. Another matter that is published here for the first time is the reduction of the characteristic determinant in the theory of linear differential equations with constant coefficients, in Chapter XV. Another is the use of identities derived from the fundamental determinant in the treatment of linear differential equations with periodic coefficients, in Chapter XVII. These identities are analogous to those of the characteristic determinant employed by Nyswander in the case of linear differential equations with constant coefficients. Still another is the treatment of an infinite universe by an application of infinite systems of differential equations in infinitely many variables, in Chapter XVIII. This investigation was completed fifteen years ago, but only the simplified purely mathematical part of it was published. There are, besides, numerous matters of lesser importance which have arisen in organizing the whole subject and bringing it under a unified notation.

It has been necessary, in the discussions, to make frequent reference to a number of standard theorems of analysis. For convenience, these theorems have been proved in the notations of this book and placed together in appendices A to H.

The entire manuscript of this book has been read with close attention by Professor Walter Bartky, of The University of Chicago, and a considerable part of it has been read with equal care by Professor James A. Nyswander, of the University of

Michigan.   Each of these mathematicians has read all the proofs and Professor Elton J. Moulton, of Northwestern University, has read certain sections.   It is a pleasure to acknowledge appreciation of this generous and laborious assistance, for it has resulted in the elimination of many errors and faults which otherwise might have escaped attention.

F. R. MOULTON

327 SOUTH LASALLE STREET
   CHICAGO, ILLINOIS
      March, 1930

TABLE OF CONTENTS

DIFFERENTIAL EQUATIONS

CHAPTER I

GENERALITIES AND DEFINITIONS

1. The Point of View in Analysis. In elementary mathematics, explicit formulas play a predominant rôle. They describe the subjects treated and they are the objects which are manipulated in order to arrive at conclusions or to obtain solutions which are assumed to exist.

In analysis, on the contrary, explicit formulas are not essential nor are they generally used. Analysis is concerned with classes of functions which are represented by suitable general symbols that do not in themselves define the properties of the functions which they represent. The functions of analysis have general and logically important properties, such as continuity or analyticity, rather than special ones. The generality of analysis makes possible the development of powerful and widely applicable mathematical machinery of a high order of logical precision. Instead of assuming that a problem necessarily has a solution which can be found by some artifice, the point of view in analysis is that a complete statement and treatment of a problem normally consists of the four parts:

(1) A definite formulation of the problem in terms of the properties of the functions which it involves.

(2) A proof of the existence of a solution of the problem.

(3) A determination of the properties of the solution whose existence has been established.

(4) A development of practical means of obtaining the solution in any special case under the general problem treated.

For brevity, a problem in analysis may be said to consist of its formulation, the existence of a solution, the properties of the solution, and suitable means of obtaining the solution. The first of the four steps necessarily precedes the remainder, but the last three do not always follow sequentially in the order in which they have been enumerated.

As an illustration of the foregoing general remarks on the nature of analysis, consider definite integrals. The definite integral of the function $f(t)$ from a to x is, by definition,

$$(1) \quad \begin{cases} \int_a^x f(t)dt = \lim_{\delta=0} \sum_{i=1}^{n_\delta} f(\tau_i)(t_i - t_{i-1}), \\ t_0 = a, \quad t_{n_\delta} = x, \quad t_{i-1} \leqq \tau_i \leqq t_i, \quad t_i - t_{i-1} \leqq \delta. \end{cases}$$

The fact that the integral may be interpreted as a plane area, and in many other ways as well, is interesting and valuable for beginners, but such an interpretation is not a definition of an integral; the definition is contained in the relations (1).

The existence of a definite integral may not be assumed without proof. In order to prove the existence of the limit in equation (1), it is necessary to know at least some general properties of $f(t)$ in the interval $a \leqq t \leqq x$. If, for example, a and x are both finite and $f(t)$ is a continuous function of t in the interval, then the integral can be shown to exist. That is, the second part of the problem is solved.

In this particular illustration, the third part of the problem is largely solved simultaneously with the second, but it is advisable to fasten attention first upon the existence of the limit and then upon the properties of the integral. Among the most general properties of the limit are that its value is independent of the mode of subdivision of the interval a to x by t_1, t_2, $\cdots$ and of the relationship of τ_i to t_i and t_{i-1}, except for the general limitations $t_{i-1} \leqq \tau_i \leqq t_i$.

The foregoing properties of the integral are established as a by-product of the proof of its existence, but there are others that require independent treatment. The value of the integral depends upon its upper limit x, a fact which may be indicated by writing

$$(2) \quad F(x) = \int_a^x f(t)dt.$$

Then it can be shown that within any finite interval on which $f(t)$ is a continuous function of t, $F(x)$ is not only a continuous function of x, but its derivative with respect to x exists and is

$f(x)$. If $f(t)$ depends upon a parameter μ, the function $F(x)$ also depends upon μ, and its properties as a function of μ may be examined.

The final problem is the development of practical means of obtaining the solution in a particular case. Reference to the details of the proofs of the foregoing statements will show that they do not provide a means of obtaining the integral except in the special case in which $f(t)$ is a formula and in which a formula $\Phi(t)$ can be found such that the derivative of $\Phi(t)$ with respect to t is $f(t)$. In this case

$$(3) \qquad \int_a^x f(t)dt = \Phi(x) - \Phi(a).$$

The integral exists, however, even if $\Phi(t)$ cannot be found, and there are other means, such as Simpson's method, of computing it with any required degree of approximation.

Statements of the type that have been made respecting definite integrals might be made respecting all ordinary problems in analysis. In the following pages attention will be directed continually to: (1) the formulation of the problems presented in differential equations; (2) proofs of the existence of solutions under various hypotheses; (3) determination of the properties of the solutions in the respective cases; and (4) the development of practical means of finding the solutions. There will appear nothing of the elementary point of view that differential equations are a moderate extension of calculus, or that the theory of differential equations consists of artifices for separating variables and performing quadratures. Such methods are useful in simple problems, but they fall very far short of the requirements for the treatment of the general problems that will be discussed in this work.

2. Normal Systems of Differential Equations. A system of differential equations of the form

$$(4) \qquad \begin{cases} \dfrac{dx_1}{dt} = f_1(x_1, \cdots, x_n; t), \\ \cdot \quad \cdot \quad \cdot \quad \cdot \quad \cdot \quad \cdot \quad \cdot \\ \dfrac{dx_n}{dt} = f_n(x_1, \cdots, x_n; t), \end{cases}$$

where $x_1, \cdots, x_n$ are variables that are to be determined in terms of the variable t, and where $f_1, \cdots, f_n$ are given functions of $x_1, \cdots, x_n, t$, constitutes, by definition, a normal system. The essential properties of a normal system are that the left members are first derivatives of the variables that are to be determined, and the right members are functions of the variables $x_1, \cdots, x_n$ and the variable t, but do not involve any of the derivatives.

Since $x_1, \cdots, x_n$ all vary, equations of the form of (4) are in general mutually dependent; that is, no one can be solved without treating all of them simultaneously. In special problems, however, one or more differential equations of a normal system may be independent of the remainder.

3. Reduction of Differential Equations to Normal Systems. A large part of the special differential equations that arise have their origin in dynamical problems. Consequently the illustrations of reducing differential equations to the normal form will be taken from that field.

The differential equation that is satisfied by the variables which define the motion of a body falling under the constant acceleration $-g$ is

$$(5) \qquad \frac{d^2x}{dt^2} = -g.$$

The transformation

$$(6) \qquad x = x_1, \qquad \frac{dx}{dt} = x_2$$

reduces equation (5) to the equivalent normal system

$$(7) \qquad \begin{cases} \dfrac{dx_1}{dt} = x_2, \\[2mm] \dfrac{dx_2}{dt} = -g, \end{cases}$$

which obviously is a special case of equations (4). The system (7) is equivalent to the equation (5), for each implies the other by mediation of the notation (6).

If the falling body is subject also to a resistance that is proportional to the first power of the velocity, the differential equation corresponding to equation (5) is

$$(8) \qquad \frac{d^2x}{dt^2} = -k^2 \frac{dx}{dt} - g,$$

and the transformation (6) leads to the equivalent normal system

(9) $$\frac{dx_1}{dt} = x_2, \qquad \frac{dx_2}{dt} = -k^2 x_2 - g.$$

The differential equations (5) and (8) are included as special cases in the differential equation

(10) $$\frac{d^n x}{dt^n} = f\left(x, \frac{dx}{dt}, \cdots, \frac{d^{n-1}x}{dt^{n-1}}; t\right).$$

This differential equation is reduced by the transformation

$$\begin{cases} x = x_1, \\ \dfrac{dx}{dt} = x_2, \\ \cdot \quad \cdot \quad \cdot \quad \cdot \\ \dfrac{d^{n-1}x}{dt^{n-1}} = x_n \end{cases}$$

to the equivalent normal system of differential equations

$$\begin{cases} \dfrac{dx_1}{dt} = x_2, \\ \cdot \quad \cdot \quad \cdot \quad \cdot \\ \dfrac{dx_{n-1}}{dt} = x_n, \\ \dfrac{dx_n}{dt} = f(x_1, \cdots, x_n; t). \end{cases}$$

The differential equations that arise in problems of dynamics often consist of several simultaneous equations. For example, the differential equations satisfied by a body moving subject to gravity $- g$, and to a resistance opposite to its direction of motion and proportional to its velocity, are

(11) $$\begin{cases} \dfrac{d^2x}{dt^2} = -k^2 \dfrac{dx}{dt}, \\ \dfrac{d^2y}{dt^2} = -k^2 \dfrac{dy}{dt} - g. \end{cases}$$

The transformation

(12) $$\begin{cases} x = x_1, \qquad y = x_3, \\ \dfrac{dx}{dt} = x_2, \qquad \dfrac{dy}{dt} = x_4 \end{cases}$$

reduces these equations to the equivalent normal system

$$(13) \quad \begin{cases} \dfrac{dx_1}{dt} = x_2, \\[2mm] \dfrac{dx_2}{dt} = -k^2 x_2, \\[2mm] \dfrac{dx_3}{dt} = x_4, \\[2mm] \dfrac{dx_4}{dt} = -k^2 x_4 - g. \end{cases}$$

Some problems give rise to a larger number of simultaneous differential equations. For example, the problem of three bodies is defined by nine differential equations, the left members of which are second derivatives of the nine variables that define the positions of the three bodies. A transformation similar to that in equations (12) reduces these differential equations to an equivalent system of eighteen normal differential equations. And, obviously, any finite number of differential equations of the types under consideration can be reduced to an equivalent normal system, and the steps of the reduction present no difficulties whatever.

4. Reduction of Normal Systems of Differential Equations to Single Differential Equations. Normal systems of differential equations of the form (4) can usually be reduced, at least theoretically, to a single equation of the form (10). In order to illustrate the procedure, suppose $n = 3$ and that the differential equations are

$$(14) \quad \begin{cases} \dfrac{dx_1}{dt} = f_1(x_1,\, x_2,\, x_3;\, t), \\[2mm] \dfrac{dx_2}{dt} = f_2(x_1,\, x_2,\, x_3;\, t), \\[2mm] \dfrac{dx_3}{dt} = f_3(x_1,\, x_2,\, x_3;\, t). \end{cases}$$

The problem is to eliminate two of the three variables x_1, x_2, x_3, say x_1 and x_2, and the first derivatives of the same variables. Since four quantities cannot in general be eliminated from three equations, it is necessary that additional equations be adjoined to the three equations (14).

The first derivatives of equations (14) are

$$(15) \quad \begin{cases} \dfrac{d^2x_1}{dt^2} = \dfrac{\partial f_1}{\partial x_1}\dfrac{dx_1}{dt} + \dfrac{\partial f_1}{\partial x_2}\dfrac{dx_2}{dt} + \dfrac{\partial f_1}{\partial x_3}\dfrac{dx_3}{dt} + \dfrac{\partial f_1}{\partial t}, \\[2mm] \dfrac{d^2x_2}{dt^2} = \dfrac{\partial f_2}{\partial x_1}\dfrac{dx_1}{dt} + \dfrac{\partial f_2}{\partial x_2}\dfrac{dx_2}{dt} + \dfrac{\partial f_2}{\partial x_3}\dfrac{dx_3}{dt} + \dfrac{\partial f_2}{\partial t}, \\[2mm] \dfrac{d^2x_3}{dt^2} = \dfrac{\partial f_3}{\partial x_1}\dfrac{dx_1}{dt} + \dfrac{\partial f_3}{\partial x_2}\dfrac{dx_2}{dt} + \dfrac{\partial f_3}{\partial x_3}\dfrac{dx_3}{dt} + \dfrac{\partial f_3}{\partial t}. \end{cases}$$

Usually the six equations (14) and (15) can be solved for the six quantities x_1, x_2 and their first and second derivatives in terms of x_3 and its first and second derivatives. If this solution is made and if the results are substituted into the derivative of the third of equations (15), the result has the form

$$(16) \quad \frac{d^3x_3}{dt^3} = f\left(x_3, \frac{dx_3}{dt}, \frac{d^2x_3}{dt^2}; t\right),$$

which is of the form of equation (10) for $n = 3$.

Equation (16) is the equivalent of the system (14) in the sense that the solution of equation (16) expresses not only x_3, but also x_1 and x_2 as well, in terms of t. For, if the solution of equation (16) for x_3 in terms of t is substituted into the solution of equations (14) and (15) for x_1 and x_2 in terms of x_3 and its derivatives, the latter variables are expressed in terms of t.

It is to be observed that the problem of solving equations (14) and (15) for two of the variables and their derivatives in terms of the third and its derivatives may be of great practical difficulty. In this respect, the simplicity of the reduction of a single equation to a normal system presents a sharp contrast. Consequently, in adopting a single form for general discussions, the normal system should be chosen. Moreover, as will be seen later, the normal system has important notational advantages.

Before passing on, consider the problem of reducing the general normal system (4) to an equivalent single equation. There are $n - 1$ variables and $n - 1$ first derivatives of these variables, or in all $2(n - 1)$ quantities to be eliminated. Equations (4) and their first derivatives provide $2n$ equations; but, in the process of forming the derivatives, $n - 1$ second derivatives have been introduced that also must be eliminated. Since $3(n - 1)$ is greater than $2n$ if n is greater than three, additional equations must be adjoined to those under consideration. The second derivatives of equations (4) add n new equations and $n - 1$ quantities to be eliminated—a net gain of one. Equations (4) and their $n - 2$ successive derivatives give $n(n - 1)$ equations, and they contain an equal number of quantities to be eliminated. If these equations are solved for $x_1, \cdots, x_{n-1}$ and their $n - 1$ derivatives and the results are substituted into the $(n - 1)$st derivative of the last equation, the result is an equation of the form of (10). Moreover, the order of the derivative of the left member in general equals the number of original equations.*

Apparently the order of the left member of a single equation equivalent to a normal system is in every case equal to the number of equations in the normal system, but there are exceptions as will be illustrated. The illustration will show that in certain respects the normal system is more general than a single equation.

Consider the normal system

$$(17) \quad \begin{cases} \dfrac{dx_1}{dt} = 7x_1 + 2x_2 - 3x_3, \\[2mm] \dfrac{dx_2}{dt} = 18x_1 + 7x_2 - 9x_3, \\[2mm] \dfrac{dx_3}{dt} = 24x_1 + 8x_2 - 11x_3, \end{cases}$$

and their first derivatives

$$(18) \quad \begin{cases} \dfrac{d^2x_1}{dt^2} = 7\dfrac{dx_1}{dt} + 2\dfrac{dx_2}{dt} - 3\dfrac{dx_3}{dt}, \\[2mm] \dfrac{d^2x_2}{dt^2} = 18\dfrac{dx_1}{dt} + 7\dfrac{dx_2}{dt} - 9\dfrac{dx_3}{dt}, \\[2mm] \dfrac{d^2x_3}{dt^2} = 24\dfrac{dx_1}{dt} + 8\dfrac{dx_2}{dt} - 11\dfrac{dx_3}{dt}. \end{cases}$$

These two sets of equations are linear in x_1, x_2, x_3, and their first and second derivatives.

Now consider the problem of solving equations (17) and (18) for x_1 and x_2 and their first and second derivatives in terms of x_3 and its first and second derivatives. The determinant of the coefficients is found to be zero. Therefore the condition that

---

* For an alternative method of reduction, see Problem (6), page 20.

the six equations shall be consistent is that the determinant shall be zero when any one of its columns is replaced by the terms in x_3 and its first and second derivatives. The formation and reduction of this determinant gives

$$\frac{d^2x_3}{dt^2} - 2\frac{dx_3}{dt} + x_3 = 0$$

as the equation that x_3 must satisfy. The highest derivative in this equation is of the second order instead of the third, which would, in general, be the lowest order satisfied by one of the three variables related through three normal differential equations. A similar result would have been found if equations (17) and (18) had been solved for either of the other pairs of variables.

5. Notations for General Systems of Differential Equations. Since single equations of the type of equation (10), and even systems of equations of the type

$$\begin{cases} \frac{d^{n_1}x_1}{dt^{n_1}} = f_1\left(x_1, \cdots, x_m, \cdots, \frac{d^{n_1-1}x_1}{dt^{n_1-1}}, \cdots, \frac{d^{n_m-1}x_m}{dt^{n_m-1}}; t\right), \\ \cdots \cdots \cdots \cdots \cdots \cdots \cdots \cdots \cdots \\ \frac{d^{n_m}x_m}{dt^{n_m}} = f_m\left(x_1, \cdots, x_m, \cdots, \frac{d^{n_1-1}x_1}{dt^{n_1-1}}, \cdots, \frac{d^{n_m-1}x_m}{dt^{n_m-1}}; t\right) \end{cases}$$

can in every case be reduced to an equivalent normal system of the form of equations (4), the general normal system will be the form adopted for discussion.

The normal system of equations (4) can be written more compactly in the form

$$(19) \qquad \frac{dx_i}{dt} = f_i(x_j; t) \qquad (i, j = 1, \cdots, n).$$

Since in general discussions the range of the variables x_i is from 1 to n, the explicit statement of this fact may be omitted for the sake of brevity. Consequently, the whole system (19) has the simplicity of form of a single equation of the first order.

Although the form of equation (19) will generally be used, in Chapter 12 it will be found convenient to reduce it still further to

$$(20) \qquad \frac{dx}{dt} = f(x; t),$$

where it is to be understood that in all cases x and f represent the n variables $x_1, \cdots, x_n$ and the n functions $f_1, \cdots, f_n$ respectively. This reduction is permissible in theoretical discussions, for all the variables and all the functions respectively have the same general properties, and the subscripts are useful in distinguishing one variable or function from another variable or function only in particular examples.

6. Independent and Dependent Variables. In the solution of a differential equation of the type

$$\frac{dy}{dx} = f(x, y),$$

the variable y may be expressed in terms of x, or x may be expressed in terms of y, as may be convenient. But in the normal system of differential equations (19), the problem is to express the variables $x_1, \cdots, x_n$ in terms of *the independent variable* t. The variable t is regarded as independent, at least on some limited range or in some limited domain.

In physical problems the variable t usually represents the time, but it may represent any other variable. In fact, equations (19) having the independent variable t may be changed to another system having x_n, for example, as the independent variable. Since

$$\frac{dx_i}{dt} = \frac{dx_i}{dx_n} \frac{dx_n}{dt},$$

$$\frac{dt}{dx_n} = \frac{1}{f_n(x_j; t)},$$

the transformed system is

$$(21) \quad \begin{cases} \dfrac{dx_i}{dx_n} = \dfrac{f_i(x_j; t)}{f_n(x_j; t)} & (i = 1, \cdots, n-1; j = 1, \cdots, n), \\ \dfrac{dt}{dx_n} = \dfrac{1}{f_n(x_j; t)}. \end{cases}$$

In the system of differential equations (19) the variables $x_1, \cdots, x_n$ are called *the dependent variables*, because they are to be determined as functions of the independent variable t.

7. Order of a System of Differential Equations. The order of a differential equation of the type of equation (10) is the order of its highest derivative, or n. The equivalent system of the form of equation (19) is also of the order n; that is, the order of a normal system is equal to the number of dependent variables or to the number of equations. This terminology is used even though the dependent variables may in special cases individually satisfy differential equations of lower order, as was illustrated by the system (17).

It happens sometimes in physical problems that a normal system of differential equations contains one or more equations that are independent of the remainder. For example, the first two and the last two equations of the system (13) constitute mutually independent groups of equations, each involving only two dependent variables. From the practical point of view this set consists of two systems of differential equations, each of the second order.

In some problems there occurs only one group of differential equations that are independent of the remainder. For example, in the system

$$(22) \quad \begin{cases} \dfrac{dx_1}{dt} = f_1(x_1, x_2; t), \\[2mm] \dfrac{dx_2}{dt} = f_2(x_1, x_2; t), \\[2mm] \dfrac{dx_3}{dt} = f_3(x_1, x_2, x_3; t), \end{cases}$$

the first two equations are independent of the third, for they do not involve the dependent variable x_3; but the third equation is not independent of the first two, for it depends upon both x_1 and x_2. As a practical matter, the first two of equations (22) would be solved so as to express x_1 and x_2 in terms of t; then these values of x_1 and x_2 would be substituted into the third equation, which would then contain only the variables x_3 and t.

Although it is practically important to make use of the existence of independent subgroups of differential equations, for general theoretical purposes these special properties may be ignored. In normal systems of differential equations, the order of the system equals the number of equations, which equals the number of dependent variables.

8. Definition of a Solution of a Normal System of Differential Equations. In the definition of a solution of differential equations, an important difference exists between the elementary theory and the more general theory. In the former, the differential equations are regarded as constituting the complete set of conditions, and in solving them arbitrary constants are introduced which may be determined in particular problems by the initial conditions. In the latter, the initial conditions are adjoined to the differential equations as a part of the conditions that a solution must satisfy.

For example, according to the elementary theory the solution of the differential equation (5) is

$$x = -\tfrac{1}{2}gt^2 + c_1t + c_2,$$

where c_1 and c_2 are arbitrary. This equation defines a double infinity of curves (in an xt-plane) depending upon the arbitrary parameters c_1 and c_2. According to the general theory, initial values for x and dx/dt would be adjoined to equation (5), and the complete system of equations would define a single curve. For example, if $x = 1$, $dx/dt = 2$ at $t = 0$, the solution is

$$x = -\tfrac{1}{2}gt^2 + 2t + 1.$$

Obviously the difference in points of view is not important in so simple a problem.

Suppose $x_i = a_i$ at $t = t_0$. Then the complete problem for the normal system of differential equations is

$$(23) \qquad \begin{cases} \dfrac{dx_i}{dt} = f_i(x_j; t), \\[2mm] x_i(t_0) = a_i. \end{cases}$$

It is clear that in order that the problem shall have meaning, the functions $f_i(x_j; t)$ must be defined for $x_i = a_i$ and $t = t_0$.

By *definition*, the functions

$$(24) \qquad x_1 = \phi_1(t), \cdots, x_n = \phi_n(t)$$

constitute a solution of equations (23) if they satisfy the relations

$$(25) \qquad \begin{cases} \dfrac{d\phi_i}{dt} \underset{t}{\equiv} f_i(\phi_i(t); t), \\[2mm] \phi_i(t_0) = a_i, \end{cases}$$

where the notation in the first line means that the left and right members are equal for *all values* of t in some domain including t_0. The domain may be in special cases only real values of t, and, in others, complex values.

It is obvious that a solution depends upon the initial values of the x_i and t, namely, the a_i and t_0. Moreover, the differential equations in general depend upon one or more parameters $\mu_1, \cdots, \mu_m$, which are constants with respect to the x_i and t, and a solution also depends upon these parameters. Hence, upon expressing explicitly the fact that a solution depends upon the a_j, t_0, and the μ_k, equations (24) become

$$(26) \qquad x_i = \phi_i(t_0; a_1, \cdots, a_n; \mu_1, \cdots, \mu_m; t).$$

As will appear in later chapters, the principal problems of differential equations consist in proving the existence of functions ϕ_i that satisfy the relations (25), and in finding the properties of the ϕ_i as functions of $t_0; a_1, \cdots, a_n; \mu_1, \cdots, \mu_m$; and t.

9. Simple Illustrations of Solutions. Consider the normal form of equation (5); namely,

$$(27) \qquad \begin{cases} \dfrac{dx_1}{dt} = x_2, \\[2mm] \dfrac{dx_2}{dt} = -g, \\[2mm] x_1(t_0) = a_1, \\[1mm] x_2(t_0) = a_2. \end{cases}$$

The constant g plays the rôle of a parameter μ which varies only with the latitude on the surface of the earth.

A solution of equations (27) is

$$(28) \qquad \begin{cases} x_1 = -\tfrac{1}{2}g(t - t_0)^2 + a_2(t - t_0) + a_1, \\ x_2 = -g(t - t_0) + a_2, \end{cases}$$

for it satisfies the relations corresponding to (25), as can be verified by direct substitution. The right members of these equations are polynomials in both t_0 and t, and they are linear in the constants a_1, a_2, and g.

In general, the solutions of differential equations do not have such simple properties as those of the right members of equations (28). For example, the differential equation satisfied by the variables defining the motion of a simple pendulum is

$$(29) \qquad \frac{d^2\theta}{dt^2} = -\frac{g}{l}\sin\theta,$$

where l is the length of the pendulum and θ is the angle between the vertical downward and the line of the pendulum.

Let the initial values of the dependent variables θ and $d\theta/dt$ be

$$(30) \qquad \theta = \theta_0, \qquad d\theta/dt = 0 \text{ at } t = t_0.$$

It is shown in treatises on dynamics * that the solution defined by equations (29) and (30) is

$$(31) \qquad \sin \frac{\theta}{2} = \sin \frac{\theta_0}{2} \operatorname{sn} \left[\sqrt{\frac{g}{l}} (t - t_0 + \tfrac{1}{4}P) \right],$$

where $\operatorname{sn} [\sqrt{g/l}(t - t_0)]$ is the sine-amplitude elliptic function having the modulus $\kappa = \sin \tfrac{1}{2}\theta_0$ and the real period P. That (31) is a solution can be established by direct substitution and making use of the properties of the sine-amplitude function. Although this problem is relatively simple from the physical point of view, its solution is a transcendental function of the arguments. Corresponding results are true for the problem of the top, or that of the motion of two bodies attracting each other according to the law of gravitation.

10. Definition of a Solution of an nth Order Differential Equation. It follows from equation (10) and its reduction to an equivalent normal system that the complete set of conditions for defining a solution are in this case

$$(32) \qquad \begin{cases} \dfrac{d^n x}{dt^n} = f \left(x, \dfrac{dx}{dt}, \cdots, \dfrac{d^{n-1}x}{dt^{n-1}}; t \right), \\ x(t_0) = a_1, \\ \qquad \cdot \qquad \cdot \qquad \cdot \\ \dfrac{d^{n-1}x(t_0)}{dt^{n-1}} = a_n. \end{cases}$$

It also follows consistently with the definition of a solution of a normal system that $x = \phi(t)$ is a solution of equations (32) if

$$(33) \qquad \begin{cases} \dfrac{d^n \phi}{dt^n} \underset{t}{\equiv} f \left(\phi, \dfrac{d\phi}{dt}, \cdots, \dfrac{d^{n-1}\phi}{dt^{n-1}}; t \right), \\ \phi(t_0) = a_1, \\ \qquad \cdot \qquad \cdot \qquad \cdot \\ \dfrac{d^{n-1}\phi(t_0)}{dt^{n-1}} = a_n, \end{cases}$$

* Appel, *Mécanique Rationnelle*, 3d ed., Vol. 1, p. 307.

where the identity in t holds for some domain including t_0. The solution $\phi(t)$ is a function of t_0, a_1, $\cdots$, a_n, as well as of t, and of the parameters that occur in the differential equation.

11. Definition of an Integral of a Normal System of Differential Equations. The differential equations under consideration are

$$(4) \qquad \frac{dx_i}{dt} = f_i(x_j; t).$$

By *definition*,

$$(34) \qquad F = F(x_1, \cdots, x_n; t)$$

is *an integral* of the differential equations (4) provided F is such a function that

$$(35) \qquad F(\phi_1, \cdots, \phi_n; t) \underset{t}{\equiv} C$$

for every solution $\phi_1(t)$, $\cdots$, $\phi_n(t)$ of equations (4), corresponding to every set of initial values $x_i(t_0) = a_i$ in the neighborhood of some particular set $a_i^{(0)}$, and where C is a constant depending upon the initial conditions. It is, of course, not necessary in every case that the integral shall involve explicitly all the variables.

Suppose the derivatives of the function F with respect to the x_i and t exist for these variables in the neighborhood of their initial values. Then

$$\frac{dF}{dt} = \frac{\partial F}{\partial x_1} \frac{dx_1}{dt} + \cdots + \frac{\partial F}{\partial x_n} \frac{dx_n}{dt} + \frac{\partial F}{dt},$$

which becomes as a consequence of equations (4)

$$(36) \quad \frac{dF}{dt} = \frac{\partial F}{\partial x_1} f_1 + \cdots + \frac{\partial F}{\partial x_n} f_n + \frac{\partial F}{\partial t} = \Phi(x_1, \cdots, x_n; t).$$

It follows from the identity (35) and the equation (36) that

$$(37) \qquad \Phi(\phi_1, \cdots, \phi_n; t) \underset{t}{\equiv} 0.$$

Since, by definition, the identity (35) is satisfied for every solution ϕ_1, $\cdots$, ϕ_n, corresponding to every set of initial conditions near the $a_i^{(0)}$, it follows that the identity (37) is an identity in the ϕ_i, as well as in t. Inasmuch as the notation for the variables in an identity is not essential, $F(x_1, \cdots, x_n; t)$, a function having first derivatives with respect to the x_i and t in the neighborhood of a_i and t_0, is an integral of the normal system of differential equations (4) if

$$(38) \quad \frac{dF}{dt} = \frac{\partial F}{\partial x_1} f_1 + \cdots + \frac{\partial F}{\partial x_n} f_n + \frac{\partial F}{\partial t} = \Phi(x_1, \cdots, x_n; t) \underset{x_i, t}{\equiv} 0.$$

This second definition does not require that a solution shall be known in order to determine whether or not a function is an integral.

It will be noted that solutions and integrals are entirely different, and the two terms will henceforth be used with the meanings defined in Arts. 8 and 11.

12. Illustrations of Integrals. Consider the differential equations for the motion of a falling body; namely,

$$\begin{cases} \dfrac{dx_1}{dt} = x_2, \\[2mm] \dfrac{dx_2}{dt} = -g. \end{cases}$$

The function

$$F = 2gx_1 + x_2^2$$

s an integral, for it satisfies the first definition of an integral, as can be verified by substituting into it the solution (28); and it satisfies the second definition, because

$$\frac{dF}{dt} = 2g \frac{dx_1}{dt} + 2x_2 \frac{dx_2}{dt} = 2gx_2 - 2x_2 g \underset{x_1, x_2, t}{\equiv} 0.$$

The integral that has just been given is independent of t, but this property is exceptional. For example,

$$F_1 = -\tfrac{1}{2}g(t - t_0)^2 - x_2(t - t_0) + x_1$$

is also an integral of the differential equations for the motion of a falling body, because it satisfies both the identities (37) and (38).

In general, integrals of differential equations are not so simple as those that have been given as illustrations. For example, the differential equation (29) has the integral ($\theta = x_1$, $d\theta/dt = x_2$)

$$F_2 = -\frac{2g}{l} \cos x_1 + x_2^2,$$

which is a transcendental function of x_1, but it is simpler than the solution (31). Many differential equations originating in physical problems have relatively simple integrals even though their solution consists of transcendental functions.

Integrals are generally of great importance in physical problems. Consider, for example, the problem of determining the motion of three bodies that attract one another according to the law of gravitation, but are subject to no other forces. Except for very special initial conditions, the solution functions are incapable of being expressed in terms of a finite number of elementary functions. Yet these differential equations have ten independent simple algebraic integrals, seven of which do not depend upon the time. Six of the ten are the mathematical expressions for the fact that the center of gravity of the three bodies moves with respect to the axes of reference in a straight line with uniform speed. Three of the integrals express the fact that the projections of the areal velocity of the system upon the three planes of reference are constant. And one integral expresses the fact that the sum of the kinetic and the potential energies of the system is constant.

The integrals describe invariants of the system, and their importance is easily seen. If, for example, one should wish to determine whether or not some existing system of three bodies might have evolved from some earlier hypothetical system, one would determine first whether the corresponding constants of their ten integrals were equal. If the corresponding constants were not all equal, the hypothesis would be false; if they were all equal, the hypothesis might be true.

13. Partial Differential Equations. This book is concerned primarily and almost exclusively with *ordinary* differential equations; that is, with differential equations of the type that have so far been considered. But there are other differential equations having quite different general characteristics. A brief description of a differential equation of a different kind, a so-called *partial differential equation*, will help to make clear the precise domain of ordinary differential equations.

One of the characteristics of a system of ordinary differential equations is that it has one *independent* variable, the variable t in present notation, and one or more *dependent* variables, the x_i. In partial differential equations there are several independent variables and one or more dependent variables. Many physical problems give rise to partial differential equations.

Suppose, for example, that the temperature v of a spherical body, such as the earth, is given at every point in the body at the time $t = t_0$ by the equation

$$(39) \qquad v = f(x, y, z; t_0).$$

At any later instant the temperature will vary with x, y, z, and t. If the sphere cannot radiate heat from its surface, the temperature v can be shown to satisfy the *partial differential equation*

$$(40) \qquad \frac{\partial v}{\partial t} = \kappa \left[\frac{\partial^2 v}{\partial x^2} + \frac{\partial^2 v}{\partial y^2} + \frac{\partial^2 v}{\partial z^2} \right],$$

where κ depends upon the properties of the material of the sphere, and may be either a constant or a function of v, x, y, and z. In equation (40) the t, x, y, and z are independent variables, and v is the dependent variable.

There might be several simultaneous partial differential equations in several dependent variables and any number of independent variables. It is evident that partial differential equations provide greater opportunities for complexities than do ordinary differential equations. In order to show how very great the difference is in the two classes of problems, a relatively simple partial differential equation will be solved.

Let R represent a uniform circular ring at whose surface heat can be neither lost nor gained. Suppose the temperature v is initially uniform on every perpendicular cross section of the ring; then the temperature will vary only with the longitude θ of points of the ring, the origin being at its center. Suppose the temperature at $t = 0$ satisfies the equation

$$(41) \qquad v = f(\theta),$$

where θ varies from $-\pi$ to $+\pi$ and $f(-\pi) = f(+\pi)$. Fourier, who first treated this problem, showed that the temperature at any later time and at any point in the ring satisfies the partial differential equation

$$(42) \qquad \frac{\partial v}{\partial t} = \kappa^2 \frac{\partial^2 v}{\partial \theta^2},$$

where κ^2 is a constant.

The problem is to solve equation (42) and to satisfy the initial condition (41), which is a functional relation rather than a special constant value of the dependent variable. At first glance nothing seems simpler. It is readily verified that the function

(43) $$v = \cos j\theta \, e^{-j^2\kappa^2 t},$$

where j is any number, satisfies (42). If the right member of equation (43) is multiplied by any constant, it still satisfies equation (42); it is also true if $\cos j\theta$ is replaced by $\sin j\theta$. Therefore the infinite series

(44) $$v = \sum_{j=0}^{\infty} [a_j \cos j\theta + b_j \sin j\theta] e^{-j^2\kappa^2 t},$$

where j takes all positive integral values and the a_j and b_j are arbitrary constants, formally satisfies (42).

The function v must satisfy the initial conditions (41), or

(45) $$\sum_{j=0}^{\infty} [a_j \cos j\theta + b_j \sin j\theta] \underset{\theta}{\equiv} f(\theta).$$

It is shown in the theory of Fourier series that if $f(\theta)$ is an analytic function of θ on the interval $-\pi \leqq \theta \leqq +\pi$, and if $f(-\pi) = f(+\pi)$, then the coefficients a_i and b_i can be so determined that the left member of equation (45) converges and equals the right member for every value of θ in the interval from $-\pi$ to $+\pi$ inclusive. Under these strong conditions on the function $f(\theta)$, the series (45) converges *absolutely* for every value of θ in the interval, and therefore the right member of equation (44) converges for $t = 0$ and for all positive values of t. Moreover, the derivatives of all orders of the left member of equation (45) exist and equal the corresponding derivatives of the right member for every value of θ in the interval. Consequently under these strong hypotheses the expression (44) satisfies both equations (41) and (42).

A function $f(\theta)$ is expansible as a converging Fourier series under much weaker hypotheses than those which have been stated, but then delicate questions arise respecting the existence of derivatives before the function (44) can be shown to be a solution of the differential equation (42). These questions are quite aside from those which are of chief interest here; the mention of them merely serves to emphasize the difficult type of problems which may be encountered even in simple problems in partial differential equations.

I. QUESTIONS AND PROBLEMS

1. What is Simpson's method for computing definite integrals? Write the explicit formulas.

2. If $f(t)$ is continuous from $t = a$ to $t = b$ except for $t = c$, under what conditions on $f(t)$ at $t = c$ does $\int_a^b f(t)dt$ exist?

3. Under what conditions on $f(t)$ at $t = \infty$ does $\int_0^\infty f(t)dt$ exist?

4. Write the precise definition of the derivative of $\int_{a(\mu)}^{b(\mu)} f(\mu; t)dt$ with respect to μ. Under what conditions does the derivative exist?

5. Write the differential equations for the motion of a body moving in a plane and subject to an acceleration downward that varies inversely as the square of its height above the earth's surface, and to a head-on resistance that varies as the square of the velocity. Reduce the equations to a normal system.

6. Consider the problem of reducing a normal system of differential equations to a single equation in the dependent variable x. Take successive derivatives of the nth equation, eliminating each time from its right member the first derivatives of $x_1, \cdots, x_{n-1}$ by means of the first $n - 1$ of the original equations. Determine what in general will be the order of the final equation. Apply the method to equations (17) as written, and also after changing one of the coefficients in the right member by unity.

7. Transform equation (8) to an equivalent differential equation having x as the independent variable. Transform equation (8) to an equivalent equation having dx/dt as the independent variable.

8. Does the definition of a solution of a system of differential equations involve directly or implicitly the existence of a formula? How many values of t are involved in the definition?

9. Prove by direct substitution and reduction that the function defined by equation (31) is a solution of equations (29) and (30).

10. Prove in detail that the definition of a solution given in Art. 8 implies that the relations (33) must be satisfied in order that $x = \phi(t)$ shall be a solution of equation (32).

11. The first definition of an integral having first derivatives with respect to $x_1, \cdots, x_n$ implies the second definition. Does the second definition imply the first?

CHAPTER II

ANALYTIC DIFFERENTIAL EQUATIONS

I. Construction and Existence of a Solution

14. Properties of Analytic Differential Equations. The normal system of differential equations

$$(1) \quad \begin{cases} \dfrac{dx_i}{dt} = f_i(x_1, \cdots, x_n; t), \\ x_i(t_0) = a_i \end{cases}$$

is said to be analytic if the $f_i(x_j; t)$ are analytic functions of their arguments simultaneously in a certain domain D,

$$(2) \quad |x_i - a_i| \leqq r_i, \qquad |t - t_0| \leqq \rho,$$

including the initial values of the variables. It will be noted that the domain defined by the relations (2) is closed; that is, the domain includes its boundaries.

The hypotheses satisfied by the $f_i(x_j; t)$ are from the logical point of view very strong, for they imply that these functions have the following properties:

Property 1. The absolute values of the functions $f_i(x_j; t)$ have finite upper bounds M_i in the closed domain D (see Appendix A). That is, for every set of values of the x_j and t in the domain D the absolute value of the function $f_i(x_j; t)$ is not greater than some finite constant M_i. If the domain were not closed, this conclusion would not necessarily follow. Moreover, the upper bound M_i is, in general, a function of the domain.

Property 2. The functions $f_i(x_j; t)$ are uniquely expansible as power series in the $x_j - a_j$ and $t - t_0$ which converge for all values of the x_j and t in the domain D. The series are the Taylor expansions in $n + 1$ variables

21

$$(3) \begin{cases} f_i(x_j; t) = f_i(a_j; t_0) + \sum_{j=1}^{n} \frac{\partial f_i}{\partial x_j}(x_j - a_j) + \frac{\partial f_i}{\partial t}(t - t_0) \\ \quad + \frac{1}{2} \sum_{j=1}^{n} \sum_{k=1}^{n} \frac{\partial^2 f_i}{\partial x_j \partial x_k}(x_j - a_j)(x_k - a_k) \\ \quad + \sum_{j=1}^{n} \frac{\partial^2 f_i}{\partial x_j \partial t}(x_j - a_j)(t - t_0) \\ \quad + \frac{1}{2} \frac{\partial^2 f_i}{\partial t^2}(t - t_0)^2 + \cdots, \end{cases}$$

where the x_j and t are replaced by the a_j and t_0 respectively in all the partial derivatives.

The series (3) converge *absolutely* and *uniformly* in the domain D. Their term-by-term derivatives and integrals with respect to their several arguments also converge absolutely and uniformly in the domain D. The sums and products of finite numbers of power series of the type and properties of the series (3), when formed as in the case of polynomials, also converge absolutely and uniformly in the domain D.

The functions $f_i(x_j; t)$ are expansible also about any other point b_j; t_1 in the domain D as Taylor series in the $x_j - b_j$ and $t - t_1$, and these series converge for all values of the x_j and t in any circles having the b_j and t_1 as origins that lie entirely within the domain D. These power series have all the general properties of the series (3).

Property 3. There exist power series that dominate * the series (3) and converge for all values of the x_j and t in the domain D', which is any domain included within the domain D. That is, there exist power series in the $x_j - a_j$ and $t - t_0$ whose coefficients are real and positive and greater than the absolute values of the corresponding coefficients in the series (3), and which converge for all values of the variables x_j and t for which $|x_j - a_j| \leqq r_j' < r_j$, $|t - t_0| \leqq \rho' < \rho$.

The expansions of the right members of the equations

$$(4) \quad P_i(x_j; t) = \frac{M_i}{\left(1 - \dfrac{x_1 - a_1}{r_1'}\right) \cdots \left(1 - \dfrac{x_n - a_n}{r_n'}\right)\left(1 - \dfrac{t - t_0}{\rho'}\right)}$$

are series that dominate the right members of equations (3) and

* See Appendix B.

converge in the domain D'. It will be noted that these expansions are geometric series in the $n + 1$ variables $x_j - a_j$ and $t - t_0$. If the M_i are replaced by an M such that $M_i \leqq M$, the series dominate the right members of equations (3). If the r_i' are replaced by an r such that $r_i' \geqq r$, the series still dominate the right members of equations (3), but they converge only in the domain $|x_j - a_j| < r$. This domain is in general more restricted than the domain D', but this fact is of no practical importance in the theoretical discussions for which the dominating series will be used.

Finally, the expansion of the right member of the equation

$$(5) \quad F_i(x_j; t) = \frac{M}{\left[1 - \dfrac{(x_1 - a_1) + \cdots + (x_n - a_n)}{r}\right]\left[1 - \dfrac{t - t_0}{\rho'}\right]}$$

dominates the right members of equations (3) and converges for all values of the x_j and t for which $|x_j - a_j| < r/n$ and $|t - t_0| < \rho'$. This domain is more restricted than that of the convergence of the expansion of the right member of equation (4).

That the expansion of the right member of equation (5) dominates the right members of equations (3) follows from the fact that it dominates the expansion of equation (4). The expansion of equation (4) contains all powers of the arguments; the numerical coefficients are unity; and the denominators are products of the powers of the r_i' and ρ'. The expansion of equation (5) contains all powers of the arguments; the numerical coefficients are the binomial coefficients, and hence are equal to or greater than unity; and the denominators are powers of r and ρ', which are equal to or less than the corresponding powers of the r_i' and ρ'.

15. Formal Construction of the Solution of Equations (1). Under the strong conditions satisfied by the functions $f_i(x_j; t)$, it might be conjectured that there is a solution $x_i = \phi_i(t)$ which is analytic in t, at least in a sufficiently restricted domain. If such should be the case, the x_i would be expansible as power series in $t - t_0$ of the form

$$(6) \quad \begin{cases} x_1 - a_1 = c_1^{(1)}(t - t_0) + c_1^{(2)}(t - t_0)^2 + \cdots, \\ \quad \cdot \quad \cdot \quad \cdot \quad \cdot \quad \cdot \quad \cdot \quad \cdot \quad \cdot \quad \cdot \\ x_n - a_n = c_n^{(1)}(t - t_0) + c_n^{(2)}(t - t_0)^2 + \cdots, \end{cases}$$

where the $c_i^{(j)}$ are constants that remain to be determined.

Let it be assumed for the moment that the series (6) converge for sufficiently small values of $|t - t_0|$, and consider the problem of so determining the coefficients $c_i^{(j)}$ that these series shall be a solution of equations (1). Substitute the series (6) into the right members of equations (3) and rearrange the results as power series in $t - t_0$. Under the hypotheses, these series will converge * for all values of t for which $|t - t_0|$ is sufficiently small. Consequently it follows from equations (1) that the derivatives of the assumed solution (6) will equal these series in the domain of convergence, and, therefore, the coefficients of corresponding powers of $t - t_0$ in the left and the right members will be equal.

On performing the indicated substitutions, rearrangements, and equating of coefficients, it is found that if the functions (6) are a solution, the $c_i^{(k)}$ satisfy the equations

$$(7) \begin{cases} c_i^{(1)} = f_i(a_j; t_0) \quad (i = 1, \cdots, n), \\ 2c_i^{(2)} = \sum_{j=1}^{n} \frac{\partial f_i}{\partial x_j} c_j^{(1)} + \frac{\partial f_i}{\partial t}, \\ 3c_i^{(3)} = \sum_{j=1}^{n} \frac{\partial f_i}{\partial x_j} c_j^{(2)} + \frac{1}{2} \sum_{j=1}^{n} \sum_{k=1}^{n} \frac{\partial^2 f_i}{\partial x_j \partial x_k} c_j^{(1)} c_k^{(1)} \\ \qquad + \sum_{j=1}^{n} \frac{\partial^2 f_i}{\partial x_j \partial t} c_j^{(1)} + \frac{1}{2} \frac{\partial^2 f_i}{\partial t^2}, \\ \cdots \cdots \cdots \cdots \cdots \cdots \cdots \cdots \cdots \cdots \\ kc_i^{(k)} = p_i^{(k)}(c_j^{(1)}, \cdots, c_j^{(k-1)}). \end{cases}$$

The $p_i^{(k)}(c_j^{(1)}, \cdots, c_j^{(k-1)})$ of the general term have the following properties:

(a) The $p_i^{(k)}$ are polynomials in the $c_j^{(1)}, \cdots, c_j^{(k-1)}$.

(b) The coefficients of the $p_i^{(k)}$ are linear functions of the coefficients of the expansions of the f_i given in equations (3).

(c) The numerical multipliers of the literal coefficients of the $f_i^{(k)}$ are positive numbers; namely, the numbers arising in Taylor's expansions and in forming products of various powers of series.

The first set of equations of (7) uniquely determine the $c_i^{(1)}$, the first coefficients of the right members of equations (6). Then the second set of equations uniquely determine the $c_i^{(2)}$.

* See Appendix C.

In general, the kth set of equations (7) uniquely determine the kth set of coefficients in the assumed solution (6).

The conclusion is that equations (1) have a formal analytic solution (6) and that it is unique. If the series (6) converge, the formal solution is an actual solution, for it will then satisfy the initial conditions and the identities (25), of Art. 8. Therefore, in order to complete the solution of the problem, the convergence of the series (6) must be proved.

16. Solution of an Auxiliary Problem. In order to prepare the way for a proof of the convergence of the formal solution (6), consider the differential equations

$$
(1') \begin{cases}
\dfrac{dX_1}{dt} = F_1(X_j; t) \\[2mm]
\quad = \dfrac{M}{\left[1 - \dfrac{(X_1 - a_1) + \cdots + (X_n - a_n)}{r}\right]\left[1 - \dfrac{t - t_0}{\rho'}\right]}, \\[4mm]
\cdots \cdots \cdots \cdots \cdots \cdots \cdots \cdots \\[2mm]
\dfrac{dX_n}{dt} = F_n(X_j; t) \\[2mm]
\quad = \dfrac{M}{\left[1 - \dfrac{(X_1 - a_1) + \cdots + (X_n - a_n)}{r}\right]\left[1 - \dfrac{t - t_0}{\rho'}\right]}, \\[4mm]
X_i(t_0) = a_i.
\end{cases}
$$

If $r < r_i$, $\rho' < \rho$ and $M \geqq |f_i(x_i; t)|$ for all values of the x_j and t in the domain D, the expansions of the right members of equations $(1')$ dominate the right members of equations (1). The constants r, ρ' and M will be so chosen that such is the case.

Since the right members of equations $(1')$ are identical, it 'ollows that

$$
\frac{dX_1}{dt} = \cdots = \frac{dX_n}{dt},
$$

which give, on making use of the initial values of the X_i,

$$
(8) \qquad X_1 - a_1 = \cdots = X_n - a_n = X,
$$

where, for simplicity, X is written for the common difference $X_i - a_i$. It follows from these equations that the value of X at $t = t_0$ is zero.

It follows from equations (1') and (8) that X satisfies the differential equation

(1'')
$$\begin{cases} \dfrac{dX}{dt} = \dfrac{M}{\left[1 - \dfrac{nX}{r}\right]\left[1 - \dfrac{t - t_0}{\rho'}\right]}, \\ X(t_0) = 0. \end{cases}$$

On separating the variables in equation (1'') in the usual way and performing the quadratures, it is found that

(9)
$$\frac{nX^2}{2r} - X = M\rho' \log\left[1 - \frac{t - t_0}{\rho'}\right] + C,$$

and the initial condition $X(t_0) = 0$ implies that $C = 0$.

The solution of equation (9) for X gives

(10)
$$X = \frac{r}{n}\left[1 \pm \sqrt{1 + \frac{2n}{r}M\rho' \log\left(1 - \frac{t - t_0}{\rho'}\right)}\right].$$

The negative sign must be taken before the radical in order to satisfy the condition $X(t_0) = 0$.

Now consider the expansion of the right member of equation (10) as a power series in $t - t_0$. The right member is an analytic function of t in the neighborhood of $t = t_0$, and it can, therefore, be expanded as a power series in $t - t_0$. Hence it follows from equations (8) that the $X_i - a_i$ can be expanded as power series in $t - t_0$ of the form

(6')
$$\begin{cases} X_1 - a_1 = C_1^{(1)}(t - t_0) + C_1^{(2)}(t - t_0)^2 + \cdots, \\ \cdot \quad \cdot \quad \cdot \quad \cdot \quad \cdot \quad \cdot \quad \cdot \quad \cdot \quad \cdot \quad \cdot \quad \cdot \quad \cdot \\ X_n - a_n = C_n^{(1)}(t - t_0) + C_n^{(2)}(t - t_0)^2 + \cdots, \end{cases}$$

which converge for sufficiently small values of $|t - t_0|$. It follows from equations (8) that the values of the $C_i^{(j)}$ are the same for $i = 1, \cdots, n$, but the subscripts have been written in order to emphasize the relationship between equations (6) and equations (6').

It is easy to determine the exact domain of convergence of the right members of the series (6'), which is obviously the same as the domain of convergence of the expansion of equation (10). The circle of convergence extends out to the nearest singular point of the function. There are two singular points of the right member of equation (10); namely, the essentially singular point $t - t_0 = \rho'$ and the branch-point given by the equation

$$1 + \frac{2n}{r} M\rho' \log\left(1 - \frac{t - t_0}{\rho'}\right) = 0.$$

The value of $t - t_0$ satisfying this equation is

$$t - t_0 = \rho'\left[1 - e^{-(r/2nM\rho')}\right].$$

Since the modulus of this branch-point is less than that of the singular point, it follows that the right members of equations (6′) converge for all values of t for which

$$(11) \qquad |t - t_0| < \rho'\left[1 - e^{-(r/2nM\rho')}\right].$$

The particular case in which the right members of the differential equations (1) do not involve t explicitly merits special mention for the reason that most differential equations arising in physical problems have this property. It is evident that the corresponding dominating differential equations can be obtained by putting $\rho' = \infty$ in equations (1′). Instead of starting from these equations and going through all the steps of the solution, it is simpler to determine the limit of the right member of the inequality (11) for $\rho' = \infty$. It is found that

$$\lim_{\rho'=\infty} \rho'\left[1 - e^{-(r/2nM\rho')}\right] = \lim_{\rho'=\infty} \rho'\left[1 - 1 + \frac{r}{2nM\rho'}\cdots\right]$$
$$= \frac{r}{2nM}.$$

Therefore, when the right members of equations (1′) are independent of t, the solution corresponding to the series (6′) converges for all values of t for which

$$(12) \qquad |t - t_0| < \frac{r}{2nM}.$$

17. Proof of Convergence of the Solution (6). The series (6′) are a solution of equations (1′) by their derivation. Therefore if the series (6′) are substituted into the expansions of (1′) as power series in their arguments, the results will be identities in $t - t_0$.

Equations (1′) can be solved by the methods of Art. 15 and the result will be of the form of the series (6′). Since the power series solution is formally unique, the result will be precisely the series (6'). The equations corresponding to equations (7) that determine the $C_i{}^{(i)}$ are

$$(7') \quad \begin{cases} C_i{}^{(1)} = F_i(a_j; t_0) \qquad (i = 1, \cdots, n), \\ 2C_i{}^{(2)} = \sum_{j=1}^{n} \dfrac{\partial F_i}{\partial X_j} C_j{}^{(1)} + \dfrac{\partial F_i}{\partial t}, \\ \;\cdot\;\;\cdot\;\;\cdot\;\;\cdot\;\;\cdot\;\;\cdot\;\;\cdot\;\;\cdot\;\;\cdot\;\;\cdot \\ kC_i{}^{(k)} = P_i{}^{(k)}(C_j{}^{(1)}, \cdots, C_j{}^{(k-1)}), \end{cases}$$

where the $P_i{}^{(k)}$ have the general Properties (a), (b), (c) of the $p_i{}^{(k)}$ of equations (7).

On making use of the fact that the expansions of the functions $F_i(X_j; t)$ dominate the expansions of the functions $f_i(x_j; t)$, and on comparing the first set of equations (7) with the first set of equations (7'), it is found that $C_i{}^{(1)} \geqq |c_i{}^{(1)}|$. Then it follows from the second sets of equations of (7) and of (7') that $C_i{}^{(2)} \geqq |c_i{}^{(2)}|$; and it follows sequentially from these results and the Properties (a), (b), and (c) that

$$C_i{}^{(k)} \geqq |c_i{}^{(k)}| \qquad (i = 1, \cdots, n; k = 1, 2, \cdots).$$

Therefore the power series (6') dominate the power series (6). Since the series (6') converge if the inequality (11) is satisfied, the solution series (6) also converge for all values of t satisfying the inequality (11).

It must not be inferred that the solution series (6) in every case converge only if the inequality (11) is satisfied; in many cases the domain of convergence is much larger. The reason is that the domain defined by (11) is one in which the series converge for all problems having the general properties possessed by the original differential equations. In most special cases the differential equations possess additional properties that give their solutions a wider domain of convergence. A larger domain of convergence would, indeed, have been obtained if the various M_i and the form of equations (4) had been used; but that result would likewise be too restricted. Since the method is important because it establishes the *existence* of a solution rather than the domain of its validity, the simple equations (1') are as useful as the more general ones would be. It should be remarked that there is no general method of determining the true domain of convergence of the solutions of differential equations of the type under discussion.

18. The Case of Linear Differential Equations. The true domain of convergence of the solutions can be determined, however, if the differential equations are linear; that is, if the variables x_i and their derivatives enter only linearly. Linear systems can be written in the form

$$
(13) \quad
\begin{cases}
\dfrac{dx_i}{dt} = \theta_{i1}(t)x_1 + \cdots + \theta_{in}(t)x_n + \theta_i(t) \quad (i = 1, \cdots, n), \\[2mm]
\phantom{\dfrac{dx_i}{dt}} = \displaystyle\sum_{j=1}^{n} \theta_{ij}(t)(x_j - a_j) + \sum_{j=1}^{n} \theta_{ij}(t)a_j + \theta_i(t), \\[2mm]
x_i(t_0) = a_i.
\end{cases}
$$

If the $\theta_i(t)$ are all identically zero, the equations are *homogeneous*. By hypothesis, the $\theta_{ij}(t)$ and the $\theta_i(t)$ are analytic functions of t, and they are, therefore, expansible as power series in $t - t_0$ of the form

$$
(14) \quad
\begin{cases}
\theta_{ij}(t) = \displaystyle\sum_{k=0}^{\infty} \theta_{ij}{}^{(k)}(t - t_0)^k, \\[2mm]
\theta_i(t) = \displaystyle\sum_{k=0}^{\infty} \theta_i{}^{(k)}(t - t_0)^k,
\end{cases}
$$

where the $\theta_{ij}{}^{(k)}$ and the $\theta_i{}^{(k)}$ are constant coefficients. Suppose the right members of equations (14) converge if $|t - t_0| \leqq \rho$.

Since the problem of linear differential equations is included as a special case in that of the general analytic differential equations treated in Arts. 15–17, it has an analytic solution

$$
(15) \quad x_i - a_i = \sum_{k=1}^{\infty} c_i{}^{(k)}(t - t_0)^k.
$$

On substituting the series (14) and (15) into equations (13), rearranging the right members as power series in $t - t_0$, and equating coefficients of corresponding powers of $t - t_0$, it is found that the coefficients $c_i{}^{(k)}$ are defined by the equations

$$
(16) \quad
\begin{cases}
c_i{}^{(1)} = \displaystyle\sum_{j=1}^{n} \theta_{ij}{}^{(0)}a_j + \theta_i{}^{(0)} \quad (i = 1, \cdots, n), \\[2mm]
2c_i{}^{(2)} = \displaystyle\sum_{j=1}^{n} \left[\theta_{ij}{}^{(1)}a_j + \theta_{ij}{}^{(0)}c_j{}^{(1)} \right] + \theta_i{}^{(1)}, \\[2mm]
\cdots \cdots \cdots \cdots \cdots \cdots \cdots \cdots \cdots \cdots \cdots \\[2mm]
kc_i{}^{(k)} = \displaystyle\sum_{j=1}^{n} \left[\theta_{ij}{}^{(k-1)}a_j + \theta_{ij}{}^{(k-2)}c_j{}^{(1)} + \cdots \right. \\[2mm]
\left. \hspace{4cm} + \theta_{ij}{}^{(0)}c_j{}^{(k-1)} \right] + \theta_i{}^{(k-1)}.
\end{cases}
$$

In order to secure advantageous dominating differential equations, let M be an upper bound of the $\theta_{ij}(t)$ and the

$$\sum_{j=1}^{n} \theta_{ij}(t)a_j + \theta_i(t)$$

for $|t - t_0| \leqq \rho$. Then the right members of the differential equations

$$(13')\quad \begin{cases} \dfrac{dX_i}{dt} = \dfrac{M\left[(X_1 - a_1) + \cdots + (X_n - a_n) + 1\right]}{1 - \dfrac{t - t_0}{\rho'}} \\[4mm] X_i(t_0) = a_i, \end{cases} \qquad (i = 1, \cdots, n),$$

dominate the right members of equations (13) and converge for all values of t for which $|t - t_0| < \rho' < \rho$.

It follows from equations (13') that the X_i have the relations

$$X_1 - a_1 = \cdots = X_n - a_n = X,$$

and that X satisfies the simple differential equation

$$(13'')\quad \begin{cases} \dfrac{dX}{dt} = \dfrac{M[nX + 1]}{1 - \dfrac{t - t_0}{\rho'}}, \\[4mm] X(t_0) = 0. \end{cases}$$

The solution of the equation (13'') subject to the initial condition $X(t_0) = 0$ is

$$(15')\qquad X = \frac{1}{n}\left[-1 + \left(1 - \frac{t - t_0}{\rho'}\right)^{-n\rho'M} \right],$$

the right member of which is expansible as a power series in $t - t_0$ that converges for all values of t for which $|t - t_0| < \rho'$. That is, the domain of convergence of the solution is coextensive with the common domain of convergence of the expansions of the coefficients of the differential equations (13). But in the non-linear case the domain of convergence of a solution is in general much less than that of the right members of the differential equations expanded as power series $t - t_0$.

In the special case in which the expansions of the $\theta_{ij}(t)$ and the $\theta_i(t)$ are permanently converging, as they would be if these functions were constants or polynomials in t, the solution series converge for all finite values of t.

II. Properties of the Analytic Solution

19. The Solution as Functions of t and of t_0. It follows from the form of the solution series (6) that the solution series are analytic functions of t. Moreover, the analytic solution is unique.

Now consider the solution as functions of t_0. If the functions $f_i(x_j; t)$ involve t explicitly, the coefficients of the expansions (3) will be functions of t_0; and it follows from the properties of these functions that they are expansible as power series in $t_0 - t_0^{(0)}$, where $t_0^{(0)}$ is any special value of t for which the $f_i(x_j; t)$ are all regular. Then it follows from Weierstrass' theorem, Appendix C, that the solution series (6) are expansible as power series in $t_0 - t_0^{(0)}$, converging if $\left| t_0 - t_0^{(0)} \right|$ is sufficiently small. That is, the solution is analytic in t_0, as well as in t, and it is therefore continuous in t_0; it may be differentiated any number of times with respect to t_0; it may be integrated with respect to t_0, etc.

In the special case in which the right members of equations (1) do not involve t explicitly, the $c_i^{(k)}$ are independent of t_0, and t_0 enters in the solution only in the combination $t - t_0$.

20. The Solution as Functions of the Initial Conditions. Under the hypotheses satisfied by equations (1), the coefficients of the right members of equations (3) are analytic functions of the a_i. Therefore the $c_i^{(k)}$ defined in equations (7) are analytic functions of the a_i; and then it follows from the theorem of Weierstrass that the solution series (6) are analytic functions of the a_i. The solution can be expanded as power series in $a_i - a_i^{(0)}$, where the $a_i^{(0)}$ are any set of values of the x_i for which the right members of the functions $f_i(x_j; t)$ are analytic.

The conclusion just stated is of great practical interest. It means, for example, that if the initial conditions were varied continuously in any physical system whose coördinates satisfy analytic differential equations, then the coördinates of the system at any time within the domain of convergence of the solution would also vary continuously. Although there are no exceptions to this theorem, the rates at which the coördinates vary with changes of the initial conditions may differ widely. For example, consider the solution in which a pendulum hangs vertically downward at rest. If the initial conditions are varied slightly by giving the pendulum a small initial displacement, then it is obvious that its coördinates and velocity at any subsequent time, say after an hour has elapsed, will differ only slightly from the position of rest. But if the initial solution is that in which the pendulum is vertically upward at rest, the problem seems different, for in this case an initial displacement, however small, will cause the pendulum to depart, in sufficient time, 180° from its initial position. Nevertheless, the theorem is true. If the initial displacement is sufficiently small, the displacement will be arbitrarily small after an hour or after any other finite interval. In the one case, the coördinates are slowly changing functions of the initial conditions; in the other, they are much more rapidly changing functions for a given initial displacement. This simple problem illustrates the importance of additional properties of solutions, such as stability, periodicity, and the like. The general properties now being given are only the first steps toward establishing all the special properties of the solution in any particular problem.

It will now be shown that the solutions of linear differential equations are linear functions of the initial values of the dependent variables. It follows from the first set of equations (16) that the $c_i^{(1)}$ are linear functions of the a_j; then it follows from the second set that the $c_i^{(2)}$ are linear functions of the a_j; and so on. Therefore the coefficients of the right members of equations (15) are linear functions of the a_j.

Although equations (15) converge for all values of t for which $|t - t_0| < \rho$, it does not follow from this fact alone that the convergence will still hold if the terms are broken up into their parts and regrouped with respect to the a_j. But the convergence after the rearrangement does hold, as can be established by simple considerations. The only condition to which the a_j are subject is that they shall all be finite. Suppose all the a_i are zero. The solution converges. Then suppose all of them except one are zero. The solution also converges. Similarly, each a_j in turn may be taken different from zero with all the remainder zero. It follows from the fact that the $c_i^{(k)}$ are linear in the a_j that these several solutions are precisely those that are obtained by breaking up the $c_i^{(k)}$ in the general case and rearranging them with respect to the a_j. The solutions of linear differential equations may, therefore, be written in the form

$$(17) \quad \begin{cases} x_1 = a_1 p_{11}(t) + \cdots + a_n p_{1n}(t) + p_1(t), \\ \cdots \cdots \cdots \cdots \cdots \cdots \cdots \\ x_n = a_1 p_{n1}(t) + \cdots + a_n p_{nn}(t) + p_n(t), \end{cases}$$

where the $p_{ij}(t)$ and the $p_i(t)$ are power series in $t - t_0$ that converge for all values of t for which $|t - t_0| < \rho$. The solutions of linear differential equations are thus seen to be sums of products of which one factor is a function that is independent of the initial conditions and of which the other is a constant. The functions of t converge for all values of t for which the inequality $|t - t_0| < \rho$ is satisfied.

One additional property of the solution (17) remains to be noted. It follows from equations (15) and (16) that the coefficients $p_{ij}(t)$ of the a_j depend only upon the $\theta_{ij}(t)$ of (13), but that the $p_i(t)$ depend upon both the $\theta_{ij}(t)$ and the $\theta_i(t)$.

21. The Solution as Functions of Parameters. Suppose the differential equations are

$$(18) \quad \begin{cases} \dfrac{dx_i}{dt} = f_i(x_j; \mu; t), \\ x_i(t_0) = a_i, \end{cases}$$

where μ is a parameter that is independent of the x_j and t.

As a first hypothesis, suppose the functions $f_i(x_j; \mu; t)$ are analytic functions of the x_j, μ, and t in the domain D defined by the inequalities $|x_j - a_j| \leqq r_j$, $|\mu| \leqq \sigma$, $|t - t_0| \leqq \rho$. The methods of Arts. 15–17 prove that an analytic solution in t exists having a domain defined by the inequality (11) within which the power series in $t - t_0$ certainly converge. But in this case the $c_i^{(k)}$, defined by equations analogous to (7), are analytic functions of μ for $|\mu| \leqq \sigma$. These coefficients can be expanded as power series in μ, and then by the theorem of Weierstrass it follows that the x_i of equations (6) are analytic functions of μ for all values of μ such that $|\mu| < \sigma$, provided t satisfies the inequality (11). It should be noted that in this case the upper bound M must be an upper bound of the $|f_i(x_j; \mu; t)|$ for all values of μ that satisfy $|\mu| \leqq \sigma$.

Now suppose the functions $f_i(x_j; \mu; t)$ are analytic in the x_j and t uniformly with respect to μ and continuous in μ in the domain D, but are not analytic in μ. It follows from Appendix A that the $|f_i(x_j; \mu; t)|$ are continuous in the x_j, μ, and t simultaneously in the closed domain D, and hence (Appendix A) have an upper bound M for the x_j, μ, and t in D. Consequently the methods of Arts. 15–17 hold, but the $c_i{}^{(k)}$ are now only continuous functions of μ. Each of the series (6) is, therefore, an infinite sum of continuous functions of μ that converges for all values of μ and t for which $0 \lessgtr \mu \leqq \sigma$ and t satisfies the inequality (11). Since M is an upper bound for all values of μ on its range, and since all the other quantities in the right member of the inequality (11) are independent of μ, it follows that the series (6) converge uniformly with respect to μ for $0 \lessgtr \mu \leqq \sigma$ and t satisfying the inequality (11). Therefore it follows from Appendix D that the solutions are continuous functions of μ.

The derivatives of the solution with respect to t are given by equations (18). Since the $f_i(x_j; \mu; t)$ are continuous functions of the x_j and μ for $|x_j - a_j| \leqq r_j$, $0 \leqq \mu \leqq \sigma$, $|t| \leqq \rho$, and since the x_j are continuous functions of μ for $0 \lessgtr \mu \leqq \sigma$ and t satisfying the inequality (11), it follows from Appendix F that the dx_i/dt are continuous functions of μ for all values of μ and t for which $0 \lessgtr \mu \leqq \sigma$, $|t - t_0| < \rho'[1 - e^{-(r/2nM\rho')}]$.

22. Illustrative Example.

Consider the differential equations

$$(19) \quad \begin{cases} \dfrac{dx_1}{dt} = f_1(x_1, x_2; t) = \dfrac{1}{(1 - x_1)(1 - x_2)(1 - t)}, \\[2mm] \dfrac{dx_2}{dt} = f_2(x_1, x_2; t) = \dfrac{1}{(1 + x_1)(1 + x_2)(1 + t)}, \\[2mm] t_0 = \tfrac{1}{4}, \\[1mm] x_1(\tfrac{1}{4}) = 0, \\[1mm] x_2(\tfrac{1}{4}) = \tfrac{1}{2}. \end{cases}$$

In order to obtain the solution, the right members of the first two of these equations must be expanded as power series in x_1, $x_2 - \tfrac{1}{2}$, and $t - \tfrac{1}{4}$. Since

$$1 - x_2 = \tfrac{1}{2}[1 - 2(x_2 - \tfrac{1}{2})], \qquad 1 + x_2 = \tfrac{3}{2}[1 + \tfrac{2}{3}(x_2 - \tfrac{1}{2})],$$

$$1 - t = \tfrac{3}{4}[1 - \tfrac{4}{3}(t - \tfrac{1}{4})], \qquad 1 + t = \tfrac{5}{4}[1 + \tfrac{4}{5}(t - \tfrac{1}{4})],$$

the expansions of the right members of equations (19) as power series in x_1, $x_2 - \frac{1}{2}$, and $t - \frac{1}{4}$ give the differential equations

$$(20) \quad \begin{cases} \dfrac{dx_1}{dt} = \dfrac{8}{3}[1 + x_1 + 2(x_2 - \tfrac{1}{2}) + \tfrac{4}{3}(t - \tfrac{1}{4}) \cdots], \\[2mm] \dfrac{dx_2}{dt} = \dfrac{8}{15}[1 - x_1 - \tfrac{2}{3}(x_2 - \tfrac{1}{2}) - \tfrac{4}{5}(t - \tfrac{1}{4}) \cdots], \end{cases}$$

which are in a convenient form for determining the coefficients of the solution.

The solution, by equations (6), can be expressed in the form

$$(21) \quad \begin{cases} x_1 - 0 = c_1{}^{(1)}(t - \tfrac{1}{4}) + c_1{}^{(2)}(t - \tfrac{1}{4})^2 + \cdots, \\[1mm] x_2 - \tfrac{1}{2} = c_2{}^{(1)}(t - \tfrac{1}{4}) + c_2{}^{(2)}(t - \tfrac{1}{4})^2 + \cdots. \end{cases}$$

Then the equations corresponding to equations (7) give

$$(22) \quad \begin{cases} c_1{}^{(1)} = \dfrac{8}{3}, \\[3mm] c_2{}^{(1)} = \dfrac{8}{15}, \\[3mm] 2c_1{}^{(2)} = \dfrac{8}{3} c_1{}^{(1)} + \dfrac{16}{3} c_2{}^{(1)} + \dfrac{32}{9} = + \dfrac{608}{45}, \\[3mm] 2c_2{}^{(2)} = -\dfrac{8}{15} c_1{}^{(1)} - \dfrac{16}{45} c_2{}^{(1)} - \dfrac{32}{75} = -\dfrac{1376}{675}, \\[3mm] \cdots \cdots \cdots \cdots \cdots \cdots \cdots \cdots, \end{cases}$$

and the solution to terms of the second degree in $t - \frac{1}{4}$ is

$$(23) \quad \begin{cases} x_1 = \dfrac{8}{3}\left(t - \dfrac{1}{4}\right) + \dfrac{304}{45}\left(t - \dfrac{1}{4}\right)^2 + \cdots, \\[3mm] x_2 = \dfrac{1}{2} + \dfrac{8}{15}\left(t - \dfrac{1}{4}\right) - \dfrac{688}{675}\left(t - \dfrac{1}{4}\right)^2 + \cdots \end{cases}$$

Now consider the determination of the domain of convergence defined by the inequality (11). It follows from equations (19) that the expansions converge only if $|x_1| < 1$, $|x_2 - \frac{1}{2}| < \frac{1}{2}$, and $|t - \frac{1}{4}| < \frac{3}{4}$. Therefore r_1, r_2, and ρ must be so chosen that $r_1 < 1$, $r_2 < \frac{1}{2}$, $r < \frac{1}{2}$, $\rho < \frac{3}{4}$. It follows from the inequality (11) that the smaller r and ρ' for a given value of M, the smaller the proved domain of convergence of the solution. On the other hand, it follows from equations (19) that in this problem the nearer r_1, r_2, and ρ are to their limits 1, $\frac{1}{2}$, and $\frac{3}{4}$, the larger is M; and it follows from the inequality (11) that the larger M

is, the smaller is the proved domain of convergence of the solution. It is evident from this simple illustration that in general the problem of finding the largest of (or the least upper bound to) the possible domains of convergence, as defined by the inequality (11), is one of considerable difficulty.

Let the problem of finding the largest domain as defined by the inequality (11) be omitted, and take simply $r_1 = r_2 = r = 0.4$, $\rho' = 0.5$. Then it follows from equations (19) that $M_1 = 200/3$, $M_2 = 200/99$, and therefore $M = 200/3$. Therefore the inequality (11) becomes in this problem

$$|t - \tfrac{1}{4}| < \tfrac{1}{2}[1 - e^{-(3/1000)}] = 0.0015 \cdots.$$

This proved domain of convergence appears to be small, but it must be remembered that it may be far less than the true domain. Another choice of r and ρ' might, indeed, increase it considerably.

II. QUESTIONS AND PROBLEMS

1. What are the precise conditions that must be satisfied in order that a function of several variables shall be analytic in a given domain?

2. Write out in full the terms of equations (3) of the fourth degree in all the arguments.

3. Write explicitly the definition of absolute and of uniform convergence. If a power series in the n variables $x_i - a_i$ converges for all $|x_i - a_i| < r_i$, is the convergence absolute at every point in this open region? Is the convergence necessarily uniform in the open region?

4. What are the facts respecting the convergence of the power-series expansion of the quotient of two power series?

5. Expand $\dfrac{1}{1 + 2x + 2x^2}$ as a power series in x and also in $x - 1$ to three terms. Determine the true domain of convergence for each series. Develop explicit dominating series for each of the expansions.

6. Determine and compare the true radii of convergence of the power-series solutions of the following differential equations:

$$\begin{cases} \dfrac{dX}{dt} = A(1 + X)^n \\ \dfrac{dX}{dt} = A[1 + X + \cdots + X^n], \\ X(t_0) = 0. \end{cases}$$

Note and use the fact that $(1 - X)[1 + X + \cdots + X^n] = 1 - X^{n+1}$, and refer to Art. 61. Determine radii of convergence of the solutions by the method of Art. 16 and the inequality (11).

7. Construct the solution of the differential equations

$$\begin{cases} \dfrac{dx_1}{dt} = 1 + 3x_1 - 4x_1x_2{}^2 - 5x_1{}^4, \\[2mm] \dfrac{dx_2}{dt} = 2 + x_1 - 3x_1{}^2x_2 - 4x_1x_2{}^3, \\[2mm] x_1(0) = 0, \qquad x_2(0) = 1 \end{cases}$$

to the fifth power of t. Construct a dominating series for this problem and determine a domain of convergence corresponding to the inequality (12).

8. Derive the inequality (12) directly from the equation (1'') with $\rho' = \infty$.

9. Start from equations (1') and derive the inequality corresponding to that in (11). Prove that this domain is greater than defined by (11) unless

$$M_1 = \cdots = M_n, \qquad r_1' = \cdots = r_n'.$$

10. Make a direct proof by using dominating functions that the power-series solutions of linear differential equations whose coefficients are polynomials in t converge for all finite values of t.

11. Prove in detail that if the right members of equations (18) possess continuous derivatives with respect to the parameter μ, the solution functions and their first derivatives with respect to t possess continuous first derivatives with respect to μ. Do the higher derivatives of the solution with respect to t possess derivatives with respect to μ?

12. Prove that if the expansions of the functions $f_i(x_j; t)$ as power series in the $x_j - a_j$ and t converge for all finite values of t provided $|x_j - a_j| < r_j$, then the inequality (12) defines a domain within which the solution converges.

13. It was proved in Arts. 19 and 20 that the solution functions are continuous in t, t_0, and the a_i individually. Prove that they are continuous in these arguments simultaneously. (See Appendix A.)

HISTORICAL SKETCH

The formal construction of solutions of analytic differential equations dates back to Euler in the middle of the eighteenth century, but the proof that the formal solution converges within sufficiently restricted limits is due to Cauchy, though Weierstrass independently discovered essentially the same proof (*Ges. Werke*, Vol. 2, p. 67). The theory and application of dominant functions in the proof of the existence of solutions of differential equations, and in related fields, which evidently had to await the founding of the theory of analytic functions, formed the subject matter of a series of papers published by Cauchy during the years 1839 to 1842 in *Comptes Rendus de l'Académie des Sciences de Paris*. Cauchy's most important contributions to the theory of analytic differential equations were published on August 5 and November 21, 1839; on June 29, October 26, and November 2 and 9, 1840; and on June 20 and July 4, 1842. These papers are collected in Cauchy's *Oeuvres Complètes*, first series, Vols. 4 to 7 and Vol. 10. The theory was called by Cauchy "*Calcul des Limites*," because it provides lower limits within which the solutions certainly converge.

Cauchy's demonstration of the existence of solutions was simplified by Briot and Bouquet, in *Comptes Rendus*, Vol. 40 (1855), p. 787. Since the proved limits of convergence of a solution are, in general, more restricted than the actual domain of its convergence, numerous papers have been published for the purpose of extending the proved limits. They were notably increased in Picard's *Cours d'Analyse* (p. 292), edited by Caron and Philippe and lithographed in 1887. They have also been extended by Stöckel [*Comptes Rendus*, Vol. 126 (1898), p. 203] and by Lindelöf [*Acta Société Scientifique de Fennicae*, Vol. 21 (1896), pp. 1–13]. Such extensions are of no theoretical importance; and, since they do not give the true domain of convergence, they are of little practical interest.

It was noted in Art. 15 that the analytic solution of analytic differential equations is unique. The question arises whether there are other solutions which are not analytic for which the x_i tend toward the a_i as t tends toward t_0. Briot and Bouquet [*Journal de l'École Polytechnique*, Vol. 36 (1856), p. 31] proved that there exists no other solution in which the x_i tend toward the a_i along paths of finite length as t tends toward t_0. Picard [*Traité d'Analyse*, second edition, Vol. 2, p. 357] has demonstrated the uniqueness of the solution subject to the condition that the x_i tend toward the a_i as t tends toward t_0 in the sense that, corresponding to every positive ϵ, there exists a $\delta_\epsilon > 0$ such that, for all values of t satisfying the inequality $|t - t_0| < \delta_\epsilon$, the x_i of the solution satisfy the inequalities $|x_i - a_i| < \epsilon$. This demonstration depends upon the use of implicit functions.

It will be noted that the theorem of Briot and Bouquet and that of Picard are quite distinct, for the latter makes no use of the notion of the length of a path described by a variable. Such notions grew up quite naturally in connection with the origin of differential equations in dynamical problems, but they have no essential relationship to the logical definition of a solution. A solution of a system of differential equations is a set of functions having certain properties at all points in some domain, but in these properties there is nothing pertaining to the paths of variables.

The theorem that the analytic solution of a system of analytic differential equations is the only continuous solution will be proved in Art. 128.

CHAPTER III

DIFFERENTIAL EQUATIONS ANALYTIC IN
A PARAMETER

I. Construction and Existence of a Solution

23. Differential Equations of Special Type. It is advisable to treat first a special class of differential equations having the form

$$(1) \quad \begin{cases} \dfrac{dx_i}{dt} = \mu f_i(x_j; \mu; t), \\[2mm] x_i(t_0) = a_i, \end{cases}$$

where μ represents a parameter that is constant with respect to the x_j and t. In the special class of equations now under consideration, the right members contain the parameter μ as a factor. The constants a_i are assumed to be independent of μ.

It is assumed that the $f_i(x_j; \mu; t)$ have the following properties:

Property 1. The $f_i(x_j; \mu; t)$ are analytic functions of the x_j and μ, but not necessarily of t, for all values of the x_j, μ, and t for which $|x_j - a_j| \leqq r_j$, $|\mu| \leqq \sigma$, $t_0 \leqq t \leqq T$.

Property 2. The $f_i(x_j; \mu; t)$ are continuous functions of t for all values of the x_j, μ, and t for which $|x_j - a_j| \leqq r_j$, $|\mu| \leqq \sigma$, $t_0 \leqq t \leqq T$. Hence, by Appendix A, the $f_i(x_j; \mu; t)$ are continuous functions of the x_j, μ, and t simultaneously.

It is to be noted that in this case the independent variable t is assumed to be real, although the discussions that follow, with slight modifications, would apply if the range of t were any curve of finite length in the complex plane. Moreover, the functions $f_i(x_j; \mu; t)$ need be only continuous in t instead of being analytic as in Chapter II. Hence these differential equations are more general functions of t than those of Chapter II.

It follows from Properties 1 and 2 and Appendix A that the

absolute values of the functions $f_i(x_j; \mu; t)$ have upper bounds M_i in the domains of the variables. Moreover, the functions $f_i(x_j; \mu; t)$ are expansible as power series in the $x_j - a_j$ and μ, but not in $t - t_0$, that converge for all values of x_j, μ, and t for which $|x_j - a_j| \leqq r_j$, $|\mu| \leqq \sigma$, $t_0 \lessgtr t \leqq T$. It follows from Appendix B that power series in the $x_j - a_j$ and μ exist that dominate the power series expansions of the functions $f_i(x_j; \mu; t)$ for all values of t for which $t_0 \lessgtr t \leqq T$, and that converge for all values of the x_j, μ, and t for which $|x_j - a_j| < r_j' < r_j$, $|\mu| < \sigma' < \sigma$, and $t_0 \lessgtr t \leqq T$.

24. Formal Construction of the Solution. There exists a formal solution of equations (1) in the power series form

(2) $$x_i = a_i + x_i^{(1)}(t)\mu + x_i^{(2)}(t)\mu^2 + \cdots,$$

where the $x_i^{(j)}(t)$ are functions of t which are to be determined.

On substituting equations (2) into equations (1) after their right members have been developed as power series in the $x_j - a_j$ and μ, rearranging the terms according to powers of μ, and equating coefficients of corresponding powers of μ, the infinite series of systems of differential equations is obtained:

(3) $$\begin{cases} \dfrac{dx_i^{(1)}}{dt} = f_i(a_j; 0; t) & (i = 1, \cdots, n), \\[2mm] \dfrac{dx_i^{(2)}}{dt} = \sum_{j=1}^{n} \dfrac{\partial f_i}{\partial x_j} x_j^{(1)} + \dfrac{\partial f_i}{\partial \mu}, \\[2mm] \dfrac{dx_i^{(\kappa)}}{dt} = p_i^{(\kappa)}(x_j^{(1)}, \cdots, x_j^{(\kappa-1)}; t) & (\kappa = 1, 2, \cdots), \end{cases}$$

where the $p_i^{(\kappa)}$ are polynomials in the $x_j^{(1)}, \cdots, x_j^{(\kappa-1)}$, but not in $t - t_0$, whose coefficients are linear functions of the coefficients of the expansions of the functions $f_i(x_j; \mu; t)$ as power series in the $x_j - a_j$ and μ, and the coefficients have positive numerical multipliers.

Since the $f_i(a_j; 0; t)$ are continuous functions of t, the first set of equations (3) gives

(4) $$x_i^{(1)} = \int f_i(a_j; 0; t)dt = F_i^{(1)}(t) + c_i^{(1)},$$

where the $c_i^{(1)}$ are arbitrary constants.

Upon substituting the $x_i^{(1)}$ of equations (4) into the second set of equations (3), the right members of the latter become known continuous functions of t, and therefore the $x_i^{(2)}$ are defined by quadratures. Then the right members of the third set become known continuous functions of t, and so on sequentially. The general step of the process gives

$$(5) \qquad x_i^{(\kappa)} = \int p_i^{(\kappa)}(x_j^{(1)}, \cdots, x_j^{(\kappa-1)})dt = F_i^{(\kappa)}(t) + c_i^{(\kappa)},$$

where the $c_i^{(\kappa)}$ are arbitrary constants.

The infinitely many sets of constants $c_i^{(\kappa)}$ must be determined in terms of the a_i. Upon substituting the right members of equations (5) into equations (2) and putting $t = t_0$, it follows that

$$a_i \underset{\mu}{\equiv} a_i + [F_i^{(1)}(t_0) + c_i^{(1)}]\mu + [F_i^{(2)}(t_0) + c_i^{(2)}]\mu^2 + \cdots.$$

These identities in μ imply that the $c_i^{(\kappa)}$ have the values

$$c_i^{(1)} = -F_i^{(1)}(t_0), \qquad \cdots, \qquad c_i^{(\kappa)} = -F_i^{(\kappa)}(t_0), \qquad \cdots.$$

Therefore the functions $x_i^{(\kappa)}$ are the definite integrals

$$(6) \qquad x_i^{(\kappa)} = \int_{t_0}^{t} p_i^{(\kappa)}(x_j^{(1)}, \cdots, x_j^{(\kappa-1)}; t)dt$$
$$(i = 1, \cdots, n; \kappa = 1, 2, \cdots),$$

and they are uniquely determined by the process.

It follows that, in the method of solving differential equations now under consideration, the coefficients are determined by quadratures rather than from linear equations as in Art. 15. This method, however, presents no difficulties theoretically and but few practically. In fact, in physical problems it is often greatly superior to that of Chapter II.

25. Proof of Convergence of the Formal Solution. The steps taken in writing equations (3) are purely formal unless equations (2) converge in some positive domain; and if equations (2) converge in any domain not zero, then it follows from Appendix C that all the steps taken in deriving equations (3) are valid.

The general method of procedure in the proof of the convergence of equations (2) is similar to that employed in Arts. 16 and 17. If $M \geqq M_i$, $\sigma' < \sigma$, $r < r_i$, the expansions of the right members of equations (1) as power series in the $x_j - a_j$ and μ are dominated, for all values of t for which $t_0 \leqq t \leqq T$, by the expansions of the right members of the differential equations

$$(1')\quad \begin{cases} \dfrac{dX_i}{dt} = \dfrac{\mu M}{\left(1 - \dfrac{\mu}{\sigma'}\right)\left[1 - \dfrac{(X_1 - a_1) + \cdots + (X_n - a_n)}{r}\right]}, \\ X_i(t_0) = a_i. \end{cases}$$

It follows from equations $(1')$ that $X_1 - a_1 = \cdots = X_n - a_n = X$ and that X satisfies the differential equation

$$(1'')\quad \begin{cases} \dfrac{dX}{dt} = \mu F_i(X_i; \mu) = \dfrac{\mu M}{\left(1 - \dfrac{\mu}{\sigma'}\right)\left[1 - \dfrac{nX}{r}\right]}, \\ X(t_0) = 0. \end{cases}$$

The solution of the equation $(1'')$ subject to the initial condition $X(t_0) = 0$, when solved for X, gives the equation

$$(2')\quad X = \frac{r}{n}\left[1 - \sqrt{1 - \frac{2nM\mu(t - t_0)}{r\left(1 - \dfrac{\mu}{\sigma'}\right)}}\right].$$

The two singularities of the right member of this equation are given by the equations

$$\begin{cases} \mu = \sigma', \\ 2nM\mu(t - t_0) = r\left(1 - \dfrac{\mu}{\sigma'}\right). \end{cases}$$

It follows from the second of these equations that the expansion of the right member of $(2')$ as a power series in μ converges, for any particular value of t, if

$$(7)\quad |\mu| < \frac{\sigma'}{1 + 2nM\dfrac{\sigma'}{r}(t - t_0)}.$$

The expansions of the X_i as power series in the parameter μ converge under the same condition.

Since the right members of equations $(1')$ have all the properties ascribed to the right members of equations (1), these differential equations can be solved in a similar manner as power series in μ. Since the power-series solution is unique, it is identical with that obtained by expanding the right member of equation $(2')$ and it converges if the inequality (7) is satisfied.

The coefficients in the solution of (1′) are defined by

$$(5') \quad \begin{cases} X_i{}^{(1)} = \int_{t_0}^t F_i(a_j; 0)dt \qquad (i = 1, \cdots, n), \\ X_i{}^{(\kappa)} = \int_{t_0}^t P_i{}^{(\kappa)}(X_j{}^{(1)}, \cdots, X_j{}^{(\kappa-1)})dt, \end{cases}$$

where the $P_i{}^{(\kappa)}$ are polynomials in the $X_i{}^{(j)}$ having the general properties of the polynomials $p_i{}^{(\kappa)}$.

It is found on comparing equations (4) and (5) with equations (5′) that

$$(8) \quad \begin{cases} X_i{}^{(1)} \geqq |x_i{}^{(1)}| \qquad (t_0 \geqq t \leqq T), \\ X_i{}^{(\kappa)} \geqq |x_i{}^{(\kappa)}| \qquad (t_0 \geqq t \leqq T; \kappa = 1, 2, \cdots). \end{cases}$$

Therefore the solution series (2) converge at least if the inequality (7) is satisfied; that is, the series (2) constitute a solution in the domain defined by the inequality (7).

26. Various Formulations of the Conditions under which the Solution Series Converge. The method of solution now under consideration is capable of application in so many theoretical and practical problems that the conditions under which its validity has been established merit careful consideration. The foregoing treatment has been so arranged that all the conclusions that have heretofore been reached in this problem flow from the inequality (7). They are contained in the following theorems:

THEOREM * I. *It follows from the inequality* (7) *that it is possible to determine a σ_1 and a T_1 such that the solution of the differential equations* (1) *as power series in μ will converge for all values of μ and of t for which* $|\mu| < \sigma_1$, $t_0 \geqq t \leqq T_1$.

THEOREM † II. *It follows from the inequality* (7) *that for an arbitrary T_1, such that $t_0 < T_1 \leqq T$, it is possible to determine a σ_1 such that the solution of the differential equations* (1) *as power series in μ will converge for all values of μ and of t for which* $|\mu| < \sigma_1$, $t_0 \geqq t \leqq T_1$.

The difference in Theorems I and II is simply that in the former both σ_1 and T_1 are restricted; in the latter, T_1 is arbitrary in its domain. In the present derivation the difference seems trivial; yet the second theorem, which played a major rôle in

* Cauchy, *Collected Works*, Series I, Vol. 7, p. 62.
† Poincaré, *Les Méthodes Nouvelles de la Mécanique Céleste*, Vol. 1, page 48.

the work of Poincaré on the problem of three bodies, followed the first by fifty years.

THEOREM III. *It follows from the inequality* (7) *that for every arbitrary* μ' *such that* $|\mu'| < \sigma$ *it is possible to determine a* T_1 *such that the solution of the differential equations* (1) *as power series in* μ *will converge for all values of* μ *and of* t *for which* $|\mu| < |\mu'|$, $t_0 \leqq t \leqq T_1$.

In Theorem III the value of μ is arbitrary in its domain, and the convergence is assured by restricting t.   In order to illustrate the force of this theorem, consider the differential equations

$$(9) \qquad \begin{cases} \dfrac{dx_i}{dt} = f_i(x_j; t), \\[2mm] x_i(t_0) = a_i, \end{cases}$$

of which the right members are continuous in t and are expansible as converging power series in $x_j - a_j$ for all $|x_j - a_j| \leqq r_j$ and $t_0 \leqq t \leqq T$, and do not depend upon a parameter μ.   Inasmuch as the functions $f_i(x_j; t)$ are not supposed to be analytic in t, the methods of Chapter II cannot be applied; and since there is no parameter μ present, apparently the method of this chapter is not applicable.   But let the right member of equations (9) be multiplied by the factor μ.   Then the method of this chapter can be applied and it is valid if the inequality (7) is satisfied. After the solution has been formed, place μ equal to unity and the problem reduces simply to that of equations (9).   By Theorem III, the solution is valid for $t_0 \leqq t \leqq T_1$.

Consider the question of the domain of convergence in this problem.   Since the functions $f_i(x_j; t)$ do not depend upon μ, the constant σ' in equations (1') and (1'') is infinite.   The limit of the inequality (7) for $\sigma' = \infty$ is

$$(10) \qquad |\mu| < \frac{r}{2nM(t - t_0)},$$

which is a sufficient condition for the convergence of the solution when the $f_i(x_j; t)$ of equations (1) are multiplied by the factor μ, but do not depend upon μ.   In the problem under consideration $\mu = 1$, and therefore the inequality (10) gives

$$(11) \qquad 0 \leqq t - t_0 < \frac{r}{2nM} = T_1 - t_0$$

as sufficient conditions for the convergence of the solution as power series in the artificially introduced parameter μ.

In the special case in which the functions $f_i(x_j)$ do not depend upon t, the solution may be expanded as power series in $t - t_0$ by the method of Arts. 15–17, or as power series in μ by the method of the present chapter. The limitation (11) on $t - t_0$ is identical with the real part of the limitation on $t - t_0$ of the inequality (12) of Art. 16.

27. Differential Equations for the General Problem. The differential equations (1) contain the parameter μ as a factor of their right members. This particular property will now be waived, and for convenience and without loss of generality the differential equations will be written in the form

$$(12) \quad \begin{cases} \dfrac{dx_i}{dt} = g_i(x_j; t) + \mu f_i(x_j; \mu; t), \\ x_i(t_0) \equiv a_i. \end{cases}$$

These differential equations include equations (1) as a special case; namely, that in which $g_i(x_j; t) \equiv 0$. But when the functions $g_i(x_j; t)$ are not identically zero, the difficulty of the problem is considerably increased.

Before specifying in detail the properties of the functions $g_i(x_j; t)$ and the functions $f_i(x_j; \mu; t)$, consider the related problem

$$(13) \quad \begin{cases} \dfrac{dx_i^{(0)}}{dt} = g_i(x_i^{(0)}; t), \\ x_i^{(0)}(t_0) = a_i. \end{cases}$$

It will be assumed either that the functions $g_i(x_i^{(0)}; t)$ are analytic in the $x_i^{(0)}$ and t for all values of the $x_i^{(0)}$ and t for which $|x_i^{(0)} - a_i| \leq r_i^{(0)}$, $|t - t_0| < \rho^{(0)}$, or that the $g_i(x_i^{(0)}; t)$ are analytic in the variables $x_i^{(0)}$ and that they may be only continuous in t for all $|x_i^{(0)} - a_i| \leq r_i^{(0)}$, $t_0 \leqq t \leqq T^{(0)}$. In the former case, the solution can be obtained for a sufficiently restricted domain for t by either the method of Art. 15 or that of Art. 24; in the latter case, the solution cannot be obtained by the method of Art. 15, but it can be obtained by the method of Art. 24. It will be seen in Chapters XI, XII, and XIII that there are still other methods of obtaining the solution of equations of the type (13). In physical problems equations (13) are often very simple and can be solved by elementary methods.

Suppose that by some suitable method the solution

$$(14) \qquad x_i^{(0)}(t) = \phi_i(t)$$

has been obtained for $t_0 \lesseqgtr t \leqq T^{(0)}$, and that the $\phi_i(t)$ are continuous functions of t in the interval.

It is now assumed that the right members of equations (12) have the following properties:

Property 1. The functions $g_i(x_j; t)$ are analytic in the $x_j - x_i^{(0)}$ and continuous in t for all x_j and t for which $\left| x_j - x_i^{(0)} \right| \leqq r_j$, $t_0 \lesseqgtr t \leqq T^{(0)}$.

Property 2. The $f_i(x_j; \mu; t)$ are analytic in the $x_j - x_i^{(0)}$ and μ uniformly with respect to t and are continuous in t for all x_j, μ, and t for which $\left| x_j - x_i^{(0)} \right| \leqq r_j$, $|\mu| \leqq \sigma$, $t_0 \lesseqgtr t \leqq T \leqq T^{(0)}$.

The expansions of the right members of equations (12) will be in powers of the $x_j - x_i^{(0)}$ and μ. Since the $x_i^{(0)}$ are functions of t, the expansions are about the variable point $x_i^{(0)}$ instead of about a fixed point a_j, as in the case of equations (1). It is important for applications to understand the precise meaning of this difference. To fix the ideas, suppose the differential equations (1) represent those satisfied by the coördinates of a planet in its motion around the sun. The a_i are the initial values of the coördinates, and the $x_i - a_i$ are the coördinates at any other time within the domain of convergence of the solution.

Now, by way of contrast, suppose equations (12) are satisfied by the motion of the moon about the earth, and that the functions $g_i(x_j; t)$ contain all the accelerations due to the earth, while the functions $\mu f_i(x_j; \mu; t)$ contain the much smaller ones due to the sun. In this case the solution (14) is elliptic motion and holds for all finite values of t. The variables $x_j - x_i^{(0)}$, which become in effect the actual dependent variables of the problem, are simply the differences between the coördinates of the moon in its orbit, as slightly modified by the attraction of the sun, and the coördinates $x_i^{(0)}$ it would have if it were subject to the earth's attraction alone. It is obvious that in this problem the $x_j - x_i^{(0)}$ are very much smaller than the $x_j - a_j$, and for this reason the method is often of very great use in problems of this type. It will be noted that the method is advantageous when, by omitting relatively small terms from the right members of the differential equations, the problem reduces to one that can be simply solved.

28. Formal Construction of the Solution of Equations (12). The solution of equations (12) will be developed as power series in μ of the form

$$(15) \qquad x_i - x_i^{(0)} = x_i^{(1)}(t)\mu + x_i^{(2)}(t)\mu^2 + \cdots,$$

where the $x_i^{(0)}(t)$ satisfy equations (13) and the $x_i^{(\kappa)}(t)$ are functions of t which are to be determined.

Upon substituting the right members of equations (15) into the expansions of the right members of equations (12) as power series in the $x_j - x_j^{(0)}$ and μ, rearranging the terms as power series in μ, and equating coefficients of corresponding powers of μ, it is found that

$$(16) \quad \begin{cases} \dfrac{dx_i^{(1)}}{dt} - \displaystyle\sum_{j=1}^{n} \dfrac{\partial g_i}{\partial x_j} x_j^{(1)} = f_i(x_j^{(0)}; 0; t) \qquad (i = 1, \cdots, n), \\[2ex] \dfrac{dx_i^{(2)}}{dt} - \displaystyle\sum_{j=1}^{n} \dfrac{\partial g_i}{\partial x_j} x_j^{(2)} = \dfrac{1}{2} \displaystyle\sum_{j=1}^{n} \sum_{\kappa=1}^{n} \dfrac{\partial^2 g_i}{\partial x_j \partial x_\kappa} x_j^{(1)} x_\kappa^{(1)} \\[2ex] \qquad\qquad\qquad\qquad\qquad + \displaystyle\sum_{j=1}^{n} \dfrac{\partial f_i}{\partial x_j} x_j^{(1)} + \dfrac{\partial f_i}{\partial \mu}, \\[1ex] \cdots \cdots \cdots \cdots \cdots \cdots \cdots \cdots \cdots \\[1ex] \dfrac{dx_i^{(\kappa)}}{dt} - \displaystyle\sum_{j=1}^{n} \dfrac{\partial g_i}{\partial x_j} x_j^{(\kappa)} = p_i^{(\kappa)}(x_j^{(1)}, \cdots, x_j^{(\kappa-1)}; t), \\[1ex] \cdots \cdots \cdots \cdots \cdots \cdots \cdots \cdots \cdots \end{cases}$$

where the x_j and μ are repiaced by the $x_j^{(0)}$ and 0 respectively in the partial derivatives, and where the $p_i^{(\kappa)}(x_j^{(1)}, \cdots, x_j^{(\kappa-1)}; t)$ are polynomials in the $x_j^{(1)}, \cdots, x_j^{(\kappa-1)}$, but not in t, whose coefficients are linear functions of the coefficients of the expansions of the functions $g_i(x_j; t)$ and the functions $f_i(x_j; \mu; t)$ as power series in the $x_j - x_j^{(0)}$ and μ, and have positive numerical multipliers. It will be noted that the left members of each set of differential equations (16) have the same coefficients as every other set, but that the right members vary with the superscript κ on the x_j.

Consider the solution of the first set of equations (16). The dependent variables are the $x_i^{(1)}$. Except for notation, they are of the form of equations (13), of Art. 18, and are consequently linear differential equations. Therefore, in case the $g_i(x_j; t)$ are analytic functions of t, the solution has the properties of equations (17), of Art. 20. And if the $g_i(x_j; t)$ are not analytic functions of t, the solution can be found by the method of Art. 24. An examination of this method in the case in which the functions $f_i(x_j; \mu; t)$, of equations (1), are linear in the x_j shows that the solution functions are linear functions of the initial values of the $x_i^{(1)}$, and hence are of the form of equations (17), of Art. 20.

For notation, let the solution of the first set of equations (16) be written

$$(17) \quad \begin{cases} x_1^{(1)} = A_1^{(1)}\phi_{11}(t) + \cdots + A_n^{(1)}\phi_{1n}(t) + \phi_1^{(1)}(t), \\ \cdot \quad \cdot \quad \cdot \quad \cdot \quad \cdot \quad \cdot \quad \cdot \quad \cdot \quad \cdot \quad \cdot \quad \cdot \quad \cdot \\ x_n^{(1)} = A_1^{(1)}\phi_{n1}(t) + \cdots + A_n^{(1)}\phi_{nn}(t) + \phi_n^{(1)}(t), \end{cases}$$

where the $A_i^{(1)}$ are constants that depend upon the initial values of the $x_i^{(1)}$.

It follows from the final property for the solution of linear differential equations derived in Art. 20 that the ϕ_{ij} of equations (17) depend only upon the left members of the first set of equations (16). Since all the sets of equations (16) have the same coefficients in their left members, the ϕ_{ij} will be the same for all sets. It was for this reason that they have not been given superscripts. On the other hand, the functions $\phi_i^{(1)}(t)$ depend upon both the left and the right members of the differential equations (16), and since the right members vary from one set to another, these parts of the solution have been given superscripts. The constants $A_i^{(1)}$ have been given superscripts because they depend upon the initial values of the $x_i^{(1)}$, which may vary with the superscript on the x_i.

Now consider the second set of differential equations of (16). The right members are known functions of t by virtue of equations (17), and consequently are linear and non-homogeneous. Since the coefficients of the left members of this set are the same as the corresponding coefficients of the first set, the solution in the notation of equations (17) is

$$(18) \quad \begin{cases} x_i^{(2)} = A_1^{(2)}\phi_{11}(t) + \cdots + A_n^{(2)}\phi_{1n}(t) + \phi_1^{(2)}(t), \\ \cdot \quad \cdot \quad \cdot \quad \cdot \quad \cdot \quad \cdot \quad \cdot \quad \cdot \quad \cdot \quad \cdot \quad \cdot \quad \cdot \\ x_n^{(2)} = A_1^{(2)}\phi_{n1}(t) + \cdots + A_n^{(2)}\phi_{nn}(t) + \phi_n^{(2)}(t). \end{cases}$$

Similarly, the solution of the general set of differential equations of (16) is

$$(19) \quad \begin{cases} x_1^{(\kappa)} = A_1^{(\kappa)}\phi_{11}(t) + \cdots + A_n^{(\kappa)}\phi_{1n}(t) + \phi_1^{(\kappa)}(t), \\ \cdots\cdots\cdots\cdots\cdots\cdots\cdots \\ x_n^{(\kappa)} = A_1^{(\kappa)}\phi_{n1}(t) + \cdots + A_n^{(\kappa)}\phi_{nn}(t) + \phi_n^{(\kappa)}(t). \end{cases}$$

The constants $A_i^{(\kappa)}$ $(i = 1, \cdots, n; \kappa = 1, 2, \cdots)$ remain to be determined from the initial conditions. Since $x_i(t_0) \equiv x_i^{(0)}(t_0) = a_i$, it follows upon substituting the $x_i^{(\kappa)}$ of equations (19) into equations (15) that

$$(20) \quad \begin{cases} A_1^{(\kappa)}\phi_{11}(t_0) + \cdots + A_n^{(\kappa)}\phi_{1n}(t_0) = -\phi_1^{(\kappa)}(t_0), \\ \cdots\cdots\cdots\cdots\cdots\cdots\cdots \\ A_1^{(\kappa)}\phi_{n1}(t_0) + \cdots + A_n^{(\kappa)}\phi_{nn}(t_0) = -\phi_n^{(\kappa)}(t_0). \end{cases}$$

These linear equations uniquely determine the $A_i^{(\kappa)}$ for all values of κ provided the determinant of the coefficients is not zero.

Consider equations (17) whose coefficients have the same determinant as that of equations (18). The functions $\phi_{ij}(t)$ are the same whatever the right members of the first set of equations (16) by which they are defined. Hence suppose for the purpose of the present discussion that these right members are identically zero; then the $\phi_i^{(1)}(t)$ of equations (17) are identically zero. Let $A_i^{(1)}$ be the value of $x_i^{(1)}$ at $t = t_0$; then it follows from equations (17) that $\phi_{ii}(t_0) = 1$ $(i = 1, \cdots, n)$ and $\phi_{ij}(t_0) = 0$ $(j \neq i)$. The determinant of the coefficients of equations (17) is therefore unity at $t = t_0$; and since the $\phi_{ij}(t)$ are continuous functions of t, the determinant is distinct from zero for all values of t for which $|t|$ is sufficiently small. Consequently the $A_i^{(\kappa)}$ are uniquely determined. When they are substituted into equations (19) and these results are substituted into equations (15), the formal solution is complete.

It will be noted on comparing the construction of the solution of Art. 24 with that given here that the simple quadratures of the former have been replaced in the latter by the more difficult problem of solving linear differential equations.

29. Proof of Convergence of the Formal Solution. The proof of the convergence of the formal solution is by the same general method as that employed in Art. 25. There is, however, more difficulty in choosing suitable dominating functions.

In order to make use effectively of the fact that the actual dependent variables of the problem are the $x_i - x_i^{(0)}$, let equations (13) be subtracted from equations (12). The results are

$$(21) \quad \begin{cases} \dfrac{d}{dt}(x_i - x_i^{(0)}) = g_i(x_j; t) - g_i(x_j^{(0)}; t) + \mu f_i(x_j; \mu; t), \\ x_i - x_i^{(0)} = 0 \quad \text{at} \quad t = t_0. \end{cases}$$

The expansions of the right members of these equations as power series in the $x_i - x_i^{(0)}$ and μ do not contain any terms independent of these arguments. The same property must be possessed by the dominating differential equations.

Let M represent a common upper bound for the functions $|g_i(x_j; t) - g_i(x_j^{(0)}; t) + \mu f_i(x_j; \mu; t)|$ for the $|x_j - x_j^{(0)}| \leqq r_j$, $|\mu| \leqq \sigma$, $t_0 \leqq t \leqq T$. Then the expansions of the right members of equations (21) as power series in the $x_j - x_j^{(0)}$ and μ are dominated by the expansions of the right members of the equations

$$(21') \quad \begin{cases} \dfrac{dX_i}{dt} = \dfrac{M\left[\dfrac{X_1 + \cdots + X_n}{r} + \dfrac{\mu}{\sigma'}\right]\left[1 + \dfrac{X_1 + \cdots + X_n}{r} + \dfrac{\mu}{\sigma'}\right]}{\left[1 - \dfrac{X_1 + \cdots + X_n}{r} - \dfrac{\mu}{\sigma'}\right]}, \\ X_i(t_0) = 0, \end{cases}$$

where r and σ' satisfy the inequalities $r < r_j$ and $\sigma' < \sigma$. The second factor in the numerator of the right members of the first set of equations is to make them vanish when $X_i = \mu = 0$; the denominator is to provide terms of every degree in all the arguments of the expansion; and the third factor in the numerator, which it will be noted does not interfere with the dominance property, is inserted in order to simplify the problem of solving for the X after integration.

It follows from the right members of equations (21') that

$$X_1 = \cdots = X_n = \frac{r}{n}\left[X - \frac{\mu}{\sigma'}\right],$$

and that the variable X satisfies the differential equation

$$(21'') \quad \begin{cases} \dfrac{dX}{dt} = \dfrac{nM}{r}\dfrac{X(1 + X)}{1 - X}, \\ X(t_0) = \dfrac{\mu}{\sigma'}. \end{cases}$$

The variables in this equation can be separated, and the solution is found to be

$$\log \frac{\left(1 + \frac{\mu}{\sigma'}\right)^2}{\frac{\mu}{\sigma'}} \frac{X}{(1 + X)^2} = \frac{nM(t - t_0)}{r}.$$

The solution of this equation for X, satisfying the initial condition $X(t_0) = \mu/\sigma'$, is

(22) $\begin{cases} X + 1 = \dfrac{1 + \mu/\sigma'}{2\mu/\sigma'} e^{-nM(t-t_0)/r} \left[\quad \right] \\ \left[\quad \right] = 1 + \mu/\sigma' - \sqrt{(1 + \mu/\sigma')^2 - 4\mu/\sigma' e^{nM(t-t_0)/r}}. \end{cases}$

The right member of this equation can be expanded as a power series in μ.

The domain of convergence of the expansion of the right member of equation (22) as a power series in μ is determined by the location of the singularities of the function. The only finite singularities are the branch-points defined by the equation

(23) $$\left(1 + \frac{\mu}{\sigma'}\right)^2 - \frac{4\mu}{\sigma'} e^{nM(t-t_0)/r} = 0.$$

The roots of this equation are

$$\frac{\mu}{\sigma'} = -1 + 2e^{nM(t-t_0)/r} \pm \sqrt{[1 - 2e^{nM(t-t_0)/r}]^2 - 1},$$

the one with the negative sign before the radical being the smaller. Therefore it follows after some reductions that the condition for the convergence of the expansion of the right member of equation (22) as a power series in μ is

(24) $$|\mu| < \sigma' \frac{[1 - \sqrt{1 - e^{-nM(t-t_0)/r}}]}{1 + \sqrt{1 - e^{-nM(t-t_0)/r}}}.$$

The expansions of the X_i as power series in μ also converge under the same condition.

The differential equations (21') can be solved directly as power series in μ by the method of Art. 28, for they have all the properties of equations (12) and of the equivalent equations

(21) that were used in constructing the solution. Since this solution is unique, it will be identical with that obtained by expanding the right member of equation (22) as a power series in μ; and it will therefore converge if the inequality (24) is satisfied. The $X_i^{(\kappa)}$ will be determined by equations having the form of equations (16).

The ultimate goal of this discussion is the proof that the series (15) converge in some domain for μ and t. The proof will be completed by showing that the series (15) are dominated by the corresponding series for the X_i. Consider the first set of equations (16) and the corresponding set for the $X_i^{(1)}(t)$. Since these equations have all the properties of equations (9), they can be solved by introducing the factor μ. Moreover, since they are linear, it can easily be shown that the series converge for $\mu = 1$ and $t_0 \leqq t \leqq T$. And, further, each term of the infinite series defining the $X_i^{(1)}(t)$ is positive and greater than the absolute values of the corresponding terms of the infinite series for the $x_i^{(1)}(t)$, because they are defined by definite integrals, and the integrands of the former dominate the integrands of the latter. Therefore

$$X_i^{(1)}(t) > \left| x_i^{(1)}(t) \right| \qquad (t_0 \leqq t \leqq T).$$

The corresponding result is true successively for terms with higher indices. Therefore the series (15) converge whenever the inequality (24) is satisfied. It should be remarked, however, that the series (15) may converge for some values of μ for which the inequality (24) is not satisfied.

In Art. 26 the condition for the convergence of the solution of equations (1) was formulated in three somewhat different theorems. It follows from the inequality (24) that the same three theorems hold respecting the convergence of the solution of the more general differential equations (12). That is, the inequality (24) can be satisfied by imposing restrictions upon both μ and t, or upon μ alone for all $t_0 \leqq t \leqq T$, or on t alone for all $|\mu| < \sigma'$.

II. PROPERTIES OF THE SOLUTION FUNCTIONS

30. The Solution as Functions of t and of t_0. The properties of the solution (2), of equations (1), and of the solution (15), of equations (12) or (21), are under consideration. Since, by hypotheses, the $f_i(x_j; \mu; t)$ of equations (1) and the $g_i(x_j; t)$ and the $f_i(x_j; \mu; t)$ of equations (12) are continuous functions of t for all values of the x_j, μ, and t for which $\left| x_j - x_j{}^{(0)} \right| \leqq r_j$, $\left| \mu \right| \leqq \sigma$, $t_0 \leqq t \leqq T$, it follows from equations (4) and (5), in the first problem, and from equations (16) in the second problem, that the individual terms of the series are continuous functions of both t and t_0. It follows from the inequalities (7) and (24) that, for any prescribed range $t_0 \leqq t \leqq T_1 \leqq T$ for t, an upper bound σ_1 for $\left| \mu \right|$ can be so determined that the conditions for convergence will be satisfied *uniformly* with respect to t on the interval. Therefore, by Appendix D, the solutions in both problems are continuous functions of t and of t_0.

The derivatives of the solutions with respect to t are defined by equations (1) and (12). Since the functions $x_i(t)$ are continuous in t, and the $g_i(x_j; t)$ and the $f_i(x_j; \mu; t)$ are continuous in the x_j and t, it follows from Appendix F that in both problems the dx_i/dt are continuous functions of t and of t_0.

The $x_i(t)$ are not, however, necessarily analytic functions of t, for the $x_i{}^{(\kappa)}(t)$ are not necessarily analytic functions of t.

31. The Solution as Functions of the a_i and of μ. It follows from equations (4) and (5) for $\kappa = 2, 3, \cdots$ sequentially that the $x_i{}^{(\kappa)}$ of equations (2) are analytic functions of the a_j in sufficiently restricted domains. Since in any closed domain for the a_i the upper bound M of the functions $f_i(x_j; \mu; t)$ is finite, it follows from the inequality (7) that a σ_1 and a T_1 can be so determined that the series (2) will converge *uniformly* with respect to the a_j in their prescribed domains for all values of μ and t such that $\left| \mu \right| < \sigma_1$, $t_0 \leqq t \leqq T_1$. Therefore, by Appendix C, the solution series (2) are analytic functions of the a_j.

The derivatives of the x_i with respect to t are given by equations (1). Since the $f_i(x_j; \mu; t)$ are analytic functions of the x_j, which in turn are analytic functions of the a_κ, it follows from Appendix C that the dx_i/dt also are analytic functions of the a_j.

Since the solution series (2) are converging power series in μ, they are analytic functions of μ. Also the dx_i/dt are analytic functions of μ.

It will now be shown that the series (15), which are the solution of the general differential equations (12), are analytic functions of the a_j. Consider the $x_i{}^{(1)}$, defined by the first set of equations of (16). The functions involved in these differential equations are analytic in the a_j in certain domains. Suppose these equations are solved by the method used to obtain the solution of the differential equations (9). Since this is the method used in solving the differential equations (1), the solution consists of functions that are analytic in the a_j. The result is similar in the case of the $x_i{}^{(2)}$, $x_i{}^{(3)}$, $\cdots$. It follows from the inequality (24) that domains for μ and t can be so defined that the series (15) will all converge for μ and t in these domains uniformly with respect to the a_j in certain domains. Therefore the x_i are analytic functions of the a_j.

It follows, as in the case of equations (1), that the dx_i/dt are analytic functions of the a_j; and the x_i and dx_i/dt are analytic functions of μ.

32. Differential Equations Whose Right Members Vanish with the Dependent Variables.

As a special class of differential equations, consider

$$(25) \quad \begin{cases} \dfrac{dx_i}{dt} = f_i(x_j; t), \\[2mm] x_i(t_0) = a_i, \qquad |a_j| < r_j, \end{cases}$$

where the functions $f_i(x_j; t)$ are analytic in the x_j and continuous in t for all values of the x_j and t for which $|x_j| \leqq r_j$, $t_0 \lesseqgtr t \leqq T$, and where

$$(26) \qquad f_i(0; t) \underset{t}{\equiv} 0.$$

The solution of equations (25) consists of functions that are analytic in the a_j, by Art. 31. These functions can therefore be expanded as power series in the a_j.

This problem can be transformed into that treated in Art. 27 by the substitution

$$x_i = y_i \mu.$$

After dividing out the factor μ, the differential equations take the form of equations (12) with the functions $g_i(y_j; t)$ linear in the y_j, and with the functions $f_i(y_j; \mu; t)$ power series in the y_j, starting with terms of the second degree. The terms of degree p in the y_j are multiplied by μ^{p-1}.

The equations for the y_i can be solved by the method of Art. 27. After the solution is formed, it is necessary to put the parameter $\mu = 1$. The result will be power series in the a_j, the coefficients of μ^p being homogeneous of degree $p + 1$ in the a_j.

The problem under consideration includes those that arise in determining the stability of fixed solutions of physical systems, and the character of the motion in their neighborhoods. The first terms of the solution are regarded as determining the character of the stability; the terms of higher order are required to give the complete solution. (See Arts. 133 and 138.)

33. Illustration of Equations (25). Consider the problem of the simple pendulum. The differential equation that its coordinates satisfy is

$$(27) \qquad \frac{d^2\theta}{dt^2} = -c^2 \sin\theta,$$

where θ is the angle between the line of the pendulum and the vertical downward.

There are two solutions of (27) in which θ and $d\theta/dt$ are constants, namely $\theta = 0$ and $\theta = \pi$. For values of θ near $\theta = 0$, equation (27) becomes

$$(28) \qquad \frac{d^2\theta}{dt^2} = -c^2 \left[\theta - \frac{\theta^3}{6} \cdots \right].$$

This equation can, of course, be written in the form of an equivalent normal system.

Now let

$$(29) \qquad \theta = y\mu,$$

which transforms equation (28) into the differential equation

$$(30) \qquad \frac{d^2y}{dt^2} = -c^2y + \frac{c^2}{6}y^3\mu^2 + \cdots.$$

This differential equation is of the type of equations (12), and its solution can be developed in series of the form

$$(31) \qquad y = y_0 + y_1\mu + y_2\mu^2 + \cdots.$$

Suppose the initial conditions are $y(0) = a$, $y'(0) = 0$, where a is small.

The differential equation corresponding to equations (13) is

$$(32) \qquad \begin{cases} \dfrac{d^2y_0}{dt^2} = -c^2y_0, \\ y_0(0) = a, \qquad y_0'(0) = 0, \end{cases}$$

the solution of which is the simple trigonometric function

$$(33) \qquad y_0 = a \cos ct.$$

The differential equation corresponding to the first set of equations (16) is

$$\begin{cases} \dfrac{d^2y_1}{dt^2} + c^2y_1 = 0, \\[2mm] y_1(0) = 0, \qquad y_1'(0) = 0, \end{cases}$$

the solution of which is

$$y_1 \equiv 0.$$

The differential equation corresponding to the second set of equations (16) is

$$(34) \qquad \begin{cases} \dfrac{d^2y_2}{dt^2} + c^2y_2 = \dfrac{c^2}{6}\,y_0{}^3 = \dfrac{c^2}{24}\,a^3[\cos 3ct + 3\cos ct], \\[2mm] y_2(0) = 0, \qquad y_2'(0) = 0. \end{cases}$$

The solution of this system of equations is found to be

$$(35) \qquad y_2 = \left[\frac{c}{16}\,t \sin ct + \frac{c^2}{192}(\cos ct - \cos 3ct) \right] a^3.$$

The method of continuing the process is clear. It will be found upon comparison that the solution has the properties listed in detail in Art. 32.

Since the first term of the solution, given in equation (33), is periodic, the solution is said to be stable for obvious reasons. The next non-zero term, given in equation (35), is not, however, periodic, but a more profound study of the problem than can be taken up here shows that the motion is periodic. [Compare Arts. 75 and 76.] The period is not exactly $2\pi/c$, and the expansion (31) is not suited to exhibit its periodicity.

34. Generalizations with Respect to Parameters. The differential equations (1) or (12) might be functions of a finite number of parameters $\mu_1, \cdots, \mu_m$. The solution functions can be developed in a similar manner in all of these parameters simultaneously, or the problem can be reduced to those already treated by the substitution

$$(36) \qquad \mu_i = \alpha_i \mu,$$

the single parameter being μ. After the solution is formed, the original parameters can be restored by the inverse substitution.

Suppose the differential equations (1) or (12) involve the parameter μ in two ways: one in a simple analytic form, and the other in a complicated or even non-analytic form. Wherever μ occurs in the first way it may be left unchanged, and wherever it occurs in the second way it may be given an accent. Then equations (12) become

$$(37) \qquad \frac{dx_i}{dt} = g_i(x_j; t) + \mu f_i(x_j; t; \mu; \mu'; t).$$

The solution of these equations can be developed as power series in μ (not in μ') by the method of Art. 28. The result will be of the form

$$(38) \qquad x_i = x_i{}^{(0)}(t) + x_i{}^{(1)}(\mu'; t)\mu + x_i{}^{(2)}(\mu'; t)\mu^2 + \cdots,$$

the coefficients being functions of μ' and t. After the solution has been formed, μ' is replaced by μ, and the solution will then be arranged in powers of μ with the coefficients as functions of μ. It is obvious that in special cases, even where the $f_i(x_j; \mu; \mu'; t)$ are analytic functions of μ', this artifice might be of great practical value. In fact, it might be advisable in both equations (1) and (12) to replace μ in the $f_i(x_j; \mu; t)$ by μ' until the solution is formed. In certain cases this artifice will increase the proved domain of convergence of the solution. This is true, for example, if the functions $f_i(x_j; \mu; t)$ are linear in the x_i and their domain of expansion as power series in μ is limited by branch-points at which the $f_i(x_j; \mu; t)$ are all finite.

III. QUESTIONS AND PROBLEMS

1. In Property 1, Art. 23, why is the range for t given in specifying the domain in which the functions $f_i(x_j; \mu; t)$ are analytic in the x_j and μ? Invent an example that illustrates the answer.

2. In Property 2, Art. 23, why are the domains for the x_j and μ given in specifying the range on which the functions $f_i(x_j; \mu; t)$ are continuous in t? Invent an example that illustrates the answer.

3. Assume that the a_i are the given power series in μ,

$$a_i = a_i{}^{(0)} + a_i{}^{(1)}\mu + a_i{}^{(2)}\mu^2 + \cdots,$$

converging if $|\mu| \leqq \sigma$, and then make the formal construction of the solution corresponding to that given in Art. 24.

4. The solutions obtained by the method of Chapter II are valid for all values of t whose moduli are sufficiently small. The domain of validity of the processes of this chapter is a real interval in t. Is it necessarily real?

5. Formally solve Problem 7, on page 37, by the method of Art. 24, introducing the factor μ as suggested in the latter part of Art. 26.

6. Solve the differential equations

$$\begin{cases} \dfrac{dx_1}{dt} = x_1\sqrt{1 - t^2} + x_2{}^2 t, \\[2mm] \dfrac{dx_2}{dt} = x_1{}^2 t^2 + x_2 t \sqrt{1 - t^2}, \end{cases}$$

both by the method of Art. 15 and by that of Art. 24, to terms of the third order inclusive. In applying the method of Art. 24, introduce the factor μ in the right members, as suggested in Art. 26, and in the solution set $\mu = 1$.

7. Determine and compare the domains of convergence for the solutions of Problem 6, as defined by the inequality (11), p. 27, and as defined by the inequality (11), p. 44.

8. The differential equations (1) in general involve the independent variable t explicitly. But the right members of (1′) do not involve t. Note that this is contrary to what was given in (1′), of Art. 16, in proving the convergence of the solutions of Chapter II. Explain the reason for the difference. Might the terms in t be omitted from the right members of (1′), of Art. 16?

9. Prove that if the differential equations are linear, the method used in solving equations (9) is valid for $t_0 \leqq t \leqq T$.

10. Find a domain of convergence as power series in μ for the solution of the equations of Problems 6, page 36, and compare the results with those obtained for the solution as power series in $t - t_0$.

11. Suppose the functions $f_i(x_j; \mu; t)$ are small relatively to the functions $g_i(x_j; t)$ of equations (12). Discuss the relative practical advantages of the solution of Art. 28 and that which might be obtained by introducing a parameter ν in the right members to be put equal to unity at the end.

12. Why were the functions $g_i(x_j; t)$ and $f_i(x_j; \mu; t)$ expanded as power series in the $x_j - x_j{}^{(0)}$ rather than as power series in the $x_j - a_j$? Is the reason practical or theoretical or both?

13. Prove in detail that the solution functions of the first set of equations (16) are linear in the initial values of the $x_i{}^{(1)}$.

14. Carry through the demonstration of the convergence of the solution as power series in μ starting from equations (21′), with the last factor in the numerator omitted.

15. Prove in detail that the $X_i{}^{(\kappa)}(t)$, of Art. 29, dominate the $|x_i{}^{(\kappa)}|$, of Art. 28.

16. Prove from the inequality (24) that the theorems of Art. 26 hold for the solution of equations (12) by the method of Art. 28.

17. If the differential equations (12) are analytic (or continuous) functions of a parameter μ', prove in detail that their solution by the method of Art. 28,

and also the first derivative of the solution with respect to t, are functions that are analytic (or continuous) functions of μ'.

18. Solve to terms of the third degree the differential equation (27) in the neighborhood of the constant solution $\theta = \pi$ by the method of Art. 32.

19. Solve the differential equations

$$\begin{cases} \dfrac{dx_1}{dt} = x_2 + \mu\, x_1 x_2^2, \\[2mm] \dfrac{dx_2}{dt} = -\sqrt{1-\mu}\, x_1 + \mu\, x_1^2 x_2 \end{cases}$$

by the methods of both Arts. 28 and 34.   Determine and compare proved domains of convergence in the two cases.

20. Prove that for small values of $t - t_0$ the right member of the inequality (24) is smaller than the right member of the inequality (7).

HISTORICAL SKETCH

Among the numerous mathematical theories that had their origin with Euler is that of the solution of differential equations as power series in a parameter.   The process was used by Euler in his work on the theory of the motion of the moon, and it has had numerous other applications in the field of celestial mechanics, although the complicated details necessary for the numerical applications of it have often obscured its general mathematical aspects.

In spite of the fact that differential equations had been solved as power series in their parameters from the time of Euler (about 1750), it was Cauchy who first put the method on a firm logical basis [*Oeuvres Complètes*, first series, Vol. VII].   The far-reaching importance of the method and the significance of Cauchy's contributions to its theory were not appreciated until Poincaré began his epoch-making researches on the problem of three bodies.   In his prize memoir [*Acta Mathematica*, Vol. 13 (1890)] he proved Theorem II, of Art. 26, both for the special case in which the right members of the differential equations have the parameter as a factor, and also for the general problem of Art. 27.   The proof contained in this memoir involved certain delicate questions respecting the uniform applicability of certain extensions of the initial proved domain of convergence, but in his *Les Méthodes Nouvelles de la Mécanique Céleste*, Vol. I, p. 58, Poincaré gave a new demonstration of Theorem II which in directness and rigor left nothing to be desired.

CHAPTER IV

VARIATION OF PARAMETERS

35. The Differential Equations. Let the right members of each of the differential equations

$$\frac{dx_i}{dt} = F_i(x_j; t)$$

be broken up into the sum of two functions, $g_i(x_j; t)$ and $f_i(x_j; t)$, so that the resulting form is

$$(1) \quad \begin{cases} \dfrac{dx_i}{dt} = g_i(x_j; t) + f_i(x_j; t), \\ x_i(t_0) = a_i. \end{cases}$$

It will be assumed that the functions $g_i(x_j; t)$ and $f_i(x_j; t)$ are analytic in the x_j and t for all values of the x_j and t for which $|x_j - a_j| \leqq r_j$, and $|t - t_0| \leqq \rho$; or, that the $g_i(x_j; t)$ and the $f_i(x_j; t)$ are analytic in the x_j and only continuous in t for all values of the x_j and t for which $|x_j - a_j| \leqq r_j$, $t_0 \leqq t \leqq T$. Under the first set of hypotheses the solution exists in a sufficiently restricted domain and can be constructed by the methods of both Chapter II and Chapter III; under the second set of hypotheses the solution exists in a sufficiently restricted domain and can be constructed by the method of Chapter III.

Under both sets of hypotheses the solution functions are analytic in the a_j and are continuous in t, and their derivatives with respect to t possess these same properties.

36. The Method of Variation of Parameters. The name of the process that will now be explained is historical and consequently is retained, although it is not really descriptive of the essence of the method in the general case. As will be seen, the method is really a transformation of variables in which the equations of transformation are so chosen as to simplify the results to the greatest possible extent.

Instead of treating equations (1), consider in the first instance

$$(2) \qquad \begin{cases} \dfrac{dx_i}{dt} = g_i(x_j;\, t), \\[2mm] x_i(t_0) = y_i, \end{cases}$$

the initial values of the x_i being represented by the y_i for certain reasons of notation that will become evident.

Let the solution of equations (2) be written in the form

$$(3) \qquad x_i = \phi_i(y_1, \,\cdots,\, y_n;\, t).$$

The right members of these equations are analytic in the y_j, and their derivatives with respect to t exist and are analytic in the y_j and are continuous in t. Since the functions (3) are a solution of equations (2), it follows from the definition of a solution that

$$(4) \qquad \begin{cases} \dfrac{d\phi_i}{dt}_{\!t} \equiv g_i(\phi_j;\, t), \\[2mm] \phi_i(t_0) = y_i. \end{cases}$$

Now regard equations (3) as equations for transforming equations (1) from the original variables x_i to a new set y_i. Since the derivatives of the $\phi_i(y_j;\, t)$ with respect to the y_j and to t exist in sufficiently restricted domains, the result of substituting equations (3) into equations (1) is

$$(5) \qquad \frac{\partial \phi_i}{\partial y_1}\frac{dy_1}{dt} + \cdots + \frac{\partial \phi_i}{\partial y_n}\frac{dy_n}{dt} + \frac{\partial \phi_i}{\partial t} = g_i(\phi_j;\, t) + f_i(\phi_j;\, t).$$

The solution of these equations for the dy_i/dt gives a normal system of differential equations.

Before equations (5) are solved, use will be made of the fact that the equations of transformation (3) are a solution of the differential equations (2). The last term in the left members of equations (5) is identical with the left members of the identities (4), the difference in the differential notation being due to the fact that in equations (3), regarded as a *solution* of equations (2), the y_j are constants, while in equations (3), regarded as *equations of transformation*, the y_j may be variables. The right members of the identities (4) are identical with the first terms of the right members of equations (5). Consequently it is found that equations (5) become as a consequence of the identities (4)

$$(6) \quad \begin{cases} \dfrac{\partial \phi_1}{\partial y_1} \dfrac{dy_1}{dt} + \cdots + \dfrac{\partial \phi_1}{\partial y_n} \dfrac{dy_n}{dt} = f_1(\phi_i; t), \\ \cdots \cdots \cdots \cdots \cdots \cdots \\ \dfrac{\partial \phi_n}{\partial y_1} \dfrac{dy_1}{dt} + \cdots + \dfrac{\partial \phi_n}{\partial y_n} \dfrac{dy_n}{dt} = f_n(\phi_i; t). \end{cases}$$

Equations (6) can be solved uniquely for the dy_i/dt provided the determinant of their coefficients is not zero. It follows from equations (2) and (3) that

$$(7) \quad y_i = \phi_i(y_1, \cdots, y_n; t_0).$$

Since $y_1, \cdots, y_n$ are mutually independent and the derivatives of the ϕ_i with respect to t exist, it follows from equations (7) that

$$(8) \quad \phi_i = y_i + (t - t_0)\psi_i(y_1, \cdots, y_n; t),$$

where the functions $\psi_i(y_j; t)$ are analytic in the y_j and are at least continuous in t.

Now consider the determinant of the coefficients of equations (6). It follows from equations (8) that this determinant equals unity for $t = t_0$; and it follows from the continuity of the ϕ_i in t that it is distinct from zero for all values of t for which $t_0 \leqq t \leqq T_1$, where $T_1 - t_0$ is sufficiently small. Therefore the solution of equations (6) for the dy_i/dt gives

$$(9) \quad \begin{cases} \dfrac{dy_i}{dt} = h_i(y_1, \cdots, y_n; t), \\ y_i(t_0) = a_i, \end{cases}$$

where the $h_i(y_j; t)$ are analytic in the y_j and continuous in t in sufficiently restricted domains. There are, however, two special points that are to be noted. The first point is that since the functions $h_i(y_j; t)$ are the quotients of two determinants, the zeros of the denominator may restrict the domain of validity of equations (9) in t below the domain of validity of equations (1). The second point is that the functions $h_i(y_j; t)$ are linear and homogeneous in the $f_j(\phi_\kappa; t)$, and consequently vanish with the $f_j(\phi_\kappa; t)$. The $h_i(y_j; t)$ depend upon the functions $g_i(\phi_j; t)$ only through the solution functions (3). Since the initial value of the determinant of the coefficients of equations (6) is unity, it follows that the order of magnitude of the right members of equations (9) does not exceed the order of magnitude of the functions $f_i(x_j; t)$.

Suppose the functions $f_i(x_j; t)$ are numerically small relative to the $g_i(x_j; t)$; then the right members of equations (9) are numerically small relative to the right members of equations (1). Consequently the y_i vary more slowly than the x_i, and the domain of validity of the solution is likely enlarged. This can also be inferred from the fact that the upper bound M of the right members of equations (9) is less than that of the right members of equations (1) in corresponding domains. In this fact often lies an important advantage of the method.

Equations (9) can be solved by the methods of either Chapter II or Chapter III if the right members are analytic functions of t. If they are only continuous functions of t, the solution can be found by the method of Chapter III, giving the y_i explicitly in terms of t. When these expressions for the y_i are substituted into equations (3), the x_i are expressed in terms of t and the problem is solved.

37. Illustrative Problem. Suppose equations (1) are the differential equations satisfied by the coördinates of two mutually attracting planets in their motion around the sun. Suppose the accelerations due to the sun are expressed by the functions $g_i(x_j; t)$, and that those due to the mutual attractions of the planets are given by the functions $f_i(x_j; t)$. The masses of the planets are so small in comparison with the mass of the sun that the functions $f_i(x_j; t)$ are in all cases numerically less than one-thousandth the functions $g_i(x_j; t)$.

Now consider equations (2) for this problem. They reduce simply to those which are satisfied by the elliptic motion of the two planets about the sun in undisturbed orbits. Their solution functions (3) are easily found and are valid for all finite values of t. The y_j of equations (3) are the elements of the elliptic orbits, such as the major semi-axes, the eccentricities, the inclinations of the orbits to the reference plane, etc.

In the case of the problem of two bodies the elements of the orbits are constants. When the two planets mutually attract each other, they do not move in fixed elliptic orbits, but their motions can be regarded as being in elliptic orbits whose elements constantly vary, though slowly, because the right members of equations (9) are very small in this problem. Equations (9) define the way they vary, and when the solutions of equations (9) are substituted into equations (3), the latter give the coördinates x_i in terms of t and the continually varying elliptic elements y_i.

It can be shown by a discussion that cannot be entered into here * that the y_i can be so chosen that the determinant of the coefficients of equations (6) is unity, and also that in the ordinary elements it is independent of t. Therefore equations (9) in this problem are valid for all finite values of t, provided the orbits of the two planets remain finite and neither pass through the sun nor intersect each other.

Now it is easy to grasp the essentials of the problem. The coördinates x_i defined by equations (1) vary rapidly and undergo large changes in the course of a few days or weeks. On the other hand, the elements y_i defined by equations (9) vary slowly and undergo important changes only after the lapse of centuries or thousands of years. In fact, if the formulas are not to be applied for a very great interval of time, the y_j in the right members of equations (9) may be regarded as constants without making important errors, and the y_j are therefore determined with this approximation by quadratures.

38. Application to Linear Differential Equations. Consider the differential equations

$$(10) \quad \begin{cases} \dfrac{dx_1}{dt} = \theta_{11}(t)x_1 + \cdots + \theta_{1n}(t)x_n + \theta_1(t), \\ \phantom{\dfrac{dx_1}{dt}} \cdot \quad \cdot \quad \cdot \quad \cdot \quad \cdot \quad \cdot \quad \cdot \quad \cdot \quad \cdot \quad \cdot \quad \cdot \quad \cdot \\ \dfrac{dx_n}{dt} = \theta_{n1}(t)x_1 + \cdots + \theta_{nn}(t)x_n + \theta_n(t), \end{cases}$$

where the $\theta_{ij}(t)$ and the $\theta_i(t)$ are continuous functions of t for $t_0 \leqq t \leqq T$. In this problem, the terms in $x_1, \cdots, x_n$ are the $g_i(x_j; t)$, and the $\theta_i(t)$ are the $f_i(x_j; t)$, which here are independent of the x_j.

The equations corresponding to equations (2) are now

$$(11) \quad \begin{cases} \dfrac{dx_i}{dt} = \sum_{j=1}^{n} \theta_{ij}(t)x_j, \\ x_i(t_0) = y_i, \end{cases}$$

* Moulton, *Introduction to Celestial Mechanics*, Art. 213.

and since these equations are linear and homogeneous, the solution corresponding to equations (3) has the form

$$(12) \quad \begin{cases} x_1 = y_1\phi_{11}(t) + \cdots + y_n\phi_{1n}(t), \\ \cdot \quad \cdot \quad \cdot \quad \cdot \quad \cdot \quad \cdot \quad \cdot \quad \cdot \quad \cdot \\ x_n = y_1\phi_{n1}(t) + \cdots + y_n\phi_{nn}(t). \end{cases}$$

Since equations (12) are linear in the y_i, the coefficients of the equations corresponding to equations (6) are independent of the y_j; and consequently the equations corresponding to the general equations (9) are

$$(13) \quad \frac{dy_i}{dt} = h_i(t).$$

These equations are quadratures whose integrals may be written

$$(14) \quad y_i = \int_{t_0}^{t} h_i(t)dt + c_i = F_i(t) + c_i,$$

where the $F_i(t)$ are known functions of t and the c_i are arbitrary constants.

Upon substituting equations (14) into equations (12), the final solution

$$(15) \quad \begin{cases} x_1 = c_1\phi_{11}(t) + \cdots + c_n\phi_{1n}(t) + \Phi_1(t), \\ \cdot \quad \cdot \quad \cdot \quad \cdot \quad \cdot \quad \cdot \quad \cdot \quad \cdot \quad \cdot \\ x_n = c_1\phi_{n1}(t) + \cdots + c_n\phi_{nn}(t) + \Phi_n(t) \end{cases}$$

is obtained, where

$$(16) \quad \begin{cases} \Phi_1 = F_1(t)\phi_{11}(t) + \cdots + F_n(t)\phi_{1n}(t), \\ \cdot \quad \cdot \quad \cdot \quad \cdot \quad \cdot \quad \cdot \quad \cdot \quad \cdot \quad \cdot \\ \Phi_n = F_1(t)\phi_{n1}(t) + \cdots + F_n(t)\phi_{nn}(t). \end{cases}$$

That is, in the case of linear differential equations the method of the variation of parameters transforms the problem of determining the parts of the solution that depend upon the non-homogeneous terms to one involving only quadratures; viz., equations (14). Therefore in all cases in which the solution of the homogeneous system (11) can be found simply, the solution of the non-homogeneous system can also be found simply.

39. Transformation of Differential Equations of the Type of Those of Art. 27 to the Type of Those of Art. 23. The problem of solving the differential equations (1), of Art. 23, was found to be much simpler from a practical point of view than that of solving the differential equations (12), of Art. 27. The method of this chapter can be used to transform the latter problem into the former.

The equations to be solved are

$$(17) \quad \begin{cases} \dfrac{dx_i}{dt} = g_i(x_j; t) + \mu f_i(x_j; \mu; t), \\ x_i(t_0) \underset{\mu}{\equiv} a_i, \end{cases}$$

in which the functions $g_i(x_j; t)$ are analytic in the x_j and continuous in t, and the functions $f_i(x_j; \mu; t)$ are analytic in the x_j and μ and continuous in t for all values of the x_i, μ, and t for which $|x_i - a_i| \leqq r_j$, $|\mu| \leqq \sigma$, $t_0 \leqq t \leqq T$.

Let the solution of the equations

$$(18) \quad \begin{cases} \dfrac{dx_i}{dt} = g_i(x_j; t), \\ x_i(t_0) = y_i \end{cases}$$

be

$$(19) \quad x_i = \phi_i(y_1, \cdots, y_n; t).$$

Then, on applying the method of Art. 36, the differential equations corresponding to equations (9) are in this case

$$(20) \quad \begin{cases} \dfrac{dy_i}{dt} = \mu \, h_i(y_j; \mu; t), \\ y_i(t_0) = a_i, \end{cases}$$

in which the h_i are analytic in the y_j and μ and continuous in t for all values of the y_j, μ, and t for which $|y_j - b_j| \leqq r_j'$, $|\mu| \leqq \sigma$, $t_0 \leqq t \leqq T'$. The domain in the y_j and t is not necessarily the same as that of the right members of equations (17) because the functions $h_i(y_j; \mu; t)$ are quotients of two determinants, and the determinant in the denominator in general is a function of the y_j and t. On the other hand, the domain in μ is unchanged because it occurs only in the numerators.

It follows from the properties of the right members of equations (20) that these differential equations are solvable by the method of Art. 24. The problem of solving equations (18) is precisely that of solving equations (13), of Art. 27. The labor of constructing the equations corresponding to equations (6) and solving them so as to obtain the set of differential equations corresponding to equations (9), and the quadratures to be performed in solving equations (20) as power series in μ, may be contrasted with solving the systems of linear differential equations (16), of Art. 28. In dynamical problems the y_i can usually be so chosen that the determinant of the transformation shall be unity, and the method of this chapter combined with that of Art. 24 is usually preferable from a practical point of view to that of Arts. 27 and 28.

In case the y_i are so chosen that the determinant of the coefficients of equations (6) is constant, the domain of validity of equations (9) is the same as that of equations (1). The proved domain of convergence of the solution of equations (9) in this case is given by the inequality (7) of Art. 25. On the other hand, if equations (1) were solved by the method of Arts. 27 and 28, the proved domain of validity would be the smaller one that is given by the inequality (24) of Art. 29. Of course, the true domain in special cases may be the same for both methods.

40. Successive Applications of the Method of the Variation of Parameters. Let the original differential equations be

$$(21) \quad \begin{cases} \dfrac{dx_i}{dt} = F_i(x_j;\, t) = g_i(x_j;\, t) + f_i(x_j;\, t), \\[2mm] x_i(t_0) = a_i, \end{cases}$$

where the functions $F_i(x_j;\, t)$ have the properties of the right members of equations (1). Let the solution of the differential equations

$$\frac{dx_i}{dt} = g_i(x_j;\, t)$$

be

$$(22) \quad x_i = \phi_i(x_1^{(1)},\, \cdots,\, x_n^{(1)};\, t).$$

Equations (21) are transformed by means of equations (22) and the method of Art. 36 into equations corresponding to equations (9), that will now be written in the form

$$(23) \quad \frac{dx_i^{(1)}}{dt} = F_i^{(1)}(x_j^{(1)};\, t).$$

It has been shown that in suitable domains the functions $F_i^{(1)}(x_j^{(1)};\, t)$ have the properties ascribed to the $F_i(x_j;\, t)$.

Now the right members of equations (23), having the general properties of the right members of equations (21), may similarly be broken up into the sums of two functions, and then transformed by the solution functions of a part of the differential equations. The final result of the step will be a new set of differential equations

$$(24) \qquad \frac{dx_i^{(2)}}{dt} = F_i^{(2)}(x_i^{(2)}; t),$$

whose right members have the general properties of the right members of equations (21) and (23). Obviously the process can be repeated as many times as is desirable.

The first thing to be noticed is that the steps of the process are not unique, for the $F_i^{(\kappa)}(x_i^{(\kappa)}; t)$ of the κth transformation may be broken up into sums of two functions in infinitely many ways. It follows that it is not possible to formulate definitely and uniquely the problem of proving the limit of the process for $\kappa = \infty$. Consequently, the process in itself is not, except in the case of linear differential equations, a general method of solving differential equations. It is in reality a method of transforming a problem in differential equations so that it can be treated more satisfactorily by other methods.

In case the variables of the successive transformations are so chosen that the determinants of the coefficients of the equations corresponding to (6) are constants, the domains of validity of the successive sets of differential equations are the same as the domain of validity of the original set. Moreover, if the functions $F_i^{(\kappa)}(x_i^{(\kappa)}; t)$ are broken up into the sums of two functions in such a way that the absolute values of the right members of the successive sets of differential equations decrease, the rates at which the successive $x_i^{(\kappa)}$ vary with t decrease as κ increases.

The method of Delaunay in his lunar theory is that which is being described. He divided up the right members of the differential equations successively in such a way that the partial systems corresponding to equations (2) had solutions corresponding to equations (3) possessing certain periodicity properties; and, moreover, he chose the new variables at each step in such a way that the determinant of the coefficients of the equations corresponding to equations (6) was unity. Finally, he broke up the successive sets of differential equations in such a way that their right members were continually reduced in numerical magnitude. After making 57 complete transformations and 440 partial transformations, and making quadratures of the final differential equations, regarding the dependent variables in their right members as constants, he had implicitly an approximate solution of the problem. To complete the expressions for the coördinates, he substituted the final variables back into the expressions of the last step corresponding to equations (3), and these back into the corresponding equations of the preceding step, and so on back to the first transformation. The stupendous task of carrying out these transformations required twenty years of arduous labor, and the final expressions for the coördinates, in very condensed notation, filled two hundred and forty quarto pages.

The fact that the lunar theory of Delaunay was carried out literally, rather than partly numerically, as had been the case of other lunar theories, led many astronomers to think that it was logically perfect. The successive transformations made by Delaunay were valid, but his final equations contained all the logical difficulties of the original. It is probable, however, that each of the transformations increased the domain of rapid convergence of his solution series.

IV. QUESTIONS AND PROBLEMS

1. Solve the linear system of differential equations

$$\begin{cases} \dfrac{dx_1}{dt} = -x_2, \\[2mm] \dfrac{dx_2}{dt} = +x_1 + \mu \sin ct, \\[2mm] x_i(0) = a_i \end{cases}$$

by the method of Art. 38. Note the identities corresponding to those used in reducing equations (5) to equations (6). What is the value of the determinant corresponding to the determinant of the coefficients of equations (6)? Interpret the problem physically. Find the solution also when $c = 1$ and interpret the problem physically in this case.

2. Solve the differential equations

$$\begin{cases} \dfrac{dx_1}{dt} = -x_2, \\[2mm] \dfrac{dx_2}{dt} = +x_1 + \mu x_2^2, \\[2mm] x_i(0) = a_i \end{cases}$$

by the methods of Chapters II, III, and IV.

3. Transform the differential equations of Problem 2 by the method of this chapter to equivalent differential equations having the form of those treated in Art. 23.

4. Prove that if the functions $f_i(x_j; t)$ are small relative to the functions $g_i(x_j; t)$, and if the determinant of the coefficients of equations (6) is constant, the proved domain of convergence of the expansion of the solution as a power series in μ is increased.

HISTORICAL SKETCH

The method of the variation of parameters, in essence, had its origin in Newton's *Principia*. After having established the fact that the undisturbed orbit of the moon about the earth is an ellipse, Newton took account of the effects of the sun upon the moon's orbit by determining the variations in its elements. Although the work of Newton was not expressed in the symbolism of analysis, it undoubtedly exercised a great influence upon the form taken by the researches of his successors Clairaut, d'Alembert, and Euler, a generation later. Moreover, the method is peculiarly appropriate to the problems in celestial mechanics presented by the solar system, as is clear from the illustration in Art. 37.

The use of the method of variation of parameters in solving non-homogeneous linear differential equations (Art. 38) dates back to the time of Euler, but it is not known when it was first used. In the domain of pure mathematics this is the connection in which the method is usually found, but, as is clear from Art. 36, it is not at all limited to linear differential equations.

As was explained in Art. 40, Delaunay in his *Théorie de la Lune* carried out the successive transformations of the method to an extent not approached by anyone else.

CHAPTER V

INTEGRALS OF DIFFERENTIAL EQUATIONS

41. Existence of Integrals of Differential Equations. Consider the differential equations

$$(1) \qquad \begin{cases} \dfrac{dx_i}{dt} = f_i(x_j; t), \\ x_i(t_0) = a_i, \end{cases}$$

in which the functions $f_i(x_j; t)$ are analytic in the x_j and continuous in t for all values of the x_j and t for which $|x_j - a_j| \leqq r_j$, $t_0 \lessgtr t \leqq T$. It was shown in Chapter III that, under these hypotheses, the differential equations have a solution

$$(2) \qquad x_i = \phi_i(t_0; a_j; t),$$

in which the functions $\phi_i(t_0; a_j; t)$ are analytic in the a_j and continuous in t in sufficiently restricted domains, and in which the derivatives $d\phi_i/dt$ also have the same properties.

According to the definition of Art. 11, the function

$$(3) \qquad F = F(x_1, \cdots, x_n; t)$$

is an integral of equations (1) provided

$$(4) \qquad F(\phi_1, \cdots, \phi_n; t) \underset{t}{\equiv} C,$$

where C is a constant. The ϕ_i are the solution functions for every set of constants a_j sufficiently near a particular set $a_i^{(0)}$ and for every t_0 sufficiently near a particular $t_0^{(0)}$.

Suppose $t^{(1)}$ is some value of t within the domain of the existence of the solution (2), and designate the corresponding values of the x_i by $x_i^{(1)}$. Then

$$(5) \qquad x_i^{(1)} = \phi_i(t_0; a_j; t^{(1)}).$$

71

The same solution can also be defined by the initial conditions $x_i(t^{(1)}) = x_i^{(1)}$. Since the functions $\phi_i(t_0; a_j; t)$ are the solution functions for every a_j and t_0 near $a_j^{(0)}$ and $t_0^{(0)}$, the solution with the initial conditions $x_j^{(1)}$ at $t^{(1)}$ is

$$(6) \qquad x_i = \phi_i(t^{(1)}; x_i^{(1)}; t).$$

Since this is the same solution as that given by equations (2), it follows that $x_i(t_0) = a_i$, and therefore equations (6) give

$$(7) \qquad a_i = \phi_i(t^{(1)}; x_i^{(1)}; t_0).$$

The $t^{(1)}$ is any value of t sufficiently near t_0 and the $x_i^{(1)}$ are corresponding values of the x_i. Consequently, on omitting the superscripts, equations (7) become

$$(8) \qquad a_i = \phi_i(t; x_j; t_0),$$

where the x_j are a solution of the differential equations (1) corresponding to the initial conditions $x_i(t_0) = a_i$. On comparing equations (8) with equations (2), it is seen that n integrals can be obtained from the n solution functions by interchanging in the latter the x_j and the a_j and t_0 and t respectively.

It follows from the properties of the solution (2) that the integrals (8) are analytic in the x_j and continuous in t and t_0 in sufficiently restricted domains, and that their derivatives with respect to t have the same properties.

It is to be noted that the n functions $\phi_i(t_0; a_j; t)$ of equations (2) together constitute a solution, while each of the $\phi_i(t; x_j; t_0)$ individually is an integral.

42. Independence of the n Integrals (8). Consider the integrals (8) as functions of the x_j. A necessary and sufficient condition that there shall be no analytic relation among the $\phi_i(t; x_j; t_0)$ is that the Jacobian determinant

$$(9) \qquad J = \begin{vmatrix} \dfrac{\partial \phi_1}{\partial x_1}, & \cdots, & \dfrac{\partial \phi_1}{\partial x_n} \\ \cdot & \cdot \cdot \cdot & \cdot \\ \dfrac{\partial \phi_n}{\partial x_1}, & \cdots, & \dfrac{\partial \phi_n}{\partial x_n} \end{vmatrix}$$

shall be not identically zero in the x_j.

Since the functions $\phi_i(t; x_j; t_0)$ equal the a_i at $t = t_0$ and possess partial derivatives with respect to t that are analytic in the x_j and continuous in t and t_0 in sufficiently restricted domains, it follows that

$$(10) \qquad \phi_i = x_i + (t - t_0)\psi_i(t; x_j; t_0),$$

where the functions $\psi_i(t; x_j; t_0)$ are analytic in the x_j and continuous in t and t_0 in sufficiently restricted domains. It follows from equations (10) that, at $t = t_0$,

$$\frac{\partial \phi_i}{\partial x_i} = 1 \quad (i = 1, \cdots, n); \qquad \frac{\partial \phi_i}{\partial x_j} = 0 \quad (j \neq i).$$

Therefore $J = 1$ at $t = 0$, and consequently it is not identically zero. Moreover, the x_j being continuous functions of t, and the functions $\phi_i(t; x_j; t_0)$ being analytic in the x_j and continuous in t, it follows that the determinant J is not zero for any value of t near t_0. Therefore *the integrals* (8) *are functionally independent.*

43. The Integrals (8) Constitute a Fundamental Set of Integrals. The set of functions

$$(11) \qquad \phi_i = \phi_i(t; x_j; t_0),$$

by definition, constitute a *fundamental set* of integrals of the differential equations (1) provided every integral of equations (1) can be expressed as a function of the ϕ_i alone.

Since the function ϕ_i is an integral, it follows by the definition in Art. 11 that

$$(12) \qquad \frac{\partial \phi_i}{\partial x_1}f_1 + \cdots + \frac{\partial \phi_i}{\partial x_n}f_n + \frac{\partial \phi_i}{\partial t}\Big|_{x_j,\, t} \equiv 0.$$

Now consider any function $F = F(\phi_1, \cdots, \phi_n)$ possessing first derivatives with respect to the ϕ_i. It follows that

$$(13) \qquad \begin{cases} \dfrac{\partial F}{\partial t} = \dfrac{\partial F}{\partial \phi_1}\dfrac{\partial \phi_1}{\partial t} + \cdots + \dfrac{\partial F}{\partial \phi_n}\dfrac{\partial \phi_n}{\partial t}, \\[2mm] \dfrac{\partial F}{\partial x_i} = \dfrac{\partial F}{\partial \phi_1}\dfrac{\partial \phi_1}{\partial x_i} + \cdots + \dfrac{\partial F}{\partial \phi_n}\dfrac{\partial \phi_n}{\partial x_i} \qquad (i = 1, \cdots, n). \end{cases}$$

Therefore

$$\frac{\partial F}{\partial t} + \sum_{i=1}^{n}\frac{\partial F}{\partial x_i}f_i = \sum_{i=1}^{n}\frac{\partial F}{\partial \phi_i}\left[\frac{\partial \phi_i}{\partial x_1}f_1 + \cdots + \frac{\partial \phi_i}{\partial x_n}f_n + \frac{\partial \phi_i}{\partial t}\right],$$

the right member of which, by the identities (12), is identically zero in the x_j and t. Therefore the function $F(\phi_1, \cdots, \phi_n)$ is, by definition, an integral of the differential equations (1).

It will now be shown that every integral possessing the properties of the functions $\phi_i(t; x_j; t_0)$ can be expressed in terms of the ϕ_i alone. Let $\Phi(x_j; t)$ be an integral of the differential equations (1). The x_j must be eliminated in order to express this function in terms of the ϕ_i.

The right members of equations (11) are independent analytic functions of the x_j whose Jacobian is not zero at $x_j = a_j$, $t = t_0$. Therefore, as will be shown in Chapter VI, these equations can be solved for the x_j in terms of the ϕ_i, giving the solution

$$(14) \qquad x_j = \psi_j(\phi_i; t) \qquad (j = 1, \cdots, n),$$

where the $\psi_j(\phi_i; t)$ are analytic functions of the ϕ_i in sufficiently restricted domains. In fact, this solution is identical with equations (2), for equations (11) and (8) are identical and the inverse of equations (8) is the system (2).

The result of substituting the expressions for the x_j, of equations (14), into the integral $\Phi(x_j; t)$ is the equation

$$(15) \qquad \Phi(x_j; t) = \Psi(\phi_j; t),$$

where $\Psi(\phi_j; t)$ is an analytic function of the ϕ_j in a sufficiently restricted domain. To complete the theorem it is necessary to show that the function Ψ does not involve t explicitly.

Since the function $\Phi(x_j; t)$ is an integral of the differential equations (1), it follows that

$$(16) \qquad \frac{\partial \Phi}{\partial x_1} f_1 + \cdots + \frac{\partial \Phi}{\partial x_n} f_n + \frac{\partial \Phi}{\partial t} \underset{x_i, t}{\equiv} 0.$$

It follows from equation (15) that

$$(17) \qquad \begin{cases} \dfrac{\partial \Phi}{\partial x_i} = \dfrac{\partial \Psi}{\partial \phi_1} \dfrac{\partial \phi_1}{\partial x_i} + \cdots + \dfrac{\partial \Psi}{\partial \phi_n} \dfrac{\partial \phi_n}{\partial x_i} \qquad (i = 1, \cdots, n), \\[2ex] \dfrac{\partial \Phi}{\partial t} = \dfrac{\partial \Psi}{\partial \phi_1} \dfrac{\partial \phi_1}{\partial t} + \cdots + \dfrac{\partial \Psi}{\partial \phi_n} \dfrac{\partial \phi_n}{\partial t} + \dfrac{\partial \Psi}{\partial t}. \end{cases}$$

Therefore the identity (16) gives the identity

$$\frac{\partial \Psi}{\partial t} + \sum_{i=1}^{n} \frac{\partial \Psi}{\partial \phi_i} \left[\frac{\partial \phi_i}{\partial x_1} f_1 + \cdots + \frac{\partial \phi_i}{\partial x_n} f_n + \frac{\partial \phi_i}{\partial t} \right] \underset{x_i, t}{\equiv} 0.$$

By the identities (12), each of the brackets in this expression is identically zero; therefore

$$\frac{\partial \Psi}{\partial t} \Big|_t \equiv 0. \tag{18}$$

That is, the function Ψ does not involve t explicitly, and the right member of (15) is a function of the integrals ϕ_i alone.

44. Reduction of Order of Differential Equations by Means of Integrals. Suppose the differential equations (1) have the integral

$$F(x_1, \cdots, x_n; t) = c, \tag{19}$$

where the constant c is determined by the initial values of the variables. In general, equation (19) can be solved for one of the x_i in terms of the remainder and of the constant c. Suppose the equation solved for x_n gives

$$x_n = \psi(x_1, \cdots, x_{n-1}; t). \tag{20}$$

This equation can be used to eliminate x_n from the first $n - 1$ of equations (1), giving a system of $n - 1$ differential equations in $n - 1$ dependent variables. That is, the integral can be used to decrease the order of the differential equations by unity. In general, κ independent integrals can be used to reduce a system of differential equations by κ equations.

It is not always advisable to use integrals to reduce the order of a system of differential equations, for the functional complexities introduced in doing so may more than counterbalance any advantages that may result from a smaller number of equations. For example, the differential equations

$$\begin{cases} \dfrac{dx_1}{dt} = x_2, \\[2mm] \dfrac{dx_2}{dt} = -\kappa^2 x_1 \end{cases}$$

have the integrals

$$\begin{cases} \kappa^2 x_1{}^2 + x_2{}^2 = c_1, \\[2mm] x_1 \cos \kappa(t - t_0) - \dfrac{x_2}{\kappa} \sin \kappa(t - t_0) = c_2. \end{cases}$$

Either of these equations can be solved for x_1 or x_2, and by means of the solution the variable can be eliminated from the differential equations, but the resulting equations are more complicated than the original.

It is only in the elementary theory of differential equations, in which the aim is to separate the variables, that the reduction of the order of a system of differential equations is regarded as of particular importance. If the integrals do not involve t explicitly, they are often of great significance in physical problems, as was explained in Art. 12. Whether or not they are independent of t, they may be used as a check upon a solution, for they reduce to constants when the solution values of the x_j are substituted into them.

The integrals of the differential equations of the problem of three bodies have long been of interest. Ten simple integrals of the problem have been known since the time of Newton; their physical meanings were given in Art. 12. It was long supposed that progress toward a general solution of the problem depended upon the discovery, by some ingenious means, of additional integrals. Finally, Bruns proved * that no more integrals exist that are algebraic in the rectangular coördinates as dependent variables. Poincaré, using the osculating elliptic elements as dependent variables, proved † that no new single-valued transcendental integrals exist, even when two of the masses are very small relative to the third. These theorems have sometimes been supposed to prove that the problem of three bodies is completely insoluble. The differential equations satisfy the hypotheses of both Chapters III and IV and hence can be solved in sufficiently restricted domains by either of these methods. Moreover, the differential equations of the problem, which are of the eighteenth order, possess eighteen integrals formed from the solution by the method of Art. 41. In interpreting the theorems of Bruns and Poincaré, the conditions under which they hold must be kept in mind. Bruns used one set of dependent variables; Poincaré, another. The results might differ using other variables. In fact, Levi-Civita has shown ‡ that, using suitable variables, uniform integrals exist for a special problem that comes under those covered by the theorem of Poincaré.

* *Acta Mathematica*, Vol. 11, pp. 25–96.
† *Acta Mathematica*, Vol. 13; *Les Méthodes de la Mécanique Céleste*, Chap. V.
‡ *Acta Mathematica*, Vol. 30, pp. 305–327.

V. QUESTIONS AND PROBLEMS

1. Solve the differential equations

$$\begin{cases} \dfrac{dx_1}{dt} = + x_2, \\[2mm] \dfrac{dx_2}{dt} = - \kappa^2 x_1, \\[2mm] x_i(t_0) = a_i. \end{cases}$$

Show that if the solution functions are given the notation of equations (2), then the functions (8) are integrals.

2. Prove that $F = \phi_1{}^2 + 2\phi_2$, where ϕ_1 and ϕ_2 are the solution functions of the differential equations of Problem 1, is an integral of these equations.

3. Prove that $\kappa^2 x_1{}^2 + x_2{}^2$ is an integral of the differential equations of Problem 1. Express it as a function of ϕ_1 and ϕ_2.

4. Would equations (10) necessarily follow if the functions $\phi_i(t; x_j; t_0)$ were continuous in t, but did not have continuous first partial derivatives with respect to t? Would equations (10) necessarily follow if the functions $\phi_i(t; x_j; t_0)$ possessed derivatives with respect to t that were not continuous in t?

5. Would equations (10) necessarily follow if the functions $\phi_i(t; x_j; t_0)$ were not analytic in the x_j, but only continuous in the x_j?

6. If $P = P(x_1, x_2)$ is a polynomial in x_1 and x_2 of any degree in the variables, prove that the Jacobian of $\phi_1 = P^m$ and $\phi_2 = \sin P$ is identically zero in x_1 and x_2.

7. Reduce the order of the differential equations of Problem 1 by the use of the integral of Problem 2.

8. Solve the differential equations

$$\begin{cases} \dfrac{dx_1}{dt} = x_2, \\[2mm] \dfrac{dx_2}{dt} = \dfrac{1 + x_3[1 - 2x_1 - x_3 + x_1{}^2 + 2x_1 x_3 - x_1{}^2 x_3]}{(1 - x_1)^2(1 - x_3)}, \\[2mm] \dfrac{dx_3}{dt} = x_4, \\[2mm] \dfrac{dx_4}{dt} = \dfrac{1 + x_1[1 - x_1 - 2x_3 + x_3{}^2 + 2x_1 x_3 - x_1 x_3{}^2]}{(1 - x_1)(1 - x_3)^2}, \\[2mm] x_1(0) = 0, \quad x_2(0) = 1, \quad x_3(0) = 0, \quad x_4(0) = 1 \end{cases}$$

by the methods of Chapter II.   Prove that

$$F(x_i) = x_2{}^2 + x_4{}^2 - 2x_1 x_3 - \frac{2}{(1 - x_1)(1 - x_3)} = c$$

is an integral of the differential equations, using the second definition of an integral (Art. 11). Verify the fact that the solution, as far as it has been worked out, satisfies the integral identically in t.

9. Prove that the solution of the reduced system, Art. 44, satisfies the differential equations (1).

CHAPTER VI

ANALYTIC IMPLICIT FUNCTIONS

45. The Problem of Implicit Functions. Suppose there are given the equations of condition

$$(1) \quad \begin{cases} F_1(x_1, \cdots, x_n; \mu) = 0, \\ \cdots \cdots \cdots \cdots \cdots \\ F_n(x_1, \cdots, x_n; \mu) = 0, \end{cases}$$

where the functions F_i have certain specified properties. The parameter μ may take all values in some domain or on some range. The problem is (a) to prove the existence of values for $x_1, \cdots, x_n$ such that equations (1) will be satisfied for all values of μ in at least a part of its domain; (b) to determine the properties of the solution; and (c) to devise means of obtaining the solution practically. The characteristics of this problem are similar to those of the problem presented by differential equations; the difference in the two problems lies in the differences between the conditions that define the solution functions.

If a solution of equations (1) exists, it can be written

$$(2) \quad x_i = \phi_i(\mu),$$

where the functions $\phi_i(\mu)$ satisfy the identities

$$(3) \quad F_i(\phi_j(\mu); \mu) \underset{\mu}{\equiv} 0$$

in some domain for μ.

In this chapter it will be assumed that the functions $F_i(x_j; \mu)$ are analytic in the x_j and μ for all values of the x_j and μ for which $|x_j - a_j| \leq r_j$, $|\mu| \leq \sigma$. The problem is not generally solvable without the further conditions

$$(4) \quad F_i(a_j; 0) = 0,$$

which will be assumed to be satisfied. These equations in effect define a point on the solution and are the analogue of the initial conditions in the theory of differential equations. The solution that will be obtained may be interpreted in the domain of reals as a curve passing through the point $x_j = a_j$, $\mu = 0$.

The problem of implicit functions is one of great importance in analysis, and it is one that has frequent applications in differential equations. For example, in Art. 43 equations (11) had to be solved for the x_j to give equations (14). Again, in Art. 44 equation (19) was assumed to be solved for x_n. In the next chapter the results obtained in the present chapter will be frequently used.

The theory of implicit functions includes as simple special cases the inversion of a series; namely, the solution of

$$\mu = a_1 x + a_2 x^2 + \cdots$$

for x in terms of μ. It includes also the solution of the equation

$$0 = a_{10}x + a_{01}\mu + a_{20}x^2 + a_{11}x\mu + a_{02}\mu^2 + \cdots$$

for x in terms of μ, or for μ in terms of x. It will be sufficient here to treat the more general cases.

46. Case in Which the Determinant of the Coefficients of the Linear Terms Is Not Zero. Suppose the origin of coördinates is so chosen that the a_i of equations (4) are zero. Since the functions $F_i(x_j; \mu)$ of equations (1) are, by hypothesis, analytic in the x and μ for all values of the x_j and μ for which $|x_j| \leqq r_i$, $|\mu| \leqq \sigma$, it follows that equations (1) may be written in the form

$$(5) \quad \begin{cases} a_{11}x_1 + \cdots + a_{1n}x_n = c_1\mu + p_1(x_j; \mu), \\ \\ a_{n1}x_1 + \cdots + a_{nn}x_n = c_n\mu + p_n(x_j; \mu), \end{cases}$$

where the a_{ij} and c_i are constants and the $p_i(x_j; \mu)$ are power series in the x_j and μ, containing no terms of degree lower than the second in the x_j and μ, and converging for all values of x_j and μ for which $|x_j| \leqq r_i$, $|\mu| \leqq \sigma$. Moreover, the determinant of the coefficients of the left members is not zero.

If the right members of equations (5) are regarded as known, these equations can be uniquely solved for $x_1, \cdots, x_n$ of the left members in terms of μ and the functions $p_1, \cdots, p_n$. The result will be of the form

$$(6) \quad x_i = a_i\mu + f_i(x_j; \mu) \qquad (i = 1, \cdots, n),$$

where the functions $f_i(x_j;\ \mu)$ are power series in the x_j and μ, starting with terms of the second degree in these variables, and converging if $|x_j| \leqq r_j$, $|\mu| \leqq \sigma$. The problem is to solve equations (6) for the x_i.

47. Formal Solution of Equations (6). Equations (6) have a formal solution for the x_i as power series in μ, a result that would be expected. Let the solution be written in the notation

$$(7) \qquad x_i = a_i^{(1)}\mu + a_i^{(2)}\mu^2 + \cdots \qquad (i = 1, \cdots, n),$$

where the $a_i^{(\kappa)}$ are constants that are to be so determined that equations (7) shall be a solution of equations (6).

On assuming the convergence of the right members of equations (7) for sufficiently restricted values of μ, substituting these series into equations (6), rearranging the right members as power series in μ, and equating the coefficients of corresponding powers of μ in the left and right members, it is found that the conditions that must be satisfied by the $a_i^{(\kappa)}$ are

$$(8) \quad \begin{cases} a_i^{(1)} = a_i \qquad (i = 1, \cdots, n), \\ a_i^{(2)} = \dfrac{1}{2}\sum_{j=1}^{n}\sum_{\kappa=1}^{n} \dfrac{\partial^2 f_i}{\partial x_j \partial x_\kappa} a_j^{(1)} a_\kappa^{(1)} + \sum_{j=1}^{n} \dfrac{\partial^2 f_i}{\partial x_j \partial \mu} a_j^{(1)} + \dfrac{1}{2}\dfrac{\partial^2 f_i}{\partial \mu^2}, \\ \cdot\ \cdot\ \cdot\ \cdot\ \cdot\ \cdot\ \cdot\ \cdot\ \cdot\ \cdot\ \cdot\ \cdot\ \cdot\ \cdot\ \cdot\ \cdot\ \cdot\ \cdot \\ a_i^{(\kappa)} = p_i^{(\kappa)}(a_j^{(1)}, \cdots, a_j^{(\kappa-1)}) \qquad (\kappa = 1, 2, \cdots), \end{cases}$$

where the functions $p_i^{(\kappa)}(a_j^{(1)}, \cdots, a_j^{(\kappa-1)})$ are polynomials in the $a_j^{(1)}, \cdots, a_j^{(\kappa-1)}$ whose coefficients are linear functions of the coefficients of the power-series expansions of the $f_i(x_j;\ \mu)$ and have positive numerical multipliers.

The $a_i^{(\kappa)}$ ($\kappa = 1, 2, \cdots$) are uniquely determined by equations (8). Hence the formal power-series solution (7) of equations (5) exists and is unique.

48. Proof of Convergence of the Series (7). The steps taken in determining the coefficients $a_i^{(\kappa)}$ are valid only if the series (7) converge. In order to prove the convergence of these series, consider first the solution of a system of equations corresponding to equations (6) whose right members dominate the right members of equations (6) and have the property of having no terms of the first degree except the term in μ. If M represents an upper bound to the functions $|f_i(x_j;\ \mu)|$ for $|x_j| \leqq r_j$, $|\mu| \leqq \sigma$, then functions which have all the required properties are

$$(6')\quad X_i = M\frac{\mu}{\sigma'} + \frac{M}{\left(1 - \dfrac{\mu}{\sigma'}\right)\left[1 - \dfrac{X_1 + \cdots + X_n}{r}\right]}$$
$$- M\left[1 + \frac{X_1 + \cdots + X_n}{r} + \frac{\mu}{\sigma'}\right],$$

where $\sigma' < \sigma$, $M > \sigma'|a_i|$ $(i = 1, \cdots, n)$, and $r < r_i$. The expansions of the right members of equations (6') dominate the right members of equations (6). The last terms in the right members of equations (6') cancel out the linear terms with the exception of $M\mu/\sigma'$.

It follows from equations (6') that $X_1 = \cdots = X_n = X$, and that X satisfies the equation

$$(6'')\quad X = M\frac{\mu}{\sigma'} + \frac{M}{\left(1 - \dfrac{\mu}{\sigma'}\right)\left[1 - \dfrac{nX}{r}\right]} - M\left[1 + \frac{nX}{r} + \frac{\mu}{\sigma'}\right].$$

The solution of this equation for X, vanishing with $\mu = 0$, is

$$(9)\quad 2\frac{n}{r}\left[1 + \frac{n}{r}M\right]X = 1 - \sqrt{1 - \frac{4n}{r}M\frac{\left[1 + \dfrac{n}{r}M\right]\dfrac{\mu}{\sigma'}}{1 - \dfrac{\mu}{\sigma'}}}\,.$$

Consider the expansion of the right member of equation (9) as a power series in μ. The singular points are the infinity for $\mu = \sigma'$ and the branch-point defined by the equation

$$r\left(1 - \frac{\mu}{\sigma'}\right) = 4nM\left[1 + \frac{n}{r}M\right]\frac{\mu}{\sigma'}.$$

Therefore the expansion of the right member of equation (9) as a power series in μ converges for all values of μ such that

$$(10)\quad |\mu| < \frac{\sigma'}{1 + \dfrac{4n}{r}M\left[1 + \dfrac{n}{r}M\right]},$$

and the expansions of the solution equations (6') as power series in μ converge under the same conditions.

Equations (6′) can be solved by the methods of Art. 47 in power-series of the form

$$(7') \qquad X_i = A_i{}^{(1)}\mu + A_i{}^{(2)}\mu^2 + \cdots.$$

Since the power-series solution is unique, it is identical with that obtained from the expansion of the right members of (9). Therefore the series (7′) converge provided the inequality (10) is satisfied, and hence the steps of Art. 47 are valid for the problem defined by equations (6′).

The $A_i{}^{(\kappa)}$ in the right members of equations (7′) are defined by equations corresponding to equations (8). It follows from the fact that the expansions of the right members of equations (6′) dominate the corresponding expansions of equations (6), and from the properties of the power series in the right members of equations (8), that $A_i{}^{(\kappa)} > |a_i{}^{(\kappa)}|$ $(i = 1, \cdots, n; \kappa = 1, 2, \cdots)$. Therefore the solution series (7) converge at least for all values of μ for which the inequality (10) is satisfied. In general the domain of convergence of the solution series is much greater than that defined by the inequality (10).

It follows from the form and convergence of equations (7) that the solution is analytic in μ for all values of μ for which the inequality (10) is satisfied. If the terms in the right members of equations (5) that are of lowest degree in μ alone are of degree p, then the terms in the right members of equations (6) that are of lowest degree in μ alone are also of degree p. And it follows from equations (8) that at least one of the solution equations (7) starts with a term of degree p at the lowest. If the right members of equations (5) do not contain any term in μ alone, the solution is simply $x_1 = \cdots = x_n = 0$.

49. Case of Several Parameters. Suppose the right members of equations (5) are power series in the x_j and in the m parameters $\mu_1, \cdots, \mu_m$. The right members of equations (6) will also be power series in $\mu_1, \cdots, \mu_m$. The solution can be constructed as power series in all these parameters by obvious modifications of the method of Art. 47. Or, if it is preferred, the substitution $\mu_j = b_j \mu$, where the b_j are constants, throws the problem back upon the single parameter μ. After the solution has been formed, the original parameters may be restored by the inverse substitution.

Suppose all terms in the right members of equations (5) that are independent of the x_j contain at least one of the parameters $\mu_1, \cdots, \mu_\kappa$ ($\kappa < m$) as a factor. Then every term of the solution (7) will contain at least one of the parameters $\mu_1, \cdots, \mu_\kappa$ as a factor. If the terms in the right members of equations (5) that are of lowest degree in μ_κ are of degree p, then the terms in the solution (7) of lowest degree in μ_κ are of degree p at the lowest.

50. Generalization of the Parameter. If equations (1) involve the parameter μ analytically and also non-analytically or in a very complicated way, the problem may be advantageously treated by replacing μ as it occurs in the second way by μ' and making the expansions only with respect to μ. The method of Art. 47 can be applied provided there are no terms in the right members of the equations corresponding to equations (5) that do not vanish with the x_j and μ.

After the solution has been constructed, the parameter μ' is replaced by μ. The result will be power series in μ whose coefficients are functions of μ that may not be analytic. Consequently in this case the solution series are not necessarily analytic functions of μ.

Suppose the right members of equations (5) are analytic in x_j and μ and continuous in μ' for $|x_j| \leqq r_j$, $|\mu| \leqq \sigma$, $0 \leqq \mu' \leqq \sigma_1$. Under these conditions the upper bound M of equations (6′) is an upper bound for all $0 \leqq \mu' \leqq \sigma_1$. Hence it follows from a demonstration parallel to that given in Art. 48 that the solution series converge uniformly with respect to μ' for all values of μ satisfying the inequality (10). Then, after μ' has been replaced by μ, it follows from Appendix D that within the smaller of the limits σ_1 and that imposed by the inequality (10) the solution series are continuous functions of μ.

51. Case in Which the Determinant of the Coefficients of the Linear Terms Is Zero and at Least One First Minor Is Not Zero. Suppose the determinant of the coefficients of the left members of equations (5) is zero, and that at least one of its first minors is not zero. Let the notation be so chosen that the determinant of the first $n - 1$ rows and columns is one that is not zero. Under the hypotheses that have been made, the first $n - 1$ of equations (5) can be solved for the $x_1, \cdots, x_{n-1}$ of their left members linearly in terms of x_n, μ, and $p_1(x_j; \mu), \cdots, p_{n-1}(x_j; \mu)$.

If A_{ij} represents the co-factor of a_{ij}, the solution, so far as it involves x_n to the first degree, will be

$$(11) \qquad x_i = \frac{A_{ni}}{A_{nn}} x_n \qquad (i = 1, \cdots, n-1).$$

Therefore the left member of the last equation gives

$$a_{n1}x_1 + \cdots + a_{nn}x_n = \frac{(a_{n1}A_{n1} + \cdots + a_{nn}A_{nn})}{A_{nn}} x_n,$$

and the coefficient of x_n is zero because the terms contained in the parentheses are the expansion of the determinant, which is zero by hypothesis, and the denominator is a non-zero first minor. Therefore the result of substituting the solution of the first $n-1$ of equations (5) for $x_1, \cdots, x_{n-1}$ in terms of x_n, μ, and $p_1(x_j; \mu), \cdots, p_{n-1}(x_j; \mu)$ into the last of equations (5) is an equation that contains no term in x_n alone of the first degree. Let this equation be written in the form

$$(12) \qquad P(x, \mu) = 0,$$

the subscript n being omitted from x_n for convenience. The $P(x, \mu)$ is a power series in x and μ that converges provided $|x|$ and $|\mu|$ satisfy the inequalities $|x| \leqq r_j$, $|\mu| \leqq \sigma$.

52. First Special Form of Equation (12).

Before taking up the general case, two special cases will be treated that are easily thrown back on the results derived in Arts. 47 and 48.

Suppose equation (12) can be written in the form

$$(13) \qquad x^\kappa p(x; \mu) = \mu^\lambda q(x; \mu),$$

where $\kappa \geqq 2$, $\lambda \geqq 1$ and $p(x; \mu)$ and $q(x; \mu)$ are power series in x and μ such that $p(0, 0)$ and $q(0, 0)$ are both different from zero. Under these conditions, the κth root can be taken of each member of equation (13), giving

$$(13') \qquad x\, p_\kappa(x; \mu) = \eta\, \mu^{\lambda/\kappa} q_\kappa(x; \mu),$$

where η is any κth root of unity, and

$$\begin{cases} [p_\kappa(x; \mu)]^\kappa \underset{x,\,\mu}{\equiv} p(x; \mu), \\ [q_\kappa(x; \mu)]^\kappa \underset{x,\,\mu}{\equiv} q(x; \mu). \end{cases}$$

It follows from these relations and $p(0, 0) \neq 0$ that $p_\kappa(0, 0) \neq 0$. Therefore, for each value of η, equation (13′) can be solved uniquely for x as a power series in $\mu^{1/\kappa}$ that will converge for $|\mu|$ sufficiently small. Since η has κ distinct values, there are κ distinct solutions. Interpreted geometrically, there are κ branches of the curves defined by equation (13) that pass through the origin.

Suppose the coefficients of the functions $p(x; \mu)$ and $q(x; \mu)$ of equation (13) are all real. Suppose $p(0, 0)$ and $q(0, 0)$ are both positive and that κ is even. Then there are two real branches of the function if μ^λ is positive, and none if it is negative. If κ is odd, there is one real branch if μ^λ is positive and also one if μ^λ is negative. If $p(0, 0)$ and $q(0, 0)$ have opposite signs, corresponding results hold with the signs of μ^λ interchanged.

53. Second Special Form of Equation (12). There is a second simple form of equation (12) that merits attention; namely,

$$(14) \qquad 0 = p_\kappa(x; \mu) + Q(x; \mu),$$

where $p_\kappa(x, \mu)$ is a homogeneous polynomial in x and μ of degree κ with the coefficient of x^κ not zero, and where $Q(x; \mu)$ is a power series in x and μ with no term of degree less than $\kappa + 1$ in the two variables taken together.

Suppose the roots of the equation $p_\kappa(x; \mu) = 0$ are $c_1\mu, \cdots, c_\kappa\mu$ so that

$$(15) \qquad p_\kappa(x; \mu) = C(x - c_1\mu) \cdots (x - c_\kappa\mu).$$

Suppose $c_1\mu$ is a simple root, and let

$$(16) \qquad x = c_1\mu + y_1\mu.$$

This substitution transforms equation (14) into a power series in y_1 and μ from which μ^κ can be divided out. Since $c_1\mu$ is a simple root, the part of the equation coming from the function $p_\kappa(x; \mu)$ will have a term of the first degree in y_1 whose coefficient is not zero. Every term coming from the function $Q(x; \mu)$ will contain μ as a factor. Consequently the equation that results from the substitution can be solved uniquely for y_1 as a power series in μ by the method of Art. 47. Upon substituting the result of this solution into the right member of equation (16), one solution of equation (14) is obtained. A solution can be obtained similarly for each distinct c_j of equation (15). If the c_j are all distinct, κ distinct solutions are obtained in this way.

54. The General Case of Equation (12). In the general case, equation (12) can be written in the form

$$(17) \qquad P(x, \mu) = \sum_{i=0}^{\infty} \sum_{j=0}^{\infty} c_{ij} x^i \mu^j = 0 \qquad (i + j > 0).$$

Suppose $c_{i0} = 0$ for $i < \kappa$, $c_{0j} = 0$ for $j < \lambda$, and $c_{\kappa 0} \neq 0$, $c_{0\lambda} \neq 0$.

The first problem is the determination of the number of solutions of equation (17) for x in terms of μ that vanish with μ. Weierstrass has proved * that, under the hypotheses given, the function $P(x, \mu)$ can be written in the form

$$P(x; \mu) = [x^\kappa + p_1(\mu)x^{\kappa-1} + \cdots + p_{\kappa-1}(\mu)x + p_\kappa(\mu)]Q(x; \mu),$$

where $p_1(\mu)$, $\cdots$, $p_\kappa(\mu)$ are power series in μ, vanishing with μ, and $Q(x; \mu)$ is a power series in x and μ for which $Q(0, 0) \neq 0$. It follows from the theory of algebraic equations that for $|x|$ and $|\mu|$ sufficiently small there are κ solutions of equation (17). The proof of the theorem of Weierstrass will not be given here, but methods of finding the solutions will be developed.

It will be noted that in the special cases treated in Arts. 52 and 53 the existence and forms of the solution were inferred from certain groups of terms of low degree. The general case is more complicated, but it is treated by a systematic selection of groups of terms that together give all the solutions under consideration.

Newton has given a geometrical representation of the essential facts that enables one to pick out and treat the groups of terms that define the solutions. Take a rectangular set of axes, an i-axis and a j-axis, and plot on their plane the points whose coördinates are the exponents of the terms of equation (17) for which $i \leqq \kappa$, $j \leqq \lambda$. There will be one point on the i-axis having the coördinates $(\kappa, 0)$ and one on the j-axis having the coördinates $(0, \lambda)$. All the remaining points will be in the first quadrant.

Now imagine that pegs are placed on the diagram at all

* *Abhandlungen aus der Funktionlehre*, p. 107. See also Bliss, *Bulletin of the American Mathematical Society*, Vol. XVI (1910), pp. 356–359; MacMillan, *Bulletin of the American Mathematical Society*, Vol. XVII (1910), pp. 116–120.

points corresponding to the exponents of the terms of $P(x; \mu)$ that are being considered. Imagine a thread to be fastened to the peg at the point $(\kappa, 0)$ and drawn down along the i-axis to the origin, and then along the j-axis to the point $(0, \lambda)$. Imagine it to be drawn tightly around the peg at the point $(0, \lambda)$. The part of the thread between the points $(\kappa, 0)$ and $(0, \lambda)$ will consist of one or more straight-line segments at whose corners will be points corresponding to the exponents of the terms of $P(x; \mu)$. There will be no points on the side of the thread toward the origin; one will be at each corner where the segments of the thread join; there may be others on the segments; but in general most of the points will be on the side of the thread remote from the origin.

The terms whose exponents define each segment give rise to a group of solutions in number equal to the difference of the ordinates of the ends of the segments. All the segments together give rise to κ solutions.

Consider the general segment whose end points have the coördinates (i_1, j_1) and (i_2, j_2), where $i_1 > i_2, j_1 < j_2$. There may be points defined by the exponents of other terms of $P(x; \mu)$ on the segment. Now make the transformation

$$(18) \qquad x = \mu^\alpha y,$$

where

$$(19) \qquad \alpha = \frac{j_2 - j_1}{i_1 - i_2} = \frac{m}{n},$$

and m and n are relatively prime integers. Let the terms defining the ends of the segment be $c_{i_1 j_1} x^{i_1} \mu^{j_1}$ and $c_{i_2 j_2} x^{i_2} \mu^{j_2}$. After the transformation defined by equations (18) and (19) they become $c_{i_1 j_1} \mu^{\alpha'} y^{i_1}$ and $c_{i_2 j_2} \mu^{\alpha'} y^{i_2}$, where

$$(20) \qquad \alpha' = i_1\alpha + j_1 = \frac{i_1 j_2 - i_2 j_1}{i_1 - i_2}.$$

If there is any other point (i', j') on the segment corresponding to a term of the function $P(x; \mu)$, its coördinates satisfy the equation

$$(21) \qquad i'(j_2 - j_1) + j'(i_1 - i_2) + i_2 j_1 - i_1 j_2 = 0.$$

Hence after the transformation (18) the term $c_{i'j'} x^{i'} \mu^{j'}$ becomes $c_{i'j'} \mu^{\alpha'} y^{i'}$. This term after the transformation contains μ to the same power as that of the transformed terms corresponding to the ends of the segment.

Now consider any term $c_{ij} x^i \mu^j$ not on the segment. Since there are no representative points defined by the terms of the function $P(x; \mu)$ that are on the side of the segment toward the origin, it follows that i and j satisfy the inequality

$$(22) \qquad i(j_2 - j_1) + j(i_1 - i_2) + i_2 j_1 - i_1 j_2 > 0.$$

Consequently after the transformation (18) the term $c_{ij} x^i \mu^j$ becomes $c_{ij} \mu^{\alpha''} y^i$, where

$$(23) \qquad \alpha'' = \frac{i(j_2 - j_1) + j(i_1 - i_2)}{i_1 - i_2} > \alpha'.$$

Therefore after the transformation this term contains μ to a higher power than it is contained in the terms corresponding to points on the segment. Consequently, after the transformation, the equation becomes divisible by $\mu^{\alpha'}$; the terms corresponding to the segment contain y alone; and those which correspond to the points not on the segment contain μ to some integral or fractional power as a factor. Since α' is not necessarily an integer, it is convenient to introduce the parameter $\mu' = \mu^{1/(i_1 - i_2)}$, for the resulting series will then be in integral powers of the variables y and μ'.

The equation (17) becomes as a consequence of the transformation (18) an equation of the form

$$(24) \qquad c_{i_1 j_1} y^{i_2} \left[y^{i_1 - i_2} + \cdots + \frac{c_{i_2 j_2}}{c_{i_1 j_1}} \right] + \mu' P'(y, \mu') = 0,$$

where $P'(y; \mu')$ is a power series in y and μ'. Let the roots of the bracket set equal to zero be $c_1, \cdots, c_{i_1 - i_2}$. Suppose c_ν is a simple root of the equation and let

$$(25) \qquad y = c_\nu + z.$$

The resulting equation will be a power series in z and μ', vanishing with z and μ'; and it will converge for any finite values of c_ν and z if $|\mu'|$ is sufficiently small, because of the fact that the series $P(x; \mu)$ converges if $|x|$ and $|\mu|$ are sufficiently small; and it follows from the transformation (18) and the definition of μ' that $|x|$ and $|\mu|$ can be made as small as may be desired by making $|\mu'|$ small. Since c_ν is a simple root of the polynomial, the equation in z and μ' contains a term of the first degree in z alone. Therefore it follows from Arts. 47 and 48 that the equation can be solved uniquely for z as a power series in μ', vanishing with μ'. Let the result of the solution be written

$$(26) \qquad z = \mu'p'(\mu'),$$

where $p'(\mu')$ is a power series in μ', converging for $|\mu'|$ sufficiently small. Then it follows from equations (18) and (25) that

$$(27) \qquad x = [c_\nu + \mu'p'(\mu')]\mu^\alpha = [c_\nu + \mu'p'(\mu')]\mu'^{i_2-i_1}.$$

The process that has just been described gives a solution of equation (17) corresponding to each of the simple roots of the bracket of equation (24) set equal to zero. If the $i_1 - i_2$ roots are all simple, the $i_1 - i_2$ solutions associated with the segment are obtained. If they are not simple, each multiple root gives rise to a power series in z and μ' whose term of lowest degree in z alone has the degree equal to the multiplicity of the root. The resulting equation in z and μ' is of the type of (17) in x and μ, and can be treated by the same methods. Unless $P(x; \mu) = 0$ has two or more solutions that are identical in μ, the roots corresponding to the segment will be separated sooner or later by successive applications of the method. The terms corresponding to the other segments can be treated in a similar manner.

55. Comments on the Process.

The process of Art. 54 gives $i_1 - i_2$ solutions of equation (17) corresponding to the segment whose end points have the coördinates (i_1, j_1) and (i_2, j_2). The total number of solutions obtained by the process is

$$\kappa = (\kappa - i_1) + (i_1 - i_2) + \cdots + (i_{p-1} - i_p) + (i_p - 0).$$

It follows from the theorem of Weierstrass that this is the total number of solutions of equation (17) that vanish with μ.

When κ is greater than unity, there is more than one branch of the function defined by equation (17) passing through the origin of the x- and μ-axes. The branches, which may be real or complex, are grouped according to the segments of the broken line that has been defined. If α, of equation (19), is unity, the group of solutions consists of curves whose common tangent at the origin is in general distinct from the axes. If α is different from unity, the group consists of curves whose common tangent coincides with either one axis or the other.

Equation (18) is a sort of magnifier that, by means of equation (24), in general separates the curves of a group having close contact at the origin. If the curves of a part of a group have a contact of high order at the origin, further magnification by a similar transformation may be required to separate them.

The process is applicable to polynomials; and, since the convergence of the original function corresponding to that in equation (17) and of all of its transformations by equations corresponding to equation (18) holds for all values of the arguments, it can be extended to include the infinite branches of the curves defined by the polynomial set equal to zero. The branches of the function for which x is infinite and μ is finite can be treated by the methods of Art. 54 after the original equation has been transformed by the substitution $x = 1/\xi$, $\mu = \mu$. The branches for which x is finite and μ is infinite can be treated by transforming the original equation by the substitution $x = x$, $\mu = 1/\nu$. The branches for which both coördinates are infinite can be treated by the transformation $x = 1/\xi$, $\mu = 1/\nu$.

The problem of Art. 54 arises from equations (5) when the determinant of the coefficients of the left member is zero and when at least one of its first minors is not zero. Now suppose that all first minors are zero, but that there is a second minor which is not zero. Then equations (5) can be solved for $n - 2$ of the x_i in terms of two of the x_i and μ. If the results of the solution are substituted into the two remaining equations, two equations in two of the x_i and μ will be obtained which have no linear terms in the two x_i in which the solution is expressed; that is, the resulting power series begin with terms of the second degree in the x_i.

The problem presented by two power series not having linear terms is extraordinarily complicated and no completely general solution of it has been obtained. Nevertheless, MacMillan has given a treatment * that is applicable save in very exceptional cases, even for any number of simultaneous equations.

* Wm. D. MacMillan, *Mathematische Annalen*, Vol. 72 (1912), pp. 157–202.

VI. QUESTIONS AND PROBLEMS

1. If equations (1) were satisfied by $x_j = a_j$, $\mu = \mu_0$, what would be the difference in the definition of the domain of validity of the equations? What would be the difference in the definition of a solution of the problem?

2. Invert the series

$$\mu = x + \frac{1}{3}x^2 + \frac{1}{7}x^3 + \frac{1}{72}x^4 + \cdots$$

to four terms.

3. Solve the equation

$$0 = 2x - \mu + \frac{1}{2}x^2 + \frac{1}{3}x\mu + \frac{1}{4}\mu^2 + \frac{1}{3}x^3 + \frac{1}{4}x^2\mu + \frac{1}{2}x\mu^2 + \frac{1}{5}\mu^3 + \cdots$$

for x in terms of μ to terms of the third degree.

4. Formally solve equations (5) for $x_1, \cdots, x_n$ as power series in μ without going through equations (6).

5. Prove the convergence in a sufficiently restricted domain of the solution of Problem 4.

6. Prove the convergence of the solution series (7) of equations (6), using upper bounds M_i for the functions $|f_i(x_j; \mu)|$.

7. Would it be possible to use

$$\frac{M}{1 - \dfrac{X_1 + \cdots + X_n}{r} - \dfrac{\mu}{\sigma'}}$$

in place of the second term in the right member of (6')? If so, complete the proof of convergence, using this dominating function.

8. Prove in detail the statements in the last paragraph of Art. 49.

9. Suppose equation (12) has the form

$$x^\kappa + b_1 x^{\kappa-1} + \cdots + b_\kappa + \mu p(x; \mu) = 0,$$

where the b_i are constants and $p(x, \mu)$ is a power series in x and μ that converges if $|x| < r$, $|\mu| < \sigma$. Under what circumstances can this equation be solved by the methods of this chapter for x in terms of μ?

10. Is it essential for the method of Art. 53 that the polynomial $p_\kappa(x; \mu)$ should be homogeneous in x and μ?

11. Suppose $p_\kappa(x, \mu)$ is homogeneous in x and μ^m of degree κ and discuss the problem.

12. Construct the Newtonian diagram for the equation

$$0 = x^7 + 2x^4\mu + 3x^2\mu^2 - x\mu^3 + 2\mu^5 + 5x^3\mu^2 - 3x^2\mu^3 + x\mu^4 + 2x^3\mu^2,$$

and find the first terms of all the solutions.

13. Find the first terms of the solutions for all of the infinite branches of the curves defined by the equation of Problem 12.

14. From the results of Problems 12 and 13, sketch the real branches of the curves.

CHAPTER VII

THE PROBLEM OF ELLIPTIC MOTION

56. Purpose of Illustrative Problems. In order that the continuity of the demonstrations should not be seriously broken, the illustrations that were given in the preceding chapters were for the most part trivial. One would not easily infer from them the wide applicability in practical problems of the methods that were developed, nor the ease and certainty with which important conclusions can be deduced by their use. Instead of being purely theoretical, the processes that were discussed are, as a matter of fact, of the greatest practical value.

In order to elucidate still further the theories that have been developed, and to show how to choose among them and to employ them in physical and theoretical applications, a number of practical problems will be treated in this chapter and the three that immediately follow. The problems chosen are not trivial nor without historical interest. They will be treated fully and in some cases by various methods in order to compare the advantages of the different processes in the situations presented.

The problem treated in this chapter is that of the elliptic motion of a particle moving subject to a force which is directed toward a fixed point and which varies inversely as the square of the distance of the particle from the point. This is the problem of two bodies which was solved first by Newton in the *Principia*, and which has been treated in somewhat different ways by many mathematicians. The discussion that will be given here is wholly different from those usually given, and is based directly upon the general theories of the preceding chapters.

57. The Differential Equations. Suppose a particle moves under the attraction of a central force which varies inversely as the square of the distance of the particle from the origin. It will be taken as known that the path described by the particle is a plane curve. Suppose its motion is in the xy-plane; then its coördinates satisfy the differential equations

(1)
$$\begin{cases} \dfrac{d^2x}{dt^2} = -k^2\dfrac{x}{r^3}, \\[2mm] \dfrac{d^2y}{dt^2} = -k^2\dfrac{y}{r^3}, \\[2mm] r^2 = x^2 + y^2, \end{cases}$$

where k^2 is a factor depending upon the central force and the units employed.

On transforming to polar coördinates by the substitution $x = r\cos\theta$, $y = r\sin\theta$, equations (1) give the equivalent system

(2)
$$\begin{cases} \dfrac{d^2r}{dt^2} - r\left(\dfrac{d\theta}{dt}\right)^2 + \dfrac{k^2}{r^2} = 0, \\[2mm] \dfrac{d}{dt}\left(r^2\dfrac{d\theta}{dt}\right) = 0. \end{cases}$$

The second of these equations has the integral

(3)
$$r^2\frac{d\theta}{dt} = c_1,$$

where c_1 is a constant that depends upon the initial conditions.

The differential equations can be so transformed that it is easy to determine the geometrical properties of the orbit by letting $r = 1/u$ and eliminating t by means of equation (3). Since

$$\begin{cases} \dfrac{dr}{dt} = \dfrac{dr}{du}\dfrac{du}{dt} = -\dfrac{1}{u^2}\dfrac{du}{d\theta}\dfrac{d\theta}{dt} = -c_1\dfrac{du}{d\theta}, \\[2mm] \dfrac{d^2r}{dt^2} = \dfrac{d}{dt}\left(\dfrac{dr}{dt}\right) = -c_1\dfrac{d}{dt}\left(\dfrac{du}{d\theta}\right) = -c_1\dfrac{d}{d\theta}\left(\dfrac{du}{d\theta}\right)\dfrac{d\theta}{dt} = -c_1^2u^2\dfrac{d^2u}{d\theta^2}, \\[2mm] r\left(\dfrac{d\theta}{dt}\right)^2 = c_1^2u^3, \end{cases}$$

it follows from the first of equations (2) that

(4)
$$\frac{d^2u}{d\theta^2} + u = \frac{k^2}{c_1^2}.$$

This is the differential equation satisfied by the coördinates of the particle.

58. The Path of the Particle. The differential equation (4) is so simple that it can be solved by elementary methods. Suppose $u = u_0$, $du/d\theta = 0$ for $\theta = \theta_0$; then the solution of equation (4) satisfying these conditions is easily found to be (since $u = 1/r$)

$$(5) \qquad r = \frac{c_1{}^2}{k^2 \left[1 + \left(\dfrac{u_0 c_1{}^2}{k^2} - 1 \right) \cos (\theta - \theta_0) \right]}.$$

The polar equation of a conic section with the origin at a focus is

$$r = \frac{p}{1 + e \cos (\theta - \theta_0)},$$

where p and e are the parameter and eccentricity respectively. On comparing this equation with equation (5), it is found that the path of the particle is a conic section whose focus is at the origin, and that

$$\begin{cases} k^2 p = c_1{}^2, \\ k^2 e = u_0 c_1{}^2 - k^2. \end{cases}$$

It will be assumed in the following discussion that c_1 and u_0 have such values that $-1 < e < +1$. That is, the case will be treated in which the path of the particle is an ellipse, including the circle as a special case. The methods that will be given do not apply if the orbit is a parabola or an hyperbola. In the case of elliptic motion henceforth considered, the parameter p and the constant c_1 are expressed in terms of the eccentricity e and the major semi-axis a by the equations

$$(6) \qquad \begin{cases} p = a(1 - e^2), \\ c_1 = k\sqrt{a(1 - e^2)}. \end{cases}$$

The period of revolution of the particle in its elliptic orbit can easily be determined. Equation (5) expresses r in terms of $\theta - \theta_0$, and equation (3) then gives a relation between θ and t. On using equations (3), (5), and (6), the formula for the period is found to be

$$(7) \qquad P = \frac{c_1{}^3}{k^4} \int_{\theta_0}^{\theta_0 + 2\pi} \frac{d\theta}{[1 + e \cos (\theta - \theta_0)]^2} = \frac{2\pi a^{3/2}}{k}.$$

At the end of a revolution the dependent variables r and θ

and their first derivatives retake their original values, and equations (2), not involving the time explicitly, are unchanged. Therefore the solution for the second revolution will be identical with that for the first. That is, the motion in the case under discussion is periodic with the period P.

In a certain sense a defines the size of the orbit and e its shape. It follows from equation (7) that the period P depends upon a alone. This remarkable property is exceptional, for the periods of revolution of particles revolving under other laws of central force are in general functions of the parameters that define their shapes.

Although the character of the orbit and the period of revolution have been determined, the problem is far from being solved. The complete solution consists in expressing the dependent variables r and θ, or others that are equivalent, in terms of the independent variable t. This problem, which so far in this discussion has not even been considered, is the one that presents practically all the difficulties.

59. The Solution as Power Series in t. The simplest method of determining the solution is that given in Chapter II. It is not so valuable, however, as others in this problem, but it will be used to throw additional light upon its characteristics and to furnish a contrast with others that will be also used.

Before developing the solution functions, equations (2) will be simplified as much as possible by using the facts that have been established and by simplifying the notation. Let θ be eliminated from the first of equations (2) by means of equation (3) and substitute the value of c_1 from equation (6). Then transform from the independent variable t to the variable τ by the equation

$$(8) \qquad t - t_0 = \frac{a^{3/2}}{k}\,\tau,$$

where t_0 is so chosen that r has its smallest value $a(1 - e)$ when $t = t_0$. Then the first of equations (2) and equation (3) become

$$(9) \qquad \begin{cases} \dfrac{d^2 r}{d\tau^2} - \dfrac{a^4(1 - e^2)}{r^3} + \dfrac{a^3}{r^2} = 0, \\[2mm] \dfrac{d\theta}{d\tau} = \dfrac{a^2\sqrt{1 - e^2}}{r^2}. \end{cases}$$

It follows from equation (8) that the period of revolution is 2π in terms of the variable τ. The first of equations (9) is independent of the second, and after the first has been solved the second is reduced to a quadrature.

Consider the first of equations (9). It might be replaced by an equivalent system of two equations of the first order, but it is not necessary to do so. It follows from the choice of τ and the fact that the orbit is an ellipse that $r(0) = a(1 - e)$, $r'(0) = 0$. Therefore the power-series solution has the form

$$(10) \qquad r = a(1 - e) + a_2\tau^2 + a_3\tau^3 + a_4\tau^4 + \cdots.$$

On substituting this series into the first of equations (9) and equating coefficients of corresponding powers of τ, it is found that

$$(11) \qquad \begin{cases} 2a_2 = \dfrac{ae}{(1 - e)^2}, \\ 6a_3 = 0, \\ 12a_4 = -\dfrac{ae(1 + 3e)}{2(1 - e)^5}, \\ \cdots\cdots\cdots\cdots \end{cases}$$

Therefore equation (10) and the second of equations (9) give as the explicit expressions for r and θ

$$(12) \qquad \begin{cases} r = a(1 - e)\left[1 + \dfrac{e}{2(1 - e)^3}\,\tau^2 - \dfrac{e(1 + 3e)}{24(1 - e)^6}\,\tau^4 \cdots\right], \\ \theta = \theta_0 + \dfrac{\sqrt{1 - e^2}}{(1 - e)^2}\,\tau\left[1 - \dfrac{e}{3(1 - e)^3}\,\tau^2 \cdots\right]. \end{cases}$$

So far as the solution has been developed, r is even in τ and $\theta - \theta_0$ is odd in τ. That these are general properties of the solution functions is easily established. If τ is replaced by $-\tau'$, the form of the first of equations (9) is unchanged. Moreover, the values of r and $dr/d\tau'$ at $\tau' = 0$ are the same as the values of r and $dr/d\tau$ at $\tau = 0$. Since both the differential equations and the initial conditions are unchanged, it follows from the uniqueness of the solution that it is unchanged. Hence if $\phi(\tau)$ represents the solution of the first of equations (9), then

$$r = \phi(\tau) = \phi(\tau') = \phi(-\tau).$$

That is, r is an even function of τ. Then it follows from the second of equations (9) that $\theta - \theta_0$ is an odd function of τ.

60. A Domain of Convergence of the Power-Series Solution.
The method of Art. 16 will be used to determine a domain
within which the solution (12) certainly converges; then, in
Art. 61, the *true* domain of convergence of these series will be
determined by a special method which is applicable in this
particular problem.

If r is replaced by r_1a, both the differential equations (9)
and the initial conditions are independent of a. Therefore the
domain of convergence of the solution depends upon e alone, as
is evident also from the form of equations (12).

The first of equations (9) is equivalent to the two equations

$$(13) \qquad \begin{cases} \dfrac{dr}{dt} = r', \\[2mm] \dfrac{dr'}{dt} = \dfrac{a^4(1 - e^2)}{r^3} - \dfrac{a^3}{r^2}. \end{cases}$$

Since the initial values of r and r' are $a(1 - e)$ and 0 respectively,
the right members of these equations are to be expanded as
power series in $r - a(1 - e)$ and $r' - 0$. The second equation
involves second and third powers of the function

$$\frac{1}{r} = \frac{1}{[a(1 - e) + r - a(1 - e)]},$$

the expansion of which as a power series in $r - a(1 - e)$ con-
verges provided $|r - a(1 - e)| < a(1 - e)$. As was seen in
Arts. 16 and 17, the dependent variables in this discussion must
be considered in their respective complex planes. Therefore
the values of r satisfying this inequality are those interior to
the circle whose center is at $a(1 - e)$ and whose radius is also
$a(1 - e)$. Since the perimeter of this circle passes through the
origin, the greatest lower bound of $|r|$ in the region is zero;
consequently, the absolute value of the right member of the
second of equations (13) does not have a finite upper bound in
the *open* region. This illustrates the reason for taking *closed*
regions for the variables in Arts. 14–17.

In the following discussion the variable r will be limited to
the *closed* domain defined by the relation

$$(14) \qquad |r - a(1 - e)| \leqq \eta a(1 - e) \qquad (0 < \eta < 1).$$

The values of r satisfying this inequality can be written in the parametric form

$$r = a(1 - e) + a\rho e^{i\phi} \qquad (\rho \leqq \eta(1 - e); 0 \leqq \phi < 2\pi).$$

In these variables the right member of the second of equations (13) becomes

$$(15) \qquad \frac{a^4(1 - e^2)}{r^3} - \frac{a^3}{r^2} = \frac{a[e(1 - e) - \rho e^{i\phi}]}{[(1 - e) + \rho e^{i\phi}]^3}.$$

The problem now is to find an upper bound for the absolute value of the right member of equation (15) for $\rho \leqq \eta(1 - e)$, $0 \leqq \phi < 2\pi$. If a function is continuous in a closed domain, it has a finite upper bound in the domain. But this does not imply that the function has a maximum in the domain at which its derivatives with respect to its arguments are zero. For this reason it is often difficult to determine the least upper bound of the absolute value of a function in a closed domain. But in this problem, it is seen that for all values of ρ the numerator of the right member of equation (15) is a maximum while the denominator is a minimum for $\phi = \pi$. Consequently, the least upper bound to the absolute value of the right member of the second of equations (13) in the domain of r is

$$(16) \qquad M_2 = \frac{a[e(1 - e) + \rho]}{[(1 - e) - \rho]^3}.$$

A corresponding upper bound must be found for the absolute value of the right member of the first of equations (13). On integrating the second of these equations and determining the constant of integration by the initial conditions $r(0) = a(1 - e)$, $r'(0) = 0$, it is found that

$$r' = \frac{a}{r} \sqrt{a^2 e^2 - (a - r)^2}.$$

This equation becomes in the parametric form for the variable r

$$r' = \frac{a e^{i(\phi/2)} \sqrt{\rho(2e - \rho e^{i\phi})}}{[(1 - e) + \rho e^{i\phi}]}.$$

In the case of this expression also the numerator is a maximum and the denominator is a minimum for $\phi = \pi$. Therefore the least upper bound to the absolute value of the right member of the first of equations (13) in the domain is

$$(17) \qquad M_1 = \frac{a\sqrt{\rho(2e + \rho)}}{[(1 - e) - \rho]}.$$

The upper bound M, of Arts. 14–17, is the larger of M_1 and M_2. Both M_1 and M_2 increase with ρ, which is subject to the inequality $\rho \leqq \eta(1 - e)$, where $0 < \eta < 1$. The ratio of M_1^2 to M_2^2 for $\rho = \eta(1 - e)$ is

$$\frac{M_1^2}{M_2^2} = \eta(1 - \eta) \frac{[\eta + e(2 - \eta)]}{(e + \eta)^2},$$

which is zero for $\eta = 0$ and $\eta = 1$. Therefore M_1 is less than M_2 for values of η near zero and near unity. A numerical examination of the function indicates that the ratio is less than unity for all values of η from zero to unity. Therefore, in the notation of Art. 16, $M = M_2$.

The n, of Art. 16, in this problem is 2, and the r, of Art. 16 (not the r of this Art.), is seen by the relation (14) to be $\eta a(1 - e)$. Therefore the proved domain of convergence of the solution, given by equation (12), of Art. 16, is in this problem

$$|\tau| < \frac{r}{2nM} = \frac{\eta(1 - e)^3(1 - \eta)^3}{4(e + \eta)}.$$

The right member of this expression vanishes for $\eta = 0$ and $\eta = 1$ and it is positive for $0 < \eta < 1$. It is found in the usual way that the values of η which correspond to a maximum or a minimum of the right member are

$$\eta = \frac{-2e \pm \sqrt{4e^2 + 3e}}{3}.$$

Only the one with the positive sign before the radical lies between zero and unity and corresponds to a maximum of the function. With this value of η, the values of τ for which the convergence of the solution is established by this method are found to be limited by the inequality

$$(18) \quad |\tau| < \frac{(1-e)^3[-2e+\sqrt{4e^2+3e}][(3+2e)-\sqrt{4e^2+3e}]^3}{108[e+\sqrt{4e^2+3e}]}.$$

61. The True Domain of Convergence of the Solution as Power Series in τ. In general, the true domain of convergence of the power series solution of a system of non-linear differential equations cannot be determined by known methods. The present problem, however, has special properties that make a precise determination of the domain of convergence possible. It must be remembered that the method which will be employed is not capable of general application.

Let the first of equations (9) be transformed by the substitution

$$(19) \qquad r = a[1 - e \cos E].$$

The result of this substitution is the simple differential equation

$$(20) \qquad \frac{dE}{d\tau} = \frac{1}{1 - e \cos E}.$$

Consider the solution of equation (20) as a power series in τ for the initial conditions $E(0) = E_0$, where E_0 is any arbitrary constant, real or complex. The solution, by Arts. 15 and 16, is analytic in τ in a sufficiently restricted domain for τ unless

$$(21) \qquad 1 - e \cos E_0 = 0,$$

and for such an initial value E_0 the solution is not analytic because, by equation (20), the first derivative with respect to τ is then infinite for $\tau = 0$. Consequently equation (21) defines the values of E_0 for which the solution is not analytic in τ.

Since E_0 is a complex quantity in this theoretical discussion, it will be written

$$(22) \qquad E_0 = u + \sqrt{-1}\, v,$$

where u and v are real. On substituting the right member of equation (22) into equation (21) and equating the real and imaginary parts of the resulting expression, it is found that

$$(23) \qquad \begin{cases} 1 - e \cos u \cosh v = 0 & (0 < e < 1), \\ \sin u \sinh v = 0. \end{cases}$$

The second of these equations is satisfied by $v = 0$, but the first cannot then be satisfied. The second is also satisfied by $u = j\pi$, where j is any integer. Then the first equation becomes

$$1 - (-1)^j e \cosh v = 0.$$

Since $\cosh v$ is positive, this equation cannot be satisfied unless j is even. Therefore the solutions of equations (23) are

$$(24) \quad \begin{cases} u = 2j\pi \quad (j = 0, \pm 1, \pm 2, \cdots), \\ \cosh v = \dfrac{1}{e}, \end{cases}$$

the second equation of which has two solutions, $\pm v_1$, for every value of e between zero and unity. Therefore the solution of equation (20) as a power series in τ ceases to be regular for those values of τ, if there are such, for which $E = 2j\pi \pm \sqrt{-1}v_1$.

It remains to find the values of τ for which $E = 2j\pi \pm \sqrt{-1}v_1$. It follows from equation (19) and the initial value of r, namely, $r = a(1 - e)$, that $E(0) = 0$ in the problem under consideration. Therefore it follows from equation (20) that

$$(25) \quad \tau = E - e \sin E.$$

In this discussion τ also must be considered in the complex domain. For notation, let

$$(26) \quad \tau = \xi + \sqrt{-1}\eta,$$

the quantities ξ and η being real. On substituting this expression for τ and $E = 2j\pi \pm \sqrt{-1}v_1$ into equation (25), and equating real and imaginary parts, it is found that

$$(27) \quad \begin{cases} \xi = 2j\pi \quad (j = 0, \pm 1, \pm 2, \cdots), \\ \eta = \pm (v_1 - e \sinh v_1). \end{cases}$$

These equations determine an infinite number of values of τ for which the solution series have singular points. The radius of convergence of the solution functions as power series in τ is the distance from the origin to the nearest of these singular points, which are the two for which $j = 0$. These singular points are on the imaginary axis of τ, and the solution (12) converges if τ satisfies the inequality

$$(28) \quad |\tau| < |v_1 - e \sinh v_1| = |\eta|,$$

and diverges if the sign of the inequality is reversed.

The domain of convergence of the solution for any other initial value of τ is the distance from that origin to the nearest of the singular points defined by equations (27). If the initial value of E is not zero, the τ of equation (25) will be changed by an additive constant and the first of equations (27) will have a corresponding modification.   For a given value of e the domain of convergence of the solution is smallest when $E(0) = 0$, for one pair of the singular points is on the imaginary axis, and all the remainder are at an equal distance from the real axis.

It will be of interest to compare the true domain of convergence of series (12) with the domain defined by the inequality (18). In the following table the unit is a radian.

e	TRUE RADIUS OF CONVERGENCE	RADIUS DEFINED BY INEQUALITY (18)
0	∞	0.250
.1	1.998	0.067
.2	1.313	0.034
.3	0.920	0.018
.4	0.650	0.009
.5	0.451	0.005
.6	0.299	0.002
.7	0.181	0.001
.8	0.093	0.000
.9	0.031	0.000
1.0	0.000	0.000

The true domain of convergence of the solution as power series in τ is of importance in the theory of the determination of the orbits of planetoids.   In order to express the result in days it is necessary to go back to $t - t_0$ by means of equation (8) and to adopt a value of a.   In the case of the asteroids the average value of a is about 2.65 in astronomical units and $e < .5$.   Since $k = 0.01720$, the number of days corresponding to the first six entries in the second column of the table are ∞, 501, 329, 231, 163, 113.   For origins corresponding to other points on the orbit the intervals are longer.   For example, if $r(0) = a(1 + e)$, the corresponding numbers are ∞, 934, 854, 821, 805, 796.   The time-intervals used in determining the orbits of the planetoids are much smaller than the smallest of the foregoing intervals.

62. Solution as Power Series in the Parameter e.   The eccentricity e can be made to play the rôle of the parameter μ, of Chapter III.

In order to simplify the algebraic work, make the substitution

(29) $r = a(1 - \rho e)$

in equations (9).   The resulting equations are

(30) $$\begin{cases} \dfrac{d^2\rho}{d\tau^2} + \dfrac{\rho - e}{(1 - \rho e)^3} = 0, \\[2mm] \dfrac{d\theta}{d\tau} - \dfrac{\sqrt{1 - e^2}}{(1 - \rho e)^2} = 0. \end{cases}$$

It follows from equation (29) and the initial values of r and r' that $\rho(0) = 1$, $\rho'(0) = 0$.

Since $|e|$ is less than unity and ρ varies from -1 to $+1$, the right members of equations (30) can be expanded as power series in e that converge for all *real* values of τ.   (In the present method τ takes only real values.)   Therefore equations (30) become

(31) $$\begin{cases} \dfrac{d^2\rho}{d\tau^2} + \rho = \dfrac{1}{2}\sum_{i=1}^{\infty}(i+1)[i - (i+2)\rho^2]\rho^{i-1}e^i, \\[2mm] \dfrac{d\theta}{d\tau} = \sqrt{1 - e^2}\sum_{i=0}^{\infty}(i+1)\rho^i e^i. \end{cases}$$

The first of these differential equations is of the type treated in Art. 27; the second reduces to a quadrature upon the solution of the first.   The solution of the first is a power series in e of the form

(32) $\rho = \rho_0 + \rho_1 e + \rho_2 e^2 + \cdots,$

where ρ_0, ρ_1, $\cdots$ are functions of τ to be determined.

Before determining the coefficients of the right member of equation (32), some of their properties will be established.

Property 1.   The variable ρ is periodic in τ with the period 2π for every value of e between -1 and $+1$.   On making use of equation (32), this property gives the identities

$$\rho(\tau) = \sum_{i=0}^{\infty}\rho_i(\tau)e^i \underset{\tau,\,e}{\equiv} \sum_{i=0}^{\infty}\rho_i(2\pi + \tau)e^i.$$

Therefore, on using the identity in e, it follows that

$$\rho_i(\tau) \underset{\tau}{\equiv} \rho_i(2\pi + \tau).$$

That is, each ρ_i separately is periodic in τ with the period 2π. It follows from the theory of Fourier series that each ρ_i can be expressed as a sum of sines and cosines of integral multiples of τ.

Property 2. Since the solution ρ is an even function of τ (Art. 59) for all values of e between -1 and $+1$, the ρ_i are sums of cosines of multiples of τ and do not involve sines.

Property 3. It follows from the geometry of the problem that a change of the sign of e is equivalent to transferring the origin to the other focus of the ellipse. Hence, if the sign of e is changed and τ is increased by π, the value of r will be unchanged, and it follows from equation (29) that the sign of ρ will be changed. Therefore for all values of e for which the series (32) converges, it follows that

$$\sum_{i=0}^{\infty} \rho_i(\tau) e^i \underset{\tau, e}{\equiv} - \sum_{i=0}^{\infty} \rho_i(\pi + \tau)(-e)^i,$$

from which it follows that

$$\rho_i(\tau) e^i \underset{\tau}{\equiv} - \rho_i(\pi + \tau)(-e)^i.$$

Hence if i is even, $\rho_i(\tau) = - \rho_i(\pi + \tau)$; and if i is odd, $\rho_i(\tau) = \rho_i(\pi + \tau)$. Since the ρ_i are sums of cosines of multiples of τ, it follows that ρ_{2j} is a sum of cosines of odd multiples of τ, and ρ_{2j+1} is a sum of cosines of even multiples of τ.

Property 4. The initial values are $\rho(0) = 1$, $\rho'(0) = 0$, whatever value e may have between zero and unity. Therefore

$$\begin{cases} \sum_{i=0}^{\infty} \rho_i(0) e^i \underset{e}{\equiv} 1, \\ \sum_{i=0}^{\infty} \rho_i'(0) e^i \underset{e}{\equiv} 0. \end{cases}$$

It follows from these identities that

$$(33) \quad \begin{cases} \rho_0(0) = 1, & \rho_i(0) = 0 \quad (i = 1, 2, \cdots), \\ \rho_i'(0) = 0, & (i = 0, 1, 2, \cdots), \end{cases}$$

which define the initial conditions for the solution.

On substituting the right member of equation (32) into the first of equations (31) and equating coefficients of corresponding powers of e, it is found that the equations corresponding to equations (16), of Art. 28, are

$$(34) \quad \begin{cases} \dfrac{d^2\rho_0}{d\tau^2} + \rho_0 = 0, \\[2ex] \dfrac{d^2\rho_1}{d\tau^2} + \rho_1 = 1 - 3\rho_0{}^2, \\[2ex] \dfrac{d^2\rho_2}{d\tau^2} + \rho_2 = 3\rho_0(1 - 2\rho_1 - 2\rho_0{}^2), \\[1ex] \cdots \cdots \cdots \cdots \cdots \cdots \end{cases}$$

Equations (34) can be solved sequentially and arbitrary constants can be determined so as to satisfy the initial conditions given in (33). The solution of the first equation is

$$(35) \qquad \rho_0 = \cos \tau,$$

after which the second of equations (34) becomes

$$(36) \qquad \frac{d^2\rho_1}{d\tau^2} + \rho_1 = -\tfrac{1}{2} - \tfrac{3}{2} \cos 2\tau.$$

The general solution of the left member of equation (36) set equal to zero is

$$\rho_1 = y_1 \cos \tau + y_2 \sin \tau,$$

where y_1 and y_2 are arbitrary constants. The solution of the complete differential equation including the right member can be obtained by the method of Art. 38, but it is not advisable to use that general method in so simple a problem. Since the solution is an identity in τ, it is evident from inspecting equation (36) that the solution of the complete equation will have a constant term and one in $\cos 2\tau$. The coefficients of these terms can be determined by assigning them literal values, substituting the expression into equation (36), and imposing the conditions that the result shall be an identity in τ. By this method the general solution of equation (36) is found to be

$$\rho_1 = c_1{}^{(1)} \cos \tau + c_2{}^{(1)} \sin \tau - \tfrac{1}{2} + \tfrac{1}{2} \cos 2\tau,$$

where $c_1{}^{(1)}$ and $c_2{}^{(1)}$ are constants that are to be determined by the initial conditions (33). The initial conditions imply $c_1{}^{(1)} = c_2{}^{(1)} = 0$, and the solution of equation (36) is simply

$$(37) \qquad \rho_1 = -\tfrac{1}{2}[1 - \cos 2\tau].$$

On substituting the values of ρ_0 and ρ_1 from equations (35) and (37) into the third equation of (34), the result is

$$\frac{d^2 \rho_2}{d\tau^2} + \rho_2 = -3 \cos 3\tau.$$

The solution of this equation subject to the initial conditions of equations (33) for $i = 2$ is

(38) $$\rho_2 = -\tfrac{3}{8}[\cos \tau - \cos 3\tau].$$

The process that has been explained evidently can be continued as far as may be desired. The solution (32) up to the term of the second degree in e is

(39) $$\rho = \cos \tau - \tfrac{1}{2}[1 - \cos 2\tau]e - \tfrac{3}{8}[\cos \tau - \cos 3\tau]e^2 \cdots.$$

After ρ has been determined, the second equation of (31) is reduced to a quadrature. On choosing the axis of reference so that $\theta(0) = 0$, it is found that

(40) $$\theta = \tau + 2e \sin \tau + \tfrac{5}{4}e^2 \sin 2\tau \cdots.$$

In this manner ρ and θ can be determined for any values of e and τ for which the series (39) and (40) converge.

63. General Expressions for the Solution. Four general properties of the solution were established in Art. 62, and there is an additional one of importance that will now be proved.

So far as the solution (39) has been worked out, it has been found that ρ_κ is a sum of cosines of τ of which the highest multiple is $\kappa + 1$. It will be proved by induction that this property holds for all values of κ. Suppose it is known that the property holds for $\kappa = 0, \cdots, i - 1$. It follows from the first of equations (31) that the right member of the differential equation satisfied by ρ_i is composed of terms of the type

(41) $$A \rho_0{}^{j_0} \rho_1{}^{j_1} \cdots \rho_{i-1}{}^{j_{i-1}},$$

where A is a number. It follows from the first of (31) that

(42) $$j_0 + j_1 + \cdots + j_{i-1} \leqq i + 1.$$

When the series (32) is substituted into the first of equations (31), each ρ_κ carries with it the factor e^κ, and since the entire term under consideration carries e^i as a factor, the j_κ are subject to the additional condition

(43) $[j_1 + 2j_2 + \cdots + (i - 1)j_{i-1}]$
$$+ [j_0 + j_1 + \cdots + j_{i-1}] - 1 \leqq i.$$

Finally, since ρ_κ contains $\cos (\kappa + 1)\tau$ as the term involving the highest multiple of τ, it follows that $\rho_\kappa{}^{j_\kappa}$ contains $\cos j_\kappa(\kappa + 1)\tau$ as the term involving the highest multiple of τ. Therefore the highest multiple of τ coming from the general term (41) is

$$N_i = j_0 + 2j_1 + \cdots + ij_{i-1},$$

which becomes as a consequence of the inequality (42)

(44) $N_i \leqq i + 1.$

It follows from the properties of the solution established in Art. 62 and the one given in the relation (44) that the differential equation satisfied by $\rho_{2\kappa}$ has the form

(45) $\dfrac{d^2\rho_{2\kappa}}{d\tau^2} + \rho_{2\kappa} = A_{2\kappa}{}^{(3)} \cos 3\tau + \cdots + A_{2\kappa}{}^{(2\kappa+1)} \cos (2\kappa + 1)\tau,$

where the $A_{2\kappa}{}^{(2i+1)}$ are constants that are known as soon as $\rho_0, \cdots, \rho_{2\kappa-1}$ have been determined.

The solution of the equation (45) has the form

(46) $\rho_{2\kappa} = a_{2\kappa}{}^{(1)} \cos \tau + \cdots + a_{2\kappa}{}^{(2\kappa+1)} \cos (2\kappa + 1)\tau.$

On substituting the expression (46) into the equation (45), imposing the conditions that the result shall be an identity in τ, and imposing the initial conditions (33) for $i = 2\kappa$, it is found that

(47)
$$
\begin{cases}
a_{2\kappa}{}^{(2j+1)} = \dfrac{- A_{2\kappa}{}^{(2j+1)}}{(2j + 1)^2 - 1} = - \dfrac{A_{2\kappa}{}^{(2j+1)}}{4j(j + 1)} \quad (j = 1, \cdots, \kappa), \\[2ex]
a_{2\kappa}{}^{(1)} = - \displaystyle\sum_{j=1}^{\kappa} a_{2\kappa}{}^{(2j+1)}.
\end{cases}
$$

The equations which correspond to (45), (46), and (47) when $i = 2\kappa + 1$ are

(48)
$$
\begin{cases}
\dfrac{d^2\rho_{2\kappa+1}}{d\tau^2} + \rho_{2\kappa+1} = A_{2\kappa+1}{}^{(0)} + \cdots + A_{2\kappa+1}{}^{2(\kappa+1)} \cos 2(\kappa + 1)\tau, \\[2ex]
\rho_{2\kappa+1} = a_{2\kappa+1}{}^{(0)} + \cdots + a_{2\kappa+1}{}^{2(\kappa+1)} \cos 2(\kappa + 1)\tau, \\[2ex]
a_{2\kappa+1}{}^{(2j)} = - \dfrac{A_{2\kappa+1}{}^{(2j)}}{4j^2 - 1}.
\end{cases}
$$

It follows that it is sufficient to compute sequentially the coefficients of the right members of equations (34) and to use equations (46) and (47) to write down the solution when the subscript is even, and equations (48) when the subscript is odd. The work should naturally be tabularly arranged so as to reduce the writing to a minimum.

64. The True Domain of Convergence of the Solution as Power Series in e. Although there are no general methods for determining the true radius of convergence of a solution as power series in a parameter, the problem now under consideration is so simple that the domain of validity of its solution can be found by methods similar to those used in Art. 61.

Consider the solution of equation (20) as a power series in e whose coefficients are functions of τ. If the series converges for given values of τ and e, it follows from the form of equation (19) and the theorem of Weierstrass, Appendix C, that the series for r as a power series in e will also converge for the same value of τ and of e. On the other hand, if the expression for E as a power series in e does not converge, the variable r is not defined. Therefore it will be sufficient to determine the true domain of the solution of equation (20) as a power series in e.

Since e is the argument of the power series, it must be considered in the complex plane, and consequently E must also be considered in the complex plane. On the other hand, the variable τ is a real parameter in the series now under consideration; and since the solution is periodic with the period 2π, it is sufficient to consider τ on the interval from 0 to 2π.

It follows from Arts. 27–29 that the solution of equation (20) can be developed as a power series in $e - e_0$, with the initial condition $E(0) = E_0$, unless E_0 and e_0 satisfy the equation

$$(49) \qquad 1 - e_0 \cos E_0 = 0.$$

In order to provide notation for the fact that both E_0 and e_0 may be complex, let

$$(50) \qquad \begin{cases} E_0 = u + \sqrt{-1}\, v, \\ e_0 = \epsilon + \sqrt{-1}\, \eta, \end{cases}$$

in which u, v, ϵ, and η are real.

The variable τ is expressed in terms of E and e, whatever values these variables may have, by equation (25). On substituting the expressions given in equations (50) for E_0 and e_0 into equations (25) and (49), and equating real and imaginary parts, it is found that

$$(51) \quad \begin{cases} u - \epsilon \sin u \cosh v + \eta \cos u \sinh v = \tau, \\ v - \eta \sin u \cosh v - \epsilon \cos u \sinh v = 0, \\ \epsilon \cos u \cosh v + \eta \sin u \sinh v = 1, \\ \eta \cos u \cosh v - \epsilon \sin u \sinh v = 0. \end{cases}$$

For every value of τ, equations (51) define certain sets of values of u, v, ϵ, and η for which the solution of (20) as a power series in e has singular points. Let such values of η and ϵ be $\eta(\tau)$ and $\epsilon(\tau)$. Then the true radius of convergence of the solution of equation (20) as a power series in e is, for the given value of τ, the smallest value of $R(\tau)$ for the various values of η and ϵ, where

$$(52) \quad R(\tau) = \sqrt{[\epsilon(\tau)]^2 + [\eta(\tau)]^2}.$$

If R_0 represents the smallest value of $R(\tau)$ for $0 \leqq \tau \leqq 2\pi$, the series (32) converges for all finite values of τ provided $|e| < R_0$.

Equations (51) are transcendental and cannot be solved in terms of simple functions. There is no difficulty, however, in determining the general characteristics of the solution, nor in finding the solution numerically in any particular case. Laplace solved the problem * in an entirely different way and proved that $R_0 = 0.6627 \cdots$. Since the eccentricities of the orbits of all the planets and satellites in the solar system are much smaller than R_0, the series in e that astronomers frequently use are convergent. The eccentricities of the orbits of many binary stars, however, are greater than R_0.

65. Determination of the Solution from an Integral. The processes used in Arts. 62 and 63 for explicitly determining the solution are perfectly straightforward and satisfactory, but there are others that are even simpler. The first of these makes use of the properties of the solution that have been established and of an integral of the differential equations.

The integral of the first of equations (30) subject to the

---

* *Mécanique Céleste*, Vol. V, Supplement.

initial conditions $\rho(0) = 1$, $\rho'(0) = 0$, when expanded as a power series in e, is

$$(53) \qquad \left(\frac{d\rho}{d\tau}\right)^2 = \frac{1 - \rho^2}{(1 - e\rho)^2} = \sum_{i=0}^{\infty} (i + 1)[1 - \rho^2]\rho^i e^i.$$

It has been shown that the solution has the properties

$$(54) \qquad \begin{cases} \rho = \rho_0 + \rho_1 e + \rho_2 e^2 + \cdots, \\ \rho_{2\kappa} = a_{2\kappa}{}^{(1)} \cos \tau + \cdots + a_{2\kappa}{}^{(2\kappa+1)} \cos (2\kappa + 1)\tau, \\ \rho_{2\kappa+1} = a_{2\kappa+1}{}^{(0)} + \cdots + a_{2\kappa+1}{}^{2(\kappa+1)} \cos 2(\kappa + 1)\tau, \end{cases}$$

where the coefficients are constants.

On substituting the first of equations (54) into equation (53), equating coefficients of e^j, and writing explicitly all terms involving the subscript j, it is found that

$$(55) \qquad 2\rho_0'\rho_j' + 2\rho_0\rho_j = F_j(\rho_0, \rho_0', \cdots, \rho_{j-1}, \rho_{j-1}'),$$

where ρ_κ' represents the derivative of ρ_κ with respect to τ, and where $F_j(\rho_0, \cdots, \rho_{j-1}')$ is a polynomial in the several indicated arguments.

For $j = 2\kappa$, equation (55) gives as a consequence of the second of equations (54)

$$(56) \qquad \begin{cases} 2a_{2\kappa}{}^{(1)} + 2\sum_{j=1}^{\kappa}\left[-(j-1)a_{2\kappa}{}^{(2j-1)} + (j+1)a_{2\kappa}{}^{(2j+1)}\right]\cos 2j\tau \\ \quad - 2\kappa a_{2\kappa}{}^{(2\kappa+1)} \cos 2(\kappa + 1)\tau = B_{2\kappa}{}^{(0)} + B_{2\kappa}{}^{(2)} \cos 2\tau \\ \qquad\qquad\qquad\qquad + \cdots + B_{2\kappa}{}^{2(\kappa+1)} \cos 2(\kappa + 1)\tau, \end{cases}$$

where the coefficients in the right member are known numbers depending upon the coefficients in the expressions for ρ_0, ρ_1, $\cdots$, $\rho_{2\kappa-1}$, which are supposed to have been computed. On equating coefficients of corresponding trigonometric functions, the explicit equations for the coefficients of the expression for $\rho_{2\kappa}$ are found to be

$$(57) \qquad \begin{cases} 2a_{2\kappa}{}^{(1)} = B_{2\kappa}{}^{(0)}, \\ 2(j+1)a_{2\kappa}{}^{(2j+1)} = 2(j-1)a_{2\kappa}{}^{(2j-1)} + B_{2\kappa}{}^{(2j)} \\ \qquad\qquad\qquad\qquad\qquad\qquad (j = 1, \cdots, \kappa - 1), \\ 2\kappa a_{2\kappa}{}^{(2\kappa+1)} = B_{2\kappa}{}^{2(\kappa+1)}. \end{cases}$$

When $j = 2\kappa + 1$, it is found by using the third of equations

(54) that the equations corresponding to equations (56) and (57) are

$$(58) \begin{cases} \left[2a_{2\kappa+1}{}^{(0)} + 3a_{2\kappa+1}{}^{(2)}\right] \cos \tau \\ \quad + \sum_{j=1}^{\kappa} \left[-(2j-1)a_{2\kappa+1}{}^{(2i)} + (2j+3)a_{2\kappa+1}{}^{2(i+1)}\right] \cos (2j+1)\tau \\ \quad - (2\kappa+1)a_{2\kappa+1}{}^{2(\kappa+1)} \cos (2\kappa+3)\tau = \sum_{j=0}^{\kappa+1} B_{2\kappa+1}{}^{(2i+1)} \cos (2j+1)\tau, \\ (2\kappa+1)a_{2\kappa+1}{}^{2(\kappa+1)} = -B_{2\kappa+1}{}^{(2\kappa+3)}, \\ (2j-1)a_{2\kappa+1}{}^{(2i)} = (2j+3)a_{2\kappa+1}{}^{2(i+1)} - B_{2\kappa+1}{}^{(2i+1)}(j = \kappa, \cdots, 1), \\ 2a_{2\kappa+1}{}^{(0)} = -3a_{2\kappa+1}{}^{(2)} + B_{2\kappa+1}{}^{(1)}. \end{cases}$$

Equations (57) and (58) determine the coefficients of the solution sequentially for $\kappa = 1, 2, \cdots$. The constants $B_\kappa{}^{(j)}$ are computed from the $F_i(\rho_0, \rho_0', \cdots, \rho_{i-1}, \rho_{i-1}')$ of equation (55), which are easily written out from the right member of equation (53).

66. Determination of the Solution from Derivatives of the Differential Equation. The coefficients of the solution can be obtained by a still simpler method which is based upon successive derivatives of ρ with respect to τ.

It follows from the first of equations (30) that

$$(59) \begin{cases} \dfrac{d^2\rho}{d\tau^2} = \dfrac{1}{e(1-\rho e)^2} - \dfrac{1-e^2}{e(1-\rho e)^3}, \\ \dfrac{d^3\rho}{d\tau^3} = \left[\dfrac{2}{(1-\rho e)^3} - \dfrac{3(1-e^2)}{(1-\rho e)^4}\right] \dfrac{d\rho}{d\tau}, \\ \dfrac{d^4\rho}{d\tau^4} = \left[\dfrac{2}{(1-\rho e)^3} - \dfrac{3(1-e^2)}{(1-\rho e)^4}\right] \dfrac{d^2\rho}{d\tau^2} \\ \qquad\qquad + \left[\dfrac{6e}{(1-\rho e)^4} - \dfrac{12e(1-e^2)}{(1-\rho e)^5}\right] \left(\dfrac{d\rho}{d\tau}\right)^2, \\ \cdots \cdots \cdots \cdots \cdots \cdots \cdots \cdots \cdots \cdots \end{cases}$$

Since $\rho(0) = 1$, $\rho'(0) = 0$, it follows from these equations that

$$(60) \begin{cases} \rho(0) = 1, \\ \rho''(0) = \dfrac{1}{(1-e)^2} = -\left[1 + 2e + 3e^2 + 4e^3 \cdots\right], \\ \rho^{\mathrm{IV}}(0) = \dfrac{1+3e}{(1-e)^5} = 1 + 8e + 30e^2 + 80e^3 \cdots, \\ \cdots \cdots \cdots \cdots \cdots \cdots \cdots \cdots \cdots \cdots \end{cases}$$

where ρ'' and ρ^{IV} are the second and fourth derivatives of ρ with respect to τ.

It follows from equations (32) and (60) that

$$(61) \quad \begin{cases} \rho_0(0) + \rho_1(0)e + \rho_2(0)e^2 + \cdots = 1, \\[2mm] \rho_0''(0) + \rho_1''(0)e + \rho_2''(0)e^2 + \cdots \\[1mm] \qquad\qquad\qquad = -[1 + 2e + 3e^2 + 4e^3 \cdots], \\[2mm] \rho_0^{IV}(0) + \rho_1^{IV}(0)e + \rho_2^{IV}(0)e^2 + \cdots \\[1mm] \qquad\qquad\qquad = 1 + 8e + 30e^2 + 80e^3 \cdots, \\[2mm] \cdot\;\cdot\;\cdot\;\cdot\;\cdot\;\cdot\;\cdot\;\cdot\;\cdot\;\cdot\;\cdot\;\cdot\;\cdot\;\cdot\;\cdot\;\cdot\;\cdot\;\cdot\;\cdot\;\cdot \end{cases}$$

These relations are identities in e, and consequently corresponding coefficients in the left and right members are equal.

It follows from equations (61) and the general forms of the expressions for ρ_{2k} and ρ_{2k+1} given in equations (54) that

$$(62) \quad \begin{cases} \rho_0(0) = a_0^{(1)} = 1; \\[1mm] \rho_1(0) = a_1^{(0)} + a_1^{(2)} = 0, \\[1mm] \rho_1''(0) = 0 - 4a_1^{(2)} = -2; \\[1mm] \rho_2(0) = a_2^{(1)} + a_2^{(3)} = 0, \\[1mm] \rho_2''(0) = -a_2^{(1)} - 9a_2^{(3)} = -3; \\[1mm] \rho_3(0) = a_3^{(0)} + a_3^{(2)} + a_3^{(4)} = 0, \\[1mm] \rho_3''(0) = 0 - 4a_3^{(2)} - 16a_3^{(4)} = -4, \\[1mm] \rho_3^{IV}(0) = 0 + 16a_3^{(2)} + 256a_3^{(4)} = 80. \end{cases}$$

It follows from these equations and equations (54) that

$$(63) \quad \begin{cases} \rho_0 = \cos \tau, \\[1mm] \rho_1 = -\tfrac{1}{2}[1 - \cos 2\tau], \\[1mm] \rho_2 = -\tfrac{3}{8}[\cos \tau - \cos 3\tau], \\[1mm] \rho_3 = -\tfrac{1}{3}[\cos 2\tau - \cos 4\tau], \\[1mm] \cdot\;\cdot\;\cdot\;\cdot\;\cdot\;\cdot\;\cdot\;\cdot\;\cdot\;\cdot\;\cdot\;\cdot, \end{cases}$$

which agree with the results obtained by the method of Art. 62.

This process makes no explicit use of the original differential equations except in forming the simple successive derivatives in equations (59). The subsequent steps involve no trigonometric functions or anything else except the simplest algebraic processes. It is clear that as the coefficients of higher order are determined higher derivatives of ρ than those written out in equations (59) are required.

The process under consideration could fail only if the determinant of the coefficients of some set of equations corresponding to those in (62) should be zero. It follows from the process of derivation of the equations that the determinant of the coefficients that arise in connection with $\rho_{2\kappa}$ is

$$(64) \qquad D_{2\kappa} = \pm \begin{vmatrix} 1, & 1, & \cdots, & 1 \\ 1^2, & 3^2, & \cdots, & (2\kappa + 1)^2 \\ \cdot & \cdot & \cdots & \cdot \\ 1^{2\kappa}, & 3^{2\kappa}, & \cdots, & (2\kappa + 1)^{2\kappa} \end{vmatrix}.$$

This is a form of Vandermonde's determinant, the value of which is easily shown to be

$$(65) \qquad D_{2\kappa} = \pm \prod_{i,\,j=0}^{\kappa} [(2i + 1)^2 - (2j + 1)^2] \qquad (i > j),$$

which is not zero. The corresponding determinant that arises in connection with computing the coefficients of the expression for $\rho_{2\kappa+1}$ is

$$(66) \qquad D_{2\kappa+1} = \pm \prod_{i,\,j=0}^{\kappa} [(2i + 2)^2 - (2j + 2)^2] \qquad (i > j),$$

which also is not zero. Therefore the process under consideration can be used without exception in determining the coefficients of the terms of every order. In simplicity and generality it leaves nothing to be desired.

VII. QUESTIONS AND PROBLEMS

1. Derive equation (5) directly from equations (2) without making use of equation (4).

2. Find the period P directly from the first of equations (9).

3. Compute the terms in τ^6 and τ^5 respectively in equations (12).

4. Prove by mathematical induction from the properties of the first of equations (9) that r is an even function of τ.

5. Compute the series corresponding to the right members of equations (12) if $r(0) = a(1 + e)$, $r'(0) = 0$; that is, if the body is initially at the point in the ellipse most remote from the origin.

6. Derive the true domain of convergence of the solution of equation (53) as a power series in τ by the method of Art. 61, and show that the result is equivalent to that given by the inequality (28).

7. Write out and solve the differential equation defining ρ_3 in the set of equations (34).

8. Determine ρ_3 explicitly by the method of Art. 65.

9. Why is τ considered in the complex plane and e real in Art. 61, while τ is considered real and e in the complex plane in Art. 64?

10. Equation (21) determines the values of E for which E, considered as a function of τ, has singular points. What is the nature of these singularities —poles, branch-points, or essential singular points? How many sheets has the Riemann surface for E as a function of τ, and what are the connections among them?

11. What is the limit of the right member of the inequality (28) for $e = 0$? For $e = 1$?

12. Taking an e-axis and a perpendicular $|\tau|$-axis, work out and graph the curve defined by the left member of the inequality (28) set equal to the right member.

13. Find the solution of equation (20) as a power series in e to three terms satisfying the initial condition $E(0) = 0$.

14. Discuss equations (51) and establish qualitatively the distribution of the singular points that they define. Find the ones of smallest modulus, construct the curve on a τ-axis and $|e|$-axis defined by $|e|$ set equal to the distance to the nearest singular point, and compare the result with that obtained in Problem 12.

15. Discuss the true domain of convergence of the solution of the first of equations (30) as a power series in e by the method of Art. 64.

16. Establish the four properties of the solution given in Art. 62 by an induction from the first of equations (31).

17. Find the expression for θ as a power series in e from the second of equations (31) and equation (39) to the third power of e.

18. Why are not the odd derivatives used in the method of Art. 66?

19. Develop the formulas when the derivatives are taken at $\tau = \pi$ and compute ρ_1, ρ_2, and ρ_3.

20. Determine ρ_4 by the method of Art. 66

CHAPTER VIII

THE SINE-AMPLITUDE FUNCTION

67. Properties of the Sine-Amplitude Function. Among the best-known transcendental functions are the elliptic functions which, in one form, were exhaustively studied by Legendre.* The first of Legendre's elliptic functions is the sine-amplitude function, which is under discussion in this chapter. Legendre derived its properties by studying the inversion of an elliptic integral; they will be derived here from the differential equation which defines it, by the use of the methods of Chapters II, III, and VI. Moreover, convenient explicit expressions for the sine-amplitude and related functions will be developed.

The most important properties of the sine-amplitude function will be enumerated for comparison with the results that will be derived from the differential equation. Legendre reduced the elliptic integrals to three normal forms, the first of which is

$$(1) \qquad t = \int_0^x \frac{dx}{\sqrt{(1 - x^2)(1 - k^2 x^2)}} = F(x; k^2).$$

where the "modulus" k is a real positive constant less than unity. Since the infinities of the integrand are of an order less than one, equation (1) defines a value of t for every value of x. If x is real, the integral will be taken along the real axis; if x is complex, the path of integration must be specified.

The inverse of equation (1) is the sine-amplitude function

$$(2) \qquad x = \mathrm{sn}\ (t; k^2),$$

where the variable t is the "amplitude" and the constant k is the "modulus" of the function. It is shown in the theory of elliptic functions that $\mathrm{sn}\ (t; k^2)$ has the following properties:

* *Les Fonctions Elliptiques.*

Property 1. The sine-amplitude function has a real period P_1 in t such that sn $(t; k^2) \equiv$ sn $(t + P_1; k^2)$, where P_1 is defined by the equation

$$(3) \quad P_1 = 4 \int_0^1 \frac{dx}{\sqrt{(1 - x^2)(1 - k^2 x^2)}}$$

$$= 2\pi \left[1 + \left(\frac{1}{2} \right)^2 k^2 + \left(\frac{1 \cdot 3}{2 \cdot 4} \right)^2 k^4 + \left(\frac{1 \cdot 3 \cdot 5}{2 \cdot 4 \cdot 6} \right)^2 k^6 + \cdots \right],$$

the right member converging if $|k^2| < 1$.

Property 2. The sine-amplitude function has a purely imaginary period $\sqrt{-1} P_2$ such that sn $(t; k^2) \equiv$ sn $(t + \sqrt{-1} P_2; k^2)$, where P_2 is defined by the equation

$$(4) \quad \sqrt{-1} P_2 = -2 \int_1^{1/k} \frac{dx}{\sqrt{(1 - x^2)(1 - k^2 x^2)}}.$$

In order to transform this integral into a form which can more easily be computed, let

$$(5) \quad \begin{cases} k^2 = 1 - k'^2, \\ x = \dfrac{1}{\sqrt{1 - k'^2 y^2}}. \end{cases}$$

Then the expression for P_2 becomes

$$(6) \quad P_2 = 2 \int_0^1 \frac{dy}{\sqrt{(1 - y^2)(1 - k'^2 y^2)}}$$

$$= \pi \left[1 + \left(\frac{1}{2} \right)^2 k'^2 + \left(\frac{1 \cdot 3}{2 \cdot 4} \right)^2 k'^4 + \cdots \right].$$

The smaller k^2, the smaller P_1 and the larger P_2; and the nearer k^2 is to unity, the larger P_1 and the smaller P_2.

Property 3. If the whole complex t-plane is divided up into rectangles whose sides parallel to the real axis have the length P_1 and whose sides parallel to the pure imaginary axis have the length P_2, the function sn $(t; k^2)$ takes the same values at corresponding points in all the rectangles. The left and lower borders of a rectangle are taken as belonging to the rectangle, and then every point in the t-plane belongs to just one rectangle. It follows that the remaining properties of sn $(t; k^2)$ can all be given by referring to a single rectangle, for example, the one in the first quadrant having a corner at the origin and two sides along the axes. This rectangle is called "the principal rectangle."

Property 4. In the principal rectangle the sine-amplitude function is real on the real axis, varying from -1 to $+1$; real on the line $t = \frac{1}{2}\sqrt{-1}P_2$, varying from $+1/k$ through infinity to $-1/k$; a pure imaginary on the imaginary axis; and a pure imaginary on the line $t = \frac{1}{2}P_1$. For all other values of t in the principal rectangle sn $(t; k^2)$ is complex.

Property 5. The sine-amplitude function takes every value, real and complex, including zero and infinity, at least once in the principal rectangle. The infinities are poles of order one and there are no other singularities. The zeros of sn $(t; k^2)$ are at $t = 0$ and $t = \frac{1}{2}P_1$, and the infinities are at $t = \frac{1}{2}\sqrt{-1}P_2$ and $t = \frac{1}{2}P_1 + \frac{1}{2}\sqrt{-1}P_2$.

Property 6. The sine-amplitude function is expansible as a power series in t which, by Property 5, converges provided $|t| < \frac{1}{2}P_2$. It is also expansible as a power series in k^2, and there are several other forms of expansion, most of which are due to Jacobi.

68. The Differential Equation Defining the Sine-Amplitude Function. It follows from equation (1) that x and t are related by the differential equation

$$(7) \qquad \left(\frac{dx}{dt}\right)^2 = (1 - x^2)(1 - k^2x^2) = F(x).$$

The derivative of this equation with respect to t gives

$$(8) \qquad \frac{d^2x}{dt^2} = - (1 + k^2)x + 2k^2x^3 \qquad (0 < k^2 < 1),$$

and it follows from $x(0) = 0$ and equation (7) that the initial conditions are

$$(9) \qquad x(0) \underset{k^2}{\equiv} 0, \qquad x'(0) \underset{k^2}{\equiv} 1,$$

the notation indicating that x and its derivative with respect to t have the values zero and unity respectively, whatever may be the value of k^2.

Equations (8) and (9) will form the basis for the determination of the properties of the solution sn $(t; k^2)$, and no logical use will be made of the properties enumerated in Art. 67.

69. The Solution as a Power Series in t. The right member of equation (8) is a polynomial in x and therefore, for any finite initial conditions, it can be solved as a power series in t by the methods of Arts. 14–17. For the initial conditions given in equations (9), the solution of equation (8) has the form

(10) $$x = t + a_2 t^2 + a_3 t^3 + \cdots.$$

It is found on substituting this expression for x into equation (8) and determining the coefficients in the usual manner that

$$\begin{cases} a_2 = 0, \\ 6a_3 = -(1 + k^2), \\ 12a_4 = 0, \\ 20a_5 = \dfrac{1}{6}(1 + k^2)^2 + 2k^2, \\ \cdots\cdots\cdots\cdots\cdots\cdots, \end{cases}$$

and therefore that

(11) $$x = t - \frac{1}{6}(1 + k^2)t^3 + \frac{1}{120}\big[(1 + k^2)^2 + 12k^2\big]t^5 + \cdots.$$

The coefficients are real because the coefficients of the differential equations are real and the a_i are determined by rational processes. The variable x is an odd function of t, because if the signs of both x and t are changed, equations (8) and (9) are unchanged.

The solution of equation (8) can be formed for initial conditions other than (9). Suppose that for $t = t_1$ the value of x is unity; then it follows from equation (7) that x' is zero. With the initial conditions $x(t_1) = 1$, $x'(t_1) = 0$, the solution of equation (8) is found to be

(12) $$x = 1 - \frac{1}{2}(1 - k^2)(t - t_1)^2$$
$$+ \frac{1}{24}(1 - k^2)(1 - 5k^2)(t - t_1)^4 + \cdots.$$

The coefficients of (12) are all real, and, with the initial conditions of this solution, x is an even function of $t - t_1$, because a change in the sign of $t - t_1$ leaves both equation (8) and the initial conditions unchanged.

70. The Real Period of the Solution. The differential equation (8) and the initial conditions (9) define the solution (10), which gives the value of x for all values of t within the domain of convergence of the right member. A formula for computing x

for restricted values of t might be useful in a particular case, but the general properties of the function of which the series is an expansion in the neighborhood of a particular point is much more important. The solution of such a problem as that now under discussion is not considered as having been completely determined until its properties have been established in the whole domain of its existence.

It will first be proved that x is a periodic function of t having a real period that will be determined. Consider not only the differential equation (8), but also the integral (7) in the form

$$(13) \qquad \frac{dx}{dt} = \sqrt{(1 - x^2)(1 - k^2 x^2)} = \sqrt{F(x)}.$$

To assist in fixing the ideas, consider the curve whose equation is

$$(14) \qquad F = (1 - x^2)(1 - k^2 x^2).$$

It follows from the initial conditions that $\sqrt{F(x)} = 1$ at $t = 0$. Therefore it follows from equation (13) and the fact that x is a continuous function of t that x is positive for t real, positive, and sufficiently small. It follows from equation (13) and the properties of $F(x)$ indicated in Fig. 1 that the derivative of

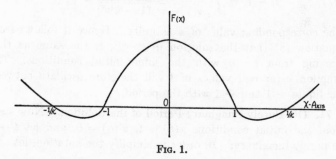

FIG. 1.

x with respect to t remains positive, and therefore that x continues to increase until $F(x)$ changes sign. Since x is a continuous function of t for all finite values of x and x', considered as initial values for defining a solution of equation (8), the function $F(x)$ cannot change sign except by passing through zero or infinity. Hence, in the solution under consideration, x will continue to increase to unity for which value of x the function $F(x)$ vanishes. The variable x attains the value unity at $t = t_1$, where

$$(15) \qquad t_1 = \int_0^1 \frac{dx}{\sqrt{(1 - x^2)(1 - k^2 x^2)}} = \frac{1}{4} P_1,$$

which is finite because all the infinities of the integrand are of the order one-half.

Now consider the solution for positive values of $t - t_1$. Since $x(t_1) = 1$, $x'(t_1) = 0$, equation (12) gives the solution, which is an even function of $t - t_1$. Therefore x decreases from unity, the negative sign belongs before the right member of (13), and x continues to decrease until $F(x)$ vanishes at $x = -1$. If t_2 represents the value of t for which $x = -1$, it is defined by the equation

$$(16) \qquad t_2 - t_1 = -\int_1^{-1} \frac{dx}{\sqrt{(1 - x^2)(1 - k^2 x^2)}} = \frac{1}{2} P_1.$$

The solution in the neighborhood of $t = t_2$ for which $x = -1$ and $x' = 0$ is an even function of $t - t_2$. Therefore for increasing positive values of $t - t_2$ the variable x increases and takes the value zero at $t = t_3$, where

$$(17) \qquad t_3 - t_2 = \int_{-1}^0 \frac{dx}{\sqrt{(1 - x^2)(1 - k^2 x^2)}} = \frac{1}{4} P_1.$$

The corresponding value of x' is unity. Hence it follows from equation (8) that the solution in $t - P_1$ is the same as that starting from $t = 0$ with the same initial conditions. The function x for real values of t will therefore oscillate between the limits -1 and $+1$ with the period P_1.

71. The Purely Imaginary Period of the Solution. Now start from the initial conditions $x(t_1) = 1$, $x'(t_1) = 0$, and let $t - t_1$ be purely imaginary. In order to simplify the notation, let

$$(18) \qquad t - t_1 = \sqrt{-1}\,\tau,$$

where τ is real. The solution (12) and all its derivatives are real, but equation (13) gives

$$\frac{dx}{d\tau} = \sqrt{-1}\sqrt{(1 - x^2)(1 - k^2 x^2)}.$$

Since the derivative of x with respect to τ is real, it follows from this equation that x increases from unity, and keeps on increasing with increasing values of τ until $F(x)$ vanishes for $x = 1/k$ at

$$(19) \qquad t_1 + \sqrt{-1}\,\tau_1 = t_1 + \int_1^{1/k} \frac{dx}{\sqrt{(1-x^2)(1-k^2x^2)}}$$

$$= \frac{1}{4}P_1 + \frac{1}{2}\sqrt{-1}\,P_2.$$

The solution in $\tau - \tau_1$ may be shown by the method heretofore used to be an even function of $\tau - \tau_1$. Therefore as τ increases x decreases from $1/k$ to unity, which it becomes at $\tau = \tau_1 + \frac{1}{2}P_2$ $= P_2$. The dependent variable x and its derivative with respect to τ have retaken their initial values, and a new cycle starts. That is, the value of x as a function of $t = t_1 + \sqrt{-1}\,\tau$ is periodic in $\sqrt{-1}\,\tau$ with the purely imaginary period $\sqrt{-1}\,P_2$.

If the solution is considered in the neighborhood of t_2, for which $x = -1$ and $x' = 0$, and if t is taken purely imaginary, the variable x will be found similarly to oscillate between -1 and $-1/k$ with the period P_2.

72. The Real Period Associated with the Infinite Branch of $F(x)$. Consider the solution starting from $t = \frac{1}{4}P_1 + \frac{1}{2}\sqrt{-1}\,P_2$ $= P'$, and let t take real increments. For this value of t it has been found that $x = 1/k$ and $x'(0) = 0$. With these initial conditions, x and its derivatives are real even functions of $t - P'$. Therefore it follows from equation (13) that x increases, and it will continue to increase until $F(x)$ vanishes or becomes infinite. The function $F(x)$ does not vanish for $x > 1/k$, but it becomes infinite for $x = \infty$. In order to discuss the problem for x very large, make the substitution

$$(20) \qquad x = \frac{1}{k\xi},$$

after which equations (8) and (7) become respectively

$$(21) \qquad \begin{cases} \dfrac{d^2\xi}{dt^2} = -(1+k^2)\xi + 2k^2\xi^3, \\[2mm] \dfrac{d\xi}{dt} = \sqrt{(1-\xi^2)(1-k^2\xi^2)} = \sqrt{F(\xi)}. \end{cases}$$

It follows from equation (20) that the initial conditions are $\xi(P') = 1$, $\xi'(P') = 0$. That is, the differential equations and the initial conditions in the variable ξ are of the same form at

$t = P'$ as they were in x at $t = 0$. Therefore ξ is a periodic function of $t - P'$, oscillating between -1 and $+1$ with the period P_1, and hence x increases from $1/k$ to infinity, and increases from minus infinity to $-1/k$ in $\frac{1}{2}P_1$; then it decreases from $-1/k$ to minus infinity, and decreases from positive infinity to $1/k$, making the complete cycle in the period P_1. That is, the function defined by equations (8) and (9) has a second set of real values including infinity that it takes periodically in the period P_1.

The facts that have been established can be conveniently represented in a diagram. Let $t = \sigma + \sqrt{-1}\tau$, and consider the complex t-plane. Let it be divided up into rectangles, or parallelograms, Fig. 2, whose real sides have the length P_1 and

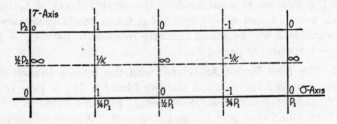

FIG. 2.   Period parallelogram of $x = \operatorname{sn}(t; k^2)$.

whose imaginary sides have the length P_2. The period rectangles are indicated in full lines; the fractional parts in dotted lines. The values of x that have been proved to correspond to certain values of t are marked on the diagram; it should be kept in mind that the numbers appearing on the diagram above the horizontal lines are not the coördinates of the points, but the values of x corresponding to the points in the t-plane.

73. The Singularities of the Solution. It follows from the general theory of Chapter II and the form of the differential equation (8) that the solution is an analytic function of t in the neighborhood of every particular value of t for which x and x' are both finite. It follows from equation (7) that x and x' become infinite for the same values of t. Consequently x is an analytic function of t for all values of t except for those for which $x = \infty$.

Suppose $x = \infty$ for $t = T$ and make the substitution (20) in order to study the nature of the function for values of t near $t = T$. It follows from equations (20) and (21) and the initial conditions $\xi(T) = 0$, $\xi'(T) = 1$, and on reference to the solution (11), that

$$(22) \quad x = \frac{1}{k\xi} = \frac{1}{k(t - T)\left[1 - \tfrac{1}{6}(1 + k^2)(t - T)^2 + \cdots\right]}.$$

Therefore $t = T$ is a pole of $x(t)$ of order one, and the only singularities of the solution for finite values of t are poles of order one. There are two poles in each period parallelogram.

The function has no other poles than those that have been determined. It will be shown first that there are no other poles on the imaginary axis than that at $t = \tfrac{1}{2}\sqrt{-1}P_2$ and points congruent to it. It has been shown that as t changes from $\tfrac{1}{4}P_1$ to $\tfrac{1}{4}P_1 + \tfrac{1}{2}\sqrt{-1}P_2$ along the line parallel to the imaginary axis, the value of $x = \operatorname{sn}(t; k^2)$ increases from unity to $1/k$. Now suppose $x = \infty$ at some point $\sqrt{-1}t'$ on the imaginary axis between zero and $\tfrac{1}{2}\sqrt{-1}P_2$. Then, if t increases by real increments from $\sqrt{-1}t'$ to $\sqrt{-1}t' + \tfrac{1}{4}P_1$, x will take the value $1/k$; for, if $x = \infty$ at any $t = \sqrt{-1}t'$, the discussion of Art. 72 shows that it will have the value $1/k$ at $t = \sqrt{-1}t' + \tfrac{1}{4}P_1$. Now consider the value of x at the same point, obtained by permitting t to increase along the real axis from zero to $\tfrac{1}{4}P_1$, and then along the line parallel to the purely imaginary axis from $\tfrac{1}{4}P_1$ to $\tfrac{1}{4}P_1 + \sqrt{-1}t'$. The value of x at this point lies between unity and $1/k$ and is not equal to $1/k$. Since the function has no singular points except simple poles, the same value for it will be obtained as t varies from zero to $\sqrt{-1}t' + \tfrac{1}{4}P_1$ along either of the paths. Therefore it is not infinite on the purely imaginary axis between zero and $\tfrac{1}{2}\sqrt{-1}P_2$. Similarly, it is not infinite on the purely imaginary axis between $\tfrac{1}{2}\sqrt{-1}P_2$ and $\sqrt{-1}P_2$.

Now suppose x is infinite at $t = a + \sqrt{-1}b$, where $a + \sqrt{-1}b$ is some point in the principal period parallelogram, and a is neither $\tfrac{1}{2}P_1$ nor P_1. Then by Art. 72, x will be real and not infinite at $t = a + \sqrt{-1}b - a = \sqrt{-1}b$. But x is a pure imaginary at $t = \sqrt{-1}b$. Therefore x has no singularities in the principal period parallelogram except the poles at $t = \tfrac{1}{2}\sqrt{-1}P_2$ and $t = \tfrac{1}{2}P_1 + \tfrac{1}{2}\sqrt{-1}P_2$.

The solution $x = \text{sn}\ (t;\ k^2)$ takes every value, both real and complex, at least once in each period parallelogram, for the integral (1) defines a value of t for every value of x with the integration taken along a finite path.

It has been shown that at corresponding points on the boundaries of the period parallelograms the function $x = \text{sn}\ (t;\ k^2)$ takes equal values. Since it is an analytic function of t, it is doubly periodic in t, satisfying the identity

$$(23) \qquad x = \text{sn}\ (t;\ k^2) \underset{t}{\equiv} \text{sn}\ (t + mP_1 + n\sqrt{-1}P_2;\ k^2).$$

where m and n are any integers.

The six properties enumerated in Art. 68 have now been inferred from equations (8) and (9) and the principles that were established in Chapter II.

74. A Generalization of the Problem. The methods of Arts. 69–73 are capable of being applied to much more general problems than that presented by equations (8) and (9). Suppose, for example, that the differential equation is

$$(24) \qquad \begin{cases} \dfrac{d^2x}{dt^2} = a_1x + a_2x^2 + a_3x^3 + a_4x^4 + a_5x^5 \\[2mm] x(0) = 0, \\[2mm] x'(0) = 1, \end{cases}$$

where $a_1, \cdots, a_4$ are real constants. This differential equation has the integral

$$(25) \qquad \left(\frac{dx}{dt}\right)^2 = 1 + a_1x^2 + \frac{2}{3}a_2x^3 + \frac{1}{2}a_3x^4 + \frac{2}{5}a_4x^5 + \frac{1}{3}a_5x^6 = G(x).$$

It is evident that the differential equation (24) can be solved as a power series in t by the method of Art. 69. The solution will be an odd function of t if $a_2 = a_4 = 0$. The domain of convergence of the solution depends upon the values of the coefficients $a_1, \cdots, a_5$.

Now consider the question of the existence of a real period of the solution. If the roots of $G(x) = 0$ are $x_1, \cdots, x_6$, and if $G(x)$ is positive for all values of x between any two real roots, then for increasing real values of t the value of x oscillates periodically through all real values from one root to the other. The conclusion can be proved by the method of Art. 70. If, on the other hand, $G(x)$ is negative for all values of x between any two real roots, the method of Art. 71 can be used to prove that for numerically increasing purely imaginary values of t the value of x oscillates periodically through all real values from one root to the other.

The infinite branches of $G(x)$ do not in this case correspond to a real period. The reciprocal transformation corresponding to equation (20) transforms equation (25) into one whose right member is infinite for $\xi = 0$. The value of t for which $x = \infty$ is a branch-point, as well as an infinity, of the function defined by equations (24).

The right member of equation (24) might be an infinite series having a positive circle of convergence, or indeed a Laurent series with a positive ring of convergence. In these cases the problem is restricted to those values of x for which the right member converges. If a real or purely imaginary period exists for which x is real, the fact can be established by the methods that are applicable when the right member of the differential equation is a polynomial, or even in more general cases.*

75. The Solution as a Power Series in k^2. The solution (11) as a power series in t converges for all values of t within the circle whose center is at the origin and whose perimeter passes through the singular points $\pm \sqrt{-1} P_2$. Consequently this series does not give, except by analytic continuation, the values of $x = \mathrm{sn}\ (t;\ k^2)$ even for all points within the period parallelogram. The expansions, however, about the points $t = \frac{1}{4} P_1$ and $t = \frac{3}{4} P_1$ and points congruent to them together define the function in the whole rectangle, as is evident from Fig. 2.

The differential equation (8) is of the type treated in Art. 27, of Chapter III. In the present problem the parameter k^2 plays the rôle of μ in the general theory. The solution will therefore have the form

$$(26) \qquad x = x_0(t) + x_2(t)k^2 + x_4(t)k^4 + \cdots.$$

On substituting this expression for x into equation (8) and equating coefficients of corresponding powers of k^2, the differential

* F. R. Moulton, *American Journal of Mathematics*, Vol. 34, pp. 177–202.

equations satisfied by the variables x_0, x_2, $\cdots$ are found to be

$$(27) \quad \begin{cases} \dfrac{d^2 x_0}{dt^2} + x_0 = 0, \\[2mm] \dfrac{d^2 x_2}{dt^2} + x_2 = -x_0 + 2x_0^3, \\[2mm] \dfrac{d^2 x_4}{dt^2} + x_4 = -x_2 + 6x_0^2 x_2, \\[2mm] \cdot \quad \cdot \quad \cdot \quad \cdot \quad \cdot \quad \cdot \quad \cdot \quad \cdot \end{cases}$$

which are to be integrated subject to the initial conditions defined by the identities (9). The solution of the first equation is

$$(28) \qquad\qquad x_0 = \sin t.$$

Then the second of equations (27) becomes

$$\frac{d^2 x_2}{dt^2} + x_2 = \frac{1}{2} \sin t - \frac{1}{2} \sin 3t.$$

The first term in the right member has the period of the solution of the left member of the equation set equal to zero. Therefore this term does not give rise to a similar term in the solution, but it is found by the method of Art. 38 that it gives rise to a term of the type $at \cos t$. The result can also be inferred from the form of the differential equation and the fact that the solution is odd in t. The coefficient a can conveniently be determined by substituting the term into the differential equation and imposing the condition that the result shall be an identity in t. This term of the solution is found in this way to be $-\frac{1}{4}t \cos t$.

The term of the type in question arises whenever the right member of a system of linear differential equations has a term whose period is the same as any period of the solution of the homogeneous parts of the differential equations set equal to zero. Such terms are known as "resonance" terms. If a musical instrument, for example, is disturbed by a periodic exterior force whose period equals the free period of the instrument, the effect is an oscillation in the free period with a continually increasing amplitude due to the factor t. In some cases resonance phenomena are disadvantageous, as in vibrations of machines; in others they are useful, as in radio reception (Art. 158).

The second term of the differential equation gives a term in the solution of its own type. The solution of this differential equation satisfying the initial conditions $x_2(0) = x_2'(0) = 0$, imposed by the identities (9), is

$$(29) \qquad x_2 = \frac{1}{16} \sin t + \frac{1}{16} \sin 3t - \frac{1}{4} t \cos t.$$

The right member of the third equation of (27) now becomes known, and its solution satisfying the conditions imposed by the identities (9) is similarly found to be

$$(30) \qquad \begin{cases} x_4 = \dfrac{7}{256} \sin t + \dfrac{1}{32} \sin 3t + \dfrac{1}{256} \sin 5t \\[2mm] \qquad\qquad - \dfrac{3}{32} t \cos t - \dfrac{1}{32} t^2 \sin t - \dfrac{3}{64} t \cos 3t. \end{cases}$$

The solution series (26) then becomes explicitly

$$(31) \qquad x = \sin t + \frac{1}{16} \left[\sin t + \sin 3t - 4t \cos t \right] k^2 + \cdots,$$

which is not periodic in form although the solution is periodic. In the corresponding solution of the problem of elliptic motion, derived in Art. 62, such a non-periodic form of the solution did not appear.

It is not necessary to look far in order to discover an important difference between the problem of elliptic motion and that of the sine-amplitude function treated here. In elliptic motion the period is independent of the parameter e; in this problem the real period, defined by equation (3), is not independent of the corresponding parameter k^2. Consequently the solution will not be periodic in form unless the process of constructing the solution is organized in such a way that the period of the trigonometric terms that arise shall be the period of the solution.

Consider, for example, the function

$$x = \sin (1 + \mu)t,$$

which is periodic with the period $2\pi/(1 + \mu)$. If the right member of this expression is expanded as a power series in μ, it will have the form

$$x = \sin t + (t \cos t)\mu + \cdots,$$

which converges for all finite values of t. It is periodic with the period $2\pi/(1 + \mu)$, but appears to be not periodic at all.

76. The Solution in Purely Periodic Form. In order to transform the problem so that the real period in a new independent variable shall be independent of the parameter k^2, let

$$(32) \quad t = \left[1 + \left(\frac{1}{2} \right)^2 k^2 + \left(\frac{1 \cdot 3}{2 \cdot 4} \right)^2 k^4 + \cdots \right] \tau = Q(k^2)\tau.$$

It follows from equation (3) that in τ the real period of x is 2π whatever value k^2 may have between zero and unity.

Equations (7) and (8) become as a consequence of the transformation (32)

$$(33) \quad \begin{cases} \left(\dfrac{dx}{d\tau} \right)^2 = Q^2(k^2)(1 - x^2)(1 - k^2x^2), \\[2mm] \dfrac{d^2x}{d\tau^2} = -(1 + k^2)Q^2(k^2)x + 2k^2Q^2(k^2)x^3. \end{cases}$$

The initial conditions are

$$(34) \quad \begin{cases} x(0) \equiv 0, \\[2mm] \left(\dfrac{dx}{d\tau} \right)_0 = Q(k^2) = 1 + \left(\dfrac{1}{2} \right)^2 k^2 + \left(\dfrac{1 \cdot 3}{2 \cdot 4} \right)^2 k^4 + \cdots. \end{cases}$$

The second of equations (33) has the properties of the differential equations treated in Arts. 27–29, with k^2 playing the rôle of the parameter μ. Therefore its solution can be developed as a power series in k^2 of the form

$$(35) \quad x = x_0(\tau) + x_2(\tau)k^2 + x_4(\tau)k^4 + \cdots,$$

where $x_0(\tau)$, $x_2(\tau)$, $\cdots$ will be different from the corresponding functions in the right member of equation (26), because both the differential equations and the initial conditions have been altered.

Since $x(\tau)$ is periodic in τ with the period 2π for all values of k^2 between zero and unity, it follows that each x_{2i} separately is periodic with the period 2π. Since $x(\tau)$ is an odd function of τ, each x_{2i} is a sum of sines of integral multiples of τ. It follows from the initial conditions of equations (34) that

$$(36) \quad \begin{cases} x_{2i}(0) = 0 \qquad (i = 0, 1, 2, \cdots), \\ x_0'(0) = 1, \\ x_{2i}'(0) = \left(\dfrac{1 \cdot 3 \, \cdots \, 2i - 1}{2 \cdot 4 \, \cdots \, 2i} \right)^2. \end{cases}$$

On substituting the expression for x given in equation (35) into the second of equations (33) and equating coefficients of corresponding powers of k^2, it is found that

$$(37) \quad \begin{cases} \dfrac{d^2 x_0}{d\tau^2} + x_0 = 0 \\ \dfrac{d^2 x_2}{d\tau^2} + x_2 = -\dfrac{3}{2} x_0 + 2x_0^3, \\ \dfrac{d^2 x_4}{d\tau^2} + x_4 = -\dfrac{3}{2} x_2 - \dfrac{27}{32} x_0 + x_0^3 + 6x_0^2 x_2, \\ \cdots \cdots \cdots \cdots \cdots \cdots \cdots \cdots \cdots \end{cases}$$

The solutions of the differential equations (37) subject to the initial conditions (36) are

$$(38) \quad \begin{cases} x_0 = \sin \tau, \\ x_2 = \dfrac{1}{16} \left[\sin \tau + \sin 3\tau \right], \\ x_4 = \dfrac{1}{256} \left[7 \sin \tau + 8 \sin 3\tau + \sin 5\tau \right], \\ \cdots \cdots \cdots \cdots \cdots \cdots \cdots \cdots \cdots \end{cases}$$

The solution now exhibits the real period and is in a form convenient for use in computation. It has the form of a power series in the parameter k^2, but on returning to the original independent variable t by means of equation (32), it is found that k^2 appears also under the trignometric signs.

The solution so far as it is given in equations (38) contains only sines of odd multiples of τ. It follows from the properties of the right member of the second of equations (33) that all the x_{2i} contain only sines of odd multiples of τ, and that the highest multiple in τ is $2i + 1$. (Compare Art. 63.)

77. Direct Proof of the Periodicity of the Solution. It will be noted that in the method of Art. 75 the periodicity of the solution was taken as known from another discussion, and the explicit expression for the period was taken as being given in advance. This information was available because of the simplicity of the problem under discussion. The corresponding information can be obtained in the more general problem in which the right member of the differential equation is a polynomial having two or more real simple roots, and the solution can be constructed in an analogous way, but the method fails completely in the case of a system of two or more simultaneous differential equations of the second order. Poincaré has developed more general methods * of proving the existence of periodic solutions of differential equations and of constructing them. One of these methods will be illustrated in this simple problem.

In order to provide for a possible dependence of the period of the solution upon the parameters of the problem and upon the initial values of the dependent variables, let an undetermined parameter δ be introduced by the equation

$$(39) \qquad t = (1 + \delta)\tau.$$

Equations (7) and (8) become as a consequence of this transformation

$$(40) \qquad \begin{cases} \left(\dfrac{dx}{d\tau}\right)^2 = (1 + \delta)^2(1 - x^2)(1 - k^2x^2) \\[2mm] \dfrac{d^2x}{d\tau^2} = - (1 + \delta)^2(1 + k^2)x + 2(1 + \delta)^2k^2x^3. \end{cases}$$

The initial values of the dependent variables are

$$(41) \qquad x(0) = 0, \qquad x'(0) = 1 + \delta.$$

The second of equations (40) can be solved as a power series in the two parameters k^2 and δ by the methods of Art. 34. Let

$$(42) \qquad x = x_{00}(\tau) + x_{20}(\tau)k^2 + x_{01}(\tau)\delta + \cdots.$$

It follows from the initial conditions that

$$(43) \qquad \begin{cases} x_{ij}(0) = 0, & x_{00}'(0) = 1, & x_{0j}'(0) = 0 \quad (j > 1), \\ x_{01}'(0) = 1, & x_{ij}'(0) = 0 & (i > 0). \end{cases}$$

---

* *Acta Mathematica*, Vol. 13; *Les Méthodes Nouvelles de la Mécanique Céleste,* Vol. I.

It is easily found upon substituting for x the right member of equation (42) into the second of equations (40), equating coefficients of corresponding powers of k^2 and δ, and solving the resulting differential equations subject to the initial values of the dependent variables defined by equations (43), that

$$(44) \quad \begin{cases} x_{00}(\tau) = \sin \tau, \\[2mm] x_{20}(\tau) = \dfrac{1}{16}\sin \tau + \dfrac{1}{16}\sin 3\tau - \dfrac{1}{4}\tau \cos \tau, \\[2mm] x_{01}(\tau) = \tau \cos \tau, \\[1mm] \cdots \cdots \cdots \cdots \cdots \cdots \cdots \\[1mm] x = \sin \tau + \dfrac{1}{16}\big[\sin \tau + \sin 3\tau - 4\tau \cos \tau\big]k^2 \\[2mm] \hspace{4cm} + \big[\tau \cos \tau\big]\delta + \cdots. \end{cases}$$

The conditions will now be imposed that the solution shall be periodic in τ with the period 2π. Since the right members of equations (40) do not involve τ explicitly, sufficient conditions that x shall be periodic with the period 2π are

$$(45) \qquad \begin{cases} x(2\pi) = x(0), \\ x'(2\pi) = x'(0). \end{cases}$$

It will be shown that the second of these equations is a consequence of the first and of the first of equations (40).

Let $x = \xi$, $x' = (1 + \delta) + \xi'$. Then it follows from the first of equations (40) that

$$2(1 + \delta)\xi' + \xi'^2 = -(1 + \delta)^2(1 + k^2)\xi^2 + (1 + \delta)^2 k^2 \xi^4.$$

Since the coefficient of ξ' is not zero, this equation can be solved (Art. 49) for ξ' as a power series in ξ, k^2, and δ, and the series will vanish with ξ whatever values k^2 and δ may have. Therefore, since $x(0) = 0$, the second of equations (45) is a consequence of the first equation and of the first of equations (40).

Now consider the first of equations (45). On making use of the last of equations (44), it becomes

$$(46) \qquad 0 = 2\pi\delta - \frac{\pi}{2}k^2 + \cdots.$$

It follows from Arts. 45–48 that the solution of this equation for δ as a power series in k^2 has the form

$$(47) \qquad \delta = \delta_2 k^2 + \delta_4 k^4 + \cdots.$$

On substituting this expression for δ into the right member of equation (42), the result is of the form

$$(48) \qquad x = x_0(\tau) + x_2(\tau)k^2 + x_4(\tau)k^4 + \cdots.$$

Since the conditions for periodicity have been satisfied for every value of k^2 for which the series converge, it follows that each $x_{2i}(\tau)$ is separately periodic in τ with the period 2π. Since $x(0) = 0$ for all values of k^2 for which the series converge, it follows that $x_{2i}(0) = 0$ for $i = 0, 1, 2, \cdots$. The initial values of the $x_{2i}{}'$ are determined by the conditions

$$x'(0) = 1 + \delta = 1 + \delta_2 k^2 + \delta_4 k^4 + \cdots,$$
whence
$$x_0{}'(0) = 1, \qquad x_{2i}{}'(0) = \delta_{2i} \qquad (i = 1, 2, \cdots).$$

78. Direct Construction of the Periodic Solution. On substituting the expressions for δ and x of equations (47) and (48) into the second of equations (40) and equating coefficients of corresponding powers of k^2, it is found that

$$(49) \quad \begin{cases} \dfrac{d^2x_0}{d\tau^2} + x_0 = 0, \\[2mm] \dfrac{d^2x_2}{d\tau^2} + x_2 = -(2\delta_2 + 1)x_0 + 2x_0{}^3, \\[2mm] \dfrac{d^2x_4}{d\tau^2} + x_4 = -(2\delta_4 + \delta_2{}^2 + 2\delta_2)x_0 - (2\delta_2 + 1)x_2 \\[2mm] \qquad\qquad\qquad\qquad\qquad\qquad + 6x_0{}^2x_2 + 4\delta_2 x_0{}^3, \\ \cdots\cdots\cdots\cdots\cdots\cdots\cdots\cdots\cdots\cdots\cdots \end{cases}$$

The solution of the first of these differential equations subject to the conditions $x_0(0) = 0$, $x_0{}'(0) = 1$ is $x_0 = \sin \tau$. Then the second equation becomes

$$\frac{d^2x_2}{d\tau^2} + x_2 = -\left(2\delta_2 - \frac{1}{2}\right)\sin \tau - \frac{1}{2}\sin 3\tau.$$

In order that the solution of this equation shall be periodic, δ_2 must satisfy $2\delta_2 - \frac{1}{2} = 0$. Then the solution satisfying the conditions $x_2(0) = 0$, $x_2{}'(0) = \delta_2 = \frac{1}{4}$ is

$$x_2 = \frac{1}{16}[\sin \tau + \sin 3\tau].$$

The process can be used to determine δ_4 and x_4, δ_6 and x_6, $\cdots$

sequentially as far as may be desired. At the general step the differential equation has the form

$$\frac{d^2x_{2i}}{d\tau^2} + x_{2i} = -(2\delta_{2i} + A_{2i}^{(1)})\sin\tau + A_{2i}^{(3)}\sin 3\tau$$
$$+ \cdots + A_{2i}^{(2i+1)}\sin(2i+1)\tau.$$

In order that the solution of this differential equation shall be periodic, the undetermined constant δ_{2i} must satisfy the relation

$$2\delta_{2i} + A_{2i}^{(1)} = 0.$$

Then the solution is periodic and is uniquely determined by the conditions $x_{2i}(0) = 0$, $x_{2i}'(0) = \delta_{2i}$.

The processes of the last two articles are applicable not only to an equation of the second order of the type treated, but also to the problem in which the right member is an infinite converging series, and, in fact, to extensive classes of simultaneous differential equations.

79. Construction of the Solution from the Integral. The co-efficients of the solution can be determined from the first of equations (33). On substituting the expression for x given in equation (35) into equation (33) and equating coefficients of corresponding powers of k^2, it is found that the general equation is

$$(50) \qquad 2x_0'x_{2i}' + 2x_0x_{2i} = P_{2i}(x_0, \cdots, x_{2i-2}; x_0', \cdots, x_{2i-2}')$$

where P_{2i} is a polynomial with known constant coefficients.

It has been shown that

$$(51) \qquad \begin{cases} x_0 = \sin\tau, \\ x_{2i} = a_{2i}^{(1)}\sin\tau + \cdots + a_{2i}^{(2i+1)}\sin(2i+1)\tau. \end{cases}$$

These properties of x_{2i} could also be inferred, by induction, from equations (33) and (50). It follows from equations (51) that the left member of equation (50) becomes

$$(52) \qquad 2x_0'x_{2i}' + 2x_0x_{2i} = 2a_{2i}^{(1)}$$
$$+ 2\sum_{j=2}^{i-1}[(j-1)a_{2i}^{(2j-1)} + (j+1)a_{2i}^{(2j+1)}]\cos 2j\tau$$
$$+ 2ia_{2i}^{(2i+1)}\cos(2i+2)\tau.$$

The right member of this expression is identically equal in τ to corresponding known terms obtained from the right member of equation (50). Therefore the coefficients of corresponding trigonometric terms in the left and right members are equal, and these relations uniquely determine the $a_{2i}^{(1)}, \cdots, a_{2i}^{(2i+1)}$. This method is just about as convenient as that given in Art. 76.

80. Construction of the Solution from Its Derivatives.

Equations (33) and the successive derivatives with respect to τ are

$$(53) \quad \begin{cases} x' = Q(k^2)\sqrt{(1-x^2)(1-k^2x^2)}, \\ x'' = Q^2(k^2)[-(1+k^2)x + 2k^2x^3], \\ x''' = Q^2(k^2)[-(1+k^2) + 6k^2x^2]x', \\ x^{\mathrm{IV}} = Q^2(k^2)[-(1+k^2) + 6k^2x^2]x'' + 12k^2Q^2(k^2)xx'^2, \\ \cdots \cdots \cdots \cdots \cdots \cdots \cdots \cdots \cdots \cdots \cdots \cdots \end{cases}$$

Since $x(0) = 0$, $x'(0) = Q(k^2)$, $x(\pi/2) = 1$, $x'(\pi/2) = 0$ for all values of k^2 between zero and unity, it follows from these equations that

$$(54) \quad \begin{cases} x(\pi/2) = 1, \\ x'(0) = Q(k^2), \\ x''(\pi/2) = -(1-k^2)Q^2(k^2), \\ x'''(0) = -(1+k^2)Q^3(k^2), \\ x^{\mathrm{IV}}(\pi/2) = (1 - 6k^2 + 5k^4)Q^4(k^2), \\ \cdots \cdots \cdots \cdots \cdots \cdots \cdots \cdots \cdots, \end{cases}$$

the right members of which can easily be expanded as power series in k^2, the explicit expression for the series $Q(k^2)$ being given in equation (34).

The series given in equation (35) and its derivatives with respect to τ are to be substituted into equations (54) for the indicated values of τ. Then coefficients of corresponding powers of k^2 are to be equated. In order to determine the coefficients of the solution, the expression for x_{2i} given in the second of equations (51) must be used. Since x_{2i} has $i + 1$ terms, $i + 1$ of equations (54) must be used in order to determine the $a_{2i}^{(j)}$. The details for $i = 1, 2, 3$ are

$$(55) \quad \begin{cases} a_2^{(1)} - a_2^{(3)} = 0 \qquad (i = 1), \\ a_2^{(1)} + 3a_2^{(3)} = (\tfrac{1}{2})^2; \end{cases}$$

$$(56) \quad \begin{cases} a_4^{(1)} - a_4^{(3)} + a_4^{(5)} = 0 \qquad (i = 2), \\ a_4^{(1)} + 3a_4^{(3)} + 5a_4^{(5)} = \left(\dfrac{1 \cdot 3}{2 \cdot 4}\right)^2, \\ -a_4^{(1)} + 9a_4^{(3)} - 25a_4^{(5)} = \dfrac{5}{32}; \end{cases}$$

$$(57) \begin{cases} a_6^{(1)} - a_6^{(3)} + a_6^{(5)} - a_6^{(7)} = 0 \qquad (i = 3), \\[2mm] a_6^{(1)} + 3a_6^{(3)} + 5a_6^{(5)} + 7a_6^{(7)} = \dfrac{25}{256}, \\[2mm] -a_6^{(1)} + 9a_6^{(3)} - 25a_6^{(5)} + 49a_6^{(7)} = \dfrac{5}{64}, \\[2mm] -a_6^{(1)} - 27a_6^{(3)} - 125a_6^{(5)} - 343a_6^{(7)} = -\dfrac{289}{256}. \end{cases}$$

These equations define the $a_{2i}^{(j)}$ uniquely so far as they have been written. The method can fail only if the determinant of the coefficients in the left member is zero for some value of i. But it is easily shown to be a special case of Vandermonde's determinant (compare Art. 66) and is therefore not zero.

For each value of i, as many of equations (54) may be used as is desired. Since there are only $i + 1$ coefficients in the expression for x_{2i}, the equations beyond the first $i + 1$ are redundant. In equations (55), (56), and (57) only those necessary have been written.

81. Simple Expressions for Legendre's Elliptic Functions. Several methods have been given in the foregoing articles for determining the coefficients of the series (35), which is an expansion of the sine-amplitude function as a power series in k^2 after the transformation of the independent variable from t to τ by equation (32). The method of Art. 80 is by far the simplest, and the explicit result obtained is

$$(58) \begin{cases} x = x_0 + x_2 k^2 + x_4 k^4 + \cdots, \\[2mm] x_0 = \sin \tau, \\[2mm] x_2 = \dfrac{1}{16} [\sin \tau + \sin 3\tau], \\[2mm] x_4 = \dfrac{1}{16^2} [7 \sin \tau + 8 \sin 3\tau + \sin 5\tau], \\[2mm] x_6 = \dfrac{1}{16^3} [67 \sin \tau + 82 \sin 3\tau + 16 \sin 5\tau + \sin 7\tau], \\[2mm] x_8 = \dfrac{1}{16^4} [738 \sin \tau + 945 \sin 3\tau + 230 \sin 5\tau \\ \hspace{5cm} + 24 \sin 7\tau + \sin 9\tau], \\[2mm] x_{10} = \dfrac{1}{16^5} [8808 \sin \tau + 11{,}661 \sin 3\tau + 3264 \sin 5\tau \\ \hspace{4cm} + 442 \sin 7\tau + 32 \sin 9\tau + \sin 11\tau], \\[2mm] \cdot \quad \cdot \quad \cdot \quad \cdot \quad \cdot \quad \cdot \quad \cdot \quad \cdot \quad \cdot \quad \cdot \quad \cdot \quad \cdot \quad \cdot \quad \cdot \end{cases}$$

Although the foregoing results are very simple, they can be transformed into expressions that are still simpler for computation. Each of the x_{2i} of equations (58) carries $\sin \tau$ as a factor, as is evident from successive reductions by the formula

$$\sin p\tau = \sin \tau \cos (p - 1)\tau + \cos \tau \sin (p - 1)\tau.$$

Moreover, since $x(\pi/2) = 1$ for all values of k^2 for which $0 \leqq k^2 < 1$, it follows that $x_{2i}(\pi/2) = 0$ $(i = 1, 2, \cdots)$. Therefore each x_{2i} beyond x_0 contains $\cos \tau$ as a factor. It is also true that $x'(\pi/2) = 0$ for $0 \leqq k^2 \leqq 1$, and therefore each x_{2i} beyond x_0 contains $\cos^2 \tau$ as a factor. After the removal of the factor $\sin \tau \cos^2 \tau$ from the x_{2i} $(i = 1, 2, \cdots)$, the expressions in the right members of equations (58) take the simpler form

$$(59) \quad \begin{cases} x_2 = \dfrac{1}{4} \sin \tau \cos^2 \tau, \\[2mm] x_4 = \dfrac{1}{64} \sin \tau \cos^2 \tau [5 + 4 \cos^2 \tau]. \\[2mm] x_6 = \dfrac{1}{256} \sin \tau \cos^2 \tau [10 + 11 \cos^2 \tau + 4 \cos^4 \tau], \\[2mm] x_8 = \dfrac{1}{128^2} \sin \tau \cos^2 \tau [389 + 500 \cos^2 \tau \\[1mm] \hspace{4cm} + 272 \cos^4 \tau + 64 \cos^6 \tau], \\[2mm] x_{10} = \dfrac{1}{256^2} \sin \tau \cos^2 \tau [1054 + 1499 \cos^2 \tau \\[1mm] \hspace{4cm} + 984 \cos^4 \tau + 368 \cos^6 \tau + 64 \cos^8 \tau], \\[2mm] \cdots \cdots \cdots \cdots \cdots \cdots \cdots \cdots \cdots \cdots \end{cases}$$

The right members of these expressions are simpler for purposes of computation than those of (58) because they involve only the argument τ and not also its multiples. It would be a simple matter to make a single-entry table for $x_0, x_2, \cdots$ and then, for any particular value of k^2, to determine x by the first of equations (58). In this development of the elliptic function sn $(t; k^2)$ the arguments t and k^2 are completely separated.

Legendre defined and discussed an associated elliptic function $y = \sqrt{1 - x^2}$, which he called the *cosine amplitude* function, cn $(\tau; k^2)$. It follows from the expansion of x as a power series in k^2 and the relation between x and y that y can be expanded as a power series in k^2, whose coefficients can be determined by the aid of equations (59). The results are

$$(60) \begin{cases} y = y_0 + y_2 k^2 + y_4 k^4 + \cdots, \\[4pt] y_0 = \cos \tau, \\[4pt] y_2 = -\dfrac{1}{4} \cos \tau \sin^2 \tau, \\[4pt] y_4 = -\dfrac{1}{64} \cos \tau \sin^2 \tau [7 + 4 \cos^2 \tau], \\[4pt] y_6 = -\dfrac{1}{256} \cos \tau \sin^2 \tau [17 + 13 \cos^2 \tau + 4 \cos^4 \tau], \\[4pt] y_8 = -\dfrac{1}{128^2} \cos \tau \sin^2 \tau [759 + 660 \cos^2 \tau \\ \qquad\qquad\qquad\qquad + 304 \cos^4 \tau + 64 \cos^6 \tau], \\[4pt] y_{10} = -\dfrac{1}{256^2} \cos \tau \sin^2 \tau [2289 + 2149 \cos^2 \tau \\ \qquad\qquad\qquad + 1192 \cos^4 \tau + 400 \cos^6 \tau + 64 \cos^8 \tau], \\[4pt] \cdot\ \cdot\ \cdot\ \cdot\ \cdot\ \cdot\ \cdot\ \cdot\ \cdot\ \cdot\ \cdot\ \cdot\ \cdot\ \cdot\ \cdot\ \cdot \end{cases}$$

The third of Legendre's elliptic functions, the *delta amplitude* function dn $(\tau;\ k^2)$, is defined in terms of x by the equation $z = \sqrt{1 - k^2 x^2}$. Therefore z can be developed as a power series in k^2, whose coefficients can be found by the aid of equations (58). The explicit results are

$$(61) \begin{cases} z = 1 + z_2 k^2 + z_4 k^4 + \cdots, \\[4pt] z_2 = -\dfrac{1}{2} \sin^2 \tau, \\[4pt] z_4 = -\dfrac{1}{8} \sin^2 \tau [1 + \cos^2 \tau], \\[4pt] z_6 = -\dfrac{1}{64} \sin^2 \tau [4 + 5 \cos^2 \tau + 2 \cos^4 \tau], \\[4pt] z_8 = -\dfrac{1}{32^2} \sin^2 \tau [40 + 56 \cos^2 \tau + 32 \cos^4 \tau + 8 \cos^6 \tau], \\[4pt] z_{10} = -\dfrac{1}{128^2} \sin^2 \tau [448 + 667 \cos^2 \tau + 454 \cos^4 \tau \\ \qquad\qquad\qquad\qquad\qquad + 176 \cos^6 \tau + 32 \cos^8 \tau], \\[4pt] \cdot\ \cdot\ \cdot\ \cdot\ \cdot\ \cdot\ \cdot\ \cdot\ \cdot\ \cdot\ \cdot\ \cdot\ \cdot\ \cdot\ \cdot\ \cdot \end{cases}$$

The right members of equations (60) and (61) are as simple as those of equations (59) and leave nothing to be desired.

82. The True Domain of Convergence of the Solution (35).
The general theorems of Chapter III imply that the solution (35) converges provided $|k^2|$ is sufficiently small, but they do

not provide a means for finding the true domain of convergence. In the present problem, however, the true domain of the solution can be found. It will be evident from the difficulties encountered in this relatively simple problem why the problem of determining the true domain of convergence of the solutions of differential equations as power series in a parameter cannot in general be solved by any known method.

It follows from equations (3) and (32) that the true domain of convergence of the series for $Q(k^2)$ is the circle whose radius is unity. Therefore, it follows from equations (33), by Arts. 27–29, that x is a regular function of k^2 and τ for all values of k^2 for which $|k^2| < 1$, and for all finite real values of τ if x and x' are finite. Since x and x' are periodic functions of τ with the period 2π, x and x' are regular functions of k^2 for all $|k^2| < 1$ provided x and x' do not become infinite for some value of τ on the interval 0 to 2π. Since k^2 is the argument of the power series whose true domain of convergence is in question, this parameter must be considered in the complex plane. Therefore x will also take complex values, but τ occurs only in the coefficients and is limited to real values.

In order to prove that x does not become infinite for any real τ for any k^2 such that $|k^2| < 1$, it will be shown that the integral

$$(62) \qquad I = \int_0^\infty \frac{dx}{Q(k^2)\sqrt{(1 - x^2)(1 - k^2 x^2)}},$$

obtained from the first of equations (33), is not real for any path of integration extending from 0 to ∞. This will mean that x cannot become infinite for any real value of τ, whatever value k^2 may have such that $|k^2| < 1$.

The integral (62) will be divided into five parts as follows:

I_1 is the integral from 0 to $1 - \epsilon$ along the real axis.

I_2 is the integral along the circle whose origin is at 1 and whose radius is ϵ from $1 - \epsilon$ to the line joining the point 1 with the point $1/k$, which in general will be complex because k is in general complex.

I_3 is the integral from the terminal point of the integral I_2 along the line joining the point 1 with the point $1/k$ to the distance ϵ of $1/k$.

I_4 is the integral from the terminal point of the integral I_3 along a circle whose center is at $1/k$ and whose radius is ϵ to the line from $1/k$ to infinity whose inclination to the real axis is the argument of $1/k$.

I_5 is the integral from the terminal point of the integral I_4 along the line to infinity whose inclination to the real axis is the argument of $1/k$. That is, for brevity,

$$(63) \quad I = I_1 + \cdots + I_5 = \int_0^1 + \int_{\epsilon(1)} + \int_1^{1/k} + \int_{\epsilon(1/k)} + \int_{1/k}^\infty .$$

Consider first the integral I_2. In order to compute it, let

$$x = 1 - \epsilon\, e^{\sqrt{-1}\theta}.$$

Then it follows that

$$I_2 = -\frac{\sqrt{-1}\,\sqrt{\epsilon}}{Q(k^2)} \int_0^{\text{amp}\,(1/k)} \frac{e^{1/2\,\sqrt{-1}\theta}d\theta}{\sqrt{(2 - \epsilon e^{\sqrt{-1}\theta})(1 - k^2x^2)}},$$

where, for convenience, the second factor in the denominator is not transformed. Since the integrand is finite for all values of θ corresponding to the path of integration, the integral is finite. Therefore,

$$\lim_{\epsilon=0} I_2 = 0.$$

Similarly, the limit of I_4 for $\epsilon = 0$ is zero. The transformation $x = 1/k\xi$ changes I_5 into the form I_1. Therefore

$$(64) \quad I = \lim_{\epsilon=0} (2I_1 + I_3) = \frac{2}{Q(k^2)} \int_0^1 \frac{dx}{\sqrt{(1 - x^2)(1 - k^2x^2)}}$$
$$+ \frac{1}{Q(k^2)} \int_1^{1/k} \frac{dx}{\sqrt{(1 - x^2)(1 - k'^2x^2)}} .$$

Equation (64) reduces as a consequence of equations (3), (4), (5), (6), and (32) to

$$(65) \quad I = \pi + \frac{\sqrt{-1}\,\pi}{2} \frac{\left[1 + \left(\frac{1}{2}\right)^2 k'^2 + \left(\frac{1\cdot3}{2\cdot4}\right)^2 k'^4 + \cdots \right]}{\left[1 + \left(\frac{1}{2}\right)^2 k^2 + \left(\frac{1\cdot3}{2\cdot4}\right)^2 k^4 + \cdots \right]}.$$

It follows at once that I is not real if k^2 is real; in fact, since the ratio of the two periods P_1 and P_2 is not real * for any value of k^2, it follows that I is not real for any value of k^2. That is, the integral from 0 to ∞ along the path chosen is not real.

Now consider any other path of integration from 0 to ∞. If none of the branch-points ± 1, $\pm 1/k$ of the integrand is included between the two paths of integration, the value of the integral I is the same. Suppose, however, that the branch-point $+ 1$ is included between the two paths. Suppose also that, in defining a Riemann surface for the function, a cross-cut joins the branch-points $- 1$ and $+ 1$, and that a cross-cut joins each of the branch-points $- 1/k$ and $1/k$ to ∞. Hence in this case

$$I = I_1 - I_3 - I_1 = - \frac{\sqrt{-1}\,\pi}{2} \frac{[1 + (\frac{1}{2})^2 k'^2 + \cdots]}{[1 + (\frac{1}{2})^2 k^2 + \cdots]},$$

which is not real.

Now suppose that the only branch-point between the original path of integration and the new one is the point $1/k$. Then it follows from the cross-cuts which have been adopted for defining a Riemann surface that the sign of the integrand differs from that on the original path of integration only from the branch-point $1/k$ to ∞. Hence in this case the integral is

$$I = I_1 + I_3 - I_1 = I_3,$$

which is not real.

If the two branch-points $+ 1$ and $+ 1/k$ alone are included between the original path of integration and the new one, the integral is similarly found to be also

$$I = 2I_1 - I_3,$$

which is not real. Finally, the integral along any path from 0 to ∞ has the value

$$I = 2I_1 + I_3 + 2n_1 I_1 + 2n_3 I_3 = 2(1 + n_1)I_1 + (1 + 2n_3)I_3,$$

where n_1 and n_3 are integers. Since this sum is not real for any integral values of n_1 and n_3, the integral I is not real. Therefore x cannot become infinite for any finite real value of τ provided $|k^2| < 1$. Therefore the solution series (35) converges for all real finite values of τ provided $|k^2| < 1$.

* Jacobi. *Werke*, Vol. II, pp. 25–26,

VIII. QUESTIONS AND PROBLEMS

1. Verify the result given in equation (3).

2. Prove by induction that the solution of equation (8) subject to the initial conditions (9) is an odd function of t.

3. Consider the problem of solving

$$\begin{cases} \dfrac{d^2x}{dt^2} = -(1 + \kappa^2 + \lambda^2)x + 2(\kappa^2 + \lambda^2 + \kappa^2\lambda^2)x^3 - 3\kappa^2\lambda^2x^5, \\ x(0) = 0, \qquad x'(0) = 1, \qquad 0 < \kappa^2 < \lambda^2 < 1. \end{cases}$$

Prove that the solution has two fundamental real periods and one purely imaginary period. Determine these periods. Find a value of t for which $x = \infty$.

4. Examine the nature of the solution of the differential equation of Problem 3 for values of t near those for which $x = \infty$. Is x a single-valued function of t?

5. Prove that $x = \operatorname{sn}(t; k^2)$ has no zeros in the principal period parallelogram except at $t = 0$ and $t = \frac{1}{2}P_1$.

6. Derive equations (38) in detail from equations (36) and (37).

7. Prove in detail that the x_{2i} of equation (35) are sines of odd multiples of τ and that the highest multiple of τ is $2i + 1$.

8. Derive equations (44) in detail.

9. Is the first of equations (45) a consequence of the second? Can the second equation of (45) be solved for δ as a power series in k^2?

10. Derive the third of equations (49).

11. Work out the first three terms of the solution by the method of Art. 78.

12. Work out the expression for x_6 by the method of Art. 79.

13. Work out the first three of equations (59) from equations (58).

14. Derive the differential equation satisfied by $y = \sqrt{1 - x^2}$.

15. In what respects would the method of Art. 82 fail if one should attempt to apply it to obtain the true domain of convergence of the solution of the differential equation of Problem 3?

CHAPTER IX

THE DEVIATIONS OF FALLING BODIES

83. Formulation of the Problem. The problem of this chapter has been chosen because the methods that are suitable for solving it are entirely different from those used in the preceding two problems.

Let it be assumed that the earth is an oblate spheroid of revolution about its axis of rotation, and that its mass is symmetrically distributed with respect to its axis and the plane of its equator. Let O, Fig. 3, be the center of the earth, P_0 a fixed point on its surface, and P_1 a point exterior to the earth on the line OP_0 prolonged. Suppose a body initially at rest with respect to the surface of the earth falls from the point P_1 and strikes the surface of the earth at the point P_2.

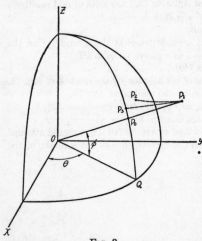

FIG. 3.

Suppose also that a plumb bob is suspended from the point P_1 by a weightless string and that it touches the surface of the earth at the point P_3. The problem is to determine the deviations of P_2 from P_3 in both longitude and latitude.

The problem obviously consists essentially of two parts, that of finding the coördinates of the point P_2 and that of finding the coördinates of the point P_3. Since the former is determined by the path described by a falling body, it depends upon the solution of differential equations. Since the latter consists in

142

finding a point P_3 such that a line through it perpendicular to the surface of the earth shall pass through the point P_1, it depends upon the solution of implicit functions.   The errors in several earlier treatments of the problem arose from the fact that the two distinct processes were not carried out in such a way that their results could be compared with sufficient accuracy.   It is obvious from physical considerations that the path of the falling body and the plumb line suspended from its point of fall will very nearly coincide, and that, consequently, the two parts of the problem must be solved with considerable approximation in order that the difference between the path of the falling body and the plumb line may be determined.

84. Differential Equations of Motion for Falling Body.   The components of acceleration to which the falling body is subject are due entirely to the attraction of the oblate earth.   Under the hypotheses that have been made respecting the shape of the earth and its distribution of mass, the resultant acceleration passes through the axis of the earth.   In other words, the components of attraction depend only upon the distance r of the body from the center of the earth and upon its geocentric latitude ϕ, but not upon its longitude θ.

The potential function * whose derivatives with respect to the coördinates give the corresponding components of gravitational acceleration is

$$(1) \qquad V = \frac{\alpha}{r} + \frac{\beta}{r^3} (1 - 3 \sin^2 \phi) \cdots,$$

where α is $k^2 E$, E being the mass of the earth and k^2 a constant depending upon the units employed, and where β is a constant which is small relative to α and which vanishes with the eccentricity of a meridian section.   In fact, the second term of the series is numerically about $1/600$ the first.   In the case of such a body as the earth, the terms of the series not written are very small in comparison with those written.

Let the origin of time be so chosen that the body starts to fall at $t = 0$.   Let the axes of reference be so chosen that $\theta(0) = 0$. Then the longitude of P_0 at any time t is ωt, the constant ω

---

* Moulton, *Introduction to Celestial Mechanics*, Art. 78.

being the rate of angular rotation of the earth. The longitude of P_1 is also ωt, but the falling body does not remain in the meridian of P_0. Hence it is convenient to let

$$(2) \qquad \theta = \omega t + \lambda,$$

where λ is the longitude from the meridian through P_0. In the case of a falling body λ and $d\lambda/dt$ are both zero at $t = 0$.

In the notations that have been adopted, the differential equations satisfied by the coördinates of the falling body are

$$(3) \qquad \begin{cases} \dfrac{d^2r}{dt^2} - r\left(\dfrac{d\phi}{dt}\right)^2 - r\left(\omega + \dfrac{d\lambda}{dt}\right)^2 \cos^2\phi = \dfrac{\partial V}{\partial r}, \\[2mm] \dfrac{d}{dt}\left(r^2\dfrac{d\phi}{dt}\right) + r^2\left(\omega + \dfrac{d\lambda}{dt}\right)^2 \sin\phi\cos\phi = \dfrac{\partial V}{\partial \phi}, \\[2mm] \dfrac{d}{dt}\left\{r^2\left(\omega + \dfrac{d\lambda}{dt}\right)\cos^2\phi\right\} = \dfrac{\partial V}{\partial \lambda} = 0. \end{cases}$$

In order to define the problem completely the initial values of the variables must be given. Let the distance OP_0 be represented by r_0 and OP_1 by $r_1 = r_0(1 + h)$. Then it follows from the conditions of the problem that the initial values of the dependent variables are

$$(4) \qquad \begin{cases} r(0) = r_0(1 + h), & \phi(0) = \phi_0, & \lambda(0) = 0, \\ r'(0) = 0, & \phi'(0) = 0, & \lambda'(0) = 0. \end{cases}$$

From this point on the problem is one purely of differential equations and implicit functions.

85. Solution of Differential Equations (3). The left members of the differential equations (3) are analytic functions of the dependent variables r, r', ϕ, ϕ', λ, and λ' in the neighborhood of every finite set of values of these quantities. It follows from equation (1) that the right members are analytic in the same arguments in the vicinity of the initial conditions defined in equations (4) provided r_0 is distinct from zero, as it is necessarily in practice. Moreover, equations (3) do not involve the independent variable t explicitly. Therefore, by Arts. 15–17, the solution is expansible as power series of the form

$$(5) \quad \begin{cases} r = r_1 + a_2 t^2 + a_3 t^3 + a_4 t^4 + \cdots, \\ \phi = \phi_0 + b_2 t^2 + b_3 t^3 + b_4 t^4 + \cdots, \\ \lambda = 0 + c_2 t^2 + c_3 t^3 + c_4 t^4 + \cdots, \end{cases}$$

which converge for all values of t for which $|t|$ is sufficiently small. The initial conditions (4) imply that the series (5) have no terms of the first degree in t.

The differential equations (3) are solved as power series in t because the properties of the motion are required for only small values of t. In the problems of the preceding chapter general properties of the solution were desired, and other methods of solving them were employed. Moreover, the other methods so far developed would not be easily applicable to this problem.

The coefficients of the right members of equations (5) are determined in the usual way by substituting these series into the expansions of the right members of equations (3) as power series in $r - r_1$, $\phi - \phi_0$, and λ, and then equating coefficients of corresponding powers of t. The coefficients of the terms of the second degree are given by the equations

$$(6) \quad \begin{cases} 2a_2 = -\dfrac{\alpha}{r_1^2} + \omega^2 r_1 \cos^2 \phi_0 - \dfrac{3\beta}{r_1^4}(1 - 3\sin^2 \phi_0), \\ 2b_2 = -\dfrac{1}{2}\left[\omega^2 + \dfrac{6\beta}{r_1^5}\right]\sin 2\phi_0, \\ 2c_2 = 0. \end{cases}$$

The coefficients a_3, b_3, and c_3 are determined by equating coefficients of t to the first degree. Since r and ϕ do not contain terms of the first degree in t, the right members of the expansions of equations (3) do not contain terms of the first degree in t. Since the first derivatives of ϕ and λ with respect to t are zero at $t = 0$, the left members of the first two of equations (3) contain no terms of the first degree in t except $6a_3 t$ and $6b_3 t$. Therefore it is found that

$$(7) \quad \begin{cases} a_3 = b_3 = 0, \\ 6c_3 = -4\omega\left[\dfrac{a_2}{r_1} - b_2 \tan \phi_0\right]. \end{cases}$$

It will be found in the sequel that the terms of the fourth degree in t of r and ϕ will be required, but that it will be sufficient to determine λ only to terms of the third degree inclusive.

The coefficients of the terms of the fourth degree in t for r and ϕ are

$$(8) \quad \begin{cases} 12a_4 = 4r_1b_2{}^2 + 2a_2 \dfrac{\partial a_2}{\partial r_1} + 2b_2 \dfrac{\partial a_2}{\partial \phi_0} + 6\omega r_1 \cos^2 \phi_0 c_3, \\[2mm] 12b_4 = \dfrac{2a_2}{r_1{}^2} \dfrac{\partial a_2}{\partial \phi_0} + 2b_2 \dfrac{\partial b_2}{\partial \phi_0} - 12 \dfrac{a_2 b_2}{r_1} - 3\omega \sin 2\phi_0 c_3. \end{cases}$$

The solution is obtained to the required number of terms by substituting the expressions for the coefficients given in equations (6), (7), and (8) into equations (5).

86. Determination of the Coördinates of the Point P_2. The point P_2 is the point at which the falling body strikes the surface of the earth. The path of the falling body is given by equations (5), $\cdots$, (8). The surface of the earth will be defined as the equipotential surface through P_0 corresponding to all the accelerations, both gravitational and rotational, to which a body at rest on its surface is subject. The potential function for the gravitational acceleration is V, equation (1). The potential for the centrifugal acceleration due to the rotation of the earth is the function $\frac{1}{2}\omega^2 r^2 \cos^2 \phi$.

For notation let the total potential be

$$(9) \qquad W = \tfrac{1}{2}\omega^2 r^2 \cos^2 \phi + V,$$

and let W_0 and W_2 be the values of W at P_0 and P_2 respectively. Then the condition that W_0 and W_2 shall be on the same equipotential surface is

$$(10) \quad \begin{cases} W_2 - W_0 = 0 = \tfrac{1}{2}\omega^2[r_2{}^2 \cos^2 \phi_2 - r_0{}^2 \cos^2 \phi_0] \\[2mm] + \alpha\left[\dfrac{1}{r_2} - \dfrac{1}{r_0}\right] + \beta\left[\dfrac{1}{r_2{}^3} - \dfrac{1}{r_0{}^3}\right] - 3\beta\left[\dfrac{\sin^2 \phi_2}{r_2{}^3} - \dfrac{\sin^2 \phi_0}{r_0{}^3}\right] + \cdots. \end{cases}$$

Let t_2 represent the value of t at which the falling body arrives at the point P_2. Then, on replacing t by t_2 in equations (5) and r_1 by $r_0(1 + h)$ in equations (6), (7), and (8), the condition expressed by equation (10) becomes

$$(11) \qquad W_2 - W_0 = P(r_2, \phi_2) = P^{(1)}(t_2, h),$$

where the function $P^{(1)}(t_2, h)$ is a power series in t_2 and h that converges for all values of t_2 and h for which $|t_2|$ is sufficiently small and $|h| < 1$. The solution of equation (11) for t_2 in terms of h gives the time at which the falling body strikes the surface of the earth, and if this value of t_2 is substituted into equations (5), the coördinates of P_2 are obtained. The result is expressed in terms of the parameter h, which is determined by the height of the point P_1 above the surface of the earth. Only the details remain to be worked out to the necessary degree of accuracy.

It follows from equations (5) that

$$(12) \quad \begin{cases} r_2 = r_0 + r_0 h + a_2 t_2^2 + a_4 t_2^4 + \cdots, \\ \phi_2 = \phi_0 + 0 \ + b_2 t_2^2 + b_4 t_2^4 + \cdots, \end{cases}$$

the values of the coefficients being given in equations (6) and (8). Since these equations do not involve terms of the first degree in t_2, equation (11) contains no term of the first degree in t_2. Hence equation (11) has the form

$$(13) \quad \begin{cases} W_2 - W_0 = P(r_2, \phi_2) = \left(\dfrac{\partial P}{\partial r_2}\right)_0 [r_0 h + a_2 t_2^2 + \cdots] \\ \qquad\qquad + \left(\dfrac{\partial P}{\partial \phi_2}\right)_0 [b_2 t_2^2 + \cdots] + \cdots \\ \qquad = a_{20} t_2^2 + a_{01} h + a_{40} t_2^4 + a_{21} t_2^2 h + a_{02} h^2 + \cdots. \end{cases}$$

It now follows from equations (11), (12), and (13) after some reductions that, if $a_2^{(0)}$, $a_4^{(0)}$, $b_2^{(0)}$ and $b_4^{(0)}$ represent the values of a_2, a_4, b_2, and b_4, defined in equations (6) and (8), for $h = 0$, then

$$(14) \quad \begin{cases} \left(\dfrac{\partial P}{\partial r_2}\right)_0 = 2a_2^{(0)}, \qquad \left(\dfrac{\partial P}{\partial \phi_2}\right)_0 = 2r_0^2 b_2^{(0)}, \\ a_{20} = 2[(a_2^{(0)})^2 + r_0^2 (b_2^{(0)})^2], \\ a_{01} = 2r_0 a_2^{(0)}, \\ a_{40} = 2a_2^{(0)} a_4^{(0)} + 2r_0^2 b_2^{(0)} b_4^{(0)} \\ \qquad + (a_2^{(0)})^2 \dfrac{\partial a_2^{(0)}}{\partial r_0} + 2a_2^{(0)} b_2^{(0)} \dfrac{\partial a_2^{(0)}}{\partial \phi_0} + r_0^2 (b_2^{(0)})^2 \dfrac{\partial b_2^{(0)}}{\partial \phi_0}, \\ a_{21} = 4r_0 a_2^{(0)} \dfrac{\partial a_2^{(0)}}{\partial r_0} + 2r_0 b_2^{(0)} \dfrac{\partial a_2^{(0)}}{\partial \phi_0} + 2r_0^3 b_2^{(0)} \dfrac{\partial b_2^{(0)}}{\partial r_0}, \\ a_{02} = r_0^2 \dfrac{\partial a_2^{(0)}}{\partial r_0}. \end{cases}$$

Let g_0 represent the acceleration of gravity at the point P_0. Then it follows from equations (12) that

$$(15) \qquad\qquad 2a_{20} = g_0^2,$$

which is not zero. Hence, if x and μ of Art. 52 are identified with t_2 and h respectively, it follows that equation (13) can be solved for t_2 as a power series in $\sqrt{h}$ that converges if $|h|$ is sufficiently small. When this value of t_2 is substituted for t in the right members of equations (5), the coördinates r_2, ϕ_2, and λ_2 are expressed as power series in $\sqrt{h}$, whose coefficients are closed expressions in the parameters ω^2 and β. Since h is less than 1/20,000 for a fall of 1000 feet, the convergence of the series is probably very rapid for any value of h that could be used in a practical experiment.

The first two of equations (5), so far as they are written, involve only even powers of t. Moreover, equation (13), so far as it is written, contains only even powers of t_2. Consequently, if the solution is not carried beyond the terms of the second degree in h, equation (13) can be solved for t_2^2 as a power series in h, instead of a power series in $\sqrt{h}$. Then it will not be necessary to square the series before substituting it for t in the first terms of the right members of equations (5).

The solution of the first five terms of equation (13) for t_2^2 as a power series in h is easily found to be

$$(16) \qquad
\begin{cases}
t_2^2 = \alpha_1 h + \alpha_2 h^2 + \cdots, \\[2mm]
\alpha_1 = -\dfrac{a_{01}}{a_{20}} = -\dfrac{4r_0 a_2{}^{(0)}}{g_0{}^2}, \\[3mm]
\alpha_2 = -\dfrac{\left[a_{40}a_{01}{}^2 - a_{21}a_{01}a_{20} + a_{02}a_{20}{}^2\right]}{a_{20}{}^3}.
\end{cases}$$

On substituting the expression for t_2 from equation (16) into the third of equations (5) in place of t, it is found that

$$(17) \qquad\qquad \lambda_2 = \left[\frac{-a_{01}}{a_{20}}\right]^{3/2} c_3{}^{(0)} h^{3/2} + \cdots.$$

Since the plumb line hangs in the meridian of P_0, the λ_3 of P_3 is zero, and consequently equation (17) gives the deviation in longitude of the falling body.

It follows directly from equations (5), (6), and (7) that

$$\begin{cases} -2a_2^{(0)} = g_0, \\ 3r_0c_3^{(0)} = g_0\omega \end{cases}$$

approximately. Therefore equation (17) reduces to

$$(18) \qquad \lambda_2 = \frac{2}{3} \omega \left(\frac{2r_0}{g_0}\right)^{1/2} h^{3/2} + \cdots.$$

Consequently, the deviation of the falling body is eastward from the plumb line, or in the direction of the earth's rotation, and its angular value is independent of the latitude except in so far as g_0 depends upon the latitude. The linear deviation, however, is proportional to the cosine of the latitude, and consequently diminishes from the equator to the poles.

An experimental verification of the eastward deviation of falling bodies would constitute a proof of the eastward rotation of the earth, but the amount of the deviation is so small for distances within the range of feasibility in practice that it is largely masked by such irregular disturbing influences as the atmosphere. For example, the deviation in longitude for a fall of 1000 feet in latitude 40° is only 3.6 inches.

The deviation in latitude remains to be found by determining the latitudes of the points P_2 and P_3. On substituting the expression for t_2, given in equation (16), in place of t in the second of equations (5), it is found that

$$(19) \qquad \begin{cases} \phi_2 = \phi_0 - \dfrac{4r_0a_2^{(0)}b_2^{(0)}}{g_0^2} h + K_2h^2 + \cdots, \\ K_2 = \alpha_2b_2^{(0)} + \alpha_1^2b_4^{(0)} + r_0\alpha_1 \dfrac{\partial b_2^{(0)}}{\partial r_0}. \end{cases}$$

The complete expression for the coefficient of h in equation (19) must be retained, but it will be sufficient to determine the approximate value of K_2. All terms in this coefficient of degree higher than the first in the small parameters ω^2 and β may be neglected. It follows from equations (6) and (8) that $b_2^{(0)}$ and $b_4^{(0)}$ are of the first order in ω^2 and β at the lowest, and therefore from the second of equations (19) that only terms of order zero in these parameters are required in α_1 and α_2. The expressions for the various quantities to the required order of accuracy are found from equations (6), (8), (14), (15), and (16) to be

$$(20) \begin{cases} a_2^{(0)} = -\dfrac{1}{2} g_0, \qquad c_3^{(0)} = \dfrac{1}{3} \dfrac{g_0}{r_0} \omega, \\[2mm] b_2^{(0)} = -\dfrac{1}{4} \left[\omega^2 + \dfrac{6\beta}{r_0^5} \right] \sin 2\phi_0, \\[2mm] a_4^{(0)} = -\dfrac{1}{12} \dfrac{g_0^2}{r_0}, \qquad \dfrac{\partial a_2^{(0)}}{\partial r_0} = \dfrac{g_0}{r_0}, \\[2mm] b_4^{(0)} = -\dfrac{g_0}{r_0} \left[\dfrac{1}{6} \omega^2 + \dfrac{9}{8} \dfrac{\beta}{r_0^5} \right] \sin 2\phi_0, \\[2mm] \dfrac{\partial a_2^{(0)}}{\partial \phi_0} = -\dfrac{r_0}{2} \left[\omega^2 - \dfrac{9\beta}{r_0^5} \right] \sin 2\phi_0, \\[2mm] \dfrac{\partial b_2^{(0)}}{\partial r_0} = \dfrac{15}{2} \dfrac{\beta}{r_0^6} \sin 2\phi_0, \qquad a_{20} = \dfrac{1}{2} g_0^2, \\[2mm] a_{01} = -r_0 g_0, \qquad a_{21} = -2 g_0^2, \\[2mm] a_{02} = r_0 g_0, \qquad a_{40} = \dfrac{1}{3} \dfrac{g_0^3}{r_0}, \\[2mm] \alpha_1 = \dfrac{2 r_0}{g_0}, \qquad \alpha_2 = \dfrac{10}{3} \dfrac{r_0}{g_0}, \\[2mm] K_2 = \dfrac{r_0}{g_0} \left[-\dfrac{3}{2} \omega^2 + \dfrac{11}{2} \dfrac{\beta}{r_0^5} \right] \sin 2\phi_0. \end{cases}$$

The value of ϕ_2 is now completely determined by substituting these expressions into equations (16) and (19). The reductions will be omitted until after the determination of the coördinates of the point P_3.

87. Determination of the Coördinates of the Point P_3.

The point P_3 at which the plumb bob touches the surface of the earth is subject to two conditions: (1) the point P_3 is on the equipotential surface that passes through the point P_0; (2) the perpendicular to the equipotential surface from the point P_3 passes through the point P_1 of suspension of the plumb line. These two conditions uniquely determine the point P_3.

The condition that the point P_3 shall be on the equipotential surface through the point P_0 is

$$(21) \qquad F_1 = W_3 - W_0 = 0,$$

where W_3 is the value of W for $r = r_3$, $\phi = \phi_3$. Suppose for the moment that the point P_0 is in the xz-plane. Then, since the direction cosines of the normal to the surface are proportional to the partial derivatives of W with respect to x and z, the equation of the line perpendicular to the equipotential surface at the point P_3 is

$$(22) \qquad (z - z_3) \left(\frac{\partial W}{\partial x} \right)_3 - (x - x_3) \left(\frac{\partial W}{\partial z} \right)_3 = 0,$$

where the subscript on the parentheses indicates that, in the expressions for the partial derivatives, x and z are replaced by x_3 and z_3 respectively.

Since the line in question must pass through the point P_1 whose rectangular coördinates are x_1 and z_1, it follows that

$$(23) \qquad F_2 = (z_1 - z_3) \left(\frac{\partial W}{\partial x} \right)_3 - (x_1 - x_3) \left(\frac{\partial W}{\partial z} \right)_3 = 0.$$

It remains to express equations (21) and (23) in terms of known quantities and the coördinates of the point P_3.

The explicit expressions for equations (21) and (23) are

$$(24) \quad \begin{cases} F_1 = \dfrac{1}{2} \omega^2 [r_3{}^2 \cos^2 \phi_3 - r_0{}^2 \cos^2 \phi_0] + \alpha \left[\dfrac{1}{r_3} - \dfrac{1}{r_0} \right] \\ \qquad + \beta \left[\dfrac{1}{r_3{}^3} - \dfrac{1}{r_0{}^3} \right] - 3\beta \left[\dfrac{\sin^2 \phi_3}{r_3{}^3} - \dfrac{\sin^2 \phi_0}{r_0{}^3} \right] \cdots = 0, \\ F_2 = \dfrac{r_1}{r_3{}^2} \left[\alpha + \dfrac{3\beta}{r_3{}^2} (1 - 5 \sin^2 \phi_3) \right] \sin (\phi_3 - \phi_0) \\ \qquad + \dfrac{6\beta}{r_3{}^4} [r_1 \cos \phi_0 - r_3 \cos \phi_3] \sin \phi_3 \\ \qquad + r_3 \omega^2 [r_1 \sin \phi_0 - r_3 \sin \phi_3] \cos \phi_3 \cdots = 0, \end{cases}$$

from which r_3 and ϕ_3 are to be determined.

In order to place equations (24) in a tractable form, let

$$(25) \quad \begin{cases} r_1 = r_0(1 + h), \\ r_3 = r_0(1 + \rho), \\ \phi_3 = \phi_0 + \sigma, \end{cases}$$

where h is an arbitrary constant defining the height of P_1 above the surface of the earth, and ρ and σ are quantities to be determined in terms of h. After the substitution of the right members of equations (25) into equations (24), the latter become

$$(26) \quad \begin{cases} F_1 = F_1(\rho, \sigma, 0) = 0, \\ F_2 = F_2(\rho, \sigma, h) = 0, \end{cases}$$

where $F_1(\rho, \sigma, 0)$ and $F_2(\rho, \sigma, h)$ are power series in ρ, σ, and h that converge provided $|\rho| < 1$, $|h| < 1$, and σ any finite quantity. The series F_1 is independent of the parameter h.

It follows from equations (24) and (25) that the series F_1 and F_2 contain no terms independent of ρ, σ, and h. Therefore equations (26) can be solved uniquely for ρ and σ as power series in h provided the determinant of the coefficients of the linear terms in ρ and σ is not zero (Arts. 46–48). It is found from equations (24) and (25) that this determinant is

$$(27) \quad D = \begin{vmatrix} \left(\dfrac{\partial F_1}{\partial \rho}\right)_0, & \left(\dfrac{\partial F_1}{\partial \sigma}\right)_0 \\[2mm] \left(\dfrac{\partial F_2}{\partial \rho}\right)_0, & \left(\dfrac{\partial F_2}{\partial \sigma}\right)_0 \end{vmatrix} = \begin{vmatrix} 2r_0 a_2^{(0)}, & 2r_0^2 b_2^{(0)} \\[2mm] 2r_0^2 b_2^{(0)}, & -2r_0 a_2^{(0)} \end{vmatrix} = -r_0^2 g_0^2,$$

which is not zero.

In order to construct the solution it will be necessary to have the expansions of F_1 and F_2 as power series in ρ, σ, and h. The expression for σ will be required to terms of the second degree in h, and in order to obtain them the terms of ρ of the first degree in h will be used. The expansions of F_1 and F_2 up to terms of the second degree inclusive in the parameters ρ, σ, and h must be considered. These series are of the form

$$(28) \quad \begin{cases} F_1 = a_{100}\rho + a_{010}\sigma + a_{200}\rho^2 + a_{110}\rho\sigma + a_{020}\sigma^2 + \cdots = 0, \\ F_2 = b_{100}\rho + b_{010}\sigma + b_{001}h + b_{200}\rho^2 + b_{110}\rho\sigma + b_{101}\rho h \\ \qquad\qquad + b_{020}\sigma^2 + b_{011}\sigma h + \cdots = 0. \end{cases}$$

The solution of equations (28) is of the form

$$(29) \quad \begin{cases} \rho = \beta_1 h + \beta_2 h^2 + \cdots, \\ \sigma = \gamma_1 h + \gamma_2 h^2 + \cdots, \end{cases}$$

where β_1, γ_1, β_2, γ_2, $\cdots$ are constants that are expressible in terms of the coefficients of equations (28). The coefficients of the terms of the first degree are given by the equations

$$(30) \quad \begin{cases} \beta_1 = \dfrac{a_{010}b_{001}}{D} = -\dfrac{a_{010}b_{001}}{r_0^2 g_0^2}, \\[4mm] \gamma_1 = -\dfrac{a_{100}b_{001}}{D} = +\dfrac{a_{100}b_{001}}{r_0^2 g_0^2}. \end{cases}$$

It was found on developing the determinant (27) that

$$(31) \quad \begin{cases} \left(\dfrac{\partial F_1}{\partial \rho}\right)_0 = a_{100} = 2r_0 a_2^{(0)}, \\[2mm] \left(\dfrac{\partial F_1}{\partial \sigma}\right)_0 = a_{010} = 2r_0^2 t_2^{(0)}, \\[2mm] \left(\dfrac{\partial F_2}{\partial \rho}\right)_0 = b_{100} = 2r_0^2 b_2^{(0)}, \\[2mm] \left(\dfrac{\partial F_2}{\partial \sigma}\right)_0 = b_{010} = -2r_0 a_2^{(0)}. \end{cases}$$

Therefore

$$(32) \quad \begin{cases} \beta_1 = \dfrac{4r_0^2 (b_2^{(0)})^2}{g_0^2}, \\[3mm] \gamma_1 = -\dfrac{4r_0 a_2^{(0)} b_2^{(0)}}{g_0^2}. \end{cases}$$

It follows from equations (6) that γ_1 is homogeneous of the first degree in the small parameters ω^2 and β, and that β_1 is homogeneous of the second degree in the same quantities. In the sequel it will be found that only terms of the first degree in ω^2 and β will be required in the coefficient of h^2.

It is found from equations (28) and (29) that

$$(33) \quad \begin{cases} D\gamma_2 = -[a_{100}b_{200} - b_{100}a_{200}]\beta_1^2 - [a_{100}b_{110} - b_{100}a_{110}]\beta_1\gamma_1 \\ \quad - [a_{100}b_{020} - b_{100}a_{020}]\gamma_1^2 - a_{100}[b_{101}\beta_1 + b_{011}\gamma_1]. \end{cases}$$

Only the last term is of the first degree in the parameters ω^2 and β. It follows from equations (24) and (28) that

$$(34) \quad b_{011} = \frac{\alpha}{r_0} + \text{terms vanishing with } \omega^2 \text{ and } \beta.$$

Therefore the expression for γ_2 becomes

$$(35) \quad \gamma_2 = -\frac{a_{100}b_{011}}{D}\gamma_1 = -\frac{2r_0}{g_0}b_2^{(0)} + \cdots,$$

and the expression for $\phi_3 = \phi_0 + \sigma$ becomes as a consequence of equations (29), (30), and (35)

$$(36) \quad \phi_3 = \phi_0 - \frac{4r_0 a_2^{(0)} b_2^{(0)}}{g_0^2} h - \left[\frac{2r_0}{g_0}b_2^{(0)} + \cdots\right]h^2 + \cdots.$$

The coefficient of h is exact; that of h^2 is given up to terms of the first order inclusive in the small parameters ω^2 and β. It is not necessary to determine r_3 in computing the deviations at the surface of the earth.

88. The Deviation in Latitude.   The deviation in latitude of the falling body from the plumb line at the surface of the earth is $\phi_3 - \phi_2$, which becomes, as a consequence of the explicit expressions given in equations (19), (20), and (36),

$$(37) \quad \phi_3 - \phi_2 = 0 \cdot h + \left[\frac{2r_0}{g_0} \left(\omega^2 - \frac{5}{4} \frac{\beta}{r_0{}^5} \right) \sin 2\phi_0 + \cdots \right] h^2 + \cdots.$$

The coefficient of h is identically zero in ω^2 and β.   The right member of equation (37) converges for all values of h for which $|h|$ is sufficiently small, and h can be taken so small that the sign of the right member is the same as the sign of the coefficient of h^2.   Since for one mile h equals approximately $1/4000$, this limitation is of no practical interest.

In the case of the earth, $4r_0{}^5\omega^2$ is about four times as great as 5β.   Therefore the deviation from the plumb line of a falling body is equatorward for all latitudes between $0°$ and $90°$.   The deviation is zero at the equator and at the poles, and it is a maximum in latitudes $\pm 45°$.   For moderate distances of fall the deviation is very slight, amounting to less than one-thousandth of an inch for a fall of 1000 feet in latitude $45°$.   Obviously so small a deviation is beyond experimental detection; and it is of no practical importance even in the much greater distances through which the vertical convection currents in the earth's atmosphere rise and descend.

The reason for the diverse results that were obtained by those who first treated this problem is now easily explained.   The expressions for the coördinates of the points in question were developed by more or less circuitous methods in all three parameters ω^2, β, and h.   Terms were omitted that seemed for one reason or another small in comparison with those that were retained.   The result was that the terms corresponding to the coefficient of h in equation (37) were not completely developed, one investigator retaining certain terms depending upon the method he used, and another investigator retaining others.   The result each obtained depended upon the terms he retained.   The straightforward processes of powerful general methods are not subject to these uncertainties.

IX. QUESTIONS AND PROBLEMS

1. What is the reason for the introduction of the variable λ by means of equation (2)?

2. Set up the differential equations of motion for the falling body in rectangular coördinates. Discuss the relative practical advantages of these equations and equations (3).

3. Which of the parameters that enter into the problem of the chapter are under the control of the experimenter?

4. Why do not equations (5) contain terms of the first degree in t?

5. Verify equations (18) and determine c_4.

6. Prove that the surface of an ideal earth is an equipotential surface with the potential function defined in equation (9).

7. What is the purpose of determining t_2? Devise and outline some other method of accomplishing the same result.

8. Verify equations (14) and (15).

9. Is it possible to solve equation (13) directly for $t_2{}^2$ as power series in h beyond terms of the second degree? Is it possible to solve such an equation as (13) directly for any power of the dependent variable?

10. Derive the expression for the linear deviation in longitude of the falling body.

11. Verify equations (19) and (20).

12. What would be the conditions corresponding to equations (22) and (23) if the rotating body were not a figure of revolution?

13. What is the physical reason that the first of equations (26) does not involve the parameter h?

14. Verify equations (30), (31), and (32).

15. Prove that the right member of equation (37) to terms of all degrees contains $\sin 2\phi_0$ as a factor.

HISTORICAL SKETCH

The eastward deviation of a falling body from a plumb line suspended from its point of fall depends upon essentially the same dynamical factors as those which are involved in the deviations of wind and ocean currents. Hence it is natural that Gauss, the founder of the theories of the circulation of the earth's atmosphere, should have treated the subject. The deviation of a falling body in the plane of its meridian depends upon the same principles, but the departure from the plumb line is much smaller than that to the eastward. In spite of the fact that meridianal deviation of a falling body is of little practical or theoretical interest, it has been the subject of a large amount of work, leading to the most diverse results.

Gauss appears to have first discussed the meridianal deviation of a falling body in March, 1803 (*Gesammelte Werke*, Vol. 5), and he reached the conclusion that the deviation is equatorward. In the following year, Laplace treated the same problem [*Bulletin de la Société Philomatique* (1804); also, *Mécanique Céleste*, Vol. 4, Chap. V]. His conclusion was that the deviation is not toward the equator. A discussion by Poisson (*Journal de l'École Polytechnique*, Vol. 16, 1838) reached the conclusion that there is no deviation in the meridian plane of the falling body. Toward the end of the century several attempts were made to test the matter experimentally; a summary of them was given by E. H. Hall in *Contributions from the Jefferson Laboratory*, Vol. 1, 1903. In 1905, M. le Compte de Sparre published two papers (*Bulletin de la Société Mathématique de France*, Vol. 33) and obtained results in substantial agreement with those of Gauss. In 1911, Wm. H. Roever published an investigation of the subject (*Transactions of the American Mathematical Society*, Vol. 12), in which he found the deviation is equatorward, but several fold greater than the results obtained by Gauss. In 1912, Roever published a second paper in the same journal, without assuming that the earth is a figure of revolution. In 1913, Robert S. Woodward treated the problem (*Astronomical Journal*, Vol. 28) and reached the conclusion that the meridianal deviation of a falling body is away from the equator. This disagreement with the results of Roever gave rise to a spirited discussion (*Science*, Vol. 38, pp. 315–319) that led the author of this book to investigate the problem by an independent method (*Annals of Mathematics*, Vol. 15). The treatment is that contained in this chapter, and the results reached are in full agreement with those of Roever, who undoubtedly was the first to treat the problem correctly.

CHAPTER X

THE DAMPED GYROSCOPE

89. The Gyroscope Problem. As considered here, the gyroscope is idealized to consist of a rotating wheel, or disc, so mounted that its axis of rotation may move freely in any direction. It is assumed in this ideal problem that there is acting a force, constant in direction, magnitude, and point of application, which tends to bring the rotating disc parallel to a fixed plane. In an actual gyroscope, the force is gravity acting on a system that is not supported at its center of mass, and hence a change in the inclination of the axis of such a gyroscope raises or lowers its center of gravity. In the ideal problem, the assumption made avoids the necessity of taking into account the effects on the center of gravity, and to this slight extent the problem treated differs from the actual problem. It is assumed, further, that there is a damping force that acts opposite to the motion of the axis of the gyroscope, and of which the magnitude is proportional to the angular velocity of the axis of the gyroscope. The problem is to determine the motion of the axis of the gyroscope and the effects of the damping force upon its motion.

The foregoing problem has been chosen because its solution illustrates the uses of important processes that have not been employed in the preceding problems. In the first place, the importance in some problems of combining the original differential equations and employing integrals in order to effect a separation of variables is illustrated. Then, too, the determination of the effects of the damping forces illustrates the great advantage of a transformation of variables of the type treated in Chapter IV.

90. The Fundamental Differential Equations. The problem of deriving the differential equations of a rotating rigid body

157

was solved by Euler. Let the origin of coördinates be at the center of gravity of the gyroscope, and take rectangular axes fixed in the rotating disc, the axes 1 and 2 being in the plane of the disc and the axis 3 in the line of its axis of rotation. Let the rates of angular rotation about these axes be ω_1, ω_2, and ω_3 respectively.

The orientation of the axis can be defined by three independent angular variables, θ, ϕ, and ψ, whose geometric meanings are indicated in Fig. 4. The variable θ corresponds to the inclination of the orbit of a planet, the variable ψ corresponds to the longitude of its ascending node, and the variable ϕ corresponds to the longitude of its perihelion point from the node in the plane of the orbit.

Let A_1, A_2, and A_3 represent the moments of inertia of the gyroscope about the axes 1, 2, and 3 respectively. It follows from the assumed symmetry of the gyroscope that $A_1 = A_2$.

Finally, let M_1, M_2, and M_3 represent the moments of the exterior forces (omitting the damping forces for the present) about the axes 1, 2, and 3. Then Euler's differential equations for the motion of the gyroscope are

$$(1) \quad \begin{cases} A_1 \dfrac{d\omega_1}{dt} - (A_2 - A_3)\omega_2\,\omega_3 = M_1, \\[2mm] A_2 \dfrac{d\omega_2}{dt} - (A_3 - A_1)\omega_3\,\omega_1 = M_2, \\[2mm] A_3 \dfrac{d\omega_3}{dt} - (A_1 - A_2)\omega_1\,\omega_2 = M_3; \end{cases}$$

$$(2) \quad \begin{cases} \sin\theta\,\dfrac{d\psi}{dt} = \omega_1 \sin\phi + \omega_2 \cos\phi, \\[2mm] \dfrac{d\theta}{dt} = \omega_1 \cos\phi - \omega_2 \sin\phi, \\[2mm] \dfrac{d\phi}{dt} = \omega_3 - \cos\theta\,\dfrac{d\psi}{dt}. \end{cases}$$

Before equations (1) and (2) can be solved, the moments M_1, M_2, and M_3 must be expressed in terms of the variables of the problem. Suppose the x-, y-, and z-axes, Fig. 4, are so chosen that the constant force to which the gyroscope is subject is parallel to the y-axis and that its direction and point of application are such that it tends to decrease the angle θ. Under these hypotheses the force tends to rotate the axis $O3$ about the line OP in the negative direction. Under the hypotheses that have been made, it easily follows that

$$(3) \quad \begin{cases} M_1 = -mA_1 \sin\theta \cos\phi \\ \qquad\qquad (m > 0), \\ M_2 = +mA_1 \sin\theta \sin\phi, \\ M_3 = 0, \end{cases}$$

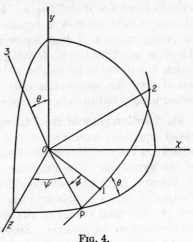

Fig. 4.

where m is a constant that depends upon the magnitude of the exterior force. The factor A_1 is taken out in the right member for later convenience, and its removal, of course, has an effect upon the definition and the magnitude of the constant coefficient m.

On making use of the fact that $A_1 = A_2$ and equations (3), the differential equations (1) become

$$(4) \quad \begin{cases} \dfrac{d\omega_1}{dt} - (1-\lambda)a_3\,\omega_2 = -m \sin\theta \cos\phi, \\[2mm] \dfrac{d\omega_2}{dt} + (1-\lambda)a_3\,\omega_1 = +m \sin\theta \sin\phi, \\[2mm] \omega_3 = a_3, \\[2mm] \lambda = \dfrac{A_3}{A_1}, \end{cases}$$

where a_3 is a constant. In the ordinary gyroscope $\lambda > 1$, but this is not an important condition.

Equations (2) and (4) constitute a set of five simultaneous differential equations, the two groups being mutually related because each involves the dependent variables of the other. The solution of these equations constitutes the solution of the problem.

If the first of equations (2) is divided by sin θ, the system (2) and (4) is in the normal form. The right members are independent of the variable t and are analytic functions of the dependent variables in the neighborhood of all finite initial values except $\theta = 0$ and $\theta = \pi$. Hence it follows from Chapter II that, if θ_0 is not 0 or π, equations (2) and (4) can be solved as power series in t that converge for $|t|$ sufficiently small. There is no difficulty in deriving the first few terms of these series, but it would be nearly useless to develop them, for they would give the coördinates only for small values of $|t|$ and would utterly fail to indicate general properties of the motion.

91. Two Integrals of the Differential Equations. The differential equations have two simple integrals that are useful in separating the variables and deriving the properties of the motion of the gyroscope. The existence of these integrals can easily be inferred from physical considerations. Since there are no dissipative forces in the problem as defined by equations (2) and (4), the total energy of the system is constant, a fact that is expressed by an integral. Since the exterior force is parallel to the y-axis, the moment of momentum about the y-axis is constant, a fact that is expressed by another integral. These integrals, however, will be derived directly from the differential equations.

It follows from the first two of equations (4) and the second of equations (2) that

$$\omega_1 \frac{d\omega_1}{dt} + \omega_2 \frac{d\omega_2}{dt} = - m \sin \theta(\omega_1 \cos \phi - \omega_2 \sin \phi)$$
$$= - m \sin \theta \frac{d\theta}{dt}.$$

The integral of this equation is

$$(5) \qquad \omega_1^2 + \omega_2^2 - 2m \cos \theta = c_1,$$

where c_1 is a constant that depends upon the initial values of the dependent variables.

As a consequence of equations (2), equation (5) becomes

$$(6) \qquad \sin^2 \theta \left(\frac{d\psi}{dt}\right)^2 + \left(\frac{d\theta}{dt}\right)^2 - 2m \cos \theta = c_1.$$

This is the integral which expresses the fact that the sum of the kinetic and potential energies of the system is constant.

On eliminating the derivatives from equation (6) by means of equations (2) and (4), it is found that the equation

$$\sin \theta \left(\sin \phi \frac{d\omega_1}{dt} + \cos \phi \frac{d\omega_2}{dt} \right) + \cos \theta (\omega_1 \sin \phi + \omega_2 \cos \phi) \frac{d\theta}{dt}$$

$$- a_3\lambda \sin \theta \frac{d\theta}{dt} + \sin \theta (\omega_1 \cos \phi - \omega_2 \sin \phi) \frac{d\phi}{dt} = 0$$

is identically satisfied. The integral of this equation is

$$\sin \theta (\omega_1 \sin \phi + \omega_2 \cos \phi) + a_3\lambda \cos \theta = c_2,$$

which becomes as a consequence of the first of equations (2)

$$(7) \qquad \sin^2 \theta \frac{d\psi}{dt} + a_3\lambda \cos \theta = c_2,$$

where c_2 is a constant that depends upon the initial values of the dependent variables. Equation (7), or the equation from which it is derived, expresses the fact that the sum of the projections upon the y-axis of the moments of momentum about the axes $O1$, $O2$, and $O3$ is a constant.

92. Differential Equation in θ and t Alone. The integrals given in equations (6) and (7) involve only the dependent variables θ and ψ. On eliminating $d\psi/dt$ between them, it is found that

$$\sin^2 \theta \left(\frac{d\theta}{dt} \right)^2 = - 2m \cos^3 \theta - (c_1 + a_3{}^2\lambda^2) \cos^2 \theta$$
$$+ 2(c_2 a_3\lambda + m) \cos \theta + (c_1 - c_2{}^2)$$
$$= F(\cos \theta).$$

On letting $u = \cos \theta$, this equation is transformed into the equivalent equation

$$(8) \quad \begin{cases} \left(\dfrac{du}{dt} \right)^2 = - 2mu^3 - (c_1 + a_3{}^2\lambda^2)u^2 + 2(c_2 a_3\lambda + m)u \\ \qquad\qquad\qquad\qquad\qquad + (c_1 - c_2{}^2) \\ = F(u) = - 2m(u - u_1)(u - u_2)(u - u_3), \end{cases}$$

where u_1, u_2, and u_3 are the roots of the equation $F(u) = 0$. For notation, let u_0 represent the initial value of u and $u_i = \cos \theta_i$.

It follows from the right member of equation (8) and the fact that du/dt is real that

$$\begin{cases} F(-\infty) = +\infty, & F(+1) = -(c_2 - a_3\lambda)^2 \leqq 0, \\ F(-1) = -(c_2 + a_3\lambda)^2 \leqq 0, & F(+\infty) = -\infty. \\ F(u_0) \geqq 0, \end{cases}$$

Therefore the three roots u_1, u_2, and u_3 are real and the curve $F = F(u)$ has the characteristics indicated in Fig. 5.

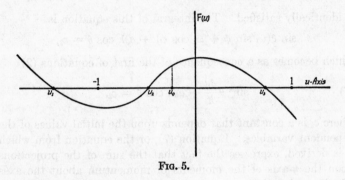

FIG. 5.

It follows from equation (8) that u satisfies the equation

$$(9) \quad \begin{cases} \dfrac{du}{dt} = \sqrt{F(u)}, \\ \dfrac{d^2u}{dt^2} = \dfrac{1}{2}\dfrac{\partial F}{\partial u} = -3mu^2 - (c_1 + a_3{}^2\lambda^2)u + (c_2 a_3\lambda + m). \end{cases}$$

These equations have the general properties of those discussed in Art. 70. Therefore u varies periodically between u_2 and u_3 in the period defined by the equation

$$(10) \quad P = \frac{2}{\sqrt{2m}} \int_{u_2}^{u_3} \frac{du}{\sqrt{-(u - u_1)(u - u_2)(u - u_3)}},$$

which is finite unless two of the three roots are equal. If $u_1 = u_2$, the value of u approaches u_2 asymptotically as t approaches infinity. If $u_2 = u_0 = u_3$, u has the constant value u_0.

In order to throw the integral (10) into Legendre's normal form of Art. 67, a linear transformation will be made such that u_1, u_2, and u_3 shall correspond to $-1/k$, -1, and $+1$ respectively, where k is as yet an undetermined constant. A transformation having the required properties is

$$(11) \quad \frac{u_2 - u_1}{u_3 - u_1} \frac{u_3 - u}{u_2 - u} = \frac{1 - k}{1 + k} \frac{v - 1}{v + 1},$$

where the new variable is v. The arbitrary k will be determined so that $u = \infty$ shall correspond to $v = 1/k$. The condition is

$$(12) \quad \begin{cases} \dfrac{(1 - k)^2}{(1 + k)^2} = \dfrac{u_2 - u_1}{u_3 - u_1} = C \leqq 1, \\[2ex] k = -\dfrac{\sqrt{C} - 1}{\sqrt{C} + 1}, \qquad k = -\dfrac{\sqrt{C} + 1}{\sqrt{C} - 1}. \end{cases}$$

The former of these two values of k will be used because it is numerically less than unity.

It follows from equation (11) that

$$(13) \quad u = \frac{[(1 - k)u_3 + (1 + k)u_2] + [(1 - k)u_3 - (1 + k)u_2]v}{2(1 - kv)},$$

by means of which the integral (10) becomes

$$(14) \quad \begin{cases} P = \dfrac{2(1 + k)}{\sqrt{2m(u_3 - u_1)}} \displaystyle\int_{-1}^{+1} \dfrac{dv}{\sqrt{(1 - v^2)(1 - k^2 v^2)}} \\[2ex] \quad = \dfrac{2\pi(1 + k)}{\sqrt{2m(u_3 - u_1)}} \left[1 + \left(\dfrac{1}{2}\right)^2 k^2 + \left(\dfrac{1 \cdot 3}{2 \cdot 4}\right)^2 k^4 + \cdots \right] \\[2ex] \quad = \dfrac{2\pi(1 + k)}{\sqrt{2m(u_3 - u_1)}} Q(k^2). \end{cases}$$

If the dependent variable is changed from u to v by equation (11) or its equivalent (13), and if the independent variable is changed from t to τ by the transformation

$$(15) \quad t - t_0 = \frac{(1 + k)Q(k^2)\tau}{\sqrt{2m(u_3 - u_1)}},$$

the differential equations (9) become

$$(16) \quad \begin{cases} \dfrac{dv}{d\tau} = Q(k^2)\sqrt{(1 - v^2)(1 - k^2 v^2)}, \\[2ex] \dfrac{d^2 v}{d\tau^2} = Q^2(k^2)\left[-(1 + k^2)v + 2k^2 v^3 \right]. \end{cases}$$

These differential equations were completely solved in Chap. VIII. Equation (7) becomes in the same notation

$$(17) \qquad \frac{d\psi}{dt} = \frac{c_2 - a_3\lambda u}{1 - u^2},$$

which is reduced to a quadrature after equations (16) have been solved.

93. Completion of the Solution of Equations (2) and (4). Since θ and ψ are now expressed in terms of t, equations (2) give

$$(18) \qquad \begin{cases} \phi = a_3 t - \displaystyle\int_0^t u \, \frac{d\psi}{dt} \, dt, \\[2mm] \omega_1 = \sin \phi \sqrt{1 - u^2} \dfrac{d\psi}{dt} + \cos \phi \dfrac{d\theta}{dt}, \\[2mm] \omega_2 = \cos \phi \sqrt{1 - u^2} \dfrac{d\psi}{dt} - \sin \phi \dfrac{d\theta}{dt}. \end{cases}$$

It follows from equations (17) and (18) that the variables have the properties indicated in the equations

$$(19) \qquad \begin{cases} \phi = At + \text{terms of period } P, \\[2mm] \omega_1 = \displaystyle\sum_{j=-\infty}^{+\infty} B_j \sin \left(A + j\frac{2\pi}{P} \right) t + \sum_{j=-\infty}^{+\infty} C_j \cos \left(A + j\frac{2\pi}{P} \right) t, \\[2mm] \omega_2 = \displaystyle\sum_{j=-\infty}^{+\infty} B_j \cos \left(A + j\frac{2\pi}{P} \right) t - \sum_{j=-\infty}^{\infty} C_j \sin \left(A + j\frac{2\pi}{P} \right) t, \end{cases}$$

where A and the B_j and C_j are constants. There is no difficulty except considerable labor in developing the detailed expressions for the right members of equations (19).

94. Some Properties of the Motion of the Gyroscope. The variable θ, which is the angle between the axis of rotation of the gyroscope and a vertical line through its center of gravity, varies periodically between θ_1 and θ_2 in the period P. The limits θ_1 and θ_2, which correspond to u_1 and u_2, are determined by the initial conditions that define the constants c_1 and c_2. Conversely, the constants c_1, c_2, and u_1 are defined if u_2 and u_3 are given. In discussing the properties of the motion of the gyroscope, it is advantageous to regard u_2 and u_3 as given, and to express c_1, c_2, and u_1 in terms of them.

It follows from equation (8) that the u_i satisfy the equations

(20)
$$\begin{cases} u_1 + u_2 + u_3 = -\dfrac{c_1 + a_3{}^2\lambda^2}{2m}, \\[2mm] u_1 u_2 + u_2 u_3 + u_3 u_1 = -\dfrac{c_2 a_3 \lambda + m}{m}, \\[2mm] u_1 u_2 u_3 = \dfrac{c_1 - c_2{}^2}{2m}. \end{cases}$$

The solution of these equations for u_1, c_1, and c_2 in terms of u_2 and u_3 is

(21)
$$\begin{cases} u_1 = -\dfrac{(1 + u_2 u_3)}{u_2 + u_3} - \dfrac{(1 + u_2 u_3)a_3{}^2\lambda^2}{(u_2 + u_3)^2 m} \\[3mm] \qquad \pm \dfrac{a_3{}^2\lambda^2 \sqrt{(1 - u_2{}^2)(1 - u_3{}^2)}\sqrt{1 + S}}{(u_2 + u_3)^2 m}, \\[3mm] c_1 = -a_3{}^2\lambda^2 - 2(u_1 + u_2 + u_3)m, \\[3mm] c_2 = \dfrac{(1 + u_2 u_3)}{u_2 + u_3} a_3 \lambda \pm a_3 \lambda \dfrac{\sqrt{(1 - u_2{}^2)(1 - u_3{}^2)}\sqrt{1 + S}}{u_2 + u_3}, \\[3mm] S = \dfrac{2(u_2 + u_3)m}{a_3{}^2\lambda^2}. \end{cases}$$

The rate of change of the variable ψ is given by equation (17). It follows from the third of equations (21) that, when $u = u_2$,

(22)
$$\frac{d\psi}{dt} = \frac{a_3\lambda}{u_2 + u_3}\left\{1 \pm \sqrt{\frac{1 - u_3{}^2}{1 - u_2{}^2}}\sqrt{1 + S}\right\};$$

and that, when $u = u_3$,

(23)
$$\frac{d\psi}{dt} = \frac{a_3\lambda}{u_2 + u_3}\left\{1 \pm \sqrt{\frac{1 - u_2{}^2}{1 - u_3{}^2}}\sqrt{1 + S}\right\}.$$

In the limiting case $u_2 = u_0 = u_3$, equations (22) and (23) become

(24)
$$\frac{d\psi}{dt} = \frac{a_3\lambda}{2u_0}[1 \pm \sqrt{1 + S}].$$

If the gyroscope spins rapidly, a_3 will be large and S will be small. In this case equation (24) becomes approximately

(25)
$$\begin{cases} \dfrac{d\psi}{dt} = \dfrac{a_3\lambda}{u_0} & \text{(for } + \sqrt{1 + S}\text{)}, \\[3mm] \dfrac{d\psi}{dt} = -\dfrac{a_3\lambda S}{4u_0} & \text{(for } - \sqrt{1 + S}\text{)}. \end{cases}$$

It follows from equations (21) to (25) that, for given values of u_2 and u_3, there are two cases depending upon the sign that belongs before the radicals. It will be supposed henceforth that $u_2 + u_3$ is positive. It follows from the last of equations (21) that S is positive in this case. For brevity, the case in which the axis of the gyroscope is inverted and $u_2 + u_3$ is negative will be omitted.

If the values of c_1 and c_2 are such that the positive sign before the radical belongs to the problem, the right members of equations (22) and (23) are both positive. Since $c_2 - a_3\lambda u_3 \leqq c_2 - a_3\lambda u$, it follows that in this case the right member of equation (17) is positive for all values of u. Therefore in this case the variable ψ continually increases.

If the values of c_1 and c_2 are such that the negative sign before the radical belongs to the problem, the right member of equation (22) is positive, zero, or negative according as

$$u_3{}^2 - u_2{}^2 \gtreqqless (1 - u_3{}^2)S.$$

The right member of equation (23) is negative.

Let Ψ represent the increase in the angle ψ in a period P. In the limiting case $u_2 = u_0 = u_3$ the parameter k, defined by equations (12), is zero and the period P, defined by equation (14), becomes

$$(26) \qquad P = \frac{2\pi}{\sqrt{2m(u_0 - u_1)}}.$$

Let the parameter m be eliminated by the last of equations (21) and consider the expression for P in the limiting case $S = 0$. On eliminating u_1 from equation (26) by the first of equations (21), it is found that for $\lim u_2 = u_0 = u_3$

$$(27) \qquad \begin{cases} P = \dfrac{2\pi u_0}{a_3\lambda} & (\lim + \sqrt{1 + S} = 1), \\[2ex] P = \dfrac{2\pi}{a_3\lambda} & (\lim - \sqrt{1 + S} = -1). \end{cases}$$

Since in these limiting cases $\Psi = P d\psi/dt$, it follows from equations (25) and (27) that for $\lim u_2 = u_0 = u_3$

$$(28) \qquad \begin{cases} \Psi = 2\pi & (\lim + \sqrt{1 + S} = 1), \\[1ex] \Psi = 0 & (\lim - \sqrt{1 + S} = -1). \end{cases}$$

In the former case, the axis of the gyroscope advances in longitude by 2π in the period P of its nutation; in the latter, it remains stationary. Consequently when u_2 and u_3 are both positive and not greatly different in value and S is small, the traces of the oscillations of the axis on the unit sphere are of the types indicated in Figs. 6–9. The case in which the positive sign belongs before the radical is illustrated in Fig. 6; the case in which the negative sign belongs before the radical and in which the right member of equation (17) is always negative is shown in Fig. 7. A

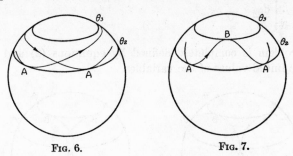

FIG. 6.   FIG. 7.

transition stage is shown in Fig. 8 in which the right member of equation (17) is zero for $u = u_2$. Finally, the case in which the right member of equation (17) is positive for $u = u_2$ and zero for some value of u between u_2 and u_3 is shown in Fig. 9.

It is clear from this description that the axis of the gyroscope undergoes a nutation between u_2 and u_3, or between the corresponding angular variables θ_2 and θ_3, in the period P, while it advances or regresses in longitude around the vertical axis. The oscillations of θ are much more complicated than a simple sine wave unless k is very small. The change in ψ consists of a constant advance or regression on which is superposed complicated oscillations in the period P. The characteristics of the variations in ϕ, ω_1, and ω_2 are easily found from equations (19).

95. The Differential Equations for Damped Motion. Equations (1) and (2) are completely general; in developing them explicitly by means of equations (3) the damping forces were neglected. Since it was assumed in Art. 90 that the damping forces are proportional to the angular velocity ω of the axis of the gyroscope and opposed to its direction of motion, it follows that their moments about the axes $O1$ and $O2$ are proportional to ω_1 and ω_2 respectively. On letting μ represent the factor of proportionality, the explicit expressions for equations (1), including the damping forces, are

$$(29) \quad \begin{cases} \dfrac{d\omega_1}{dt} - (1 - \lambda)a_3\,\omega_2 = -\,m\sin\theta\cos\phi - \mu\omega_1, \\[2mm] \dfrac{d\omega_2}{dt} + (1 - \lambda)a_3\,\omega_1 = +\,m\sin\theta\sin\phi - \mu\omega_2, \\[2mm] \dfrac{d\omega_3}{dt} = 0. \end{cases}$$

The problem is completely defined by equations (2) and (29) and the initial values of the variables.

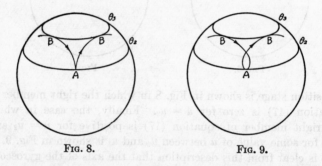

Fig. 8. Fig. 9.

96. Choice of Method of Solving Equations (2) and (29).

The problem is to determine the effects of the damping terms $-\mu\omega_1$ and $-\mu\omega_2$ upon the motion of the gyroscope. Its solution is to be obtained by treating the systems of differential equations (2) and (29).

Equations (2) and (29) can be solved as power series in t, but the results would not give any of the desired properties of the motion of the gyroscope, even in the case $\mu = 0$. They can also be solved as power series in the parameter μ. The first terms of this solution will be the solution worked out in Arts. 92 and 93.. The terms of the first degree in μ define the first approximations of the variations in ω_1, ω_2, θ, ϕ, and ψ due to the damping forces. The differential equations by which they are determined are linear with coefficients which are functions of t (compare

Art. 27), and serious practical difficulties are encountered in solving them. Moreover, the general nature of the effects of the damping forces is not easily inferred from the results.

The most important question is that of the effects of the damping forces upon the limits θ_2 and θ_3 of the nutation of the axis of the gyroscope. It is particularly important to learn whether or not the damping forces gradually bring the axis of rotation of the gyroscope toward coincidence with the vertical axis. This suggests transforming to the dependent variables θ_1, θ_2, θ_3 by the methods of Chapter IV.

In this problem the methods of Chapter IV can be advantageously modified so as to reduce the number of dependent variables. It follows from equations (29) that

$$\omega_1 \frac{d\omega_1}{dt} + \omega_2 \frac{d\omega_2}{dt} = - m \sin \theta (\omega_1 \cos \phi - \omega_2 \sin \phi) - \mu(\omega_1^2 + \omega_2^2),$$

which, as a consequence of equations (2), becomes

$$(30) \quad \frac{d}{dt}\left[\sin^2 \theta \left(\frac{d\psi}{dt}\right)^2 + \left(\frac{d\theta}{dt}\right)^2 \right] + 2m \sin \theta \frac{d\theta}{dt}$$
$$= - 2\mu \left[\sin^2 \theta \left(\frac{d\psi}{dt}\right)^2 + \left(\frac{d\theta}{dt}\right)^2 \right].$$

It is also found from equations (29) that

$$\sin \theta \left[\sin \phi \frac{d\omega_1}{dt} + \cos \phi \frac{d\omega_2}{dt} \right] + \cos \theta [\omega_1 \sin \phi + \omega_2 \cos \phi] \frac{d\theta}{dt}$$
$$- a_3 \lambda \sin \theta \frac{d\theta}{dt} + \sin \theta [\omega_1 \cos \phi - \omega_2 \sin \phi] \frac{d\phi}{dt}$$
$$= - \mu \sin \theta [\omega_1 \sin \phi + \omega_2 \cos \phi],$$

which, as a consequence of equations (2), becomes

$$(31) \quad \frac{d}{dt}\left[\sin^2 \theta \frac{d\psi}{dt} + a_3 \lambda \cos \theta \right] = - \mu \sin^2 \theta \frac{d\psi}{dt}.$$

Equations (30) and (31) involve only the dependent variables θ, $d\theta/dt$, and $d\psi/dt$. On letting $u = \cos \theta$, $\dot{u} = du/dt$, and $\dot{\psi} = d\psi/dt$, these equations may be replaced by the equivalent system of differential equations

$$(32) \quad \begin{cases} \dfrac{du}{dt} - \dot{u} = 0, \\[2mm] \dfrac{d\dot{u}}{dt} + u(1 - u^2)\dot{\psi}^2 - a_3\lambda(1 - u^2)\dot{\psi}^2 + \dfrac{u}{1 - u^2}\dot{u}^2 \\[2mm] \hspace{5cm} - m(1 - u^2) = -\mu\dot{u}, \\[2mm] \dfrac{d\dot{\psi}}{dt} + \dfrac{(a_3\lambda - 2u\dot{\psi}^2)}{1 - u^2}\dot{u} = -\mu\dot{\psi}, \end{cases}$$

in which the dependent variables are u, $\dot{u}$, and $\dot{\psi}$.

The solution of equations (32) for $\mu = 0$ is equivalent to the solution outlined in Art. 92, and it will therefore be regarded as known. Let it be written in the form

$$(33) \quad \begin{cases} u = f_1(a_1, a_2, a_3; t), \\ \dot{u} = f_2(a_1, a_2, a_3; t), \\ \dot{\psi} = f_3(a_1, a_2, a_3; t), \end{cases}$$

where a_1, a_2, and a_3 are the initial values of u, $\dot{u}$, and $\dot{\psi}$. The initial values of these dependent variables are uniquely defined by u_1, u_2, u_3, the roots of the cubic equation (8), and conversely. Therefore equations (33) can be written in the equivalent form

$$(34) \quad \begin{cases} u = \phi_1(u_1, u_2, u_3; t), \\ \dot{u} = \phi_2(u_1, u_2, u_3; t), \\ \dot{\psi} = \phi_3(u_1, u_2, u_3; t). \end{cases}$$

These equations can be used to transform the differential equations (32) from the dependent variables u, $\dot{u}$, and $\dot{\psi}$ to the new dependent variables u_1, u_2, u_3 by a direct application of the methods of Chapter IV. But in order to avoid lengthy transformations and reductions it is better to proceed somewhat indirectly.

97. Transformation of Equations (32). It follows from equations (30) and (31) that

$$(35) \quad \begin{cases} \sin^2\theta \left(\dfrac{d\psi}{dt}\right)^2 + \left(\dfrac{d\theta}{dt}\right)^2 - 2m\cos\theta = p_1, \\[2mm] \sin^2\theta \, \dfrac{d\psi}{dt} + a_3\lambda\cos\theta = p_2, \end{cases}$$

where, instead of being constants, p_1 and p_2 are functions of the independent variable t and are defined by the equations

$$(36) \quad \begin{cases} p_1 = c_1 - 2\mu \int_{t_0}^{t} \left[\sin^2 \theta \left(\frac{d\psi}{dt} \right)^2 + \left(\frac{d\theta}{dt} \right)^2 \right] dt, \\ p_2 = c_2 - \mu \int_{t_0}^{t} \left[\sin^2 \theta \frac{d\psi}{dt} \right] dt. \end{cases}$$

The result of eliminating $d\psi/dt$ between equations (35) and letting $\cos \theta = u$ is the equation

$$(37) \quad \left(\frac{du}{dt} \right)^2 = F(u) = - 2mu^3 - (p_1 + a_3{}^2\lambda^2)u^2 \\ + 2(p_2a_3\lambda + m)u + (p_1 - p_2{}^2),$$

which is analogous to equation (8).

It should be kept in mind that p_1 and p_2 are unknown variables and that they cannot be exactly determined until the problem of determining θ and $\dot{\psi}$ has been solved. In case μ is small relative to m, as would be true in a physical problem, p_1 and p_2 vary only slowly from c_1 and c_2 respectively.

It follows from the geometrical meanings of the variables that, whether p_1 and p_2 are constants or variables, the axis of the gyroscope attains a turning point in its nutation when $F(u) = 0$ for any value of u between -1 and $+1$. If $\mu = 0$ so that p_1 and p_2 are constants, the turning points are for fixed values of u, namely, u_2 and u_3, as was shown in Arts. 92–94. If p_1 and p_2 are variables, the values of u_2 and u_3 for the turning points are variables.

Equations (34), if worked out explicitly, would be precisely of the forms of the corresponding equations developed in Arts. 92–94 for the case in which u_1, u_2, and u_3 are constants. This means that the axis of the gyroscope is regarded as moving at every instant in a curve of the type illustrated in Figs. 6–9, but in one whose defining parameters, namely, p_1 and p_2, continually change. This is precisely the conception that was explained in Chapter IV. Consequently, if u_2 represents one of the limits taken by u, it satisfies the equation

$$(38) \quad F(u_2) = - 2mu_2{}^3 - (p_1 + a_3{}^2\lambda^2)u_2{}^2 \\ + 2(p_2a_3\lambda + m)u_2 + (p_1 - p_2{}^2) = 0,$$

with p_1 and p_2 variables. For certain values of t, the variable u_2 satisfies equation (38); for other values of t, equation (38) defines the value of u_2 that corresponds to a limit of the fixed curve that the axis is moving in at the instant. In this sense u_2, a variable, satisfies equation (38) for all values of t.

Since u_2 varies only because p_1 and p_2 vary, it follows that

$$(39) \qquad \frac{du_2}{dt} = \frac{\partial u_2}{\partial p_1}\frac{dp_1}{dt} + \frac{\partial u_2}{\partial p_2}\frac{dp_2}{dt}.$$

It follows from equations (35), (36), and (37) that

$$(40) \qquad \begin{cases} \dfrac{dp_1}{dt} = -2\mu\left[(1-u^2)\dot\psi^2 + \dfrac{\dot u^2}{1-u^2}\right] \\[2mm] \qquad = \dfrac{-2\mu}{1-u^2}\left[(p_2 - a_3\lambda u)^2 + F(u)\right], \\[3mm] \dfrac{dp_2}{dt} = -\mu(1-u^2)\dot\psi = -\mu(p_2 - a_3\lambda u). \end{cases}$$

Since the roots of $F(u) = 0$ are u_1, u_2, and u_3, it follows from equation (37) that

$$(41) \qquad \begin{cases} u_1 + u_2 + u_3 = -\dfrac{p_1 + a_3{}^2\lambda^2}{2m}, \\[2mm] u_1 u_2 + u_2 u_3 + u_3 u_1 = -\dfrac{p_2 a_3 \lambda + m}{m} \\[2mm] u_1 u_2 u_3 = \dfrac{p_1 - p_2{}^2}{2m}. \end{cases}$$

On using these equations to reduce the partial derivatives of u_2 with respect to p_1 and p_2, formed from equation (38), it is found that

$$(42) \qquad \begin{cases} \dfrac{\partial u_2}{\partial p_1} = \dfrac{1-u^2}{2m(u_3 - u_2)(u_1 - u_2)}, \\[3mm] \dfrac{\partial u_2}{\partial p_2} = \dfrac{-(p_2 - a_3\lambda u_2)}{m(u_3 - u_2)(u_1 - u_2)}. \end{cases}$$

Therefore equation (39) becomes after some reductions

$$(43) \qquad \frac{du_2}{dt} = \frac{\mu(1-u^2)[(p_2 - a_3\lambda u)^2 + F(u)]}{m(1-u^2)(u_3 - u_2)(u_2 - u_1)}$$
$$- \frac{\mu(p_2 - a_3\lambda u_2)(p_2 - a_3\lambda u)}{m(u_3 - u_2)(u_2 - u_1)}.$$

Since $F(u)$ and the right member of equation (43) vanish for

$u = u_2$, it follows that the right member of equation (43) contains the factor $u - u_2$. On making use of equations (37) and (38), it is found that

$$(44) \begin{cases} \dfrac{(p_2 - a_3\lambda u)^2 + F(u)}{1 - u^2} = p_1 + 2mu, \\[2mm] (p_2 - a_3\lambda u_2)(p_2 - a_3\lambda u) = p_2{}^2 - p_2 a_3\lambda u_2 - p_2 a_3\lambda u + a_3{}^2\lambda^2 u u_2 \\[1mm] \qquad\qquad\qquad = (p_1 + 2mu_2)(1 - u_2{}^2) \\[1mm] \qquad\qquad\qquad\quad - a_3\lambda(p_2 - a_3\lambda u_2)(u - u_2). \end{cases}$$

Therefore equation (43) becomes

$$(45) \qquad \frac{du_2}{dt} = \frac{\mu[a_3\lambda(p_2 - a_3\lambda u_2) + 2m(1 - u_2{}^2)](u - u_2)}{m(u_3 - u_2)(u_2 - u_1)}.$$

A final step remains to complete the reduction of equation (45) to the desired form. It follows from equations (20) that

$$\begin{cases} a_3\lambda(p_2 - a_3\lambda u_2) = \dfrac{a_3{}^2\lambda^2(1 - u_2{}^2)}{u_2 + u_3}\left[1 \pm \dfrac{\sqrt{1 - u_3{}^2}}{\sqrt{1 - u_2{}^2}}\sqrt{1 + S}\right], \\[4mm] 2m(1 - u_2{}^2) = \dfrac{a_3{}^2\lambda^2(1 - u_2{}^2)S}{u_2 + u_3}. \end{cases}$$

On substituting these expressions into the right member of equation (45) and writing the corresponding expression for du_3/dt by permuting u_2 and u_3, the final result is found to be

$$(46) \begin{cases} \dfrac{du_2}{dt} = \dfrac{\mu a_3{}^2\lambda^2(1 - u_2{}^2)\sqrt{1 + S}\left[\sqrt{1 + S} \pm \sqrt{\dfrac{1 - u_3{}^2}{1 - u_2{}^2}}\right](u - u_2)}{m(u_2 + u_3)(u_3 - u_2)(u_2 - u_1)} \\[6mm] \dfrac{du_3}{dt} = \dfrac{\mu a_3{}^2\lambda^2(1 - u_3{}^2)\sqrt{1 + S}\left[\sqrt{1 + S} \pm \sqrt{\dfrac{1 - u_2{}^2}{1 - u_3{}^2}}\right](u_3 - u)}{m(u_2 + u_3)(u_3 - u_2)(u_3 - u_1)}. \end{cases}$$

The upper sign belongs before the radicals in case of oscillations of the type illustrated in Fig. 6, and the lower sign for the types illustrated in Figs. 7–9.

The problem immediately under discussion has been the transformation of the differential equations (32) by means of equations (34) from the original dependent variables u, $\dot{u}$, and $\dot{\psi}$

to the new dependent variables u_1, u_2, and u_3. Two of the desired equations are equations (46). The third for du_1/dt could easily be derived, but it will not be required. The variable u is expressed in terms of the independent variable t and of the new dependent variables u_1, u_2, and u_3 by means of the solution of the second of equations (16) and the transformation (13). If this transformation were made, equations (46) would be expressed explicitly in terms of the independent and the dependent variables.

98. Solution of Equations (46). The complete system of differential equations corresponding to equations (46) may be written in the form

$$(47) \quad \begin{cases} \dfrac{du_1}{dt} = \dfrac{\mu}{m}\, f_1(u_1,\, u_2,\, u_3;\, t), \\[2mm] \dfrac{du_2}{dt} = \dfrac{\mu}{m}\, f_2(u_1,\, u_2,\, u_3;\, t), \\[2mm] \dfrac{du_3}{dt} = \dfrac{\mu}{m}\, f_3(u_1,\, u_2,\, u_3;\, t). \end{cases}$$

These differential equations are of the type of those that were treated in Arts. 23–26. In practice the parameter μ/m will be a small number. Therefore the solution of equations (47) can advantageously be expanded as power series μ/m of the form

$$(48) \quad \begin{cases} u_1 = u_1{}^{(0)} + u_1{}^{(1)}(t)\,\dfrac{\mu}{m} + u_1{}^{(2)}(t)\left(\dfrac{\mu}{m}\right)^2 + \cdots, \\[2mm] u_2 = u_2{}^{(0)} + u_2{}^{(1)}(t)\,\dfrac{\mu}{m} + u_2{}^{(2)}(t)\left(\dfrac{\mu}{m}\right)^2 + \cdots, \\[2mm] u_3 = u_3{}^{(0)} + u_3{}^{(1)}(t)\,\dfrac{\mu}{m} + u_3{}^{(2)}(t)\left(\dfrac{\mu}{m}\right)^2 + \cdots. \end{cases}$$

It follows from Art. 24 that the first terms of the right members of these equations are the initial values of u_1, u_2, and u_3 respectively. The succeeding terms determine the variations in u_1, u_2, and u_3 due to the damping forces whose magnitudes are measured by the parameter μ. In case μ/m is small, the terms beyond the first degree in μ/m will be inappreciable.

The terms of the first degree in μ/m are defined by the definite integrals (compare Art. 24)

$$(49) \quad \begin{cases} u_1{}^{(1)} = \int_{t_0}^{t} f_1(u_1{}^{(0)},\, u_2{}^{(0)},\, u_3{}^{(0)};\, t)dt, \\[2mm] u_2{}^{(1)} = \int_{t_0}^{t} f_2(u_1{}^{(0)},\, u_2{}^{(0)},\, u_3{}^{(0)};\, t)dt, \\[2mm] u_3{}^{(1)} = \int_{t_0}^{t} f_3(u_1{}^{(0)},\, u_2{}^{(0)},\, u_3{}^{(0)};\, t)dt. \end{cases}$$

Since these three equations are mutually independent, each may be solved regardless of the others. For this reason the terms of the first degree in μ of the solution of equations (46) can be obtained without deriving the first equation of the set.

In order to form the integrals of (46) corresponding to the second and third equations of (49), it is advisable to express the variable u in terms of the variable v by means of equation (13). It is found after some reductions that

$$(50) \quad \begin{cases} u - u_2 = \dfrac{(u_3 - u_2)(1 - k)(1 + v)}{2(1 - kv)}, \\[3mm] u_3 - u = \dfrac{(u_3 - u_2)(1 + k)(1 - v)}{2(1 - kv)}. \end{cases}$$

It is also advisable to transform from the independent variable t to the independent variable v by the first of equations (16). As a consequence of these transformations, equations (46) become after some reductions

$$(51) \quad \begin{cases} \dfrac{du_2}{dv} = \dfrac{\mu}{m} M_1 \dfrac{1 + v}{(1 - kv)\sqrt{(1 - v^2)(1 - k^2v^2)}}, \\[3mm] \dfrac{du_3}{dv} = \dfrac{\mu}{m} M_2 \dfrac{1 - v}{(1 - kv)\sqrt{(1 - v^2)(1 - k^2v^2)}}, \end{cases}$$

where

$$(52) \quad \begin{cases} M_1 = \dfrac{(1 - k^2)a_3{}^2\lambda^2(1 - u_2{}^2)\sqrt{1 + S}\left[\sqrt{1 + S} \pm \sqrt{\dfrac{1 - u_3{}^2}{1 - u_2{}^2}}\right]}{2\sqrt{2}m(u_3 - u_1)(u_2 + u_3)(u_2 - u_1)}, \\[6mm] M_2 = \dfrac{(1 - k^2)a_3{}^2\lambda^2(1 - u_3{}^2)\sqrt{1 + S}\left[\sqrt{1 + S} \pm \sqrt{\dfrac{1 - u_2{}^2}{1 - u_3{}^2}}\right]}{2\sqrt{2}m(u_3 - u_2)(u_2 + u_3)(u_3 - u_1)}. \end{cases}$$

The first terms of the solution of equations (51) as power series in μ/m are

$$(53) \quad \begin{cases} u_2^{(1)} = M_1^{(0)} \int_{v_0}^v \frac{(1+v)dv}{(1-kv)\sqrt{(1-v^2)(1-k^2v^2)}}, \\ u_3^{(1)} = M_2^{(0)} \int_{v_0}^v \frac{(1-v)dv}{(1-kv)\sqrt{(1-v^2)(1-k^2v^2)}}, \end{cases}$$

where $M_1^{(0)}$ and $M_2^{(0)}$ are the values of M_1 and M_2 respectively when $u_1 = u_1^{(0)}$, $u_2 = u_2^{(0)}$, $u_3 = u_3^{(0)}$.

The integrals in the right members of equations (53) are easily expressible in terms of Legendre's normal forms of elliptic integrals and of more elementary integrals. In the physical problem, $u_3 - u_2$ will be small relative to unity, and it follows from equations (12) that k will be small. For simplicity consider the limiting case $k = 0$, in which equations (53) become

$$(54) \quad \begin{cases} u_2^{(1)} = M_1^{(0)} \int_{v_0}^v \sqrt{\frac{1+v}{1-v}}\, dv \\ \qquad = -M_1^{(0)} \left[\sqrt{1-v^2} + 2\sin^{-1}\sqrt{\frac{1-v}{2}} \right]_{v_0}^v, \\ u_3^{(1)} = M_2^{(0)} \int_{v_0}^v \sqrt{\frac{1-v}{1+v}}\, dv \\ \qquad = +M_2^{(0)} \left[\sqrt{1-v^2} + 2\sin^{-1}\sqrt{\frac{1+v}{2}} \right]_{v_0}^v. \end{cases}$$

The quantities of chief interest in the physical problem are the variations δu_2 and δu_3 in u_2 and u_3 while u undergoes a complete oscillation from u_2 to u_3 and return in the period P. It follows from equation (11) that the corresponding limits for v are -1 and $+1$ respectively. Since $\delta u_2 = u_2^{(1)}\mu/m$, $\delta u_3 = u_3^{(1)}\mu/m$ approximately, it follows from equations (52) and (54) that

$$(55) \quad \begin{cases} \delta u_2 = \dfrac{\mu \pi a_3^2 \lambda^2 (1 - u_2^2)\sqrt{1+S}\left[\sqrt{1+S} \pm \sqrt{\dfrac{1-u_3^2}{1-u_2^2}} \right]}{m\sqrt{2m(u_3-u_1)}(u_2+u_3)(u_2-u_1)}, \\[3ex] \delta u_3 = \dfrac{\mu \pi a_3^2 \lambda^2 (1 - u_3^2)\sqrt{1+S}\left[\sqrt{1+S} \pm \sqrt{\dfrac{1-u_2^2}{1-u_3^2}} \right]}{m\sqrt{2m(u_3-u_2)}(u_2+u_3)(u_3-u_1)}, \end{cases}$$

the superscript zero being omitted from u_1, u_2, and u_3 for the sake of simplicity. The solution of the problem with the approximation adopted is therefore

(56)
$$\begin{cases} u_2 = u_2^{(0)} + \delta u_2, \\ u_3 = u_3^{(0)} + \delta u_3. \end{cases}$$

99. Properties of the Solution. In case the oscillation of the axis of the gyroscope is of the type illustrated in Fig. 6, the upper sign in the right members of equations (55) belongs to the problem. In this case both δu_2 and δu_3 are positive and the limits of the oscillations of the axis both approach the pole that is vertically over the center of the gyroscope. Since $0 < u_2^2 < u_3^2$, it follows that $1 - u_3^2 < 1 - u_2^2$. Since u_2 and u_3 are both considerably larger than u_1, which is less than -1, $u_2 - u_1$ approximately equals $u_3 - u_1$, particularly if u_2 and u_3 are positive. Therefore equations (55) give approximately

(57)
$$\frac{\delta u_2}{\delta u_3} = \frac{1 \pm \sqrt{\dfrac{1 - u_2^2}{1 - u_3^2}} \sqrt{1 + S}}{1 \pm \sqrt{\dfrac{1 - u_3^2}{1 - u_2^2}} \sqrt{1 + S}}.$$

The right member of this equation is greater than unity in the case under consideration. Therefore u_2 increases more rapidly than u_3 and they both approach the value unity.

Now suppose that the oscillations of the axis of the gyroscope are of one of the types illustrated in Figs. 7–9, for which the lower signs in the right members of equations (55) belong to the problem. The right member of the first equation is positive. Therefore u_2 always increases.

The right member of the second of equations (55) may be positive, zero, or negative, according to the values of u_2, u_3, $a_3\lambda$, and m. In case it is positive, the oscillations of the axis are of the type illustrated in Figs. 6 and 7, and the limit u_3 of the oscillation increases. It follows from equation (57) that u_2 increases faster than u_3.

In case the oscillations of the axis of the gyroscope are of the type illustrated in Fig. 8, the right member of the second of equations (55) is zero and u_3 remains stationary until u_2 increases. Then the right member of the second of equations (55) is positive and u_3 increases, but more slowly than u_2.

In case the oscillations of the axis of the gyroscope are of the type illustrated in Fig. 9, the right member of the second of equations (55) is negative and u_3 diminishes. As u_3 decreases and u_2 increases, the right member of the second of equations (55) approaches zero, after which both u_2 and u_3 increase.

In all cases u_2 and u_3 approach equality. In this limiting case of $u_2 = u_3$ the right members of equations (55) are positive and equal whether the upper or the lower sign belongs to the problem. Therefore in all cases the nutations of the axis of the gyroscope diminish and the axis tends toward a stable vertical position.

The nature of the oscillations of a gyroscope could be determined only with great difficulty by any of the methods which have been used in solving the problems of preceding chapters. The labor of treating numerically many particular cases by those methods would be enormous. Nor could the problems solved in the preceding chapters be advantageously treated by the methods of this chapter. A suitable choice of a method for treating a problem in differential equations is of the highest importance.

X. QUESTIONS AND PROBLEMS

1. Derive the differential equations corresponding to equations (4) when the gyroscope is not supported at its center of gravity.

2. Do the integrals corresponding to those given in equations (6) and (7) exist in the case of Problem 1?

3. Derive the integral of equation (7) by writing the conditions that the sum of the projections on the $O\eta$-axis of the moments of momentum about the axes $O1$, $O2$, and $O3$ is a constant.

4. What was the reason for eliminating u_1, c_1, and c_2 from the problem by means of equations (20)?

5. Derive the expression for the kinetic energy of the gyroscope, in the case of damped oscillations, from equations (29). Prove from this expression that the kinetic energy continually decreases.

6. Write out equations (34) explicitly.

7. Reduce the integrals of the right members of equations (53) to Legendre's normal forms of elliptic integrals and simpler integrals.

8. In which type of oscillations is the damping of the oscillations the faster?

9. It has been assumed that the gyroscope is suspended above its center of gravity, and, therefore, that when u_2 and u_3 are positive the effect of gravity is to tend to decrease θ. How would the equations of the problem be changed if the gyroscope were suspended at a point below its center of gravity?

10. Examine the possibility of determining qualitatively the effect of the damping forces by solving the simultaneous system of equations (2) and (29) as power series in the parameter μ/m.

CHAPTER XI

THE METHOD OF SUCCESSIVE INTEGRATIONS

100. Properties of the Differential Equations. The method
that was developed in Chapter II is applicable only to differential
equations that are analytic in the independent and dependent
variables in the vicinity of their initial values. The method
that was developed in Chapter III is applicable only to differential
equations that are analytic in the dependent variables and at
least continuous in the independent variable. From the logical
point of view these are strong restrictions. The method of this
chapter is applicable to more general differential equations.

Let the differential equations be written in the usual form

$$(1) \qquad \begin{cases} \dfrac{dx_i}{dt} = f_i(x_j; t) & (i, j = 1, \cdots, n), \\ x_i(t_0) = a_i & (i = 1, \cdots, n). \end{cases}$$

For simplicity in the exposition, the variables x_i and t will be
assumed to be real. With suitable modifications the method is
applicable to the case in which the variables are complex.

The properties of the functions $f_i(x_j; t)$ are specified in a
closed region R for these variables which is defined by the
relations

$$(2) \qquad \begin{cases} -r_i \leqq x_i - a_i \leqq r_i & (i = 1, \cdots, n), \\ 0 \leqq t - t_0 \leqq \rho. \end{cases}$$

It should be stated that the upper and lower limits to the $x_i - a_i$
are taken equal only for simplicity in the subsequent work,
and that in particular problems $t - t_0$ might take negative as
well as positive values.

Property 1. The functions $f_i(x_j; t)$ are single-valued functions
of the x_j and t in the region R.

179

Property 2.   The functions $f_i(x_j; t)$ are continuous functions of t for every set of values of the x_j and t in the region R.

Property 3.   The functions $f_i(x_j; t)$ have the Lipschitz property in the x_j uniformly with respect to t for every set of values of the x_j and t in the region R.   That is, for every two sets of values of the x_j in the region R, which may be given the notations x_j' and x_j'', the $f_i(x_j; t)$ satisfy the relations

$$(3) \quad |f_i(x_j'; t) - f_i(x_j''; t)| \leqq A \sum_{j=1}^{n} |x_j' - x_j''| \quad (i = 1, \cdots, n),$$

where A is a finite constant which is independent of the x_j and t. There might be a different A_i associated with each $f_i(x_j; t)$, but there is no actual loss in generality, while there is a gain in simplicity, in taking for the common A the largest of the A_i.

There are several consequences of the properties of the $f_i(x_j; t)$ that should be noted.   By Property 2, the $f_i(x_j; t)$ are continuous functions of t alone for every set of values of the x_j and t in the region R.   It follows from the Lipschitz Property 3 that the $f_i(x_j; t)$ are continuous functions of the x_j, taken simultaneously, for every set of values of the x_j and t in the region R.   Moreover, since A is independent of t, this continuity in the x_j is *uniform* with respect to t.   Hence it follows (Appendix A, Corollary) that the $f_i(x_j; t)$ are continuous functions of the x_j and t simultaneously for every set of values of the x_j and t in the region R.   That is, the properties of the $f_i(x_j; t)$ imply that these functions are continuous functions of their arguments in the region R.   But the continuity of a function with respect to a set of variables does not imply that the function possesses the Lipschitz property with respect to the variables.   This negative conclusion follows from the example of a continuous function of one variable having a vertical point of inflection within the domain of continuity, because no finite A exists for which the Lipschitz relation holds for every pair of points in the neighborhood of such a point of inflection.

Since, by virtue of the hypotheses, the $f_i(x_j; t)$ are continuous functions of the x_j and t in the closed region R, it follows by Appendix A that the absolute values of these functions have a finite upper bound M in R.   There might be a different upper bound associated with each $f_i(x_j; t)$, but no real increase in generality would result in making use of the fact.

The Lipschitz property of a function with respect to a variable does not imply differentiability of the function with respect to the variable. This negative conclusion is established by the fact that even though

$$\frac{|f(x') - f(x'')|}{|x' - x''|} < A,$$

where A is a finite constant and x' and x'' take every pair of distinct values of x in the region R, still

$$\lim_{x'-x''=0} \frac{f(x') - f(x'')}{x' - x''}$$

need not exist for any particular x''. For example, the absolute value of the quotient does not have a limit at a corner of the curve defined by the equation $y = f(x)$.

On the other hand, if a function possesses a continuous first derivative with respect to a variable at every point on a closed range, it has the Lipschitz property in the variable on the range. For, if $f(x)$ has a continuous first derivative with respect to x at $x = x''$, then, by the mean value theorem, it follows that

$$f(x') - f(x'') = (x' - x'')f_x(x'' + \lambda(x' - x'')),$$

where $f_x(x)$ is the first derivative of $f(x)$ with respect to x, and where $0 \leqq \lambda \leqq 1$. Since $f_x(x)$, by hypothesis, is continuous in x, its absolute value has an upper bound A in the closed range. Consequently the Lipschitz condition is satisfied.

It follows from these discussions that the Lipschitz property in a region, in the weight of the conditions it imposes, lies between the property of continuity in the region and the property of the existence of a continuous first derivative in the region. Since analytic functions have continuous first derivatives with respect to their arguments at all points at which they are regular, they possess the Lipschitz property. Therefore all the differential equations that have been considered in the earlier chapters are special cases of those that will be treated in this chapter.

101. Analogue of the Lipschitz Property in the Analytic Case. To fix the ideas, consider a function of two variables $f(x_1, x_2)$ which is analytic for all values of the variables x_1 and x_2 in a complex region R. If x_1 and x_2 are restricted to real values, a relation of the form of (3) is satisfied; if it is desired to permit x_1 and x_2

to take complex values, the form of the relation must be suitably modified.

Let (x_1', x_2') and (x_1'', x_2'') be any two points in the complex domain R. Then

$$|f(x_1', x_2') - f(x_1'', x_2'')| = |[f(x_1', x_2') - f(x_1'', x_2')]$$
$$+ [f(x_1'', x_2') - f(x_1'', x_2'')]|$$
$$\leqq |f(x_1', x_2') - f(x_1'', x_2')| + |f(x_1'', x_2') - f(x_1'', x_2'')|.$$

Let $f_{x_1}(x_1, x_2)$ and $f_{x_2}(x_1, x_2)$ be the first derivatives of $f(x_1, x_2)$ with respect to x_1 and x_2 respectively. Both of these derivatives exist and are continuous in the region R, and therefore their absolute values are bounded by a positive constant A in R.

Now, since

$$\int_{x_1''}^{x_1'} f_{x_1}(x_1, x_2') dx_1 = f(x_1', x_2') - f(x_1'', x_2'),$$

it follows that

$$\begin{cases} |f(x_1', x_2') - f(x_1'', x_2')| = \left| \int_{x_1''}^{x_1'} f_{x_1}(x_1, x_2') dx_1 \right| \leqq Al_1, \\ |f(x_1'', x_2') - f(x_1'', x_2'')| = \left| \int_{x_2''}^{x_2'} f_{x_2}(x_1'', x_2) dx_2 \right| \leqq Al_2, \end{cases}$$

where l_1 and l_2 are the lengths of the paths in their complex planes described by x_1 and x_2 respectively in going from the points x_1'' to x_1' and x_2'' to x_2'. Therefore the condition corresponding to the Lipschitz condition is, in the case of a function $f(x_1, x_2)$ of two complex variables x_1 and x_2,

$$|f(x_1', x_2') - f(x_1'', x_2'')| \leqq A(l_1 + l_2).$$

In the general case of n complex variables the relation is

$$|f(x_i') - f(x_i'')| \leqq A \sum_{j=1}^{n} l_j.$$

If the boundary of R is convex, then $l_j = |x_j' - x_j''|$.

102. Definition of the Successive Integration Process on the Picard Interval. The process of this chapter is often known as *The Method of Successive Approximations*. This terminology is not descriptive and it has often erroneously been taken to mean that the process does not have a complete logical justification.

As a matter of fact, the method is logically complete and involves approximations only in the sense that the elements of any converging sequence of functions are approximations to the limit function.

The method consists formally in determining sequences of functions $x_i^{(1)}$, $x_i^{(2)}$, $\cdots$ $(i = 1, \cdots, n)$, the superscript defining the order of the functions in the sequences. The first functions of the sequences are defined by the equations

$$(4) \qquad x_i^{(1)} = a_i + \int_{t_0}^{t} f_i(a_j; t)dt \qquad (i = 1, \cdots, n).$$

It follows from the properties of the $f_i(x_j; t)$ that the $x_i^{(1)}(t)$ are defined and are continuous functions of t for every value of t in the region R. Moreover, since

$$|x_i^{(1)} - a_i| = \left| \int_{t_0}^{t} f_i(a_j; t)dt \right|$$
$$\leqq \left| \int_{t_0}^{t} Mdt \right| = M(t - t_0),$$

it follows that the $x_i^{(1)}$ are in the region R if

$$M(t - t_0) \leqq r_i.$$

Let r be the smallest of the r_i; then the $x_i^{(1)}$ and t are in the region R if

$$(5) \qquad 0 \leqq t - t_0 \leqq \rho, \qquad t - t_0 \leqq r/M.$$

The variable t will henceforth in this article be assumed to satisfy these restrictions. The interval for t imposed by these restrictions is known as *the Picard interval* for the problem, because Picard proved * that in this interval the process converges to a solution.

The second functions of the sequences are defined by the equations

$$(6) \qquad x_i^{(2)} = a_i + \int_{t_0}^{t} f_i(x_j^{(1)}; t)dt \qquad (i = 1, \cdots, n).$$

The $f_i(x_j^{(1)}; t)$ are continuous functions of the $x_j^{(1)}$ and of t for

* *Journal de Mathématiques*, 4th series, Vol. 6 (1890), pp. 197–210; *Traité d'Analyse*, 2d edition, Vol. II, pp. 340–346.

all values of the $x_j^{(1)}$ and of t in the region R. The $x_j^{(1)}$ are continuous functions of t for all values of t in the region R, and they are in R if t is in the Picard interval. Therefore, by Appendix F, the $f_i(x_j^{(1)}; t)$ are continuous functions of t for all values of t in the Picard interval. Hence equations (6) define the $x_i^{(2)}$ as continuous functions of t for all values of t satisfying the relations (5).

The third functions of the sequences are defined similarly. The functions at the general step are defined by

$$(7) \quad x_i^{(\kappa)} = a_i + \int_{t_0}^{t} f_i(x_j^{(\kappa-1)}; t)dt \qquad (0 \lesseqgtr t - t_0 \leqq \rho, r/M).$$

If the $x_i^{(\kappa-1)}$ are defined and are continuous functions of t in the Picard interval, then the $x_i^{(\kappa)}$ are defined and are continuous functions of t in the same interval. Therefore all the functions of the sequences $x_i^{(1)}$, $x_i^{(2)}$, $\cdots$ are defined and are continuous functions of t in the Picard interval. This fact alone does not, of course, establish the conclusions that the sequences have limits and that the limits constitute a solution of equations (1). These conclusions will be proved in Arts. 105 and 106.

103. Variation in the First Step of the Process. Instead of defining the first functions of the sequences by equations (4), they may be defined by the equations

$$(8) \qquad x_i^{(1)} = a_i + \int_{t_0}^{t} f_i(a_j + \phi_j(t); t)dt,$$

where the $\phi_j(t_0) = 0$ and the $\phi_j(t)$ are continuous functions of t for all values of t in the region R, and where, moreover, the $a_j + \phi_j(t)$ are in the region R for all values of t in R.

With the values of the $x_i^{(1)}$ defined by equations (8), the second functions of the sequences are defined by equations (6), and the general set by equations (7). That is, the process differs from that of Art. 102 only in the first step, but it might likewise be made to differ similarly in any or all of a finite number of steps It will be shown in Art. 106 that these sequences converge to the same limits as those of Art. 102.

104. Geometrical Interpretation of the Process. The intuitions are generally assisted by geometrical illustrations of analytical processes. The method under consideration has a relatively simple geometrical interpretation, at least in the case in which there is only one dependent variable.

For simplicity, suppose there is but one dependent variable x and consider the xt-plane, Fig. 10. The region R lies between the lines $x = a - r$ and $x = a + r$, and the lines $t = t_0$ and $t = t_0 + \rho$. At every point in this rectangle the right member of the differential equation

$$\frac{dx}{dt} = f(x, t)$$

is defined. Suppose at each point of the region R a vector is drawn such that the tangent of the angle between its line and the t-axis is equal to the value of the function $f(x; t)$ at the point.

Now consider the function $x^{(1)}$ of the first step defined by the equation corresponding to equations (4). It follows from these

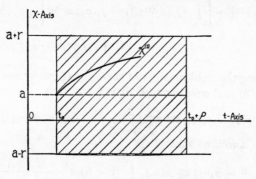

Fig. 10.

equations and the construction of the diagram that $x^{(1)}$ is a curve whose tangent for every value of t in the Picard interval is parallel to the vector at the point (a, t). Similarly, the function of the second step, defined by the equation corresponding to equations (5), has a tangent at every point t in the Picard interval that is parallel to the vector on the curve $x^{(1)}$ at the point $(x^{(1)}, t)$. The curve defined at each step is such that its tangent at every point t in the Picard interval is parallel to the vectors at corresponding points of the curve at the preceding step.

If the first approximation is defined by equation (8), the tangents to the corresponding curve are parallel to the vectors at the points defined by the curve $x = a + \phi(t)$.

It seems reasonable from this geometrical interpretation that the directions of the tangents for various values of t and the curve itself approach limits as the number of steps becomes infinitely great.

105. Convergence of the Process. The functions $x_i^{(1)}(t)$, $x_i^{(2)}(t)$, $\cdots$ are uniquely defined on the Picard interval by equations (4), (6), and (7). It will now be shown that these sequences converge to limits uniformly with respect to t.

It follows from equations (4) that

$$(9) \qquad \left| x_i^{(1)} - a_i \right| = \left| \int_{t_0}^{t} f_i(a_j; \, t) dt \right| \leqq M(t - t_0).$$

Then it follows from equations (4) and (6) that

$$\left| x_i^{(2)} - x_i^{(1)} \right| = \left| \int_{t_0}^{t} \left[f_i(x_j^{(1)}; \, t) - f_i(a_j; \, t) \right] dt \right|$$
$$\leqq \int_{t_0}^{t} \left| f_i(x_j^{(1)}; \, t) - f_i(a_j; \, t) \right| dt.$$

On reducing the right member of these equations by the Lipschitz property (3) and equations (9), it is found that

$$\left| f_i(x_j^{(1)}; \, t) - f_i(a_j; \, t) \right| \leqq A \sum_{j=1}^{n} \left| x_j^{(1)} - a_j \right| \leqq MnA(t - t_0).$$

Therefore it follows that

$$(10) \qquad \left| x_i^{(2)} - x_i^{(1)} \right| \leqq MnA \int_{t_0}^{t} (t - t_0) dt = \frac{M}{nA} \frac{[nA(t - t_0)]^2}{2}.$$

It follows by a similar series of steps that

$$\left| x_i^{(3)} - x_i^{(2)} \right| = \left| \int_{t_0}^{t} \left[f_i(x_j^{(2)}; \, t) - f_i(x_j^{(1)}; \, t) \right] dt \right|$$
$$\leqq \int_{t_0}^{t} \left| f_i(x_j^{(2)}; \, t) - f_i(x_j^{(1)}; \, t) \right| dt$$
$$\leqq A \sum_{j=1}^{n} \int_{t_0}^{t} \left| x_j^{(2)} - x_j^{(1)} \right| dt \leqq \frac{M}{nA} \frac{[nA(t - t_0)]^3}{3!}.$$

On repeating the process κ times, it is found that

$$(11) \qquad \left| x_i^{(\kappa)} - x_i^{(\kappa-1)} \right| \leqq \frac{M}{nA} \frac{[nA(t - t_0)]^\kappa}{\kappa!} \leqq \frac{M}{nA} \frac{(nA\rho)^\kappa}{\kappa!}.$$

The sequences of functions $x_i^{(1)}$, $x_i^{(2)}$, $\cdots$ converge, by definition, for any particular value of t provided that, corresponding to every positive value of ϵ, there exists a positive integer $\kappa_{\epsilon t}$, depending upon both ϵ and t, such that for every integer κ greater than $\kappa_{\epsilon t}$ it is true that

$$(12) \qquad |x_i^{(\kappa+p)} - x_i^{(\kappa-1)}| < \epsilon \qquad (p = 1, 2, \cdots).$$

The convergence is *uniform* with respect to t on an interval, such as the Picard interval, if there exists a positive integer κ_ϵ, depending upon ϵ but independent of t, such that the inequality (12) is satisfied for all values of t on the interval.

Since

$$x_i^{(\kappa+p)} - x_i^{(\kappa-1)} = \left[x_i^{(\kappa+p)} - x_i^{(\kappa+p-1)}\right] + \left[x_i^{(\kappa+p-1)} - x_i^{(\kappa+p-2)}\right]$$
$$+ \cdots + \left[x_i^{(\kappa)} - x_i^{(\kappa-1)}\right],$$

it follows from the relations (11) that

$$(13) \quad \begin{cases} |x_i^{(\kappa+p)} - x_i^{(\kappa-1)}| \\[6pt] \leqq \dfrac{M}{nA} \dfrac{(nA\rho)^\kappa}{\kappa!}\left[1 + \dfrac{nA\rho}{\kappa+1} + \cdots + \dfrac{(nA\rho)^p}{(\kappa+1)\cdots(\kappa+p)}\right] \\[6pt] < \dfrac{M}{nA}\dfrac{(nA\rho)^\kappa}{\kappa!}e^{nA\rho} \qquad (p = 1, 2, \cdots; 0 \leqq t - t_0 \leqq \rho, r/M). \end{cases}$$

It follows from these inequalities that, corresponding to every positive ϵ, an integer κ_ϵ exists such that, for every $\kappa > \kappa_\epsilon$ and every positive integer p and every value of t in the Picard interval, the inequalities $|x_i^{(\kappa+p)} - x_i^{(\kappa-1)}| < \epsilon$ are satisfied. Therefore the sequences of functions defined in Art. 102 converge to limits uniformly with respect to t on the Picard interval. It follows from Appendix D that the limits of the sequences are continuous functions of t for all values of t on the Picard interval.

106. Uniqueness of the Limits of the Process. An alternative definition of the first functions of the sequences of functions was given by equations (8). It will be proved that the limits of the sequences are independent of the functions $\phi_i(t)$, so long as they possess the properties imposed.

Let $x_{i_0}^{(\kappa)}$ represent the κth set of functions as defined by equations (7), and let $x_{i_\phi}^{(\kappa)}$ be the corresponding set, starting from equations (8). Then it follows from equations (4) and (8) that

$$\left\{ \begin{aligned} |x_{i_\phi}^{(1)} - x_{i_0}^{(1)}| &= \left| \int_{t_0}^{t} [f_i(a_j + \phi_j(t); \ t) - f_i(a_j; \ t)] dt \right| \\ &\leqq \int_{t_0}^{t} [\, |f_i(a_j + \phi_j(t); \ t)| + |f_i(a_j; \ t)| \,] dt \\ &\leqq 2M(t - t_0). \end{aligned} \right.$$

On making use of the relations (3), the second step gives

$$\left\{ \begin{aligned} |x_{i_\phi}^{(2)} - x_{i_0}^{(2)}| &\leqq \int_{t_0}^{t} |f_i(x_{i_\phi}^{(1)}; \ t) - f_i(x_{i_0}^{(1)}; \ t)| \, dt \\ &\leqq \sum_{j=1}^{n} A \int_{t_0}^{t} |x_{i_\phi}^{(1)} - x_{i_0}^{(1)}| \, dt \\ &\leqq \frac{2M}{nA} \frac{[nA(t - t_0)]^2}{2}. \end{aligned} \right.$$

At the general step, the corresponding relations are

(14) $\quad |x_{i_\phi}^{(\kappa)} - x_{i_0}^{(\kappa)}| \leqq \dfrac{2M}{nA} \dfrac{[nA(t - t_0)]^\kappa}{\kappa!} \leqq \dfrac{2M}{nA} \dfrac{(nA\rho)^\kappa}{\kappa!}.$

Therefore

$$\lim_{\kappa = \infty} |x_{i_\phi}^{(\kappa)} - x_{i_0}^{(\kappa)}| = 0$$

for all values of t on the Picard interval. That is, the limits of the process are independent of the $\phi_j(t)$ except for the conditions imposed in connection with equations (8), by which the first step of the process was modified. It follows that if the general numerical characteristics of the solution are known in advance, the $\phi_j(t)$ may be so chosen that the rapidity of convergence of the process will be increased. A practical method of making use of this property of the process will be explained in Art. 123.

107. The Limits of the Sequences Are a Solution. It follows from the definition in Art. 8 that the limits of the sequences of functions that have been defined in Arts. 102 and 103 are a solution of the differential equations (1) on the Picard interval provided

(15) $\quad \dfrac{d}{dt} [\lim_{\kappa = \infty} x_i^{(\kappa)}] - f_i(\lim_{\kappa = \infty} x_j^{(\kappa)}; \ t) \underset{t}{\equiv} 0 \quad (0 \underset{\cdot}{\leqq} t - t_0 \leqq \rho, \ r/M).$

Since the $f_i(x_j; \ t)$ are continuous functions of the x_j for all values of the x_j and t in the region R, it follows from Appendix G that

(16) $f_i(\lim_{\kappa=\infty} x_j{}^{(\kappa)}; t) \equiv \lim_{t} \lim_{\kappa=\infty} f_i(x_j{}^{(\kappa)}; t)$ $(0 \leqq t - t_0 \leqq \rho, r/M)$.

It will be proved next that

(17) $\dfrac{d}{dt}\left[\lim_{\kappa=\infty} x_i{}^{(\kappa)}\right] \equiv \lim_{t} \lim_{\kappa=\infty} \dfrac{dx_i{}^{(\kappa)}}{dt}$ $(0 \leqq t - t_0 \leqq \rho, r/M)$.

It follows from Appendix E that if the derivatives $dx_i{}^{(\kappa)}/dt$ exist in the Picard interval, and if the sequences of derivatives converge to limits uniformly with respect to t in the same interval, then the derivatives of the limits are the respective limits of the derivatives in the interval.

It follows from equations (7) that

(18) $\dfrac{dx_i{}^{(\kappa)}}{dt} \underset{t}{\equiv} f_i(x_j{}^{(\kappa-1)}; t)$ $(0 \leqq t - t_0 \leqq \rho, r/M)$.

Therefore the derivatives of the functions constituting the sequences exist in the Picard interval. It follows from the relations (3) and the inequalities (13) that

(19) $\left\{\begin{array}{l} \left|\dfrac{dx_i{}^{(\kappa+p+1)}}{dt} - \dfrac{dx_i{}^{(\kappa)}}{dt}\right| \underset{t}{\equiv} \left|f_i(x_j{}^{(\kappa+p)}; t) - f_i(x_j{}^{(\kappa-1)}; t)\right| \\[2mm] \qquad \underset{t}{\leqq} A \sum_{j=1}^{n} \left|x_j{}^{(\kappa+p)} - x_j{}^{(\kappa-1)}\right| \\[2mm] \qquad < M \dfrac{(nA\rho)^{\kappa}}{\kappa!}\, e^{nA\rho} \\[2mm] \qquad (p = 1, 2, \cdots; 0 \leqq t - t_0 \leqq \rho, r/M). \end{array}\right.$

Therefore the sequences of derivatives converge in the Picard interval uniformly with respect to t, and therefore the identities (17) are satisfied.

The identities (15), which express the conditions that the limits of the $x_i{}^{(\kappa)}$ shall be a solution, become as a consequence of the identities (16) and (17)

(20) $\dfrac{d}{dt}\left[\lim_{\kappa=\infty} x_i{}^{(\kappa)}\right] - f_i(\lim_{\kappa=\infty} x_j{}^{(\kappa)}; t) \equiv \lim_{t} \lim_{\kappa=\infty}\left[\dfrac{dx_i{}^{(\kappa)}}{dt} - f_i(x_j{}^{(\kappa)}; t)\right].$

It follows from equations (7), (3), and (11) that

$$(21) \quad \begin{cases} \lim_{\kappa=\infty} \left[\frac{dx_i{}^{(\kappa)}}{dt} - f_i(x_j{}^{(\kappa)}; t) \right] \equiv \lim_t \lim_{\kappa=\infty} \left[f_i(x_j{}^{(\kappa-1)}; t) - f_i(x_j{}^{(\kappa)}; t) \right] \\ \qquad\qquad \leqq A \lim_t \lim_{\kappa=\infty} \sum_{j=1}^n | x_j{}^{(\kappa-1)} - x_j{}^{(\kappa)} | \\ \qquad\qquad \leqq \frac{M}{nA} \lim_t \lim_{\kappa=\infty} \frac{(nA\rho)^\kappa}{\kappa!} \equiv 0 \\ \qquad\qquad\qquad (0 \leqq t - t_0 \leqq \rho, r/M). \end{cases}$$

It follows, therefore, from the identities (20) and (21) that the identities (15) are satisfied. Since these identities are the conditions that the limit functions shall be a solution of the differential equations (1), the process defines a solution on the Picard interval.

108. Extension of the Solution to a Border of the Region R. The methods given in Chapters II and III define the solution only in sufficiently restricted domains. The reason is, of course, that they both give power-series expansions which converge only in circles extending out to their nearest singular point. In the analytic sense the functions in general exist outside of their circles of convergence. The limitations of the domains of validity are particularly unfortunate when one is interested, for example, only in real values of the arguments, and the singularities are for complex values of the arguments. The point is illustrated by the expansion of the sine-amplitude function, given in Art. 69, the convergence of which is limited by the complex singular points given in Art. 73. As was noted in Chapter VIII, the locations of the singular points of solutions of differential equations cannot in general be determined.

The process of this chapter does not expand the solution functions into series, and consequently its domain of validity is not subject to the same kind of limitations as those of the methods of Chapters II and III. What is desired is the solution until it attains a border of the region R. That is, the problem is to find the solution until either t or some x_i attains a limit used in defining the region R in Art. 100.

The solution is defined in the interval $0 \leqq t - t_0 \leqq \rho, r/M$. In the case in which $r/M \leqq \rho$, the Picard interval extends to the t-border of the region R. If $r/M < \rho$, the Picard interval does not extend to the t-border of the region R. In this case one or more of the x_i may extend to a border of the region R, or no x_i may attain a border of the region R. In the former case the Picard interval contains the complete solution of the problem; in the latter case it does not, for the terminal values of the x_i at $t = r/M$ may be taken as initial values for an extension of the solution curves by the application of the process on a new Picard interval.

Suppose $r/M < \rho$ and that no x_i attains a border of the region R for any value of t on the Picard interval. The problem is to enlarge the interval so that the solution will be defined until t or some x_i shall attain a border of the region R. It will be noted on referring to Art. 102 that t was restricted to the Picard interval in order that every $x_i^{(\kappa)}$ should remain in the region R in every case that exists under the hypotheses. This restriction was made because the right members of equations (1) were not defined if any x_i or t should be outside of the region R. An obvious way to remove the restriction to the Picard interval is to enlarge * the x_i-borders of the region R in such a way that $r/M > \rho$, for then the solution will be defined by the process for all $0 \leqq t - t_0 \leqq \rho$. But the solution will belong to the original problem only if the limits of the $x_i^{(\kappa)}$ for $\kappa = \infty$ are all in the region R. Suppose that some x_i is on a border of the region R for $t = T$; then the true domain of existence of the solution is $0 \leqq t - t_0 \leqq T$, and the generalized process defines the solution functions on this interval.

The problem now is to extend the region R with respect to the x_i by defining the functions $f_i(x_j; t)$ of equations (1) for $|x_i - a_i| > r_i$ so that they shall have the Properties 1, 2, and 3, of Art. 100, and so that in the extended region r/M shall be greater than ρ. The functions $f_i(x_j; t)$ will be defined first for a single one of the x_j outside of the region R. Suppose $x_1 > a_1 + r_1$ and that $|x_j - a_j| \leqq r_j$ $(j = 2, \cdots, n)$. Then let

$$(22) \qquad f_i(x_1, \cdots, x_n; t) \underset{x_2, \cdots, x_n}{\equiv} f_i(a_1 + r_1, x_2, \cdots, x_n; t).$$

Similarly, if $x_1 < a_1 - r_1$, let

$$(23) \qquad f_i(x_1, \cdots, x_n; t) \underset{x_2, \cdots, x_n}{\equiv} f_i(a_1 - r_1, x_2, \cdots, x_n; t).$$

* Dunham Jackson, *Annals of Mathematics*, 2d series, Vol. 23 (1921), p. 75.

These equations define the $f_i(x_j; t)$ for all values of $x_2, \cdots, x_n; t$ in R and for all finite values of x_1. Moreover, the functions $f_i(x_j; t)$ possess the Properties 1, 2, and 3, of Art. 100, in the extended domain.

Now extend the domain in a similar manner sequentially with respect to $x_2, \cdots, x_n$, using $x_1, \cdots, x_{n-1}$ sequentially in their extended domains. After the extension of the domain has been made with respect to x_n, the functions $f_i(x_j; t)$ will be defined and have the Properties 1, 2, and 3 for all finite values of the x_j and for $0 \leqq t - t_0 \leqq \rho$. Denote the extended domain by R'. It follows from the definition of the $f_i(x_j; t)$ in R' that in this extended domain $|f_i(x_j; t)| < M$ and $r = \infty$.

The Picard interval for the generalized functions $f_i(x_j; t)$ is $0 \leqq t - t_0 \leqq \rho$. Suppose the solution is constructed on this interval. The solution of the original problem is determined on this interval unless some x_i attains a border of the region R for $t - t_0 = T < \rho$. Then the solution is defined for the interval $0 \leqq t - t_0 \leqq T$, but not for larger values of $t - t_0$.

It follows that the method of this chapter is applicable to very general problems, for the functions $f_i(x_j; t)$ need have only the Lipschitz property in the x_j and be continuous in t. In fact, it is not necessary that the functions $f_i(x_j; t)$ be given by formulas. Besides this, the process gives the solution in the entire domain of its existence.

109. Properties of the Solution Functions as Functions of t and of t_0. Suppose the domain of definition of the functions $f_i(x_j; t)$ is extended by the method of Art. 108 to the region R', and consider the solution in the entire domain of its existence $0 \leqq t - t_0 \leqq T \leqq \rho$.

The $x_i^{(\kappa)}(t)$ are defined by the processes of both Art. 102 and Art. 103 for all values of t for which $0 \leqq t - t_0 \leqq T$, and they are continuous functions of t and t_0 for every value of t on the interval. It follows from the inequalities (13) that the convergence of the functions $x_i^{(\kappa)}(t)$ to their limit functions $x_i(t)$ is uniform with respect to t. The convergence is similarly uniform with respect to t_0. Therefore it follows from Appendix D that the limit functions are continuous functions of t and t_0. In order to place both t and t_0 in evidence, let the solution functions be written $x_i(t_0, t)$.

It follows from the Properties 1, 2, and 3, of Art. 100, that the $f_i(x_j; t)$ are continuous functions of the x_j, t_0, and t in the region R'. It has just been shown that the x_j are continuous functions of t_0 and t in R'. Therefore it follows from equations (1) and Appendix F that the first derivatives $dx_i/dt = f_i(x_j; t)$ are continuous functions of t_0 and t in the region R'.

110. Properties of the Solution as Functions of the a_i. The solution functions $x_i(t)$ are functions of the a_i as well as of t_0 and t. The domain of existence of the solution functions evidently depends in general upon the values of the a_i. Hence let a domain D for the a_i, lying entirely within the region R, be defined by

$$a_i^{(1)} \lesseqgtr a_i \leqq a_i^{(2)}.$$

There will be a common interval $0 \lesseqgtr t - t_0 \leqq T_D$ for which the solution functions exist for every set of values of the a_i in the domain D.

Since the $f_i(x_j; t)$ are continuous functions of the x_j, it follows from Arts. 102 and 103 that the $x_i^{(\kappa)}$ are continuous functions of the a_j for the a_j in the domain D and $0 \lesseqgtr t - t_0 \leqq T_D$. It follows from the relations corresponding to the inequalities (13) that the $x_i^{(\kappa)}$ converge uniformly with respect to the a_j to the solution function x_i for the a_j in the domain D and for $0 \lesseqgtr t - t_0 \leqq T_D$. Therefore it follows from Appendix D that the functions x_i are continuous functions of the a_j for all values of the a_j in the domain D and $0 \lesseqgtr t - t_0 \leqq T_D$.

Since the $f_i(x_j; t)$ are continuous functions of the x_j for the x_j and t in the region R', and since the $dx_i/dt = f_i(x_j; t)$ for all values of the a_j in the domain D and $0 \lesseqgtr t - t_0 \leqq T_D$, it follows from Appendix F that the first derivatives of the solution functions are continuous functions of the a_j for all values of the a_j in the domain D and $0 \lesseqgtr t - t_0 \leqq T_D$.

Suppose the functions $f_i(x_j; t)$ are continuous functions of a parameter μ, and that the Properties 1, 2, and 3, of Art. 100, hold uniformly with respect to μ for $\mu_1 \lesseqgtr \mu \leqq \mu_2$ and the x_j and t in a region R_μ. Then it follows from a similar discussion that the solution functions and also the first derivatives of the solution functions with respect to t are continuous functions of μ for all values of μ for which $\mu_1 \lesseqgtr \mu \leqq \mu_2$ and $0 \lesseqgtr t - t_0 \leqq T_{\mu_1, \mu_2}$.

If the functions $f_i(x_j; t)$ satisfy the Lipschitz property with respect to μ, then the conclusion of the preceding paragraph can also be established by adjoining to the differential equations (1) the equation

$$\frac{d\mu}{dt} = 0,$$

subject to the initial condition $\mu(t_0) = \mu$. The conclusion follows from the fact that the dependent variables of the augmented system of differential equations are $x_1, \cdots, x_n, \mu$, and, as has been proved, the solution functions and their first derivatives are continuous functions of the initial values of the dependent variables $a_1, \cdots, a_n, \mu$.

111. Properties of the Solution Functions under Stronger Conditions. Suppose the functions $f_i(x_j; t)$ possess the Properties 1, 2, 3, of Art. 100, and that they have the additional property:

Property 4. The partial derivatives $\partial f_i/\partial x_j$ and $\partial f_i/\partial t$ of the functions $f_i(x_j; t)$ exist and are continuous functions of the x_j and t for all values of the x_j and t in the region R.

It will be proved that the solution functions and their first derivatives with respect to t possess first derivatives with respect to t and the a_j which are continuous functions of the a_j and t for all values of the a_j in the domain D and $0 \leqq t - t_0 \leqq T_D$.

Since the region R is closed, it follows from Appendix A that a finite constant N exists such that

$$(24) \qquad \left| \frac{\partial f_i}{\partial x_j} \right| < N, \qquad \left| \frac{\partial f_i}{\partial t} \right| < N \qquad (i, j = 1, \cdots, n)$$

for all values of the x_j and t in the region R.

It follows from equations (4), (6), and (7) and their first derivatives with respect to t, and from Property 4 that

$$(25) \qquad \frac{\partial x_i^{(\kappa)}}{\partial t}, \quad \frac{\partial x_i^{(\kappa)}}{\partial a_j}, \quad \frac{\partial}{\partial t}\left(\frac{dx_i^{(\kappa)}}{dt}\right), \quad \frac{\partial}{\partial a_j}\left(\frac{dx_i^{(\kappa)}}{dt}\right)$$

exist and are continuous functions of t and the a_j for all values of the a_j in the domain D and $0 \leqq t - t_0 \leqq T_D$. In order to complete the demonstration it will be necessary to prove the lemma that the $\left| \partial x_i^{(\kappa)}/\partial a_j \right|$ have a finite upper bound N_1 for the a_j in the domain D and $0 \leqq t - t_0 \leqq T_D$.

It follows from equations (4) for $i, j = 1, \cdots, n$ that

$$\left| \frac{\partial x_i^{(1)}}{\partial a_j} \right| \leqq 1 + \left| \int_{t_0}^{t} \frac{\partial f_i(a_j; t)}{\partial a_j} \, dt \right|$$

$$\leqq 1 + N(t - t_0) \leqq 1 + nN(t - t_0).$$

It follows from these inequalities and equations (6) that

$$\left| \frac{\partial x_i^{(2)}}{\partial a_j} \right| \leqq 1 + \left| \int_{t_0}^{t} \sum_{l=1}^{n} \left(\frac{\partial f_i}{\partial x_l} \right)_1 \frac{\partial x_l^{(1)}}{\partial a_j} \, dt \right|$$

$$\leqq 1 + nN \int_{t_0}^{t} [1 + nN(t - t_0)] dt$$

$$\leqq 1 + nN(t - t_0) + \frac{n^2 N^2 (t - t_0)^2}{2} .$$

Sequential repetitions of this process give, at the general step,

$$(26) \quad \begin{cases} \left| \dfrac{\partial x_i^{(\kappa)}}{\partial a_j} \right| \leqq 1 + nN(t - t_0) + \cdots + \dfrac{[nN(t - t_0)]^{\kappa}}{\kappa !} \\ < e^{nNp} = N_1 \qquad (\kappa = 1, 2, \cdots), \end{cases}$$

which is the lemma that was to be proved.

The next step in the demonstration is the proof that the sequences of partial derivatives $\partial x_i^{(\kappa)}/\partial a_j$ approach their limits, as κ becomes infinite, uniformly with respect to the a_j for all values of the a_j in the domain D and $0 \leqq t - t_0 \leqq T_D$.

It follows from equations (7) that

$$(27) \quad \begin{cases} \left| \dfrac{\partial x_i^{(\kappa+p+1)}}{\partial a_j} - \dfrac{\partial x_i^{(\kappa+1)}}{\partial a_j} \right| \\ = \left| \int_{t_0}^{t} \sum_{l=1}^{n} \left[\left(\dfrac{\partial f_i}{\partial x_l} \right)_{\kappa+p} \dfrac{\partial x_l^{(\kappa+p)}}{\partial a_j} - \left(\dfrac{\partial f_i}{\partial x_l} \right)_{\kappa} \dfrac{\partial x_l^{(\kappa)}}{\partial a_j} \right] dt \right| \\ = \left| \int_{t_0}^{t} \left\{ \sum_{l=1}^{n} \dfrac{\partial x_l^{(\kappa+p)}}{\partial a_j} \left[\left(\dfrac{\partial f_i}{\partial x_l} \right)_{\kappa+p} - \left(\dfrac{\partial f_i}{\partial x_l} \right)_{\kappa} \right] \right. \right. \\ \left. \left. + \sum_{l=1}^{n} \left(\dfrac{\partial f_i}{\partial x_l} \right)_{\kappa} \left[\dfrac{\partial x_l^{(\kappa+p)}}{\partial a_j} - \dfrac{\partial x_l^{(\kappa)}}{\partial a_j} \right] \right\} dt \right| . \end{cases}$$

In determining upper bounds for the right members of these equations, the inequalities (24) and (26) will be used.

It was proved in Arts. 105 and 108 that the $x_i^{(\kappa)}$ approach limits x_i as κ becomes infinite for all values of t for which $0 \leqq t - t_0 \leqq T$. Therefore, since, by Property 4, the partial derivatives $\partial f_i/\partial x_j$ are continuous functions of the x_j for all values of the x_j in the region R, it follows by Appendix F that the derivatives $(\partial f_i/\partial x_l)_\kappa$ approach limits $\partial f_i/\partial x_l$ as κ becomes infinite. That is, corresponding to every positive number ϵ_1, there exists an integer κ_{ϵ_1} such that, for every integer $\kappa > \kappa_{\epsilon_1}$, it is true that

$$(28) \qquad \left| \left(\frac{\partial f_i}{\partial x_l} \right)_{\kappa+p} - \left(\frac{\partial f_i}{\partial x_l} \right)_\kappa \right| < \epsilon_1 \qquad (p = 1, 2, \cdots).$$

Therefore equations (27) give, as a consequence of the inequalities (24), (26), and (28), the inequalities

$$(29) \quad \begin{cases} \left| \dfrac{\partial x_i^{(\kappa+p+1)}}{\cdot \, \partial a_j} - \dfrac{\partial x_i^{(\kappa+1)}}{\partial a_j} \right| < \left| \displaystyle\int_{t_0}^t \left[\epsilon_1 n N_1 + 2 n N_1 N \right] dt \right| \\[2ex] \qquad\qquad\qquad \leqq \dfrac{\epsilon_1 N_1}{N} n N (t - t_0) + 2 N_1 \, n N (t - t_0). \end{cases}$$

It is found similarly that

$$\begin{cases} \left| \dfrac{\partial x_i^{(\kappa+p+2)}}{\partial a_j} - \dfrac{\partial x_i^{(\kappa+2)}}{\partial a_j} \right| \\[2ex] \qquad = \left| \displaystyle\int_{t_0}^t \left\{ \sum_{l=1}^n \dfrac{\partial x_l^{(\kappa+p+1)}}{\partial a_j} \left[\left(\dfrac{\partial f_i}{\partial x_l} \right)_{\kappa+p+1} - \left(\dfrac{\partial f_i}{\partial x_l} \right)_{\kappa+1} \right] \right.\right. \\[2ex] \qquad\qquad \left.\left. + \sum_{l=1}^n \left(\dfrac{\partial f_i}{\partial x_l} \right)_{\kappa+1} \left[\dfrac{\partial x_l^{(\kappa+p+1)}}{\partial a_j} - \dfrac{\partial x_l^{(\kappa+1)}}{\partial a_j} \right] \right\} dt \right|, \end{cases}$$

which give, as a consequence of the inequalities (24), (26), (28), and (29), the inequalities

$$\left| \frac{\partial x_i^{(\kappa+p+2)}}{\partial a_j} - \frac{\partial x_i^{(\kappa+2)}}{\partial a_j} \right| < \frac{\epsilon_1 N_1}{N} \left\{ n N (t - t_0) + \frac{[n N (t - t_0)]^2}{2} \right\} + 2 N_1 \frac{[n N (t - t_0)]^2}{2}.$$

Sequential repetitions of the process give at the qth step

$$(30) \quad \begin{cases} \left| \dfrac{\partial x_i^{(\kappa+p+q)}}{\partial a_j} - \dfrac{\partial x_i^{(\kappa+q)}}{\partial a_j} \right| \\[2ex] \qquad < \dfrac{\epsilon_1 N_1}{N} \left\{ n N (t - t_0) + \cdots + \dfrac{[n N (t - t_0)]^q}{q!} \right\} \\[2ex] \qquad\qquad + 2 N_1 \dfrac{[n N (t - t_0)]^q}{q!} \\[2ex] \qquad < \dfrac{\epsilon_1 N_1}{N} e^{n N \rho} + 2 N_1 \dfrac{(n N \rho)^q}{q!} \qquad (p, q = 1, 2, \cdots) \end{cases}$$

for all values of the a_j in the domain D and $0 \leqq t - t_0 \leqq T_D$.

Now the conclusion is at hand, for, corresponding to every positive number ϵ, a positive number ϵ_1, depending upon ϵ, and a positive integer q_ϵ, independently depending upon ϵ, exist such that, for every integer $q > q_\epsilon$, it is true that

$$(31) \qquad \begin{cases} \dfrac{\epsilon_1 N_1}{N} e^{nN\rho} < \dfrac{\epsilon}{2}, \\[2mm] 2N_1 \dfrac{(nN\rho)^q}{q!} < \dfrac{\epsilon}{2}, \end{cases}$$

from which it follows that the right member of the inequality (30) is less than ϵ. Since this inequality holds for all values of the a_i in the domain D and $0 \leqq t - t_0 \leqq T_D$, the partial derivatives $\partial x_i{}^{(\kappa)}/\partial a_j$ approach their limits uniformly with respect to the a_j and t as κ becomes infinite. Therefore, by Appendix D, the derivatives $\partial x_i/\partial a_j$ exist and are continuous functions of the a_j and t for all values of the a_j in the domain D and $0 \leqq t - t_0 \leqq T_D$.

It follows from equations (1) that for the solution functions there are the identities

$$(32) \qquad \begin{cases} \dfrac{\partial}{\partial t}\left(\dfrac{dx_i}{dt}\right) \underset{t}{\equiv} \dfrac{\partial}{\partial t} f_i[x_j(a_l; t); t] \underset{t}{\equiv} \sum_{j=1}^{n} \dfrac{\partial f_i}{\partial x_j}\dfrac{\partial x_j}{\partial t} + \dfrac{\partial f_i}{\partial t}, \\[3mm] \dfrac{\partial}{\partial a_l}\left(\dfrac{dx_i}{dt}\right) \underset{t}{\equiv} \dfrac{\partial}{\partial a_l} f_i[x_j(a_l; t); t] \underset{t}{\equiv} \sum_{j=1}^{n} \dfrac{\partial f_i}{\partial x_j}\dfrac{\partial x_j}{\partial a_l}. \end{cases}$$

By Property 4, the partial derivatives $\partial f_i/\partial x_l$ and $\partial f_i/\partial t$ exist and are continuous functions of the a_l in the domain D and $0 \leqq t - t_0 \leqq T_D$. It has just been proved that the $\partial x_j/\partial t$ and $\partial x_j/\partial a_l$ exist and are continuous functions of the a_l and t in the same domain. Therefore the right members of equations (32) are continuous functions of the a_l and t for all values of the a_l in the domain D and $0 \leqq t - t_0 \leqq T_D$.

It can be proved similarly that if the mth derivatives of the functions $f_i(x_j; t)$ with respect to the x_j and t exist and are continuous functions of these arguments, then the mth derivatives of the solution functions x_i with respect to t and the a_j exist and are continuous functions of the a_j and t for all values of the a_j in the domain D and $0 \leqq t - t_0 \leqq T_D$.

XI. QUESTIONS AND PROBLEMS

1. In Property 2 the functions $f_i(x_j; t)$ are stated to be continuous functions of t in the region R. Why is the region for the x_i also given in stating this property?

2. Why is the domain for t given in Property 3?

3. Which of the conclusions of this chapter would follow if the functions $f_i(x_j; t)$ had the Lipschitz property with respect to t?

4. Which of the conclusions of this chapter would follow if the A of the relations (3) depended upon the variable t?

5. Prove that the functions $f_i(x_j; t)$, of Art. 100, are continuous in the x_j and t simultaneously.

6. Why are the $\phi_j(t)$, of Art. 103, assumed to have the initial values $\phi_j(t_0) = 0$ and to be continuous in t?

7. Is it necessary that the $a_i + \phi_i(t)$ should be in the region R for all values of t in the region R?

8. It was proved in Art. 105 that the functions $x_i^{(\kappa)}(t)$ converge uniformly to limits as κ becomes infinite. Suppose the fact that the convergence is uniform were not known; could it be proved that the limit functions are a solution of the differential equations (1)?

9. Prove directly, rather than by the method of Art. 106, that the process of Art. 103 converges to limits.

10. In Art. 108 the region R was extended sequentially with respect to the dependent variables $x_1, \cdots, x_n$. Do the final definitions of the functions $f_i(x_j; t)$ in the extended region R' depend upon the order in which the extensions are made?

11. Would there be any advantage in extending the region with respect to the independent variable t?

12. Prove that the first derivatives of the solution functions with respect to t_0 exist and are continuous functions of t and of t_0 for all values for which $0 \leqq t - t_0 \leqq T$.

13. Prove that the derivatives of the solution functions with respect to t_0 exist and are continuous functions of the a_j for the a_j in the domain D and $0 \leqq t - t_0 \leqq T_D$.

14. Suppose the functions $f_i(x_j; t)$ depend upon a parameter μ and that they have only the Properties 1, 2, and 3, of Art. 100, with respect to the x_j and t, uniformly with respect to μ for $\mu_1 \leqq \mu \leqq \mu_2$. Suppose, further, that the first derivatives of the $f_i(x_j; t)$ with respect to μ exist and are continuous functions of μ for all values of the x_j and t in R and for all values of μ for $\mu_1 \leqq \mu \leqq \mu_2$. Under these hypotheses do the derivatives of the solution functions with respect to μ exist?

15. Prove in detail the closing theorem of Art. 111 in the case $m = 2$.

16. Suppose the functions $f_i(x_j; t)$ are linear in the x_j. Prove that the solution exists on the entire interval for which the $f_i(x_j; t)$ are continuous functions of t and that the solution functions are linear in the a_j.

CHAPTER XII

NUMERICAL SOLUTION OF DIFFERENTIAL EQUATIONS

112. Outline of the Method. All the methods for solving differential equations that have been given in the preceding chapters are applicable numerically under the conditions that have been stated. The method of Chapter II can be employed if the differential equations are analytic in the dependent and independent variables simultaneously. The method of Chapter III can be employed if the differential equations are analytic in the dependent variables and the parameter μ and continuous in the independent variable simultaneously. The method of Chapter XI is applicable if the differential equations have the Lipschitz property with respect to the dependent variables and are continuous in the independent variable simultaneously. If the differential equations are analytic in all the variables, all three methods of solving them are applicable.

Which of the available methods for solving a system of differential equations is preferable depends upon the problem, as was illustrated in Chapters VII–X. Problems will now be considered of a general character in which the dependent variables cannot be separated. It will be supposed that the differential equations are of such a nature that the general characteristics of their solution cannot be determined. It will be assumed that it is desired to find the solution for a finite pre-assigned range of the independent variable t, and the problem is to determine a convenient method of obtaining the solution numerically.

The method that is about to be explained is based on that of Chapter XI. Therefore it is applicable if the functions $f_i(x_j; t)$ of the differential equations are analytic in the x_j and t, and also if they have only the Lipschitz property in the x_j and are continuous in t. It is not necessary that the functions $f_i(x_j; t)$ should be defined by formulas; it is sufficient that they be determined when the x_j and t are given and have the stated properties. Naturally the functions $f_i(x_j; t)$ must be defined and have the specified properties for all values of t for which the solution is desired.

The first step consists in applying the method of Art. 102 on so short an interval that a very few approximations will give the solution functions with the desired degree of accuracy. The terminal values of the first interval are then taken as initial values for forming the solution on a second interval. And the characteristics of the solution functions on the first interval are used for determining the $\phi_i(t)$ of Art. 103 so that the convergence on the second interval shall be as rapid as possible. Similarly, the characteristics of the solution functions on the first two intervals are used for determining functions $\phi_i(t)$ for the third interval, and so on sequentially.

The extrapolations of the functions $\phi_i(t)$ are made by the use of difference functions, and the necessary quadratures are carried out by means of the same functions. By these means the computations are most easily made and errors are avoided. The work is arranged so that it will be most convenient to carry out.

Finally, it is shown that the method can be so applied that it will give the solution over a preassigned interval with a preassigned degree of approximation.

The theory will be completely developed first, and then the method of applying it will be explained. Those interested only in the methods of computation might begin with Art. 118.

113. The Differential Equations. The differential equations are

$$(1) \qquad \begin{cases} \dfrac{dx_i}{dt} = f_i(x_j; t) \qquad (i, j = 1, \cdots, n), \\ x_i(t_0) = a_i, \end{cases}$$

where the functions $f_i(x_j; t)$ have the Properties 1, 2, 3, of Art. 100, in the closed region R:

$$(2) \qquad \begin{cases} -r_i \leqq x_i - a_i \leqq r_i, \\ 0 \leqq t - t_0 \leqq \rho. \end{cases}$$

A closed region R_1, interior to R, will be defined by the relations

(3)
$$\begin{cases} -r_i + \delta \gtreqless x_i - a_i \leqq r_i - \delta, \\ 0 \gtreqless t - t_0 \leqq \rho, \end{cases}$$

where δ is an arbitrarily small positive constant. The problem is to determine the solution numerically until it attains a border of the region R_1, provided the r_i and ρ are finite.

In order to simplify the notation, let equations (1) be written in the form

(4)
$$\begin{cases} \dfrac{dx}{dt} = f(x; t), \\ x(t_0) = a, \end{cases}$$

where x represents the n different x_i, which may be expressed by the notation $x \equiv (x_1, \cdots, x_n)$. Similarly, $f \equiv (f_1, \cdots, f_n)$, $a \equiv (a_1, \cdots, a_n)$. This simplification of notation is feasible because the subscripts i and j used in the general theories of the preceding chapters played no rôles except to keep in evidence that there were n similar symbols. Each of the symbols of a group has all the essential properties of each of the other symbols of the group. The fact that there are n similar symbols in each group can be kept in mind without resorting to the use of the subscripts i and j.

114. The Solution on the First Interval. The solution will be developed on a sequence of intervals $t_0 \gtreqless t \leqq t_1,\ t_1 \gtreqless t \leqq t_2,\ \cdots$. The solution on the first interval will be determined by the method of Chapter XI. The fact that the x belong to the pth interval ($p = 1, 2, \cdots$) will be indicated by the superscript p, $x^{(p)}$. The successive functions of the sequences on the pth interval will be indicated by the subscripts $1, 2, \cdots$.

With the foregoing notations, the first approximation functions on the first interval are defined by

(5) $\qquad x_1^{(1)} = a + \displaystyle\int_{t_0}^{t} f(a + \phi^{(1)}(t); t)dt \qquad (t_0 \gtreqless t \leqq t_1),$

the superscript indicating that the x are being considered on the first interval, and the subscript indicating that the $x_1^{(1)}$ are the first approximations. The $\phi^{(1)}(t)$ are functions having the properties of the $\phi_j(t)$ of Art. 103. The t_1 will be so determined that the interval does not exceed the Picard interval; that is,

$$0 \lesseqgtr t_1 - t_0 \leqq \rho, \, r/M.$$

The second approximation functions on the first interval are defined in corresponding notation by the equations

$$x_2^{(1)} = a + \int_{t_0}^{t} f(x_1^{(1)}; t) dt.$$

The succeeding approximations on the first interval are defined by

$$(6) \qquad x_\kappa^{(1)} = a + \int_{t_0}^{t} f(x_{\kappa-1}^{(1)}; t) dt \qquad (\kappa = 3, 4, \cdots).$$

It was proved in Art. 105 that the sequences converge to limits as κ becomes infinite. For notation, let

$$(7) \qquad \lim_{\kappa = \infty} x_\kappa^{(1)} = x^{(1)} \qquad (t_0 \leqq t \leqq t_1).$$

Suppose $0 \lesseqgtr t_1 - t_0 \leqq \tau \leqq \rho, \, r/M$, and that there have been determined κ_1 $(\kappa_1 \geqq \kappa)$ successive sets of functions of the sequences on the first interval. Then it follows from equations (11), of Art. 105, that

$$(8) \qquad \left| x^{(1)} - x_{\kappa_1}^{(1)} \right| \leqq \frac{2M}{nA} \frac{(nA\tau)^{\kappa+1}}{(\kappa+1)!} e^{nA\tau} = \eta(\kappa, \tau).$$

That is, on the first interval the absolute values of the differences between the exact solution functions $x^{(1)}$ and the approximation functions $x_{\kappa_1}^{(1)}$ are less than $\eta(\kappa, \tau)$, a function of the two parameters κ and τ.

115. Extension of the Solution to the Second Interval. The values of the x have been determined for every value of t on the first interval. If $t_1 - t_0 = \rho$ or if any $x_{\kappa_1}^{(1)}$ satisfies either of the relations

$$(9) \qquad \begin{cases} x_{\kappa_1}^{(1)}(t) - a \gtreqqless + r - \delta + \eta, \\ x_{\kappa_1}^{(1)}(t) - a \lesseqqgtr - r + \delta - \eta, \end{cases}$$

for any value of t in the first interval, then the solution has attained a border of the region R_1 and, consequently, the proposed problem has been solved.

If, on the other hand, the inequalities

$$(10) \quad \begin{cases} t_1 - t_0 < \rho, \\ x_{\kappa_1}^{(1)}(t) - a < + r - \delta - \eta, \\ x_{\kappa_1}^{(1)}(t) - a > - r + \delta + \eta \end{cases}$$

are satisfied for all values of t on the first interval, then the solution has not attained a border of R_1 and, consequently, the proposed problem has not been solved. Suppose the inequalities (10) are satisfied for all values of t on the first interval, and consider the problem of extending the solution to a second interval $t_1 \leqq t \leqq t_2$, where t_2 remains to be defined.

The first problem is to choose the initial conditions for the second interval. The exact terminal values of the $x(t)$ on the first interval are $x^{(1)}(t_1)$ which have been proved to exist, but which have not been determined exactly. Nevertheless, consider the solution on the second interval, using the exact $x^{(1)}(t_1)$ as initial values. The functions of the solution sequences are defined by the equations

$$(11) \quad \begin{cases} x_1^{(2)} = x^{(1)}(t_1) + \int_{t_1}^{t} f(x^{(1)}(t_1) + \phi^{(2)}(t); t)dt \quad (t_1 \leqq t \leqq t_2), \\ x_{\kappa_2}^{(2)} = x^{(1)}(t_1) + \int_{t_1}^{t} f(x_{\kappa_2-1}^{(2)}; t)dt \quad (\kappa_2 = 2, 3, \cdots), \end{cases}$$

where the $\phi^{(2)}(t)$ are functions of t having the general properties of the $\phi_i(t)$ of Art. 103.

Consider also a solution on the second interval starting with the computed approximate solution $x_{\kappa_1}^{(1)}(t_1)$ as initial values. The successive functions of these sequences of functions are defined by the equations

$$(12) \quad \begin{cases} \bar{x}_1^{(2)} = x_{\kappa_1}^{(1)}(t_1) + \int_{t_1}^{t} f(x_{\kappa_1}^{(1)}(t_1) + \phi^{(2)}; t)dt \quad (t_1 \leqq t \leqq t_2), \\ \bar{x}_{\kappa_2}^{(2)} = x_{\kappa_1}^{(1)}(t_1) + \int_{t_1}^{t} f(\bar{x}_{\kappa_2-1}^{(2)}; t)dt \quad (\kappa_2 = 2, 3, \cdots). \end{cases}$$

These functions can be actually computed. All the functions defined by equations (11) and (12) lie in the region R if

$$(13) \quad \begin{cases} t_2 - t_1 \leqq \rho - (t_1 - t_0), \\ t_2 - t_1 \leqq \dfrac{r - |x_{\kappa_1}^{(1)}(t_1) - a| - \eta}{M}, \end{cases}$$

as can be established by considerations similar to those used in defining the Picard interval in Art. 102. The value of t_2 will be so determined that the relations (13) are satisfied.

The exact solution functions on the second interval are

$$(14) \qquad x^{(2)} = \lim_{\kappa_2 = \infty} x_{\kappa_2}^{(2)}(t) \qquad (t_1 \leqq t \leqq t_2).$$

Since all the functions of the sequences (11) and (12) are in the region R, relations hold corresponding to those given in (8). Therefore, if $\kappa_2 \geqq \kappa$ and $t_2 - t_1 \leqq \tau$, it follows that

$$(15) \qquad \left| x^{(2)} - x_{\kappa_2}^{(2)} \right| \leqq \eta(\kappa, \tau).$$

That is, $\eta(\kappa, \tau)$ is an upper bound, on the second interval, to the absolute values of the differences between the exact solution functions and the approximate solution functions that are defined by the exact initial conditions and proceeding to at least κ steps in the sequences.

It will be necessary to have also an upper bound to $\left| \bar{x}_{\kappa_2}^{(2)} - x_{\kappa_2}^{(2)} \right|$ on the second interval; that is, to the absolute values of the differences between the functions of the κ_2 ($\kappa_2 \geqq \kappa$) sequence, starting with computed approximate initial conditions and those starting with the exact initial conditions. It follows from the first of equations (11) and (12) and Property 3, of Art. 100, that

$$(16) \quad \left\{ \begin{aligned} \left| x_1^{(2)} - \bar{x}_1^{(2)} \right| &\leqq \left| x^{(1)}(t_1) - x_{\kappa_1}^{(1)}(t_1) \right| + \left| \int_{t_1}^{t} [f(x^{(1)}(t_1) + \phi^{(2)}; t) \right. \\ &\qquad\qquad\qquad\qquad\qquad \left. - f(x_{\kappa_1}^{(1)}(t_1) + \phi^{(2)}; t)] dt \right| \\ &\leqq \left| x^{(1)}(t_1) - x_{\kappa_1}^{(1)}(t_1) \right| \\ &\qquad\qquad + A \sum \int_{t_1}^{t} \left| x^{(1)}(t_1) - x_{\kappa_.}^{(1)}(t_1) \right| dt \\ &\leqq \eta[1 + nA(t - t_1)] \qquad (t_1 \leqq t \leqq t_2), \end{aligned} \right.$$

the symbol $\sum$ indicating here and in the succeeding articles that a sum of n functions having similar properties is being taken.

It is found from equations (11) and (12) for $\kappa_2 = 2$ that

$$\left| x_2^{(2)} - \bar{x}_2^{(2)} \right| \leqq \left| x^{(1)}(t_1) - x_{\kappa_1}^{(1)}(t_1) \right| + \left| \int_{t_1}^{t} [f(x_1^{(2)}; t) - f(\bar{x}_1^{(2)}; t)] dt \right|$$

$$\leqq \eta \left\{ 1 + \frac{nA(t - t_1)}{1!} + \frac{[nA(t - t_1)]^2}{2!} \right\}.$$

On repeating the process, it is found at the κ_2th step that

$$(17) \quad \begin{cases} \left| x_{\kappa_2}^{(2)} - \bar{x}_{\kappa_2}^{(2)} \right| \leqq \eta \left\{ 1 + \frac{nA(t-t_1)}{1!} + \cdots + \frac{[nA(t-t_1)]^{\kappa_2}}{\kappa_2!} \right\} \\ \qquad < \eta e^{nA\tau} \qquad (t_1 \lessgtr t \leqq t_2; t_2 - t_1 \leqq \tau). \end{cases}$$

On combining the relations (15) and (17), it is found that

$$(18) \quad \left| x^{(2)} - \bar{x}_{\kappa_2}^{(2)} \right| < \eta[1 + e^{nA\tau}] = \eta_2 \qquad (t_1 \lessgtr t \leqq t_2).$$

That is, η_2 is an upper bound, on the second interval, to the absolute values of the differences between the exact solution functions and the functions of the κ_2 ($\kappa_2 \lessgtr \kappa$) sequence starting with approximate values of the $x(t_1)$.

116. Extension of the Solution to Succeeding Intervals. If the solution on the second interval has not attained a border of the region R_1, it may be extended to one or more succeeding intervals. The process is similar to that of extending the solution to the second interval. The relations on the third interval corresponding to the relations (15) and (17) are

$$(19) \quad \begin{cases} \left| x^{(3)} - x_{\kappa_3}^{(3)} \right| \leqq \eta(\kappa, \tau) \quad (\kappa_3 \lessgtr \kappa; t_2 \lessgtr t \leqq t_3; t_3 - t_2 \leqq \tau), \\ \left| x_{\kappa_3}^{(3)} - \bar{x}_{\kappa_3}^{(3)} \right| < \eta_2 \, e^{nA\tau} = \eta[1 + e^{nA\tau}]e^{nA\tau}, \end{cases}$$

from which it follows that

$$(20) \quad \left| x^{(3)} - \bar{x}_{\kappa_3}^{(3)} \right| < \eta[1 + e^{nA\tau} + e^{2nA\tau}] = \eta_3.$$

After the process has been continued in a similar way over q intervals, the corresponding inequality is

$$(21) \quad \left| x^{(q)} - \bar{x}_{\kappa_q}^{(q)} \right| < \eta[1 + e^{nA\tau} + \cdots + e^{(q-1)nA\tau}] = \eta_q,$$

provided all the $x^{(p)}$ remain in the region R for $t_{p-1} \lessgtr t \leqq t_p$, and $\kappa_p \geqq \kappa$, $t_p - t_{p-1} \leqq \tau$ for $p = 1, \cdots, q$. Since

$$\eta_q > \eta_{q-1} > \cdots > \eta,$$

it follows that η_q is an upper bound to $\left| x(t) - \bar{x}_{\kappa_p}(t) \right|$ on the whole interval $t_0 \lessgtr t \leqq t_q$.

The conditions that have been supposed to be satisfied are:

(a) The independent variable t has not attained the border of the region R.

(b) All the approximations in each interval are in the region R.

(c) None of the x has attained a border of the region R_1.

In terms of the notation that has been adopted, these conditions are explicitly

$$(22) \quad \begin{cases} \text{(a)} \quad t_p - t_0 \; < \rho, \\ \text{(b)} \quad t_{p+1} - t_p \; \leqq \dfrac{r - |\bar{x}_\kappa{}^{(p)}(t_p) - a| - \eta_p}{M}, \\ \text{(c)} \; |\bar{x}_{\kappa_p}{}^{(p)} - a| < r - \delta - \eta_p. \end{cases}$$

The upper bound η_q is a function of the two parameters κ and τ. In order that the process shall define a solution for the q intervals $t_1 - t_0, t_2 - t_1, \cdots, t_q - t_{q-1}$, one or the other of the limit equations

$$\lim_{\kappa=\infty} = \eta_q(\kappa, \tau) = 0, \qquad \lim_{\tau=0} \eta_q(\kappa, \tau) = 0$$

must be satisfied.

It follows from equations (8) and (21) that

$$(23) \qquad \lim_{\kappa=\infty} \eta_q(\kappa, \tau) = 0,$$

whatever the values of τ and q; and it follows from the same equations that

$$(24) \qquad \lim_{\tau=0} \eta_q(\kappa, \tau) = 0,$$

whatever the values of κ and q.

If q remains fixed as τ approaches zero, the interval $t_q - t_0 \leqq q\tau$ approaches zero and the limit (24) is valueless. Suppose, however, that the steps of the solution are so arranged that $t_p - t_{p-1} = \tau$ $(p = 1, \cdots, q)$ and that, as τ decreases, q increases in such a way that $\rho_0 < q\tau < \rho_1 < \rho$, where ρ_1 is any number such that the approximations on the q steps all remain within the region R. Then it follows from the inequality (21) that

$$\eta_q < \eta q \, e^{nA\rho} < \frac{\eta}{\tau} \, \rho \, e^{nA\rho}.$$

It follows from these inequalities and the relations (8) that

$$(25) \quad \lim_{\tau=0} \eta_q = \rho \, e^{nA\rho} \lim_{\tau=0} \frac{\eta(\kappa, \tau)}{\tau} = 0 \qquad (\kappa = 1, 2, \cdots).$$

That is, over any fixed interval $t_0 \leqq t \leqq t_q$ for which the relations (22) are satisfied, the process defines sequences of functions which converge for $\kappa = 1, 2, 3, \cdots$ to a solution as τ tends to zero, and the convergence is uniform with respect to t on the interval. Therefore the limits of the process with respect to both κ and τ are a solution of the differential equations (1).

The only remaining problem is to show that, for any value of κ, the parameters τ and q can be so determined in advance that either t or some x for some value of t in the interval $t_0 \leqq t \leqq t_q$ will attain a border of the region R_1. If on the pth interval any of the relations

$$(26) \quad \begin{cases} t_p - t_0 = \rho, \\ \bar{x}_{\kappa_p}{}^{(p)} - a > +r - \delta + \eta_p, \\ \bar{x}_{\kappa_p}{}^{(p)} - a < -r + \delta - \eta_p \end{cases}$$

is satisfied, then either t or at least one of the x for some value of t is on a border of the region R_1. The problem is, therefore, to define an interval $t_{p+1} - t_p$, having a positive lower bound, over which the process will always be valid whenever none of the relations (22) is satisfied, and such that one of the relations (26) eventually will be satisfied. Since the relations are expressed by inequalities, there will be infinitely many ways in which the interval can be defined.

Suppose that none of the relations (26) is satisfied; that is, that

$$(27) \quad \begin{cases} t_p - t_0 < \rho, \\ \bar{x}_{\kappa_p}{}^{(p)} - a \leqq +r - \delta + \eta_p, \\ \bar{x}_{\kappa_p}{}^{(p)} - a \geqq -r + \delta - \eta_p. \end{cases}$$

Although, if any of relations (26) is satisfied, either t or some x has attained a border of the region R_1, the opposite relations (27) do not imply the relations (22) nor that every x has not attained a border of the region R_1. Therefore assume that no x has attained a border of the region R_1. Hence the solution can be continued another step subject to the relations (22). It follows from relations (22) and relations (27) that, if the relations

$$(28) \quad \begin{cases} t_{p+1} - t_p \leqq \rho - (t_p - t_0), \\ t_{p+1} - t_p \leqq \dfrac{r - (r - \delta + \eta_p) - \eta_p}{M} = \dfrac{\delta - 2\eta_p}{M} \end{cases}$$

are satisfied, the process is valid. Hence $2\eta_p$ will be taken less than the preassigned δ for $p = 1, 2, \cdots$. In order to arrive at explicit results, suppose $4\eta_p = \delta$ for $p = 1, 2, \cdots$.

It follows from the limit equations (25) that, corresponding to every positive integer κ, a number σ_κ (depending on κ) exists such that, for every value of τ for which $\tau \leqq \sigma_\kappa$, the value of $4\eta_p \leqq \delta$ for $p = 1, 2, \cdots$. Consequently the relations (28) will hold if the relations

$$(29) \quad \begin{cases} 4\eta_p < \dfrac{4\eta(\kappa, \sigma_\kappa)}{\sigma_\kappa} \, \rho e^{nA\rho} < \delta, \\[2mm] \tau \leqq \sigma_\kappa, \\[2mm] t_{p+1} - t_p \leqq \tau \qquad (p = 0, 1, 2, \cdots, q), \\[2mm] t_{p+1} - t_p < \dfrac{\delta}{2M} \end{cases}$$

are satisfied.

Suppose the differential equations, the region R, and the initial conditions for some set of values of the variables in the region R are given. Suppose the upper bound M of the $|f(x, t)|$ and the Lipschitz constant A have been determined for the $f(x, t)$ in the region R. Suppose the positive number δ and an upper bound κ to the number of approximations on each interval have been chosen. Suppose, finally, that an upper bound ϵ to the absolute value of the possible error in the solution until it attains a border of the region R_1 is given. Let it be required to determine τ in advance so that the process can be continued until either t or some x has attained a border of the region R_1, and so that the absolute value of the error of the solution at all points in the region R_1 shall be less than ϵ.

Since $\eta_p \leqq \eta_q$ for $p = 1, 2, \cdots$, one condition is $\eta_q < \epsilon$. It follows from the limit equation (25) that τ can be so determined that this inequality will be satisfied. The first inequality of (29) puts another restriction upon τ, and therefore τ must be determined so that it will satisfy both inequalities. Finally, it follows from the last of the inequalities (29) that τ must also satisfy the inequality $2M\tau < \delta$. When τ satisfies all these relations, the process may be applied, step after step, in a routine way until the computations show that a border of the region R_1 has been attained, and for every value of t for which the computed solution is interior to the region R_1 the absolute values of the errors in the x will not exceed ϵ.

117. Effects of Approximate Quadratures. It has been tacitly assumed in the preceding articles that all the quadratures involved are carried out with numerical exactness. In practice, however, they are formed by numerical processes and consequently are subject to numerical approximations. The question is whether these approximations will impair the validity of the conclusions.

When the integrands are continuous functions of the variables of integration, as they are here, the computations can always be so made by such methods as that of Simpson, for example, that an upper bound to the absolute value of the possible error in each quadrature shall be as small as may be desired. It will now be shown that this upper bound can be made so small that the conclusion of Art. 116 holds even though the quadratures are only approximate.

Since $|f(x; t)| < M$ for all values of the x in the region R, the variation in the $|f(x; t)|$ is bounded in every interval $t_{p+1} - t_p$. Since the x are continuous functions of t and the $f(x; t)$ are continuous functions of t and the x, it follows from Appendix F that the $f(x; t)$ are continuous functions of t. Therefore the quadratures can be so arranged in advance that the absolute value of the error in each one shall not exceed an arbitrary positive number μ.

Consider the first interval $t_0 \leqq t \leqq t_1$ and let the approximate computed value of the $x_{\kappa_1}^{(1)}$ be represented by $X_{\kappa_1}^{(1)}$. Let the fact that an integral is computed only approximately with μ as an upper bound of the possible error be indicated by placing a bar over the integral sign. Then it follows that

$$(30) \quad \begin{cases} x_1^{(1)} = a + \displaystyle\int_{t_0}^{t} f(a + \phi^{(1)}; t)dt, \\[2mm] X_1^{(1)} = a + \displaystyle\overline{\int}_{t_0}^{t} f(a + \phi^{(1)}; t)dt, \\[2mm] \left| x_1^{(1)} - X_1^{(1)} \right| \leqq \mu \qquad (t_0 \leqq t \leqq t_1). \end{cases}$$

The functions $X_1^{(1)}$ will be in the region R if $t_1 - t_0 \leqq \rho, r/M$.

Now consider the computed second approximations on the first interval. They will be subject to errors due to the $X_1^{(1)}$, upon which they depend; and they will be subject to errors also due to the fact that the quadratures are only approximate.

Let $\xi_2^{(1)}$ represent the exact integrals when the arguments in the integrands are the approximate $X_1^{(1)}$. Then it follows that

$$(31) \quad \begin{cases} x_2^{(1)} = a + \displaystyle\int_{t_0}^t f(x_1^{(1)}; \, t)dt \qquad (t_0 \leqq t \leqq t_1), \\[2ex] \xi_2^{(1)} = a + \displaystyle\int_{t_0}^t f(X_1^{(1)}; \, t)dt, \\[2ex] X_2^{(1)} = a + \displaystyle\int_{t_0}^{\overline{t}} f(X_1^{(1)}; \, t)dt, \end{cases}$$

and the $X_2^{(1)}$ will be in the region R if $t_1 - t_0 \leqq \rho$, $(r - \mu)/M$. Then it follows from the fact that the $f(x; \, t)$ have the Lipschitz property in the x, from the last of relations (30), and from the definition of μ that

$$\begin{cases} |x_2^{(1)} - \xi_2^{(1)}| \leqq \left| \displaystyle\int_{t_0}^t [f(x_1^{(1)}; \, t) - f(X_1^{(1)}; \, t)dt \right| \\[2ex] \qquad \leqq A\sum \displaystyle\int_{t_0}^t |x_1^{(1)} - X_1^{(1)}| \, dt \leqq nA\mu(t - t_0), \\[2ex] |\xi_2^{(1)} - X_2^{(1)}| = \left| \displaystyle\int_{t_0}^t f(X_1^{(1)}; \, t)dt - \displaystyle\int_{t_0}^{\overline{t}} f(X_1^{(1)}; \, t)dt \right| \leqq \mu; \end{cases}$$

and, therefore, that

$$(32) \quad |x_2^{(1)} - X_2^{(1)}| \leqq \mu[1 + nA(t - t_0)] \qquad (t_0 \leqq t \leqq t_1).$$

Similarly, for the third approximation, let

$$\begin{cases} x_3^{(1)} = a + \displaystyle\int_{t_0}^t f(x_2^{(1)}; \, t)dt, \\[2ex] \xi_3^{(1)} = a + \displaystyle\int_{t_0}^t f(X_2^{(1)}; \, t)dt, \\[2ex] X_3^{(1)} = a + \displaystyle\int_{t_0}^{\overline{t}} f(X_2^{(1)}; \, t)dt, \end{cases}$$

from which it follows that

$$(33) \quad |x_3^{(1)} - X_3^{(1)}| \leqq \mu \left[1 + \frac{nA(t - t_0)}{1!} + \frac{[nA(t - t_0)]^2}{2!} \right].$$

The process can be continued in a similar way to succeeding steps. At the κ_1st step the corresponding relation is

$$(34) \quad \left| x_{\kappa_1}{}^{(1)} - X_{\kappa_1}{}^{(1)} \right| \leqq \mu \left[1 + \cdots + \frac{[nA(t - t_0)]^{\kappa_1 - 1}}{(\kappa_1 - 1)!} \right] < \mu\, e^{nA\tau}$$

$$(t_1 - t_0 \leqq \tau).$$

On combining this inequality with the relation (8), it is found that

$$(35) \quad \left| x^{(1)} - X_{\kappa_1}{}^{(1)} \right| < \eta + \mu\, e^{nA\tau} = \bar{\eta}_1 \qquad (t_0 \leqq t \leqq t_1),$$

where the $x^{(1)}$ are the exact solution functions on the first interval and the $X_{\kappa_1}{}^{(1)}$ are the approximate computed functions.

Now consider the extension of the solution to the second interval $t_1 \leqq t \leqq t_2$, where $t_2 - t_1 \leqq \tau$. Let the functions $x_1{}^{(2)}$, $\xi_1{}^{(2)}$, and $X_1{}^{(2)}$ be defined by

$$(36) \quad \begin{cases} x_1{}^{(2)} = x^{(1)}(t_1) + \displaystyle\int_{t_1}^{t} f(x^{(1)}(t_1) + \phi^{(2)}; t)dt, \\[2mm] \xi_1{}^{(2)} = X_{\kappa_1}{}^{(1)}(t_1) + \displaystyle\int_{t_1}^{t} f(X_{\kappa_1}{}^{(1)}(t_1) + \phi^{(2)}; t)dt, \\[2mm] X_1{}^{(2)} = X_{\kappa_1}{}^{(1)}(t_1) + \displaystyle\int_{t_1}^{\bar{t}} f(X_{\kappa_1}{}^{(1)}(t_1) + \phi^{(2)}; t)dt. \end{cases}$$

All these functions will lie in the region R for all values of t on the second interval provided

$$M(t_2 - t_1) \leqq r - \left| X_{\kappa_1}{}^{(1)}(t_1) - a \right| - \mu.$$

It follows from the Lipschitz property of the $f(x; t)$ and from equations (35) and (36) that

$$\begin{cases} \left| x_1{}^{(2)} - \xi_1{}^{(2)} \right| \leqq \left| x^{(1)}(t_1) - X_{\kappa_1}{}^{(1)}(t_1) \right| + \left| \displaystyle\int_{t_1}^{t} [f(x^{(1)}(t_1) + \phi^{(2)}; t) \right. \\ \left. \qquad\qquad - f(X_{\kappa_1}{}^{(1)}(t_1) + \phi^{(2)}; t)]dt \right| \\ \qquad \leqq \bar{\eta}_1[1 + nA(t - t_1)], \\ \left| \xi_1{}^{(2)} - X_1{}^{(2)} \right| < \mu \qquad (t_1 \leqq t \leqq t_2); \end{cases}$$

and, therefore, that

$$(37) \quad \left| x_1{}^{(2)} - X_1{}^{(2)} \right| < \bar{\eta}_1[1 + nA(t - t_1)] + \mu \qquad (t_1 \leqq t \leqq t_2).$$

On making use of the equations defining the second approximations on the second interval, the equations corresponding to equations (36), and the inequalities (37), it is found similarly that

$$(38) \quad \left| x_2^{(2)} - X_2^{(2)} \right| < \bar{\eta}_1 \left\{ 1 + \cdots + \frac{[nA(t - t_1)]^2}{2!} \right\} \\ + \mu[1 + nA(t - t_0)].$$

An induction to the general step of the process on the second interval gives

$$(39) \quad \left| x_{\kappa_2}^{(2)} - X_{\kappa_2}^{(2)} \right| < [\bar{\eta}_1 + \mu]e^{nA\tau} = \eta e^{nA\tau} + \mu[1 + e^{nA\tau}]e^{nA\tau}.$$

On using these inequalities and the inequalities (15), it is found that

$$(40) \quad \left| x^{(2)} - X_{\kappa_2}^{(2)} \right| < [\eta + \mu e^{nA\tau}][1 + e^{nA\tau}] = \bar{\eta}_2 \quad (t_1 \leqq t \leqq t_2).$$

The right member of these inequalities is an upper bound to the absolute values of the differences between the exact solution functions and the corresponding computed approximations to them on the second interval.

Suppose the process under consideration has been extended over q intervals. It follows by an induction that

$$(41) \quad \begin{cases} \left| x^{(q)} - X_{\kappa}^{(q)} \right| < \eta + [\bar{\eta}_{q-1} + \mu]e^{nA\tau} \\ \quad = [\eta + \mu e^{nA\tau}][1 + \cdots + e^{(q-1)nA\tau}] = \bar{\eta}_q. \end{cases}$$

Since $\bar{\eta}_q > \bar{\eta}_{q-1} > \cdots > \bar{\eta}_1$, the quantity $\bar{\eta}_q$ is an upper bound, on every interval from the first to the qth, to the absolute value of the difference between the exact solution and the computed approximations to the solution.

Let τ and q be so related that $\rho_0 < q\tau < \rho_1$, where ρ_1 is any number such that all of the approximations are in the region R. Then it follows from the inequality (41) that

$$(42) \quad \left| x^{(p)} - X_{\kappa_p}^{(p)} \right| < [\eta + \mu e^{nA\tau}] \frac{\rho}{\tau} e^{nA\rho} \quad (p = 1, \cdots, q).$$

Now, it follows from equation (8) that, whatever may be the value of $\epsilon > 0$, the parameter τ can be so determined that, for any $\kappa = 1, 2, 3, \cdots$, the inequality

$$(43) \quad \rho e^{nA\rho} \frac{\eta(\kappa, \tau)}{\tau} < \frac{\epsilon}{2}$$

will be satisfied. Moreover, the computations of the quadratures can be so arranged that μ will imply the inequality

(44) $$\mu \frac{\rho}{\tau} e^{2n A \rho} < \frac{\epsilon}{2}.$$

It follows, therefore, from the inequalities (42), (43), and (44) that the computation can be so arranged that

(45) $$|x^{(p)} - X_{\kappa_p}{}^{(p)}| < \epsilon \qquad (p = 1, \cdots, q).$$

That is, an approximation to the solution of differential equations having the properties of equations (1) can be constructed by numerical processes until it attains a border of the region R_1 in such a way that the absolute value of the error for every value of the independent variable t will be less than any positive number ϵ chosen in advance.

The restrictions upon the interval τ and the numerical processes that have been imposed in order to insure the inequalities (43) and (44) are, of course, much more severe than would be required in practice, because they provide for the worst possible case that can exist under the hypotheses. This discussion establishes the complete validity of the process, but does not furnish a suitable guide for choosing the interval τ and the method of performing the quadratures.

118. Numerical Solutions. The preceding articles have laid logical foundations for numerical work, but they are far from providing convenient means for carrying out the work. The methods to be followed in numerical problems will be developed in the remainder of this chapter. Since they will conform with the processes assumed to be used in what precedes, they will be explained without insisting at every step on their logical aspects.

It will be noted that the method that has been discussed depends upon the formation of quadratures. Since the integrands will in general be functions whose primitives cannot be found, and may be functions not even expressed by formulas, it is evident that methods of wide applicability must in general be used.

One of the most convenient methods of finding approximate numerical values of a quadrature is to substitute for the integrand function a polynomial nearly coinciding with it in the range of integration. In fact, the coefficients of the polynomial can be so determined that its numerical value shall equal that of the integrand function at a number of points. The Lagrangian formula for a polynomial $P(t)$ that agrees in value with the function $f(t)$ for $t = t_1, t_2$, and t_3 is

$$(46) \quad P(t) = \frac{(t - t_2)(t - t_3)}{(t_1 - t_2)(t_1 - t_3)} f(t_1) + \frac{(t - t_1)(t - t_3)}{(t_2 - t_1)(t_2 - t_3)} f(t_2)$$
$$+ \frac{(t - t_1)(t - t_2)}{(t_3 - t_1)(t_3 - t_2)} f(t_3),$$

and similar equations for polynomials of higher degree.

In practice it is advantageous to have $t_\kappa - t_{\kappa-1} = \tau$. When the intervals are equal, equation (46) becomes

$$(47) \quad P(t) = \frac{1}{2\tau^2} \big[(t - t_2)(t - t_3)f(t_1) - 2(t - t_1)(t - t_3)f(t_2) $$
$$+ (t - t_1)(t - t_2)f(t_3) \big].$$

It is much more convenient, however, to compute the definite integrals by means of difference functions.

119. Definition and Simple Properties of Difference Functions. Let the values of the function $f(t)$ for $t = t_0, t_1, \cdots, t_p$ be represented by $f^{(0)}, f^{(1)}, \cdots, f^{(p)}$. It will be supposed that $t_\kappa - t_{\kappa-1} = \tau$. Then the successive difference functions for the argument t_p are defined by

$$(48) \quad \begin{cases} \Delta_1 f^{(p)} = \quad f^{(p)} - \quad f^{(p-1)} \quad (p = 1, 2, \cdots), \\ \Delta_2 f^{(p)} = \Delta_1 \ f^{(p)} - \Delta_1 \ f^{(p-1)}, \\ \cdot \quad \cdot \quad \cdot \quad \cdot \quad \cdot \quad \cdot \quad \cdot \quad \cdot \quad \cdot \\ \Delta_\kappa f^{(p)} = \Delta_{\kappa-1} f^{(p)} - \Delta_{\kappa-1} f^{(p-1)} \quad (\kappa = 2, 3, \cdots), \end{cases}$$

where $\Delta_\kappa f^{(p)}$ is the κth difference function of f for $t = t_p$.

It follows from equations (48) that $f^{(0)}, \cdots, f^{(p)}$ uniquely determine $\Delta_1 f^{(p)}, \cdots, \Delta_p f^{(p)}$, but they do not determine difference functions of higher order. Conversely, $f^{(0)}, \Delta_1 f^{(p)}, \cdots, \Delta_p f^{(p)}$ uniquely determine $f^{(1)}, \cdots, f^{(p)}$, but not $f^{(p+1)}$.

Now consider the particular polynomial defined by

$$(49) \quad p_\kappa(t) = (t - T)(t - T + \tau)(t - T + 2\tau) \cdots$$
$$(t - T + (\kappa - 1)\tau) \quad (\kappa = 1, 2, \cdots),$$

with $p_0(t) = 1$. It follows from the definitions (48) that

$$(50) \quad \begin{cases} \Delta_1 p_\kappa(t) = (t - T)(t - T + \tau) \cdots \\ \qquad (t - T + (\kappa - 2)\tau)[t - T + (\kappa - 1)\tau - (t - T - \tau)] \\ = \kappa \tau p_{\kappa-1}(t). \end{cases}$$

It follows by repeated applications of this formula that

$$(51) \quad \begin{cases} \Delta_\lambda p_\kappa(t) = \kappa(\kappa-1) \cdots (\kappa-\lambda+1)\tau^\lambda p_{\kappa-\lambda}(t) & (\lambda < \kappa), \\ \Delta_\lambda p_\kappa(t) = \lambda!\,\tau^\lambda & (\lambda = \kappa), \\ \Delta_\lambda p_\kappa(t) \equiv 0 & (\lambda > \kappa). \end{cases}$$

Any polynomial $P_m(t)$, of degree m in t, can be expressed in the form

$$(52) \qquad P_m(t) = c_0 + \sum_{\kappa=1}^{m} c_\kappa\, p_\kappa(t),$$

for $c_0 = P_m(T)$ and the coefficients $c_m, \cdots, c_1$ can be determined sequentially by equating coefficients of powers of $t - T$ in the right member of the equation to the coefficients of corresponding arguments in the left member.

The problem is to express the coefficients $c_1, \cdots, c_m$ in terms of the difference functions of $P_m(t)$. It follows directly from equations (51) and (52) that

$$(53) \quad \begin{cases} \Delta_\lambda P_m(T) = \sum_{\kappa=1}^{\lambda-1} c_\kappa\,\Delta_\lambda p_\kappa(T) + c_\lambda\Delta_\lambda p_\lambda(T) \\ \qquad\qquad + \sum_{\kappa=\lambda+1}^{m} c_\kappa\kappa(\kappa-1)\cdots(\kappa-\lambda+1)\tau^\lambda p_{\kappa-\lambda}(T) \\ \qquad = 0 + c_\lambda\,\lambda!\,\tau^\lambda + 0. \end{cases}$$

Therefore

$$(54) \qquad c_\lambda = \frac{\Delta_\lambda P_m(T)}{\lambda!\,\tau^\lambda} \qquad (\lambda = 1, \cdots, m),$$

and equation (52) becomes

$$(55) \qquad P_m(t) = P_m(T) + \sum_{\lambda=1}^{m} \frac{\Delta_\lambda P_m(T)}{\lambda!\,\tau^\lambda}\, p_\lambda(t).$$

Suppose now that $P(t)$ is any continuous function of t for $T \geqq t \geqq T - m\tau$. A polynomial $P_m(t)$ can be determined that will equal the function $P(t)$ for $t = T,\ T - \tau,\ T - 2\tau,\ \cdots,$ $T - m\tau$. If the degree m of the polynomial and the interval τ are properly chosen, the polynomial and the function will have nearly equal values at all other points on the interval. Therefore an approximate expression for the function $P(t)$ on the interval $T \geqq t \geqq T - m\tau$ is

$$(56) \qquad P(t) \doteq P(T) + \sum_{\lambda=1}^{m} \frac{\Delta_\lambda P(T)}{\lambda!\,\tau^\lambda}\, p_\lambda(t).$$

120. Arrangement of Difference Tables; Extrapolation; Detection of Errors. In extensive computations it is very important to have the numerical work systematically arranged and to preserve on the work sheets all arithmetical operations. If the values of the function $P(t)$ for $t = t_0, t_1, t_2, \cdots$ are $P_0, P_1, P_2, \cdots$ respectively, the difference functions for $P(t)$ may be conveniently arranged as in the following table:

t	$P(t)$	$\Delta_1 P(t)$	$\Delta_2 P(t)$	$\Delta_3 P(t)$
t_0	P_0			
t_1	P_1	$\Delta_1 P_1$		
t_2	P_2	$\Delta_1 P_2$	$\Delta_2 P_2$	
t_3	P_3	$\Delta_1 P_3$	$\Delta_2 P_3$	$\Delta_3 P_3$
t_4	P_4	$\Delta_1 P_4$	$\Delta_2 P_4$	$\Delta_3 P_4$
...	...	...	...	...
...	...	...	...	...
...	...	...	...	...

This table is formed by subtracting each number from the one immediately beneath it and setting the remainder opposite the minuend in the column to the right.

If the function $P(t)$ is a smoothly varying continuous function, such as those usually encountered in physical problems, and if the interval τ is small enough, the differences of higher order will be numerically small in comparison with the associated values of the function, and the differences of higher order will change slowly. Consequently, it is possible to approximate closely to the value of the function at the succeeding value of t, say t_5 in the table, by inferring from the last column of differences the next succeeding difference, $\Delta_3 P_5$ in the table, and adding it to the last entry in the column to the left, and this sum to the last entry in the next column to the left, and so on to the value of the function itself.

In extensive computations numerical errors are occasionally made. The use of difference tables for functions that vary smoothly will nearly always reveal the existence and location of an error in the computed value of the function for an isolated value of the argument. Suppose an error e has been committed in computing the value of P_κ, but that the neighboring values of $P(t)$ are correct. Then it follows from equations (48) that $\Delta_1 P_\kappa$ and $\Delta_1 P_{\kappa+1}$ contain the errors $+ e$ and $- e$ respectively. Then it follows, similarly, that $\Delta_2 P_\kappa$, $\Delta_2 P_{\kappa+1}$, and $\Delta_2 P_{\kappa+2}$ contain the errors $+ e$, $- 2e$, and $+ e$ respectively; $\Delta_3 P_\kappa$, $\Delta_3 P_{\kappa+1}$, $\Delta_3 P_{\kappa+2}$, and $\Delta_3 P_{\kappa+3}$ contain the errors $+ e$, $- 3e$, $+ 3e$, and $- e$ respectively, and so on. The coefficients of e in the differences of any order are the binomial coefficients, with alternating signs, associated with the corresponding powers of the variables of the binomial.

If e is small relative to the values of the function, its existence would not be evident nor would it be noticeable from a graph of the function. But the increasing coefficients with alternating signs make the multiples of the error that occur in the relatively small differences of higher order conspicuous. That is, when an error has been committed, even of a unit or two in the last place used in the computation, the differences of higher order will become irregular. Since the coefficients of the error are the binomial coefficients with alternating signs, the sum of the differences in each difference column is independent of the error. Hence it is generally possible to determine immediately both the location and the magnitude of the error e. But if there are errors in the function for successive values of t, they cannot generally be located simply from an examination of the irregularities in the differences of higher order.

121. Interpolation by Difference Functions. Equation (56) is a formula by means of which an approximate value of $P(t)$ can be determined for any value of t near T, particularly for $T - \tau < t < T$. Let $P_0 = P(T)$, $P_{-1/\kappa} = P(T - \tau/\kappa)$, and $P_{1/\kappa} = P(T + \tau/\kappa)$. Then the most frequently used interpolating formulas are found to be

$$(57) \quad \begin{cases} P_{-1/4} \doteq P_0 - \tfrac{1}{4}\Delta_1 P_0 - \tfrac{3}{32}\Delta_2 P_0 - \tfrac{7}{128}\Delta_3 P_0 - \tfrac{77}{2048}\Delta_4 P_0 \cdots, \\ P_{-1/3} \doteq P_0 - \tfrac{1}{3}\Delta_1 P_0 - \tfrac{1}{9}\Delta_2 P_0 - \tfrac{5}{81}\Delta_3 P_0 - \tfrac{10}{243}\Delta_4 P_0 \cdots, \\ P_{-1/2} \doteq P_0 - \tfrac{1}{2}\Delta_1 P_0 - \tfrac{1}{8}\Delta_2 P_0 - \tfrac{1}{16}\Delta_3 P_0 - \tfrac{5}{128}\Delta_4 P_0 \cdots, \\ P_{1/2} \doteq P_0 + \tfrac{1}{2}\Delta_1 P_0 + \tfrac{3}{8}\Delta_2 P_0 + \tfrac{5}{16}\Delta_3 P_0 + \tfrac{35}{128}\Delta_4 P_0 \cdots, \\ P_{1/3} \doteq P_0 + \tfrac{1}{3}\Delta_1 P_0 + \tfrac{2}{9}\Delta_2 P_0 + \tfrac{14}{81}\Delta_3 P_0 + \tfrac{77}{486}\Delta_4 P_0 \cdots, \\ P_{1/4} \doteq P_0 + \tfrac{1}{4}\Delta_1 P_0 + \tfrac{5}{32}\Delta_2 P_0 + \tfrac{15}{128}\Delta_3 P_0 + \tfrac{195}{2048}\Delta_4 P_0 \cdots. \end{cases}$$

The right members of these equations can be expressed in terms of $P(t)$ and its difference functions for other values of the argument by using equations (48). For example, it is found from these equations that

$$(58) \begin{cases} P(T) &= P(T + \tau) - \Delta_1 P(T + \tau), \\ \Delta_\lambda P(T) &= \Delta_\lambda P(T + \tau) - \Delta_{\lambda+1} P(T + \tau), \\ P(T) &= P(T - \tau) + \Delta_1 P(T - \tau) + \Delta_2 P(T - \tau) + \cdots, \\ \Delta_\lambda P(T) &= \Delta_\lambda P(T - \tau) + \Delta_{\lambda+1} P(T - \tau) + \cdots. \end{cases}$$

122. Computation of Definite Integrals by Difference Functions.

Definite integrals will be required over the interval from $T - \tau$ to T. It follows from equations (49) that

$$(59) \begin{cases} \int_{T-\tau}^{T} p_1(t)dt = -\frac{1}{2}\tau^2, & \int_{T-\tau}^{T} p_3(t)dt = -\frac{1}{4}\tau^4, \\ \int_{T-\tau}^{T} p_2(t)dt = -\frac{1}{6}\tau^3, & \int_{T-\tau}^{T} p_4(t)dt = -\frac{19}{30}\tau^5. \end{cases}$$

Hence it follows from the approximate equation (56) that if $P_0 = P(T)$, then the approximate value of the integral of $P(t)$ from $T - \tau$ to T is

$$(60) \quad \int_{T-\tau}^{T} Pdt \doteq \tau[P_0 - \tfrac{1}{2}\Delta_1 P_0 - \tfrac{1}{12}\Delta_2 P_0 - \tfrac{1}{24}\Delta_3 P_0 - \tfrac{19}{720}\Delta_4 P_0 \cdots].$$

This integral can be expressed in terms of $P_1 = P(T + \tau)$ and the $\Delta_\lambda(T + \tau)$ by means of the first and second of equations (58). The result is

$$(61) \quad \int_{T-\tau}^{T} Pdt \doteq \tau[P_1 - \tfrac{3}{2}\Delta_1 P_1 + \tfrac{5}{12}\Delta_2 P_1 + \tfrac{1}{24}\Delta_3 P_1 + \tfrac{11}{720}\Delta_4 P_1 \cdots].$$

A repetition of the formulas for $P_2 = P(T + 2\tau)$ gives the corresponding formula

$$(62) \quad \int_{T-\tau}^{T} Pdt \doteq \tau[P_2 - \tfrac{5}{2}\Delta_1 P_2 + \tfrac{23}{12}\Delta_2 P_2 - \tfrac{3}{8}\Delta_3 P_2 - \tfrac{19}{720}\Delta_4 P_2 \cdots].$$

The foregoing are the integrals that will be useful in the sequel.

123. The General Step in the Construction of the Solution.

It is advisable to explain the method of forming the general step of a solution before showing how to take the first steps.

Suppose the solution of the differential equations (1) has been determined for $t = t_0, t_1, \cdots, t_p$ and that it is desired to compute the values of the x_i for the solution at $t = t_{p+1}$. It will be supposed that $t_k - t_{k-1} = \tau$ for $k = 1, \cdots, p$. Let $x_i(t_k)$ be represented by $x_i^{(k)}$ and let $f_i^{(k)} = f_i(x_j^{(k)}; t_k)$. Suppose difference tables have been constructed for the $x_i^{(k)}$ and the $f_i^{(k)}$, for $k = 1, \cdots, p$, similar to that described in Art. 120.

The first problem is to extrapolate from the difference tables by the method described in Art. 120 either the $x_i^{(p+1)}$ or the $f_i^{(p+1)}$. It is generally advisable to choose the set of variables whose differences of the highest order used vary the more slowly, though either set may be used. Suppose that the $f_i^{(p+1)}$ are extrapolated.

The next step is to compute the $x_i^{(p+1)}$. Since it follows from the differential equations (1) that

$$(63) \qquad x_i^{(p+1)} = x_i^{(p)} + \int_{t_p}^{t_{p+1}} f_i(x_j; t)dt,$$

the values of the $x_i^{(p+1)}$ can be determined by using the general formula (60); whence,

$$(64) \quad x_i^{(p+1)} \doteq x_i^{(p)} + \tau[f_i^{(p+1)} - \tfrac{1}{2}\Delta_1 f_i^{(p+1)} - \tfrac{1}{12}\Delta_2 f_i^{(p+1)} \cdots].$$

The $f_i^{(p+1)}$ in the right members of equations (64) were determined by extrapolation and, consequently, are subject to possible errors. If τ is chosen small enough, the corresponding errors in the values of the $x_i^{(p+1)}$ computed from equations (64) will be much smaller. Hence more nearly correct values of the $f_i^{(p+1)}$ are given by

$$(65) \qquad f_i^{(p+1)} = f_i(x_j^{(p+1)}; t_{p+1}),$$

for, by hypothesis, the $f_i(x_j; t)$ are in some way uniquely defined for all values of the x_j and t in the region R.

With the corrected values of the $f_i^{(p+1)}$, more nearly correct values of the $x_i^{(p+1)}$ can be determined by a repeated use of equations (64). It is not necessary, however, to repeat the entire computation, although it would not be costly to do so because the formula is very simple. Suppose the correction to the extrapolated value of $f_i{}^{(p+1)}$ is e, which in practice will be a few units in the last place used in the computation. It follows from the method of forming the difference functions that $\Delta_1 f_i{}^{(p+1)}$, $\Delta_2 f_i{}^{(p+1)}$, $\cdots$ all require the same correction e. Then it follows from equations (64) that the corresponding corrections to the $x_i{}^{(p+1)}$ are $\frac{3}{8} e \tau$, which usually can be formed and applied directly. If the corrections to the $x_i{}^{(p+1)}$ are large or if the $f_i(x_j; t)$ change rapidly with changes in the x_i near $x_i{}^{(p+1)}$, it may be necessary to recompute the $f_i{}^{(p+1)}$ and repeat the whole step. It is generally advisable in practice to take τ so small that a recomputation of the $f_i{}^{(p+1)}$ is not required.

If in the course of a computation the differences of the highest order used become very small, the interval may be doubled by forming difference tables omitting alternate entries in the last few steps of the computation. If, on the other hand, the differences of the highest order used become large or vary irregularly, the interval should be reduced to one-half its former value by interpolating values of the x_i and the f_i for the midpoints of the intervals used by the method of Art. 121. It may sometimes be found advisable in the course of a computation to double an interval or to divide an interval several times, or sometimes to increase and sometimes to decrease it in the same computation.

It will be observed that the computations outlined give the values of the x_i only for $t = t_0, t_1, t_2, \cdots$. The values of the x_i are given approximately for all intermediate values of t, however, by equation (56). On making use of equation (49), this equation gives for values of t near t_p

$$(66) \quad x_i \doteq x_i{}^{(p)} + \Delta_1 x_i{}^{(p)} \frac{(t - t_p)}{\tau} + \frac{1}{2} \Delta_2 x_i{}^{(p)} \frac{(t - t_p)(t - t_p + \tau)}{\tau^2}$$
$$+ \frac{1}{6} \Delta_3 x_i{}^{(p)} \frac{(t - t_p)(t - t_p + \tau)(t - t_p + 2\tau)}{\tau^3} + \cdots.$$

The problem is therefore completely solved.

124. The First Steps of the Solution. The method described in the preceding article for taking the general step in the construction of the solution cannot be used for the first steps, because it depends upon successive differences of various functions which cannot be formed until a few steps on the solution have been made. The method that is most convenient in practice is to compute approximate values of the functions for the first three or four steps, and then to correct them after the difference tables have been started.

Since

$$(67) \qquad \frac{dx_i}{dt} = f_i(a_j; t_0)$$

at $t = t_0$, it follows that approximate values of the x_i at $t = t_1$ are

$$(68) \qquad \bar{x}_i{}^{(1)} \doteq a_i + \tau f_i(a_j; t_0) \qquad (t_1 - t_0 = \tau).$$

The value to be chosen for τ depends upon the number of significant figures desired in the result. It will generally be found satisfactory to choose τ so that $\tau f_i(a_j; t_0)$ shall not exceed a thousand times the unit in the last place used in the computation, but no rule applicable to all cases can be given.

The derivatives of the x_i at $t = t_1$ are approximately

$$(69) \qquad \left(\frac{dx_i}{dt} \right)_{t_1} \doteq f_i(\bar{x}_i{}^{(1)}; t_1).$$

Now, since the $f_i(x_i; t)$ are continuous functions of the x_j and t, the average rates of change of the x_i in the interval $t_0 \lesseqgtr t \leqq t_1$ are approximately equal to the average of the rates of change of the x_i at the ends of the interval. Therefore more nearly correct values of the x_i at $t = t_1$ are

$$(70) \qquad \bar{\bar{x}}_i{}^{(1)} \doteq a_i + \tfrac{1}{2}\tau[f_i(a_j; t_0) + f_i(\bar{x}_j{}^{(1)}; t_1)].$$

More nearly correct values of the x_i at $t = t_1$ might be determined by a repetition of the process, but generally it is not advisable to repeat it.

It is now possible to compute the $f_i(x_j; t)$ at $t = t_1$, which are the $f_i{}^{(1)}$ in the notation of Art. 123. Since the x_i and the f_i are known exactly at $t = t_0$ and approximately known at $t = t_1$, the difference tables can be started and approximate values of the first differences can be entered.

The next approximate step is similar to the general step, with the limitation that only first differences are available for the extrapolations and for the application of equation (64). The third step can be formed similarly, with both first and second differences available for the extrapolations and the integrations.

Approximate values of the x_i are known at this stage for $t = t_1$, t_2, t_3, and the difference tables contain first, second, and third differences. It is advisable at this stage to correct the approximate values of the x_i at $t = t_1$, t_2, t_3.

It follows from equations (62), (61), and (60) that more nearly correct values of the x_i at $t = t_1$, t_2, t_3 are given respectively by

$$(71) \quad \begin{cases} x_i{}^{(1)} \doteq a_i + \tau\big[f_i{}^{(3)} - \tfrac{5}{2}\Delta_1 f_i{}^{(3)} + \tfrac{23}{12}\Delta_2 f_i{}^{(3)} - \tfrac{3}{8}\Delta_3 f_i{}^{(3)}\big], \\ x_i{}^{(2)} \doteq a_i + \tau\big[f_i{}^{(3)} - \tfrac{3}{2}\Delta_1 f_i{}^{(3)} + \tfrac{5}{12}\Delta_2 f_i{}^{(3)} + \tfrac{1}{24}\Delta_3 f_i{}^{(3)}\big], \\ x_i{}^{(3)} \doteq a_i + \tau\big[f_i{}^{(3)} - \tfrac{1}{2}\Delta_1 f_i{}^{(3)} - \tfrac{1}{12}\Delta_2 f_i{}^{(3)} - \tfrac{1}{24}\Delta_3 f_i{}^{(3)}\big]. \end{cases}$$

With these values of the x_i, the $f_i{}^{(1)}$, $f_i{}^{(2)}$, and $f_i{}^{(3)}$ are to be recomputed and all the difference tables are to be corrected.

If the changes in the $f_i{}^{(j)}$ produce appreciable changes in the right members of equations (71), the $x_i{}^{(j)}$ should be recomputed. The work can be abbreviated as follows. Suppose the corrections to the $f_i{}^{(1)}$, $f_i{}^{(2)}$, and $f_i{}^{(3)}$ are respectively e_1, e_2 and e_3. Then it follows from equations (71) that

$$(72) \quad \begin{cases} \text{correction to } x_i{}^{(1)} = \tfrac{1}{24}\tau[19e_1 - 5e_2 + e_3], \\ \text{correction to } x_i{}^{(2)} = \tfrac{1}{3}\tau[4e_1 + e_2 + 0], \\ \text{correction to } x_i{}^{(3)} = \tfrac{3}{8}\tau[3e_1, + 3e_2 - e_3]. \end{cases}$$

It follows that the correction e_1 is much more important than the corrections e_2 and e_3. This is the reason that it is advisable to make a second approximation to the $x_i{}^{(1)}$ by means of equation (70), while first approximations to the $x_i{}^{(2)}$ and $x_i{}^{(3)}$ will usually suffice. In any case, at this stage equations (71) should be applied repeatedly if necessary until further repetitions do not change the values of the $x_i{}^{(j)}$. Then, if τ is small enough, the solution can be carried forward by the method of Art. 123.

The simplicity of the method that has been described can be appreciated only by its practical application. It is advisable to apply it first to some problem, such as the problem of two bodies, that can be solved otherwise. The ease of application of the method and the correctness of the results it gives quickly inspire confidence in it.

XII. QUESTIONS AND PROBLEMS

1. Why was the region R, in Art. 113, supposed to be closed? Does this hypothesis impose important limitations on the problem from a practical point of view?

2. What was the purpose of introducing the region R_1 in Art. 113?

3. What in Art. 123 plays the rôle of the $\phi^{(1)}(t)$ and $\phi^{(2)}(t)$ of Arts. 114 and 115?

4. Inasmuch as the $x^{(1)}(t_1)$ are not known, what was the purpose in introducing equations 11 and 12?

5. Work out the details of equations (17).

6. What notational advantage is obtained by introducing the symbols $\eta_2, \eta_3, \cdots, \eta_q$ by equations (18), (20), and (21) respectively?

7. Derive the general inequality (21).

8. What is the reason for the introduction of $-\eta$ in the right member of the second of the relations (13)?

9. Verify the relations (28).

10. Choose for η_p some other value, satisfying the imposed relations, than $4\eta_p = \delta$ and derive the relations corresponding to the relations (29).

11. Prove in detail that the statements in the third paragraph of Art. 117 are correct.

12. What is the reason for the introduction of the functions $\xi_2^{(1)}$ in the second of equations (31)?

13. Verify the relations (34).

14. Make the induction that leads to the inequalities (41).

15. Write the equations corresponding to equations (46) and (47) when $P(t)$ is a polynomial in t of the fourth degree.

16. Form a difference table for values of $\sin t$ to five places with an interval of 5°. Extrapolate values of the function and compare the result with the true values. Make an error of two units in the fifth place of one of the intermediate values of $\sin t$ in the difference table and observe the effects upon the differences. From the nature of the differences discover the location and amount of the error.

17. From the difference table of Problem 16 interpolate the values of $\sin t$ for intermediate values of t by means of equations (57).

18. Derive the equation corresponding to equations (57) for $t = T - \frac{2}{3}\tau$.

19. Compute the right member of the next equation in the series (59).

20. Interpret geometrically the first two steps of Art. 124.

21. Solve the differential equation

$$\frac{dx}{dt} = x, \qquad x(0) = 1$$

by the method of Arts. 124 and 123, and compare the result with the solution function

$$x = e^t = 1 + t + \frac{t^2}{2!} + \frac{t^3}{3!} + \cdots.$$

HISTORICAL SKETCH

Newton in his *Principia* was the first to find approximate solutions of differential equations by numerical processes. Naturally the details of his methods differed much from those now in use, but the underlying principles were the same.

The successors of Newton perfected the operations used in obtaining numerical solutions of differential equations, and they applied the method to problems in celestial mechanics to which more general methods are not adapted. For example, if a comet passes near Jupiter and is for a time under the dominating influence of the planet, its motion can be most conveniently followed during the interval by numerical processes. On the other hand, such methods are useless for determining the general characteristics of the mutual interactions of the planets or of the perturbations of the motions of the moon by the sun. They are, in fact, valuable in only a few particular numerical problems on limited intervals for the independent variable. They could not be used, for example, in the analytic case to determine the locations of the singular points of the solution functions in the complex plane.

The methods of numerical integration were, however, used by Hill as an aid in difficult theoretical investigations in his celebrated researches on the Lunar Theory (*American Journal of Mathematics*, Vol. I), and in the same way by Sir George Darwin in his calculations of periodic orbits (*Acta Mathematica*, Vol. 21). From considerations of symmetry, Hill inferred in the case he treated that if the infinitesimal body should cross each of two special axes perpendicularly, then the orbit, when referred to these axes, would be closed and the motion of the body would be periodic. He and Darwin took as initial conditions the infinitesimal body crossing one axis perpendicularly and varied the initial velocity until they found that the infinitesimal body would cross the other axis perpendicularly.

During the World War extensive use was made of the method of this chapter in computing the trajectories of projectiles as a basis for the construction of range tables. The retardation to which a projectile is subject is such a complicated function of its velocity with respect to the air that no other method is suitable.

A demonstration of the validity of the process of numerical integration, in the strict sense of Art. 117, naturally could not be made until after a logical foundation had been laid for it on a restricted interval, such as that of Picard. The proof over the complete region was worked out by the author, in 1914, and was published, in 1918, in a blue-print pamphlet issued by the Ballistic Branch of the Ordnance Department of the United States Army. This proof was reproduced, in 1926, in the author's *New Methods in Exterior Ballistics*, Chapter V, in substantially the form given here.

CHAPTER XIII

THE CAUCHY-LIPSCHITZ PROCESS

125. The Formal Process. There is another general method of solving differential equations. It was originated by Cauchy and perfected logically by Lipschitz, and it is the simplest of all methods in its conception.

The right members of the differential equations

$$(1) \qquad \begin{cases} \dfrac{dx_i}{dt} = f_i(x_j; t), \\ x_i(t_0) = a_i, \end{cases}$$

are assumed to possess the Lipschitz property with respect to the x_j for all values of the x_j and t in a closed region R, and to be continuous in t for all values of the x_j and t in the region R, where the region R is defined by

$$(2) \qquad \begin{cases} -r_i \leqq x_i - a_i \leqq r_i, \\ 0 \leqq t - t_0 \leqq \rho. \end{cases}$$

The interval $t_0 \leqq t \leqq t_0 + \rho$ is divided up into a number of sub-intervals $t_0 \leqq t \leqq t_1$, $t_1 \leqq t \leqq t_2$, $\cdots$, which may be equal or unequal in length. Functions of t are defined on these respective intervals by the equations

$$(3) \qquad \begin{cases} X_i{}^{(1)}(t) = a_i + f_i(a_j; t_0)(t - t_0) & (t_0 \leqq t \leqq t_1), \\ X_i{}^{(2)}(t) = X_i{}^{(1)}(t_1) + f_i(X_j{}^{(1)}(t_1); t_1)(t - t_1) & (t_1 \leqq t \leqq t_2), \\ \cdots \cdots \cdots \cdots \cdots \cdots \cdots \cdots \cdots \cdots \cdots \cdots \cdots \cdots \cdots, \end{cases}$$

the total interval covered by the process being so limited that neither t nor any $X_i{}^{(\kappa)}(t)$ shall be outside the region R.

It is evident from equations (3) that the functions defined by the process represent a number of segments of straight lines whose initial points are the terminal points of the corresponding preceding segments, and whose directions are determined by the conditions that the tangents of their inclinations to the t-axis shall equal the numerical values of the functions $f_i(x_j; t)$ at their initial points.

Now let the process pass toward a limit by subdividing the whole interval for which t and the $X_i^{(\kappa)}(t)$ remain in the region R into a greater and greater number of sub-intervals in such a way that the length of each sub-interval shall approach zero. Obviously the whole interval for which the $X_i^{(\kappa)}(t)$ remain in the region R may vary with successive subdivisions of the intervals. The limits of the process are continuous functions of t which may be designated by $X_i(t)$. That these limit functions constitute a solution of the differential equations may not be assumed without proof.

126. Proof that the Cauchy-Lipschitz Process Converges and Defines a Solution. The direct proof that the process converges and defines a solution is not difficult, but it will be simpler here to make the demonstration depend upon the discussions contained in Chapter XII. In order to establish the necessary relationships between the two processes, let equations (3) be written in the form

$$(4) \quad \begin{cases} X^{(1)}(t) = a + \int_{t_0}^{t} f(a; t_0)dt & (t_0 \leqq t \leqq t_1), \\ X^{(2)}(t) = X^{(1)}(t_1) + \int_{t_1}^{t} f(X^{(1)}(t_1); t_1)dt & (t_1 \leqq t \leqq t_2), \\ \cdots \cdots \cdots \cdots \cdots \cdots \cdots \cdots \cdots \cdots \cdots \cdots \end{cases}$$

the subscripts being omitted from the X_i and the a_i so that the notations shall agree with those of Chapter XII.

It follows from equations (5) and (11) of Chapter XII that the corresponding functions for the first approximations on the same intervals are defined by

$$(5) \quad \begin{cases} x_1^{(1)} = a + \int_{t_0}^{t} f(a; t)dt & (t_0 \leqq t \leqq t_1), \\ x_1^{(2)} = x_1^{(1)}(t_1) + \int_{t_1}^{t} f(x_1^{(1)}(t_1); t)dt & (t_1 \leqq t \leqq t_2), \\ \cdots \cdots \cdots \cdots \cdots \cdots \cdots \cdots \cdots \cdots \cdots \cdots \end{cases}$$

the $\phi^{(p)}(t)$ being identically zero in t in this case.

Since the $f(x; t)$ are continuous functions of t for all values of the x and t in the closed region R, it follows from the first of equations (4) and of (5) that a finite number θ exists such that, for every set of values of the a, t, and t_0 in the region R, the inequalities

$$(6) \quad \begin{cases} |x_1^{(1)} - X^{(1)}| = \left| \int_{t_0}^{t} [f(a; t) - f(a; t_0)] dt \right| \\ \qquad\qquad\qquad < \theta(t - t_0) \leqq \theta\tau \qquad (t_0 \leqq t \leqq t_1) \end{cases}$$

are satisfied. It follows similarly from the second of equations (4) and of (5) that

$$|x_1^{(2)} - X^{(2)}| \leqq |x_1^{(1)}(t_1) - X^{(1)}(t_1)| + \int_{t_1}^{t} \Big\{ |f(x_1^{(1)}(t_1); t) \\ - f(x_1^{(1)}(t_1); t_1)| + |f(x_1^{(1)}(t_1); t_1) - f(X^{(1)}(t_1); t_1)| \Big\} dt,$$

which give, as a consequence of the Lipschitz property of the $f(x; t)$, the inequalities (6), and the definition of θ,

$$(7) \quad \begin{cases} |x_1^{(2)} - X^{(2)}| < \theta\tau + \theta(t - t_1) + nA \int_{t_1}^{t} |x_1^{(1)}(t_1) - X^{(1)}(t_1)| dt \\ \qquad < \theta\tau + \theta(t - t_1) + nA\theta\tau(t - t_1) \\ \qquad \leqq \dfrac{\theta}{nA} [(1 + nA\tau)^2 - 1] \qquad (t_1 \leqq t \leqq t_2). \end{cases}$$

The induction to the general step leads to the inequalities

$$(8) \quad |x_1^{(p)} - X^{(p)}| < \frac{\theta}{nA} [(1 + nA\tau)^q - 1]$$
$$(t_{p-1} \leqq t \leqq t_p;\ p = 1, \cdots, q).$$

Since $q\tau \leqq \rho$, the inequalities (8) are implied by

$$(9) \quad |x_1^{(p)} - X^{(p)}| < \frac{\theta}{nA} [(1 + nA\tau)^{\rho/\tau} - 1] \qquad (p = 1, \cdots, q).$$

It was proved in Art. 116 that the limits of the $x_1^{(p)}(t)$ for $\tau = 0$ ($\kappa = 1$) constitute a solution of the differential equations (1) until either t or some x attains a border of the region R_1. Therefore the limits of the $X^{(p)}(t)$ for $\tau = 0$ are also a solution of equations (1) if

$$(10) \quad \lim_{\tau = 0} |x_1^{(p)} - X^{(p)}| = 0 \qquad (p = 1, \cdots, q).$$

Since $\lim \theta = 0$ for $\tau = 0$, as is at once evident from the definition of the parameter θ given in equation (6), and also

$$(11) \qquad \lim_{\tau=0} (1 + nA\tau)^{\rho/\tau} = e^{nA\rho},$$

it follows from the inequalities (9) that $\lim |x_1^{(p)} - X^{(p)}| = 0$ for $\tau = 0$. Therefore the Cauchy-Lipschitz process defines a solution of the differential equations until the solution attains a border of the region R_1. Moreover, the solution is identical with that defined by the process of successive integrations, and it has all the properties of that solution which were established in Chapter XI.

127. Comparison of the Methods. It is now possible to consider the relative advantages of the method of successive integrations and the Cauchy-Lipschitz process. The former method, as set forth for practical purposes in Chapter XII, is seen to depend upon two parameters, κ and τ. It has been shown in the preceding article that in the special case $\kappa = 1$ this method is a generalization of the Cauchy-Lipschitz process.

The problem of the relative advantages of the two methods resolves itself into determining the relative advantages of integrating over an interval and of taking the straight line segments defined by equations (3). The latter corresponds closely to using only the first term in the right members of the integrating formulas (60), of Chapter XII. The first term would be sufficient only if the interval τ were very small. Consequently, in order to attain a given degree of accuracy, the intervals must, in general, be taken much shorter in the Cauchy-Lipschitz process than in that of successive approximations. Since a considerable fraction of the labor of forming a solution is usually the computing of the functions $f_i(x_j; t)$ for various values of the x_j and t, the Cauchy-Lipschitz process is by no means so satisfactory for practical use as that explained in Chapter XII.

128. Uniqueness of the Continuous Solutions. The solutions that have been shown to exist by the several methods that have been given are all continuous functions of the independent variable t. The question arises whether or not the solutions obtained are the only continuous solutions.

The differential equations (1) of this chapter include all those that have been treated, at least so far as their right members

depend upon the variables x_j and t. Suppose the solution of
equations (1) that has been proved to exist by the method of
successive integrations and by the Cauchy-Lipschitz process, or
by the other methods that are available when the $f_i(x_j; t)$ are
analytic functions of the x_j and t, is represented by

$$x_i = \phi_i(t).$$

As a consequence of the definition of a solution, the ϕ_i satisfy
the identities

$$(12) \qquad \frac{d\phi_i}{dt} \underset{t}{\equiv} f_i(\phi_j(t); t) \qquad (t_0 \leqq t \leqq T_1),$$

where $T_1 - t_0$ is sufficiently small.

Suppose there exists another solution that is continuous in
t, which may be written

$$x_i = \psi_i(t).$$

The $\psi_i(t)$ satisfy the identities

$$(13) \qquad \frac{d\psi_i}{dt} \underset{t}{\equiv} f_i(\psi_j(t); t) \qquad (t_0 \leqq t \leqq T_2),$$

where $T_2 - t_0$ is sufficiently small.

It follows from the initial conditions that $\phi_i(t_0) = \psi_i(t_0) = a_i$.
If the $\phi_i(t)$ and the $\psi_i(t)$ are respectively different for some set
of values of t near t_0, it follows from the continuity of the $\phi_i(t)$
and the $\psi_i(t)$ that an interval $t_0 \leqq t \leqq T_0$ exists such that,
for all values of t in the interval, $\delta_i(\phi_i - \psi_i)$ is zero or positive,
where δ_i is positive or negative unity. Since the $\phi_i(t)$ and the
$\psi_i(t)$ are continuous functions of t, it follows from the identities
(12) and (13) and the fact that the functions $f_i(x_j; t)$ have the
Lipschitz property with respect to the x_j that

$$(14) \quad \delta_i \frac{d}{dt}(\phi_i - \psi_i) \leqq A \sum_{j=1}^{n} \delta_j(\phi_j - \psi_j) \qquad (t_0 \leqq t \leqq T_0).$$

Now consider the related problem defined by the differential
equations

$$(15) \qquad \begin{cases} \dfrac{dy_i}{dt} = A \sum_{j=1}^{n} y_j \qquad (t_0 \leqq t \leqq T_0), \\ y_i(t_0) = 0. \end{cases}$$

It follows from a comparison of the relations (14) and (15) that

(16) $\delta_i(\phi_i - \psi_i) \leqq y_i$ $(t_0 \geqq t \leqq T_0)$.

Equations (15) imply that $y_1 = \cdots = y_n = y$. Therefore the variable y satisfies the equations

(17) $\begin{cases} \dfrac{dy}{dt} = nAy, \\ y(t_0) = 0. \end{cases}$

The general solution of the first of these equations is

$$y = Ce^{nA(t-t_0)},$$

and it follows from the initial condition that $C = 0$. Therefore $\phi_i(t) - \psi_i(t) \equiv 0$ for $t_0 \geqq t \leqq T_0$. That is, there is no continuous solution different from the solution that has been shown to exist by the various methods.

The method of successive integrations and the Cauchy-Lipschitz process are applicable to the analytic differential equations treated in Chapter II. It follows from this uniqueness proof that when the right members of the differential equations are analytic functions of the x_j and t, then the method of successive integrations defines the analytic solution.

An alternative proof, suggested by Bartky, of the uniqueness of the continuous solution depends directly upon the method of Chapter XI. Suppose the integral at the first step of the process, corresponding to that in equation (8), Art. 103, is defined by

$$x_i^{(1)} = a_i + \int_{t_0}^{t} f_i(a_i + (\psi_i - a_i); t)dt,$$

where the ψ_i constitute a second continuous solution of equations (1). The integrand has all the properties imposed upon the integrand of equation (8), Art. 103. Therefore the limits obtained by the process starting with this integral are the solution $\phi_i(t)$.

Since, by hypothesis, the ψ_i are a solution, it follows that $x_i^{(1)} \equiv \psi_i$. Then the $x_i^{(2)}, x_i^{(3)}, \cdots$ sequentially equal the ψ_i and $\lim_{\kappa=\infty} x_i^{(\kappa)} \equiv \psi_i$. Therefore $\psi_i \equiv \phi_i$, which was to be proved.

XIII. QUESTIONS AND PROBLEMS

1. Discuss the applicability of the Cauchy-Lipschitz process to analytic differential equations for complex values of the independent variable.

2. Prove from the Cauchy-Lipschitz process that if the right members of the differential equations (1) are analytic functions of a parameter μ, then the solution functions are continuous in μ.

3. Make a direct proof from the process itself that the Cauchy-Lipschitz process converges.

4. Derive the inequality (8) by a complete induction.

5. Discuss the advisability of using the Cauchy-Lipschitz process to get a rough approximation to the solution, and then to correct the approximation by the method of successive integrations.

6. Apply the Cauchy-Lipschitz process to the differential equation

$$\begin{cases} \dfrac{d^2x}{dt^2} = -x, \\ x(0) = 0, \qquad x'(0) = 1. \end{cases}$$

Compare the results with the exact solution $x = \sin t$. Solve the same problem as a power series in t and by the method of successive integrations for $0 \leqq t \leqq \pi$.

7. Suppose the right members of the differential equations are analytic functions of the dependent variables x_j and the independent variable t. Does it follow without using the uniqueness theorem of Art. 128 that the analytic solution furnished by the method of Chapter II and that given by the methods of successive integrations are identical?

8. Give the details of the proof that it follows from equations (14) and (15) that $\delta_i(\phi_i - \psi_i) \leqq y_i$ for $t_0 \leqq t \leqq T_0$.

HISTORICAL NOTE

The method of this chapter appeared first in Cauchy's lectures, published by Moigno in 1844. The refinements in the demonstration of the fact that the process defines a solution, which were added by Lipschitz, are given in his *Lehrbuch der Analysis*, page 504.

CHAPTER XIV

GENERALITIES ON LINEAR DIFFERENTIAL EQUATIONS

129. Resumé of General Properties of Solutions. Consider first the homogeneous linear differential equations

$$(1) \qquad \frac{dx_i}{dt} = \theta_{i1}(t)x_1 + \cdots + \theta_{in}(t)x_n \qquad (i = 1, \cdots, n).$$

The right members of these differential equations are analytic functions of the x_j in the vicinity of every finite set of values of these variables.

If the $\theta_{ij}(t)$ are analytic functions of t in the neighborhood of its initial value t_0, the differential equations have all the properties of those of Chapter II, and, consequently, the solutions are analytic functions of t in a sufficiently restricted domain about t_0. It was proved in Art. 18 that the domain of analyticity of the solution functions is coextensive with the common domain of analyticity of the $\theta_{ij}(t)$.

If the $\theta_{ij}(t)$ are continuous functions of t, the solutions can be obtained by the method of successive integrations for the range in t for which the $\theta_{ij}(t)$ are continuous. The solution functions are continuous in t.

The solutions of the differential equations (1) are linear homogeneous functions of the initial values of the dependent variables. This result was established in Art. 20 for the case in which the $\theta_{ij}(t)$ are analytic functions of t. It follows, too, for the case in which the $\theta_{ij}(t)$ are continuous, directly from the method of constructing the solution functions given in Art. 102.

130. Fundamental Sets of Solutions. The differential equations (1) have a solution for every finite set of initial values of the x_j. Let

$$x_1 = \phi_{11}(t), \quad \cdots, \quad x_n = \phi_{n1}(t)$$

be the solution corresponding to some particular set of initial values of the x_i. Other solutions can be defined similarly for other sets of initial values of the x_i. The m solutions corresponding to m such sets of initial conditions can be written

$$(2) \quad \begin{cases} x_1 = \phi_{11}(t). \quad \phi_{12}(t), \quad \cdots, \quad \phi_{1m}(t), \\ \cdot \quad \cdot \quad \cdot \quad \cdot \quad \cdot \quad \cdot \quad \cdot \quad \cdot \quad \cdot \quad \cdot \quad \cdot \quad \cdot \\ x_n = \phi_{n1}(t), \quad \phi_{n2}(t), \quad \cdots, \quad \phi_{nm}(t), \end{cases}$$

where the functions in each column constitute a solution of equations (1).

It follows from the definition of a solution of differential equations, Art. 8, that the functions of the jth column of equations (2) satisfy the identities

$$(3) \quad \frac{d\phi_{ij}}{dt} \equiv_t \theta_{i1}(t)\phi_{1j}(t) + \cdots + \theta_{in}(t)\phi_{nj}(t) \quad (i, j = 1, \cdots, n).$$

If each of the solutions (2) is multiplied by an arbitrary constant and their sum is taken, the result is

$$(4) \quad \begin{cases} x_1 = C_1\phi_{11}(t) + \cdots + C_m\phi_{1m}(t), \\ \cdot \quad \cdot \quad \cdot \quad \cdot \quad \cdot \quad \cdot \quad \cdot \quad \cdot \quad \cdot \quad \cdot \quad \cdot \\ x_n = C_1\phi_{n1}(t) + \cdots + C_m\phi_{nm}(t), \end{cases}$$

which is also a solution; for, upon substituting these expressions for the x_i into equations (1) and rearranging the results, it is found by using the identities (3) that

$$(5) \quad \sum_{j=1}^{m} C_j \left\{ \frac{d\phi_{ij}}{dt} - \left[\theta_{i1}(t)\phi_{1j}(t) + \cdots + \theta_{in}(t)\phi_{nj}(t) \right] \right\} \equiv_t 0.$$

A set of solutions of the form (2) is called a *fundamental set of solutions* of the differential equations (1) if every solution of equations (1) can be expressed in the form of equations (4) by a suitable determination of the coefficients C_j. Since a solution of equations (1) is determined uniquely by the initial values of the x_j, necessary and sufficient conditions that the $\phi_{ij}(t)$ shall be a fundamental set of solutions are that $C_1, \cdots, C_m$ can be so determined that

$$(6) \quad \begin{cases} a_1 = C_1\phi_{11}(t_0) + \cdots + C_m\phi_{1m}(t_0), \\ \cdot \quad \cdot \quad \cdot \quad \cdot \quad \cdot \quad \cdot \quad \cdot \quad \cdot \quad \cdot \quad \cdot \quad \cdot \\ a_n = C_1\phi_{n1}(t_0) + \cdots + C_m\phi_{nm}(t_0), \end{cases}$$

where $a_1, \cdots, a_n$ are arbitrary initial values of the x_i.

The C_j can be so determined for every set of values of the a_i that equations (6) shall be satisfied only if $m \lesseqgtr n$; and they can be so determined if, and only if, there are n of the m solutions, say the first n, such that the determinant

$$(7) \qquad D_0 = \begin{vmatrix} \phi_{11}(t_0), & \cdots, & \phi_{1n}(t_0) \\ \cdot & \cdot \cdot \cdot \cdot & \cdot \\ \phi_{n1}(t_0), & \cdots, & \phi_{nn}(t_0) \end{vmatrix}$$

is distinct from zero.

A set of n solutions can be so determined that D_0 shall be distinct from zero. For example, if $\phi_{ii}(t_0) = 1$ and $\phi_{ij}(t_0) = 0$ for $j \neq i$, it follows from equation (7) that $D_0 = 1$. There are evidently infinitely many other sets of initial values of the x_i which define fundamental sets of solutions. If the differential equations are not linear, linear functions of individual solutions of the form of equations (4) are not a solution and there are no fundamental sets of solutions.

Fundamental sets of solutions are of great practical importance, because relatively simple individual solutions can often be obtained in terms of which every solution can be expressed by equations of the form of equations (4). Fundamental sets of solutions are even more important in the development of a general theory of linear differential equations, as will be illustrated in the chapters which follow.

131. The Determinant of a Fundamental Set of Solutions. It is important in certain connections to have the determinant of a fundamental set of solutions for all values of t for which the solutions exist. Let

$$(8) \qquad D(t) = \begin{vmatrix} \phi_{11}(t), & \cdots, & \phi_{1n}(t) \\ \cdot & \cdot \cdot \cdot \cdot & \cdot \\ \phi_{n1}(t), & \cdots, & \phi_{nn}(t) \end{vmatrix} = \begin{vmatrix} \phi_{11}(t), & \cdots, & \phi_{n1}(t) \\ \cdot & \cdot \cdot \cdot \cdot & \cdot \\ \phi_{1n}(t), & \cdots, & \phi_{nn}(t) \end{vmatrix},$$

the rows and columns being interchanged, for convenience, in the second form.

The derivative of the determinant D with respect to t is

$$(9) \qquad \frac{dD}{dt} = \sum_{i=1}^{n} \begin{vmatrix} \phi_{11}(t), & \cdots, & \phi_{i1}{}'(t), & \cdots, & \phi_{n1}(t) \\ \cdot & \cdot \cdot \cdot \cdot \cdot \cdot \cdot & \cdot \\ \phi_{1n}(t), & \cdots, & \phi_{in}{}'(t), & \cdots, & \phi_{nn}(t) \end{vmatrix},$$

where $\phi_{ij}'(t)$ is the derivative of $\phi_{ij}(t)$ with respect to t. Upon eliminating the $\phi_{ij}'(t)$ by means of the identities (3), it is found that

$$(10) \quad \frac{dD}{dt} = \sum_{i=1}^{n} \begin{vmatrix} \phi_{11}(t), & \cdots, & \sum_{j=1}^{n} \theta_{ij}(t)\phi_{j1}(t), & \cdots, & \phi_{n1}(t) \\ \cdot & \cdot & \cdot & \cdot & \cdot \\ \phi_{1n}(t), & \cdots, & \sum_{j=1}^{n} \theta_{ij}(t)\phi_{jn}(t), & \cdots, & \phi_{nn}(t) \end{vmatrix}.$$

If the κth column of this determinant is multiplied by $\theta_{i\kappa}(t)$ and is subtracted from the ith column, $\kappa = 1, \cdots, n$ except $\kappa = i$, equation (10) reduces to

$$(11) \quad \begin{cases} \dfrac{dD}{dt} = \sum_{i=1}^{n} \begin{vmatrix} \phi_{11}(t), & \cdots, & \theta_{ii}(t)\phi_{i1}(t), & \cdots, & \phi_{n1}(t) \\ \cdot & \cdot & \cdot & \cdot & \cdot \\ \phi_{1n}(t), & \cdots, & \theta_{ii}(t)\phi_{in}(t), & \cdots, & \phi_{nn}(t) \end{vmatrix} \\ = D \sum_{i=1}^{n} \theta_{ii}(t). \end{cases}$$

The solution of equation (11) subject to the initial condition $D(t_0) = D_0$ is

$$(12) \quad D(t) = D_0\, e^{\int_{t_0}^{t} \sum_{i=1}^{n} \theta_{ii}(t)dt}.$$

The right member of equation (12) is finite and distinct from zero for all values of t for which the path of integration (finite in length) does not pass through a discontinuity of one or more of the $\theta_{ii}(t)$. Since the solution is defined by the processes that have been given only for values of t for which all the $\theta_{ij}(t)$ are continuous, it follows that $D(t)$ is finite and distinct from zero for all values of t for which the solution is defined.

The determinant $D(t)$ is the determinant of the coefficients of the derivatives dy_i/dt in equations (6), of Art. 36. Consequently, in the case of linear differential equations the corresponding equations can be solved for the dy_i/dt for all values of t for which the $\theta_{ij}(t)$ are continuous, and the method of variation of parameters provides the solution of the non-homogeneous differential equations for all values of t for which the $\theta_{ij}(t)$ and the $\theta_i(t)$ are continuous.

132. An Important Special Case Arising in Physical Problems.

The differential equations that arise in physical problems are usually systems of simultaneous equations of the second order each. In certain cases they are linear and homogeneous and have the form

$$(13) \quad \frac{d^2x_i}{dt^2} = \psi_{i1}(t)x_1 + \cdots + \psi_{in}(t)x_n \qquad (i = 1, \cdots, n).$$

These equations are reduced to the form of equations (1) by the transformation

$$(14) \qquad x_i = x_i, \qquad x_{n+i} = \frac{dx_i}{dt} \qquad (i = 1, \cdots, n),$$

which changes equations (13) into the equivalent system

$$(15) \quad \begin{cases} \dfrac{dx_i}{dt} = x_{n+i} \qquad (i = 1, \cdots, n), \\[2mm] \dfrac{dx_{n+i}}{dt} = \psi_{i1}(t)x_1 + \cdots + \psi_{in}(t)x_n. \end{cases}$$

On comparing equations (1) and (15), it is seen that in the case of equations (13), the following identities are satisfied:

$$(16) \begin{cases} \theta_{ij}(t) \equiv 0 & (i = 1, \cdots, n; j \not= n + i), \\ \theta_{ij}(t) \equiv 1 & (i = 1, \cdots, n; j = n + i), \\ \theta_{ij}(t) = \psi_{i-n, j} & (i = n + 1, \cdots, 2n; j = 1, \cdots, n), \\ \theta_{ij}(t) \equiv 0 & (i > n, j > n). \end{cases}$$

Therefore, in the case of equations (13), the $\theta_{ii}(t)$ are identically zero, and consequently it follows from equation (12) that $D(t) \equiv D_0$. In the case of differential equations having the properties of equations (13), the method of variation of parameters has its greatest simplicity.

133. Equations for Variations.

In the differential equations

$$(17) \quad \begin{cases} \dfrac{dx_i}{dt} = f_i(x_j; t) \qquad (i, j = 1, \cdots, n), \\ x_i(t_0) = a_i, \end{cases}$$

suppose for simplicity that the $f_i(x_j; t)$ are analytic functions of the x_j and t in the neighborhood of the a_j and t_0.

Suppose the solution of equations (17) for the special initial conditions $x_i(t_0) = a_i^{(0)}$, where the $a_i^{(0)}$ are approximately equal to the a_i, is

$$(18) \qquad x_i = \phi_i(t_0; a_i^{(0)}; t).$$

In many physical problems the solutions of the differential

equations are particularly simple for special initial conditions. For example, the problem of two bodies has a very simple solution when the initial conditions are such that the orbit of one body with respect to the other is a circle. Although the method under consideration is most useful when the solution (18) is simple, its applicability is not limited to such cases.

Suppose it is desired to obtain the solution of equations (17) for the initial conditions

$$(19) \qquad x_i(t_0) = a_i = a_i^{(0)} + \alpha_i,$$

where the α_i are small relative to the radii of convergence of the expansions of the $f_i(x_j; t)$ as power series in the $x_j - a_j^{(0)}$. Since the solution functions are continuous functions of the a_i (Art. 20), it follows that the solution of equations (17) with the initial conditions defined by equations (19) will approximately equal the right members of equations (18) for sufficiently restricted values of $|t - t_0|$. Therefore the solution may be written

$$(20) \qquad x_i = \phi_i(t) + \xi_i,$$

and the ξ_i will be small for sufficiently small values of $|t - t_0|$. It follows that the initial values of the ξ_i are

$$(21) \qquad \xi_i(t_0) = \alpha_i.$$

Upon substituting the right members of equations (20) for the x_j into equations (17) and expanding the right members as power series in the ξ_j, and then making use of the fact that the ϕ_i are a solution, it is found that

$$(22) \qquad \frac{d\xi_i}{dt} = \sum_{j=1}^n \frac{\partial f_i}{\partial x_j} \xi_j + \cdots \qquad (i = 1, \cdots, n),$$

where the x_i are replaced by the ϕ_i in all the coefficients of the right members.

Since the ξ_j are small for small values of $|t - t_0|$, the terms of degree higher than the first in the right members of equations (22) are relatively unimportant. Consequently, equations (22) are approximately equivalent to the system

$$(23) \qquad \frac{d\xi_i}{dt} = \sum_{j=1}^n \frac{\partial f_i}{\partial x_j} \xi_j.$$

These equations are, by definition, *the equations for variations* of the solution (18) of the differential equations (17). Equations (18) are the *generating solution* for the equations for variation.

The differential equations (23) are linear and homogeneous in the dependent variables ξ_i, and, consequently, they are much simpler in type than the differential equations (17) by which they are defined, unless the latter are also linear. In the special case in which the $f_i(x_j; t)$ are independent of t and the ϕ_i are constants, the coefficients of the right members of equations (23) are constants. Such a case is the circular solution of the problem of two bodies in which one of the coördinates is the distance between the bodies and the other is the angular longitude measured from axes uniformly rotating in the plane of motion with the period of the bodies.

In case the $f_i(x_j; t)$ do not involve t explicitly and the ϕ_i are periodic functions of the variable t, the differential equations are linear with periodic coefficients. This case is much more difficult than that in which the coefficients are constants. The case of constant coefficients is treated in Chapter XV, and that of periodic coefficients in Chapter XVII.

The properties of the solutions of equations (23) define the characteristics of the generating solution (18). If all the solutions of equations (23) consist of converging sums of trigonometric terms, the solution (18) is said to be stable. The simplest case is that in which the ϕ_i of equations (18) are constants. Then the coefficients of equations (23) are constants. As will be shown in the next chapter, the solutions of such equations are in general exponentials of the type $x_i = \eta_i e^{\lambda t}$, the η_i being constants. If all the values of λ are purely imaginary numbers or do not have positive real parts, the solution is stable for positive values of t; otherwise the solution is unstable.

Another important case is that in which the ϕ_i are periodic functions of t. In this case the coefficients of equations (23) and the η_i of the solution are in general also periodic with the same period. In this case also the solution is said to be stable if all the values of λ are purely imaginary numbers.

134. Particular Solutions of the Equations for Variations. Let c represent any of the a_i or any function of the a_i of equations (17), and suppose the solution functions are analytic in c in the neighborhood of c_0, where $c = c_0$ when $a_i = a_i^{(0)}$ $(i = 1, \cdots, n)$.

Then the solution functions can be expanded as power series in $c - c_0 = \gamma$ of the form

$$(24) \qquad x_i = \phi_i(c_0; t) + \frac{\partial \phi_i}{\partial c} \gamma + \cdots.$$

On comparing equations (20) and (24), it is seen that

$$(25) \qquad \xi_i = \frac{\partial \phi_i}{\partial c} \gamma + \cdots,$$

where γ is arbitrary. If the ξ_i are defined by the linear differential equations (23), instead of equations (22), the corresponding expressions in equations (25) are the first terms of the right members. The arbitrary constant γ may be taken equal to unity, and consequently a particular solution of equations (23) is

$$(26) \qquad \xi_i = \frac{\partial \phi_i}{\partial c}.$$

There is such a solution for $c = a_1, \cdots, a_n$ in turn and for c equal to any function of the a_i.

In general, the solution (26) is not of any practical value, for it is as difficult to determine it as it is to compute a solution of equations (23). There are, however, cases in which these solutions are important. Let it be recalled (Art. 130) that the problem is completely solved when a fundamental set of solutions of the differential equations has been determined. Consequently, it is important to determine as many simple independent solutions of equations (23) as possible. It frequently happens that for a particular set of the a_i the solution functions ϕ_i, of equations (18), are simple functions of c, which is a function of the a_i, and of t. In such a case the solution (26) can be easily obtained.

As an example, consider the problem of two bodies. When the a_i satisfy certain conditions, the orbit of one body with respect to the other is a circle whose radius may be represented by c. The solution $x_i = \phi_i + \partial \phi_i / \partial c$ is simply one in which the relative orbit is a circle of a different radius. It is obvious that one variation of a circular orbit is another circular orbit having a different radius. In general, in dynamical systems there is a constant c which measures the dimensions of the configuration, but not its shape.

The most important case in which the method under consideration is useful is that in which the right members of the differential equations (17) do not explicitly involve the independent variable t. In this case the constant t_0, which occurs in the solution functions but not in the differential equations, may play the rôle of the constant c. Therefore a solution of the equations for variations (23) is in this case

$$\xi_i = \frac{\partial \phi_i}{\partial t_0}.$$

In the case under consideration t and t_0 occur in the solution only in the combination $t - t_0$. Therefore

$$(27) \qquad \xi_i = \frac{\partial \phi_i}{\partial t_0} = -\frac{\partial \phi_i}{\partial t} = -f_i(\phi_i)$$

is a solution of equations (23). If the right members are multiplied by any constant, the result is still a solution.

135. Illustrations from Ballistics. If the origin is taken at the muzzle of the gun, the y-axis vertically upward, and the x-axis in the plane of fire, the differential equations of motion satisfied by the projectile are *

$$(28) \qquad \begin{cases} \dfrac{d^2x}{dt^2} = -f_1(y, x', y'), \\[2mm] \dfrac{d^2y}{dt^2} = -f_2(y, x', y') - g, \end{cases}$$

where g is the acceleration of gravity and x' and y' are the derivatives of x and y with respect to t. Since the acceleration of gravity and the resistance of the air do not depend upon the coördinate x, the right members of equations (28) do not involve x explicitly.

Let the initial values of x, x', y, and y' be x_0, x_0', y_0, and y_0' respectively. Then the solution of equations (28) can be written in the form

$$(29) \qquad \begin{cases} x = x_0 + \phi(y_0, x_0', y_0'; t - t_0), \\ y = 0 + \psi(y_0, x_0', y_0'; t - t_0). \end{cases}$$

The constant x_0 appears only in the first equation and then additively, because the right members of the differential equations (28) are independent of x.

* F. R. Moulton, *New Methods in Exterior Ballistics*, page 11.

Equations (28) can be replaced by an equivalent system of four equations of the first order each in the dependent variables. Then, on making the transformation

$$(30) \quad \begin{cases} x - x_0 = \phi + \xi, & y = \psi + \eta, \\ x' = \phi' + \xi', & y' = \psi' + \eta', \end{cases}$$

in which ϕ' and ψ' represent the derivatives of ϕ and ψ with respect to t, the equations corresponding to equations (23) are

$$(31) \quad \begin{cases} \dfrac{d\xi}{dt} = \xi', \\[2mm] \dfrac{d\xi'}{dt} = -\dfrac{\partial f_1}{\partial y}\eta - \dfrac{\partial f_1}{\partial x'}\xi' - \dfrac{\partial f_1}{\partial y'}\eta', \\[2mm] \dfrac{d\eta}{dt} = \eta', \\[2mm] \dfrac{d\eta'}{dt} = -\dfrac{\partial f_2}{\partial y}\eta - \dfrac{\partial f_2}{\partial x'}\xi' - \dfrac{\partial f_2}{\partial y'}\eta'. \end{cases}$$

These equations are convenient for determining small variations from a trajectory that may have been computed for special (normal) initial conditions.

It follows from the results of Art. 134 and the form of the solution (29) that a solution of equations (31) is

$$(32) \quad \begin{cases} \xi = \dfrac{\partial(x_0 + \phi)}{\partial x_0} = 1, & \eta = \dfrac{\partial \psi}{\partial x_0} = 0, \\[2mm] \xi' = \dfrac{\partial \phi'}{\partial x_0} = 0, & \eta' = \dfrac{\partial \psi'}{\partial x_0} = 0, \end{cases}$$

as can be easily verified.

Since the right members of equations (28) do not involve t explicitly, it follows from the principles of Art. 134 that a second solution of equations (31) is

$$(33) \quad \begin{cases} \xi = \dfrac{\partial \phi}{\partial t}, & \eta = \dfrac{\partial \psi}{\partial t}, \\[2mm] \xi' = \dfrac{\partial \phi'}{\partial t}, & \eta' = \dfrac{\partial \psi'}{\partial t}. \end{cases}$$

On making use of equations (28) and (29), this solution becomes

$$(34) \quad \begin{cases} \xi = \phi'(y_0, x_0', y_0'; t - t_0), & \eta = \psi'(y_0, x_0', y_0'; t - t_0), \\ \xi' = -f_1(\psi, \phi', \psi'), & \eta' = -f_2(\psi, \phi', \psi') - g. \end{cases}$$

The right members of these equations are known when the solution (29) has been determined.

136. Use of Integrals of the Differential Equations. In most physical problems the differential equations corresponding to equations (17) have one or more relatively simple integrals, such as the energy integral in conservative systems. Integrals of equations (17) furnish integrals of equations (23), as will be shown, which may be used to reduce the order of these equations.

Suppose the differential equations (17) have the integral

$$(35) \qquad F(x_1, \cdots, x_n; t) = C,$$

analytic in $x_1, \cdots, x_n$, and t. On substituting the expressions for the x_i from equations (20) into the function F and expanding the result as a power series in the ξ_j, it is found that

$$(36) \qquad F(\phi_1, \cdots, \phi_n; t) + \sum_{i=1}^{n} \frac{\partial F}{\partial x_i} \xi_i + \cdots = C.$$

Since $F(\phi_1, \cdots, \phi_n; t) = C_0$ is also an integral of equations (17) and C is a power series in the α_i of equations (19), it follows that

$$(37) \qquad \frac{\partial F}{\partial x_1} \xi_1 + \cdots + \frac{\partial F}{\partial x_n} \xi_n = c$$

is an integral of equations (23). This equation can obviously be used to eliminate one of the ξ_i from equations (23).

Similarly, κ independent integrals of equations (17) furnish κ corresponding independent integrals of equations (23). All integrals of equations (23) determined in this way are linear functions of the ξ_i.

137. Case in Which the Differential Equations Depend upon a Parameter. Suppose the differential equations under consideration are

$$(38) \qquad \begin{cases} \dfrac{dx_i}{dt} = f_i(x_j; \mu; t), \\ x_i(t_0) = a_i, \end{cases}$$

in which the right members are analytic functions of the arguments in the neighborhood of $x_j = a_j$, $\mu = \mu_0$, $t = t_0$.

Let

$$(39) \qquad x_i = \phi_i(t_0; a_j; \mu_0; t)$$

be a solution of the differential equations (38) and let

(40) $$x_i = \phi_i + \xi_i$$

be the solution corresponding to the initial conditions

(41) $$\begin{cases} x_i(t_0) = a_i + \alpha_i, \\ \mu = \mu_0 + \nu. \end{cases}$$

On transforming equations (38) from the variables x_i to ξ_i and from the parameter μ to ν, and expanding the right members as power series in the ξ_i and ν, it is found that

(42) $$\frac{d\xi_i}{dt} = \frac{\partial f_i}{\partial \mu} \nu + \sum_{j=1}^{n} \frac{\partial f_i}{\partial x_j} \xi_j + \cdots.$$

It should be noted that, when $\nu \neq 0$, the ξ_i do not have exactly the same meaning as they have in equations (22).

Suppose the right members of equations (42) are restricted to the terms of the first degree in ν and the ξ_i. The homogeneous parts of these equations are identical with equations (22); the part of the solution depending upon the terms in ν can be determined by the method of Art. 38. Consequently, the problem corresponding to equations (23) will be considered as solved.

The usefulness of equations (42) can be illustrated by referring again to the problem of exterior ballistics. If $\nu = 0$, the problem is that of determining the effects upon the trajectory of small variations in the initial conditions, such as the initial components of velocity, the resistance of the air remaining normal. The term in ν corresponds to a slight departure from normal atmospheric resistance, due to such things as winds or abnormal air density. If not all the α_i are zero and if ν is not zero, there are both abnormal initial conditions and abnormal accelerations.

138. General Solution of Equations (42). Since equations (42) include equations (22) as the special case in which $\nu = 0$, this discussion includes that of equations (22).

All of the general methods for solving differential equations heretofore given in Chapters II, III, XI, XII, and XIII are applicable to this problem, but it is not advisable to use them without some modification, for they take no advantage of the circumstance that the ξ_i are small, at least for restricted values of $|t - t_0|$.

In order to make use effectively of the fact that, under the hypotheses, the ξ_i are small relative to the radii of convergence of the expansions of the $f_i(x_j; t)$ as power series in the ξ_j and ν, let (compare Art. 32)

$$(43) \qquad \xi_i = \eta_i \epsilon, \qquad \nu = \sigma \epsilon,$$

where ϵ is a parameter which remains as yet undetermined. Divide out ϵ from the resulting equations, after which they can be written in the form

$$(44) \quad \frac{d\eta_i}{dt} = \frac{\partial f_i}{\partial \mu}\sigma + \sum_{j=1}^{n}\frac{\partial f_i}{\partial x_j}\eta_j + V_i^{(2)}(\sigma, \eta_i)\epsilon + V_i^{(3)}(\sigma, \eta_i)\epsilon^2 + \cdots,$$

where the $V_i^{(\kappa)}(\sigma, \eta_i)$ are homogeneous functions of the arguments σ and η_j of degree κ.

Equations (44) can be solved as power series in ϵ by the methods of Chapter III, and ϵ can be placed equal to unity in the final result. The terms independent of ϵ are precisely the equations for variations including the term in ν to the first degree. The terms of higher degrees in ϵ are defined by linear differential equations whose homogeneous parts are the same as the equations for the variations. Consequently the only difficulties are in the equations for variations, which in all cases have the relative simplicity of linear equations and which often have the additional simplifying property of having constant or periodic coefficients.

Let the solution of equations (44) as power series in the parameter ϵ be expressed in the notation

$$(45) \qquad \eta_i = \eta_i^{(0)}(t) + \eta_i^{(1)}(t)\epsilon + \eta_i^{(2)}(t)\epsilon^2 + \cdots.$$

The terms in the solution which are independent of ϵ are defined by the differential equations

$$(46) \qquad \frac{d\eta_i^{(0)}}{dt} - \sum_{j=1}^{n}\frac{\partial f_i}{\partial x_j}\eta_j^{(0)} = \frac{\partial f_i}{\partial \mu}\sigma.$$

The solutions of these equations are linear in the α_i, the initial values of the ξ_i, and in σ.

The terms of the first degree in ϵ are defined by the differential equations

$$(47) \qquad \frac{d\eta_i^{(1)}}{dt} - \sum_{j=1}^{n}\frac{\partial f_i}{\partial x_j}\eta_j^{(1)} = V_i^{(2)}(\sigma, \eta_i^{(0)}).$$

Since the initial values of the $\eta_i^{(1)}$ are zero, the solutions of these equations are of the same degree as the $V_i^{(2)}$ in σ and the α_j, which are of the second degree. By an easy induction it can be proved that the $\eta_i^{(\kappa)}$ are homogeneous functions of σ and the α_j of degree $\kappa + 1$. That is, the η_i are expanded as power series in σ and the α_j. The parameter ϵ serves simply to guide the computation so that all the terms of each degree shall be computed together.

It would be possible to solve equations (22) directly as power series in the n parameters $\alpha_1, \cdots, \alpha_n$, and to solve equations (42) in the $n + 1$ parameters ν and $\alpha_1, \cdots, \alpha_n$. This procedure would be slightly less convenient than that which has been outlined, for it would isolate the computation of each term from all the others, even of the same degree.

XIV. QUESTIONS AND PROBLEMS

1. Why is not the condition that equations (6) shall be satisfied for some particular set of values of the a_i a sufficient condition that the solutions (2) shall constitute a fundamental set?

2. Prove that linear functions of particular solutions of non-linear differential equations are not solutions. For integrals, see Art. 43.

3. Write out equations (8), $\cdots$, (11) in detail for $n = 4$.

4. Write the equations corresponding to equations (17) for the problem of two bodies in both rectangular and polar coördinates. Write the equations corresponding to equations (18) for the circular solution. Then develop explicitly the equations corresponding to equations (22).

5. Write the differential equations for the simple pendulum. Write the solution equations corresponding to equations (18) for the pendulum at rest at the bottom of its possible motion and also at the top. Develop the equations corresponding to equations (23) for both of these particular solutions. Solve the equations and determine the stability of the two generating solutions.

6. In the pendulum problems, solve the equations corresponding to equations (22) to terms of the second degree inclusive by the method of Art. 138.

7. The problem of two bodies has a circular solution in which the radius of the circular orbit of one body with respect to the other is an arbitrary constant c. Verify that in this problem, expressed both in rectangular and in polar coördinates, the equations corresponding to equations (26) are a solution of the equations for variations.

8. In the case of the problem of two bodies, verify that the equations corresponding to equations (27) are a solution of the equations for variation.

9. Verify the fact that equations (34) are a solution of equations (31).

10. Derive the equation corresponding to equation (37) for the problem of two bodies, using the energy integral for the integral (35).

CHAPTER XV

LINEAR DIFFERENTIAL EQUATIONS WITH CONSTANT COEFFICIENTS

139. The Characteristic Equation. The differential equations to be treated are the homogeneous system

$$(1) \quad \begin{cases} \dfrac{dx_1}{dt} = a_{11}x_1 + \cdots + a_{1n}x_n, \\ \cdot \quad \cdot \quad \cdot \quad \cdot \quad \cdot \quad \cdot \quad \cdot \quad \cdot \\ \dfrac{dx_n}{dt} = a_{n1}x_1 + \cdots + a_{nn}x_n, \end{cases}$$

where the a_{ij} are given finite constants. These equations can be solved by all of the methods heretofore given, but since they have special properties their solutions will also have special properties which are to be determined.

The differential equation $x' = ax$ has the solution $x = ce^{at}$, where c is an arbitrary constant. Similarly, the differential equation $x'' = ax$ has the two solutions $x = c_1 e^{\sqrt{a}\,t}$ and $x = c_2 e^{-\sqrt{a}\,t}$, where c_1 and c_2 are arbitrary constants. If this differential equation is replaced by the equivalent normal system

$$\begin{cases} \dfrac{dx_1}{dt} = x_2, \\ \dfrac{dx_2}{dt} = ax_1, \end{cases}$$

the two solutions take the forms

$$\begin{cases} x_1 = c_1 e^{\sqrt{a}\,t}, & x_1 = c_2 e^{-\sqrt{a}\,t}, \\ x_2 = c_1 \sqrt{a}\, e^{\sqrt{a}\,t}; & x_2 = -c_2 \sqrt{a}\, e^{-\sqrt{a}\,t}. \end{cases}$$

In each of the foregoing problems the solutions are exponential functions of t. The solutions of other simple linear differential equations with constant coefficients that might be written down

246

would be found to have the same property.   These particular examples make it natural to inquire whether or not a constant λ and n constants A_i exist such that

(2)
$$\begin{cases} x_1 = A_1 e^{\lambda t}, \\ \cdot \quad \cdot \quad \cdot \quad \cdot \\ x_n = A_n e^{\lambda t} \end{cases}$$

is a solution of the differential equations (1).

Upon substituting the expressions for $x_1, \cdots, x_n$ from equations (2) into equations (1), it is found that necessary and sufficient conditions that the expressions (2) shall constitute a solution of equations (1) are

(3)
$$\begin{cases} (a_{11} - \lambda)A_1 + a_{12}A_2 + \cdots + a_{1n}A_n = 0, \\ \cdot \quad \cdot \quad \cdot \quad \cdot \quad \cdot \quad \cdot \quad \cdot \quad \cdot \quad \cdot \quad \cdot \quad \cdot \\ a_{n1}A_1 + a_{n2}A_2 + \cdots + (a_{nn} - \lambda)A_n = 0, \end{cases}$$

the constant λ appearing only in the terms of the main diagonal.

A necessary and sufficient condition that equations (3) shall have a solution other than the trivial one $A_i = 0$ is

(4)
$$D(\lambda) = \begin{vmatrix} a_{11} - \lambda, & \cdots, & a_{1n} \\ \cdot & & \\ \cdot & & \\ \cdot & & \\ a_{n1} & , & \cdots, & a_{nn} - \lambda \end{vmatrix} = 0.$$

This is the *characteristic equation* of the differential equations (1). It is of degree n in λ, and for each value of λ for which $D(\lambda) = 0$ equations (3) have a solution in which at least one of the A_i is arbitrary, the remaining A_i being uniquely determined in terms of λ and the arbitrary A_i.   For each such value of λ and its associated A_i, equations (2) are a solution of equations (1).

The problem is to determine a set of n solutions that constitute a fundamental set.   Obviously there are numerous special cases to be treated, depending upon the multiplicities of the roots of equation (4) and the properties of the minors of the determinant $D(\lambda)$ for these roots.

140. Solutions When No Two Roots of the Characteristic Equation Are Equal.   Suppose the roots of the equation $D(\lambda) = 0$ are $\lambda_1, \cdots, \lambda_n$, no two of the λ_j being equal.   Under these hypotheses the derivative of the determinant $D(\lambda)$ with respect to λ is distinct from zero for $\lambda = \lambda_1, \cdots, \lambda_n$.   It follows from the form of the determinant $D(\lambda)$ that its derivative with respect to λ is the negative of the sum of its principal first minors. Therefore at least one of the first minors of the determinant $D(\lambda)$ is distinct from zero for each of the roots $\lambda_1, \cdots, \lambda_n$.

Now consider equations (3) for $\lambda = \lambda_j$. Since at least one first minor of the determinant of their coefficients is distinct from zero, these equations, for each λ_j, define $A_1, \cdots, A_n$ in terms of an arbitrary constant C_j by expressions of the form

$$(5) \qquad A_1 = \delta_{1j}C_j, \quad \cdots, \quad A_n = \delta_{nj}C_j,$$

where the δ_{ij} are first minors of the determinant $D(\lambda)$ for $\lambda = \lambda_j$. The first subscript on the δ_{ij} indicates the A_i with which they are associated; the second subscript indicates that they are functions of λ_j. For each value of j there is at least one δ_{ij} that is distinct from zero; and, in general, more than one first minor of the determinant is distinct from zero for $\lambda = \lambda_j$. The δ_{ij} are the determinants of order $n - 1$ formed from any $n - 1$ rows of the determinant $D(\lambda)$ for which at least one δ_{ij} is distinct from zero for $\lambda = \lambda_j$.

On substituting the expressions for the A_i given in equations (5) into equations (2), the n solutions associated with the n roots of $D(\lambda) = 0$ are found to be

$$(6) \qquad \begin{cases} x_1 = C_j\delta_{1j}e^{\lambda_j t} \qquad (j = 1, \cdots, n), \\ \cdots \quad \cdots \quad \cdots \\ x_n = C_j\delta_{nj}e^{\lambda_j t}. \end{cases}$$

In this case each solution is a purely exponential function of t of the type found in the simple examples of Art. 139.

141. Proof that the Solutions (6) Constitute a Fundamental Set. It follows from Art. 130 that the solutions (6) constitute a fundamental set if and only if the determinant

$$\delta = \begin{vmatrix} \delta_{11}, & \cdots, & \delta_{1n} \\ \cdot & & \cdot \\ \cdot & & \cdot \\ \cdot & & \cdot \\ \delta_{n1}, & \cdots, & \delta_{nn} \end{vmatrix}$$

is distinct from zero. The elements of the jth column of this determinant are functions of λ_j, and the λ_j are the n roots of the equation $D(\lambda) = 0$. Evidently it is not easy to establish by direct proof that this determinant is distinct from zero.

The conclusion that δ is distinct from zero will be established by an indirect proof. Under the assumption that $\delta \neq 0$, there exist n constants $B_1, \cdots, B_n$, not all of which are zero, such that

(7)
$$\begin{cases} 0 = B_1\delta_{11} + \cdots + B_n\delta_{1n}, \\ \cdots\cdots\cdots\cdots\cdots\cdots\cdots \\ 0 = B_1\delta_{n1} + \cdots + B_n\delta_{nn}. \end{cases}$$

Since

(8)
$$\begin{cases} x_1 = C_1\delta_{11}e^{\lambda_1 t} + \cdots + C_n\delta_{1n}e^{\lambda_n t}, \\ \cdots\cdots\cdots\cdots\cdots\cdots\cdots\cdots\cdots \\ x_n = C_1\delta_{n1}e^{\lambda_1 t} + \cdots + C_n\delta_{nn}e^{\lambda_n t} \end{cases}$$

is a solution of equations (1) for every set of constant values $C_1, \cdots, C_n$, it follows that $B_1, \cdots, B_n$, satisfying equations (7), when used for $C_1, \cdots, C_n$, give the solution corresponding to the initial conditions $x_1(0) = \cdots = x_n(0) = 0$. Since in this solution the x_i are identically zero, it follows that

(9)
$$\begin{cases} 0 \underset{t}{\equiv} B_1\delta_{11}e^{\lambda_1 t} + \cdots + B_n\delta_{1n}e^{\lambda_n t}, \\ \cdots\cdots\cdots\cdots\cdots\cdots\cdots\cdots \\ 0 \underset{t}{\equiv} B_1\delta_{n1}e^{\lambda_1 t} + \cdots + B_n\delta_{nn}e^{\lambda_n t}. \end{cases}$$

It has been pointed out that for each j at least one of the δ_{ij} $(i = 1, \cdots, n)$ is distinct from zero. Suppose $\delta_{pi} \neq 0$ and that there are k of the δ_{pj} $(j = 1, \cdots, n)$ that are not zero. Then the pth of the identities (9) and its $k - 1$ successive derivatives with respect to t are

(10)
$$\begin{cases} 0 \underset{t}{\equiv} B_1\delta_{p1}e^{\lambda_1 t} + \cdots + B_n\delta_{pn}e^{\lambda_n t}, \\ 0 \underset{t}{\equiv} B_1\delta_{p1}\lambda_1 e^{\lambda_1 t} + \cdots + B_n\delta_{pn}\lambda_n e^{\lambda_n t}, \\ \cdots\cdots\cdots\cdots\cdots\cdots\cdots\cdots\cdots \\ 0 \underset{t}{\equiv} B_1\delta_{p1}\lambda_1{}^{k-1}e^{\lambda_1 t} + \cdots + B_n\delta_{pn}\lambda_n{}^{k-1}e^{\lambda_n t}, \end{cases}$$

in which $n - k$ of the δ_{pj} are zero.

The identities (10) can be satisfied by values of the B_j that are not all zero only if the determinant of their coefficients is zero. This determinant, at $t = 0$, is

(11)
$$V = \Pi\delta_{pj} \begin{vmatrix} 1 & , \cdots, & 1 \\ \lambda_1 & , \cdots, & \lambda_n \\ \cdot & & \cdot \\ \cdot & & \cdot \\ \cdot & & \cdot \\ \lambda_1{}^{k-1}, & \cdots, & \lambda_n{}^{k-1} \end{vmatrix},$$

where $\Pi\delta_{pj}$ is the product of the k of the δ_{pj} $(j = 1, \cdots, n)$ that are not zero, and $\lambda_1, \cdots, \lambda_n$ are the corresponding values of the λ_j. Under the hypothesis that the λ_j are distinct, this Vandermonde determinant is not zero. Therefore the k of the B_j occurring in the identities (9) are all zero. A similar conclusion follows for each value of p from 1 to n, from which it follows that every B_j is zero. That is, the hypothesis that the determinant δ is zero, which was made for the purpose of the indirect proof, has led to the conclusion that every B_j of equations (7) must be zero, which is true only if δ is distinct from zero. Therefore the hypothesis that δ is zero is false, and consequently the solutions (6) constitute a fundamental set. It follows that in this case every solution of the differential equations (1) can be expressed in the form of equations (8). It was shown in the general theory of Art. 18 that the power-series solutions of linear differential equations with constant coefficients are permanently converging series. In this case the solution series have been separated into n simple exponential series with constant coefficients.

Proofs that the solutions which will be obtained for more complicated cases also constitute fundamental sets will be closely analogous to that for the simple case when no two of the λ_j are equal.

142. Solutions of the General nth Order Linear Differential Equation. Before considering cases in which two or more of the roots of the equation $D(\lambda) = 0$ are equal, the simpler problem of the general linear differential equation with constant coefficients will be treated.

Let the nth order differential equation be written in the form

$$(12) \qquad \frac{d^n x}{dt^n} + a_1 \frac{d^{n-1} x}{dt^{n-1}} + \cdots + a_n x = 0,$$

in which $a_1, \cdots, a_n$ are finite constants. In order to obtain the solutions of this equation, it is convenient to define an operator Δ by the identity

$$(13) \qquad \Delta(x) \equiv \frac{d^n x}{dt^n} + a_1 \frac{d^{n-1} x}{dt^{n-1}} + \cdots + a_n x.$$

It follows that the differential equation (12) in terms of the operator Δ is simply $\Delta(x) = 0$. It follows, too, that if $x = \phi(t)$ is a solution of equation (12), then $\Delta(\phi(t)) \equiv 0$.

It also follows from the definition of the operator Δ that

$$(14) \quad \begin{cases} \dfrac{d\Delta(x)}{dt} = \Delta\left(\dfrac{dx}{dt}\right), \\[2mm] \dfrac{d\Delta(x)}{d\alpha} = \Delta\left(\dfrac{dx}{d\alpha}\right), \\[2mm] \Delta(e^{\lambda t}) = e^{\lambda t}D(\lambda), \\[2mm] D(\lambda) = \lambda^n + a_1\lambda^{n-1} + \cdots + a_n, \end{cases}$$

where α is any parameter on which x may depend.   The equation $D(\lambda) = 0$ is the characteristic equation of the differential equation (12), as can be easily verified by transforming equation (12) into an equivalent normal system and forming the characteristic equation in accordance with the definition of Art. 139.

Since

$$\frac{d^\kappa e^{\lambda t}}{d\lambda^\kappa} = t^\kappa e^{\lambda t},$$

it follows from equations (14) that

$$(15) \quad \begin{cases} \Delta(t e^{\lambda t}) = \Delta\left(\dfrac{de^{\lambda t}}{d\lambda}\right) = e^{\lambda t}\left[\dfrac{dD}{d\lambda} + tD(\lambda)\right], \\[3mm] \Delta(t^2 e^{\lambda t}) = \Delta\left(\dfrac{d^2 e^{\lambda t}}{d\lambda^2}\right) = e^{\lambda t}\left[\dfrac{d^2 D}{d\lambda^2} + 2t\dfrac{dD}{d\lambda} + t^2 D(\lambda)\right], \\[3mm] \cdot\ \cdot\ \cdot\ \cdot\ \cdot\ \cdot\ \cdot\ \cdot\ \cdot\ \cdot\ \cdot\ \cdot\ \cdot\ \cdot\ \cdot\ \cdot\ \cdot \\[3mm] \Delta(t^\kappa e^{\lambda t}) = e^{\lambda t}\left[\dfrac{d^\kappa D}{d\lambda^\kappa} + \dfrac{\kappa}{1}t\dfrac{d^{\kappa-1}D}{d\lambda^{\kappa-1}} + \dfrac{\kappa}{1}\dfrac{\kappa-1}{2}t^2\dfrac{d^{\kappa-2}D}{d\lambda^{\kappa-2}}\right. \\[3mm] \qquad\qquad\qquad\qquad\qquad \left. + \cdots + t^\kappa D(\lambda)\right]\cdot \end{cases}$$

The numerical multipliers in the right members of equations (15) are the binomial coefficients.

Now suppose that $\lambda = \lambda_1$ is a root of the equation $D(\lambda) = 0$ of multiplicity κ_1.   Then it follows that

$$D(\lambda_1) = 0, \quad \frac{dD(\lambda_1)}{d\lambda_1} = 0, \quad \cdots, \quad \frac{d^{\kappa_1-1}D(\lambda_1)}{d\lambda_1^{\kappa_1-1}} = 0, \quad \frac{d^{\kappa_1}D(\lambda_1)}{d\lambda_1^{\kappa_1}} \neq 0.$$

Hence it follows from equations (14) and (15) that

$$\Delta_t(e^{\lambda_1 t}) \equiv 0, \qquad \Delta_t(t e^{\lambda_1 t}) \equiv 0, \qquad \cdots, \qquad \Delta_t(t^{\kappa_1-1} e^{\lambda_1 t}) \equiv 0.$$

It follows from the identity (13) that these functions under the operator Δ are solutions of the differential equation (12).   That is, there are associated with the root λ_1 of the characteristic equation $D(\lambda) = 0$ the solutions

$$(16) \qquad x = C_1 e^{\lambda_1 t}, \quad C_2 t e^{\lambda_1 t}, \quad \cdots, \quad C_{\kappa_1} t^{\kappa_1 - 1} e^{\lambda_1 t},$$

where $C_1, \cdots, C_{\kappa_1}$ are arbitrary constants. There are corresponding solutions associated with each of the other roots of the characteristic equation $D(\lambda) = 0$. Since the number of solutions associated with each root equals the order of its multiplicity, the process provides n solutions of the differential equation (12).

143. Proof that the Solutions Constitute a Fundamental Set.
The condition that the solutions (16) of equation (12), together with the corresponding solutions associated with the other roots of the equation $D(\lambda) = 0$, constitute a fundamental set can be derived from the equivalent normal system of differential equations and the definition of a fundamental set of solutions for these equations. It is found that the solutions of equation (12) constitute a fundamental set if the determinant formed from these functions and their first $n - 1$ derivatives with respect to t is distinct from zero. As has been seen in Art. 131, it is sufficient to consider this determinant at $t = 0$.

The solutions (16) are of the type $t^\kappa e^{\lambda t}$, where κ has various integral values. In treating various derivatives of this function at $t = 0$, it is convenient to have a recursion formula. It is at once found that

$$\left\{ \begin{aligned}
\frac{d}{dt}(t^{\kappa+1} e^{\lambda t}) &= \frac{d}{dt}(t \cdot t^\kappa e^{\lambda t}) = t^\kappa e^{\lambda t} + t\frac{d}{dt}(t^\kappa e^{\lambda t}), \\
\frac{d^2}{dt^2}(t^{\kappa+1} e^{\lambda t}) &= 2\frac{d}{dt}(t^\kappa e^{\lambda t}) + t\frac{d^2}{dt^2}(t^\kappa e^{\lambda t}), \\
\cdot \quad & \cdot \quad \cdot \quad \cdot \quad \cdot \quad \cdot \quad \cdot \quad \cdot \quad \cdot \\
\frac{d^p}{dt^p}(t^{\kappa+1} e^{\lambda t}) &= p\frac{d^{p-1}}{dt^{p-1}}(t^\kappa e^{\lambda t}) + t\frac{d^p}{dt^p}(t^\kappa e^{\lambda t}).
\end{aligned} \right.$$

At $t = 0$ the final equation of this set becomes simply

$$\frac{d^p}{dt^p}(t^{\kappa+1} e^{\lambda t}) = p\frac{d^{p-1}}{dt^{p-1}}(t^\kappa e^{\lambda t}).$$

When $\kappa = 0$ it is observed that

$$(17) \qquad \frac{d^q e^{\lambda t}}{dt^q} = \lambda^q e^{\lambda t}.$$

Therefore it is found from these equations that, at $t = 0$,

(18)
$$\begin{cases} \dfrac{d^p}{dt^p}(t^\kappa e^{\lambda t}) = p(p - 1) \cdots (p - \kappa + 1)\lambda^{p-\kappa}, \\[2mm] \dfrac{d}{d\lambda}\dfrac{d^p}{dt^p}(t^\kappa e^{\lambda t}) = \dfrac{d^p}{dt^p}(t^{\kappa+1}e^{\lambda t}). \end{cases}$$

Now return to the consideration of the determinant formed from the solutions and their first $n - 1$ derivatives with respect to t at $t = 0$. In order to illustrate the properties of this determinant, suppose $n = 5$ and that $D(\lambda) = (\lambda - \lambda_1)^2(\lambda - \lambda_2)^3$. Then it follows immediately from equation (17) and the second of equations (18) that the determinant in question is simply

(19)
$$\delta(\lambda_1, \lambda_2) = \begin{vmatrix} 1, & 0, & 1, & 0, & 0 \\ \lambda_1, & 1, & \lambda_2, & 1, & 0 \\ \lambda_1^2, & 2\lambda_1, & \lambda_2^2, & 2\lambda_2, & 2 \\ \lambda_1^3, & 3\lambda_1^2, & \lambda_2^3, & 3\lambda_2^2, & 6\lambda_2 \\ \lambda_1^4, & 4\lambda_1^3, & \lambda_2^4, & 4\lambda_2^3, & 12\lambda_2^2 \end{vmatrix}.$$

If there were only one root of the equation $D(\lambda) = 0$, the corresponding determinant would be simply the product of the main diagonal elements unity; in the present case the determinant is the sum of two others.

In order to prove that the determinant $\delta(\lambda_1, \lambda_2)$ is not zero, consider the function

(20)
$$\Lambda(\lambda) = \begin{vmatrix} 1, & 0, & 1, & 0, & 1 \\ \lambda_1, & 1, & \lambda_2, & 1, & \lambda \\ \lambda_1^2, & 2\lambda_1, & \lambda_2^2, & 2\lambda_2, & \lambda^2 \\ \lambda_1^3, & 3\lambda_1^2, & \lambda_2^3, & 3\lambda_2^2, & \lambda^3 \\ \lambda_1^4, & 4\lambda_1^3, & \lambda_2^4, & 4\lambda_2^3, & \lambda^4 \end{vmatrix}.$$

The function $\Lambda(\lambda)$ is a polynomial of the fourth degree in λ. It follows from the form of the right member of equation (20) that $\Lambda(\lambda) = 0$ for $\lambda = \lambda_1$ and $\lambda = \lambda_2$, and that the first derivative of $\Lambda(\lambda)$ with respect to λ also vanishes at $\lambda = \lambda_1$ and $\lambda = \lambda_2$. Therefore $\Lambda(\lambda)$ has the form

(21)
$$\Lambda(\lambda) = \delta_1(\lambda_1, \lambda_2)(\lambda - \lambda_1)^2(\lambda - \lambda_2)^2.$$

On comparing equations (19) and (20), it is seen that the second derivative of $\Lambda(\lambda)$ with respect to λ at $\lambda = \lambda_2$ equals

$\delta(\lambda_1, \lambda_2)$. Therefore it follows from equations (20) and (21) that

(22) $$\delta(\lambda_1, \lambda_2) = 2\delta_1(\lambda_1, \lambda_2)(\lambda_2 - \lambda_1)^2,$$

and

$$\delta_1(\lambda_1, \lambda_2) = \begin{vmatrix} 1 & , 0 & , 1 & , 0 \\ \lambda_1 & , 1 & , \lambda_2 & , 1 \\ \lambda_1^2 & , 2\lambda_1 & , \lambda_2^2 & , 2\lambda_2 \\ \lambda_1^3 & , 3\lambda_1^2 & , \lambda_2^3 & , 3\lambda_2^2 \end{vmatrix}.$$

A sequential application of this process leads finally to the result

(23) $$\delta(\lambda_1, \lambda_2) = 2(\lambda_2 - \lambda_1)^6,$$

which is not zero.

The general case of the corresponding determinant when the roots of $D(\lambda) = 0$ have any multiplicities can evidently be treated in a precisely similar manner, with the result that δ is a numerical constant times powers of the differences of the roots, and consequently is not zero.

144. Solutions When the Characteristic Equation Has a Double Root. Return now to the differential equations (1) and suppose that the associated characteristic equation $D(\lambda) = 0$ has the double root $\lambda = \lambda_1$, and that all the other roots are simple. The solutions associated with the roots $\lambda_3, \cdots, \lambda_n$ are determined precisely as in the case in which the n roots are simple. There are two cases for the solutions associated with the double root $\lambda = \lambda_1$. In the first case, all the first minors of the determinant $D(\lambda_1)$ are zero; in the second case, not all the first minors of the determinant $D(\lambda_1)$ are zero.

Case I. All the first minors of the determinant $D(\lambda_1)$ are zero. Since λ_1 is only a double root of the equation $D(\lambda) = 0$, there is at least one second minor of the determinant $D(\lambda_1)$ which is distinct from zero, and consequently equations (3), for $\lambda = \lambda_1$, are solvable for $A_1, \cdots, A_n$ linearly and homogeneously in terms of two arbitrary constants C_1 and C_2. The solutions have the form

(24) $$\begin{cases} A_1 = \eta_{11}C_1 + \eta_{12}C_2, \\ \cdot \quad \cdot \quad \cdot \quad \cdot \quad \cdot \quad \cdot \\ A_n = \eta_{n1}C_1 + \eta_{n2}C_2. \end{cases}$$

At least one of the η_{i1} and one of the η_{i2} are distinct from zero, and, moreover, the η_{i2} are not simply equal to the η_{i1} respectively multiplied by a constant factor. The solutions in this case are

$$(25) \quad \begin{cases} x_1 = C_1\eta_{11}e^{\lambda_1 t}, \ C_2\eta_{12}e^{\lambda_1 t}, \ C_3\delta_{13}e^{\lambda_3 t}, \ \cdots, \ C_n\delta_{1n}e^{\lambda_n t}, \\ \cdot \quad \cdot \quad \cdot \quad \cdot \quad \cdot \quad \cdot \quad \cdot \quad \cdot \\ x_n = C_1\eta_{n1}e^{\lambda_1 t}, \ C_2\eta_{n2}e^{\lambda_1 t}, \ C_3\delta_{n3}e^{\lambda_3 t}, \ \cdots, \ C_n\delta_{nn}e^{\lambda_n t}. \end{cases}$$

That the solutions (25) constitute a fundamental set can be proved by the indirect method of Art. 141. The equations corresponding to equations (10) are in this case

$$(26) \quad \begin{cases} 0 \equiv (B_1\eta_{p1} + B_2\eta_{p2})e^{\lambda_1 t} + \sum_{j=3}^{n} B_j\delta_{pj}e^{\lambda_j t}, \\ 0 \equiv (B_1\eta_{p1} + B_2\eta_{p2})\lambda_1 e^{\lambda_1 t} + \sum_{j=3}^{n} B_j\delta_{pj}\lambda_j e^{\lambda_j t}, \\ \cdot \quad \cdot \quad \cdot \quad \cdot \quad \cdot \quad \cdot \quad \cdot \quad \cdot \\ 0 \equiv (B_1\eta_{p1} + B_2\eta_{p2})\lambda_1^{k-2}e^{\lambda_1 t} + \sum_{j=3}^{n} B_j\delta_{pj}\lambda_j^{k-2}e^{\lambda_j t}, \end{cases}$$

in which there are $k - 1$ coefficients that are not zero. The determinant of the coefficients of the B_j at $t = 0$ is of the form (11), and consequently is not zero. Hence it follows, as in Art. 141, that the solutions form a fundamental set.

Case II. Not all first minors of the determinant $D(\lambda_1)$ are zero. Since there is at least one first minor of the determinant $D(\lambda_1)$ that is not zero, equations (3), for $\lambda = \lambda_1$, are solvable in this case for $A_1, \cdots, A_n$ in terms of one arbitrary constant C_1 by equations of the form of equations (5). Hence there is only one purely exponential solution associated with the root λ_1.

It might be surmised from the results obtained for the general nth order equation in Art. 142 that a second solution associated with the root λ_1 is of the form

$$(27) \quad \begin{cases} x_1 = C_1 P_1(t)e^{\lambda_1 t}, \\ \cdot \quad \cdot \quad \cdot \quad \cdot \quad \cdot \\ x_n = C_1 P_n(t)e^{\lambda_1 t}, \end{cases}$$

where C_1 is an arbitrary constant and where $P_1(t), \cdots, P_n(t)$ are polynomials in t, of degree one in this simple case.

The conditions that the right members of equations (27) shall be a solution of equations (1) are

$$(28) \quad \begin{cases} P_1' + \lambda_1 P_1 \underset{t}{\equiv} a_{11}P_1 + \cdots + a_{1n}P_n, \\ \cdot \quad \cdot \quad \cdot \quad \cdot \quad \cdot \quad \cdot \quad \cdot \quad \cdot \\ P_n' + \lambda_1 P_n \underset{t}{\equiv} a_{n1}P_1 + \cdots + a_{nn}P_n, \end{cases}$$

where P_i' is the derivative of P_i with respect to t. Since these relations are identities, they give rise to a set of equations corresponding to each power of t in the P_i. To fix the notation, let

$$(29) \quad \begin{cases} C_1 P_1 = A_1{}^{(0)} t + A_1{}^{(1)}, \\ \cdot \quad \cdot \quad \cdot \quad \cdot \quad \cdot \quad \cdot \\ C_1 P_n = A_n{}^{(0)} t + A_n{}^{(1)}, \end{cases}$$

where the $A_i{}^{(0)}$ and the $A_i{}^{(1)}$ are constants. Then the identities (28) are equivalent to the equations

$$(30) \quad \begin{cases} (a_{11} - \lambda_1) A_1{}^{(0)} + \cdots + a_{1n} A_n{}^{(0)} = 0, \\ \cdot \quad \cdot \quad \cdot \quad \cdot \quad \cdot \quad \cdot \quad \cdot \quad \cdot \\ a_{n1} A_1{}^{(0)} + \cdots + (a_{nn} - \lambda_1) A_n{}^{(0)} = 0; \end{cases}$$

$$(31) \quad \begin{cases} (a_{11} - \lambda_1) A_1{}^{(1)} + \cdots + a_{1n} A_n{}^{(1)} = A_1{}^{(0)}, \\ \cdot \quad \cdot \quad \cdot \quad \cdot \quad \cdot \quad \cdot \quad \cdot \quad \cdot \\ a_{n1} A_1{}^{(1)} + \cdots + (a_{nn} - \lambda_1) A_n{}^{(1)} = A_n{}^{(0)}. \end{cases}$$

The problems are to prove that equations (30) and (31) have solutions and to find the solutions. Equations (30) have a solution of the form $A_i{}^{(0)} = \delta_{i1} C_1$, where C_1 is an arbitrary constant, but it is not easy to show directly that equations (31) have a solution.

The left members of equations (30) and (31) are similar in form to the expansions of $D(\lambda)$, with the $A_i{}^{(0)}$ taking the place of the co-factors of the elements of the row with respect to which the expansions are made. This fact suggests making comparison between equations (30) and (31) and such expansions of $D(\lambda)$. To fix the notation, suppose there is a first minor in the first $n - 1$ rows of $D(\lambda_1)$ that is not zero. Then consider the identities *

$$(32) \quad \begin{cases} (a_{11} - \lambda) D_{n1}(\lambda) + \cdots + a_{1n} D_{nn}(\lambda) \underset{\lambda}{\equiv} 0, \\ \cdot \quad \cdot \quad \cdot \quad \cdot \quad \cdot \quad \cdot \quad \cdot \quad \cdot \quad \cdot \quad \cdot \\ a_{n-11} D_{n1}(\lambda) + \cdots + a_{n-1n} D_{nn}(\lambda) \underset{\lambda}{\equiv} 0, \\ a_{n1} D_{n1}(\lambda) + \cdots + (a_{nn} - \lambda) D_{nn}(\lambda) \underset{\lambda}{\equiv} D(\lambda), \end{cases}$$

where the $D_{ij}(\lambda)$ are the co-factors of the a_{ij} in $D(\lambda)$.

* The use of these and corresponding identities in the general case is due to James A. Nyswander, *American Journal of Mathematics*, Vol. 47 (1925), pp. 257–276. Their use is of great importance in the theory.

Since $D(\lambda_1) = 0$ and $D'(\lambda_1) = 0$, where $D'(\lambda)$ is the derivative of $D(\lambda)$ with respect to λ, the identities (32) and their first derivatives with respect to λ, for $\lambda = \lambda_1$, give the equations

$$(33) \quad \begin{cases} (a_{11} - \lambda_1)D_{n1}(\lambda_1) + \cdots + a_{1n}D_{nn}(\lambda_1) = 0, \\ \cdot \quad \cdot \quad \cdot \quad \cdot \quad \cdot \quad \cdot \quad \cdot \quad \cdot \quad \cdot \quad \cdot \quad \cdot \quad \cdot \\ a_{n1}D_{n1}(\lambda_1) + \cdots + (a_{nn} - \lambda_1)D_{nn}(\lambda_1) = 0; \end{cases}$$

$$(34) \quad \begin{cases} (a_{11} - \lambda_1)D'_{n1}(\lambda_1) + \cdots + a_{1n}D'_{nn}(\lambda_1) = D_{n1}(\lambda_1), \\ \cdot \quad \cdot \quad \cdot \quad \cdot \quad \cdot \quad \cdot \quad \cdot \quad \cdot \quad \cdot \quad \cdot \quad \cdot \quad \cdot \\ a_{n1}D'_{n1}(\lambda_1) + \cdots + (a_{nn} - \lambda_1)D'_{nn}(\lambda_1) = D_{nn}(\lambda_1). \end{cases}$$

The first and the second of these two sets of equations are of the same form as equations (30) and (31) respectively.

The functions $x_1, \cdots, x_n$ of the solution (27) carry an arbitrary constant as a factor, which has been denoted by C_1. Hence it is found, on comparing equations (30) and (31) with equations (33) and (34), that the former have the solution

$$(35) \quad \begin{cases} A_1{}^{(0)} = C_1D_{n1}(\lambda_1), \\ \cdot \quad \cdot \quad \cdot \quad \cdot \quad \cdot \quad \cdot \\ A_n{}^{(0)} = C_1D_{nn}(\lambda_1); \end{cases}$$

$$(36) \quad \begin{cases} A_1{}^{(1)} = C_1D'_{n1}(\lambda_1), \\ \cdot \quad \cdot \quad \cdot \quad \cdot \quad \cdot \\ A_n{}^{(1)} = C_1D'_{nn}(\lambda_1). \end{cases}$$

Equations (31) also have a solution of the form of equations (35) carrying an arbitrary C_2. This solution will be omitted, for it is not required in determining the $P_i(t)$. It follows that the solution (27) is

$$(37) \quad \begin{cases} x_1 = C_1[D'_{n1}(\lambda_1) + D_{n1}(\lambda_1)t]e^{\lambda_1 t}, \\ \cdot \quad \cdot \quad \cdot \quad \cdot \quad \cdot \quad \cdot \quad \cdot \quad \cdot \\ x_n = C_1[D'_{nn}(\lambda_1) + D_{nn}(\lambda_1)t]e^{\lambda_1 t}, \end{cases}$$

where C_1 is an arbitrary constant.

Since the relations (28) are identities in t, their derivatives with respect to t are also satisfied. Therefore $x_i = P_i{}'(t)e^{\lambda_1 t}$ are also a solution. It follows, therefore, from equations (27), (28), and (37) that

$$(38) \quad \begin{cases} x_1 = C_2D_{n1}(\lambda_1)e^{\lambda_1 t}, \\ \cdot \quad \cdot \quad \cdot \quad \cdot \quad \cdot \\ x_n = C_2D_{nn}(\lambda_1)e^{\lambda_1 t}, \end{cases}$$

is a solution, where C_2 is an arbitrary constant. This solution corresponds to the second solution of equations (34), to which reference has been made, and in this simple case it could have been obtained as easily from those equations. In the general cases, however, it will tend to simplicity to derive first the solution whose coefficients are polynomials of the highest degree in t, and then to obtain the remaining solutions of the group by replacing the $P_i(t)$ by their successive derivatives with respect to t.

145. The Solutions in Case II Constitute a Fundamental Set. It will be shown by an indirect method, analogous to that used in Art. 141, that the solutions (37) and (38), together with those associated with the simple roots $\lambda_3, \cdots, \lambda_n$ of the characteristic equation $D(\lambda) = 0$, constitute a fundamental set.

The identities corresponding to the identities (9) are in this case

$$(39) \quad \begin{cases} 0 \equiv B_1[D'_{n1}(\lambda_1) + D_{n1}(\lambda_1)t]e^{\lambda_1 t} + B_2 D_{n1}(\lambda_1)e^{\lambda_1 t} + F_1, \\ \cdot \quad \cdot \quad \cdot \quad \cdot \quad \cdot \quad \cdot \quad \cdot \quad \cdot \quad \cdot \quad \cdot \quad \cdot \quad \cdot \quad \cdot \quad \cdot \\ 0 \equiv B_1[D'_{nn}(\lambda_1) + D_{nn}(\lambda_1)t]e^{\lambda_1 t} + B_2 D_{nn}(\lambda_1)e^{\lambda_1 t} + F_n, \\ F_i = \sum_{j=3}^{n} B_j \delta_{ij} e^{\lambda_j t}. \end{cases}$$

The pth of these identities and its first $k - 1$ derivatives with respect to t give rise to identities corresponding to those in (10). Since

$$\frac{d^j}{dt^j}[D'_{np}(\lambda_1) + D_{np}(\lambda_1)t]e^{\lambda_1 t} = \lambda_1{}^j[D'_{np}(\lambda_1) + D_{np}(\lambda_1)t]e^{\lambda_1 t} \\ + j\lambda_1{}^{j-1}D_{np}(\lambda_1)e^{\lambda_1 t},$$

it follows that the determinant corresponding to that of equation (11) is

$$(40) \quad \frac{V}{D_{np}} = \Pi\delta_{pj} \begin{vmatrix} D'_{np}+0 & , & 1 & , & 1 & , & \cdots \\ \lambda_1 D'_{np}+D_{np} & , & \lambda_1 & , & \lambda_3 & , & \cdots \\ \lambda_1{}^2 D'_{np}+2\lambda_1 D_{np} & , & \lambda_1{}^2 & , & \lambda_3{}^2 & , & \cdots \\ \cdot & & \cdot & & \cdot & & \\ \cdot & & \cdot & & \cdot & & \\ \cdot & & \cdot & & \cdot & & \\ \lambda_1{}^{k-1}D'_{np}+(k-1)\lambda_1{}^{k-2}D_{np}, & \lambda_1{}^{k-1}, & \lambda_3{}^{k-1}, & \cdots \end{vmatrix},$$

where p is so chosen that $D_{np}(\lambda_1)$ is not zero, and where $\Pi\delta_{pj}$ is the product of the $k - 2$ of the $\delta_{p3}, \cdots, \delta_{pn}$ that are not zero.

This determinant easily reduces to the much simpler form

$$(41) \quad V = D^2{}_{np}\Pi\delta_{pi} \begin{vmatrix} 0 & , 1 & , 1 & , \cdots, 1 \\ 1 & , \lambda_1 & , \lambda_3 & , \cdots, \lambda_n \\ 2\lambda_1 & , \lambda_1{}^2 & , \lambda_3{}^2 & , \cdots, \lambda_n{}^2 \\ \cdot & \cdot & \cdot & \cdot \\ \cdot & \cdot & \cdot & \cdot \\ \cdot & \cdot & \cdot & \cdot \\ (k-1)\lambda_1{}^{k-2}, & \lambda_1{}^{k-1}, & \lambda_3{}^{k-1}, & \cdots, \lambda_n{}^{k-1} \end{vmatrix}.$$

It follows from a discussion similar to that used in treating the determinant (19) that the right member of equation (41) is distinct from zero. Therefore all the B_i of the identities used in obtaining the determinant (41) are zero. When p takes all values from 1 to n, all the remaining B_i will also necessarily be zero, because each solution has at least one coefficient that is not zero. But this contradicts a consequence of the assumption that the solutions do not constitute a fundamental set. Therefore they constitute a fundamental set, which was to be proved.

146. Solutions When the Characteristic Equation Has a Triple Root. The complexities of the general problem are so great that, before taking it up, it is advisable to discuss briefly the case in which the characteristic equation has one triple root $\lambda = \lambda_1$ and all other simple roots $\lambda_4, \cdots, \lambda_n$.

Since $\lambda = \lambda_1$ is a triple root of the equation $D(\lambda) = 0$, the function $D(\lambda)$ and its first and second derivatives with respect to λ vanish for $\lambda = \lambda_1$, while its third derivative is distinct from zero for $\lambda = \lambda_1$. It follows from the form of the determinant $D(\lambda)$, equation (4), that its third derivative is a constant times the sum of its principal third minors. Since the third derivative of $D(\lambda)$ with respect to λ is not zero for $\lambda = \lambda_1$, there is at least one third minor of $D(\lambda_1)$ that is not zero. The following three cases will be considered:

Case I.   All first and second minors of $D(\lambda_1)$ are zero.

Case II.   At least one first minor of $D(\lambda_1)$ is not zero.

Case III.   All first minors of $D(\lambda)$ carry the factor $(\lambda - \lambda_1)$, but not all carry the factor $(\lambda - \lambda_1)^2$, and at least one second minor of $D(\lambda_1)$ is not zero.

It will be shown in Art. 150, page 278, that there are no other cases possible when $D(\lambda) = 0$ has only a triple root.

Case I. *All first and second minors of $D(\lambda_1)$ are zero.* Necessary and sufficient conditions that the differential equations (1) shall have a solution of the form of equations (2) are equations (3). When $\lambda = \lambda_1$, these equations in this case can be solved for the A_i as linear homogeneous functions of three arbitrary constants whose coefficients are third minors of the determinant $D(\lambda_1)$. It follows from the theory of linear equations that these three solutions are linearly independent. The solutions are

$$(42) \quad \begin{cases} x_1 = C_1\delta_{113}e^{\lambda_1 t} + C_2\delta_{123}e^{\lambda_1 t} + C_3\delta_{133}e^{\lambda_1 t}, \\ \cdots \cdots \cdots \cdots \cdots \cdots \cdots \cdots \\ x_n = C_1\delta_{n13}e^{\lambda_1 t} + C_2\delta_{n23}e^{\lambda_1 t} + C_3\delta_{n33}e^{\lambda_1 t}, \end{cases}$$

where C_1, C_2, and C_3 are arbitrary constants. Moreover, the three solutions are linearly independent. It can be easily shown by the method which was used in Art. 144, Case I, that the solutions (42), together with those associated with the simple roots $\lambda_4, \cdots, \lambda_n$, constitute a fundamental set.

Case II. *At least one first minor of $D(\lambda_1)$ is not zero.* The solutions in this case are of the form of equations (27), in which $P_1(t), \cdots, P_n(t)$ are polynomials in t of the second degree. Consequently, the equations corresponding to equations (29) are

$$(43) \quad \begin{cases} C_1P_1 = A_1{}^{(0)}t^2 + A_1{}^{(1)}t + A_1{}^{(2)}, \\ \cdots \cdots \cdots \cdots \cdots \cdots \cdots \\ C_1P_n = A_n{}^{(0)}t^2 + A_n{}^{(1)}t + A_n{}^{(2)}, \end{cases}$$

where the $A_i{}^{(0)}$, $A_i{}^{(1)}$, and $A_i{}^{(2)}$ are constants.

The identities corresponding to (28) in this case give rise to the three sets of equations

$$(44) \quad \begin{cases} (a_{11} - \lambda_1)A_1{}^{(0)} + \cdots + a_{1n}A_n{}^{(0)} = 0, \\ \cdots \cdots \cdots \cdots \cdots \cdots \cdots \\ a_{n1}A_1{}^{(0)} + \cdots + (a_{nn} - \lambda_1)A_n{}^{(0)} = 0; \end{cases}$$

$$(45) \quad \begin{cases} (a_{11} - \lambda_1)A_1{}^{(1)} + \cdots + a_{1n}A_n{}^{(1)} = 2A_1{}^{(0)}, \\ \cdots \cdots \cdots \cdots \cdots \cdots \cdots \\ a_{n1}A_1{}^{(1)} + \cdots + (a_{nn} - \lambda_1)A_n{}^{(1)} = 2A_n{}^{(0)}; \end{cases}$$

$$(46) \quad \begin{cases} (a_{11} - \lambda_1)A_1{}^{(2)} + \cdots + a_{1n}A_n{}^{(2)} = A_1{}^{(1)}, \\ \cdots \cdots \cdots \cdots \cdots \cdots \cdots \\ a_{n1}A_1{}^{(2)} + \cdots + (a_{nn} - \lambda_1)A_n{}^{(2)} = A_n{}^{(1)}. \end{cases}$$

The immediate problem is to prove that equations (44), (45), and (46) have a solution for the $A_i^{(0)}$, $A_i^{(1)}$, and $A_i^{(2)}$ respectively.

In proving that equations (44), (45), and (46) have a solution, the point of departure is the identities (32). These relations and their first and second derivatives with respect to λ are, for $\lambda = \lambda_1$,

$$(47) \quad \begin{cases} (a_{11} - \lambda_1)D_{n1}(\lambda_1) + \cdots + a_{1n}D_{nn}(\lambda_1) = 0, \\ \cdot \quad \cdot \quad \cdot \quad \cdot \quad \cdot \quad \cdot \quad \cdot \quad \cdot \quad \cdot \quad \cdot \quad \cdot \quad \cdot \quad \cdot \\ a_{n1}D_{n1}(\lambda_1) + \cdots + (a_{nn} - \lambda_1)D_{nn}(\lambda_1) = 0; \end{cases}$$

$$(48) \quad \begin{cases} (a_{11} - \lambda_1)D'_{n1}(\lambda_1) + \cdots + a_{1n}D'_{nn}(\lambda_1) = D_{n1}(\lambda_1), \\ \cdot \quad \cdot \quad \cdot \quad \cdot \quad \cdot \quad \cdot \quad \cdot \quad \cdot \quad \cdot \quad \cdot \quad \cdot \quad \cdot \quad \cdot \\ a_{n1}D'_{n1}(\lambda_1) + \cdots + (a_{nn} - \lambda_1)D'_{nn}(\lambda_1) = D_{nn}(\lambda_1); \end{cases}$$

$$(49) \quad \begin{cases} (a_{11} - \lambda_1)D''_{n1}(\lambda_1) + \cdots + a_{1n}D''_{nn}(\lambda_1) = 2D'_{n1}(\lambda_1), \\ \cdot \quad \cdot \quad \cdot \quad \cdot \quad \cdot \quad \cdot \quad \cdot \quad \cdot \quad \cdot \quad \cdot \quad \cdot \quad \cdot \quad \cdot \\ a_{n1}D''_{n1}(\lambda_1) + \cdots + (a_{nn} - \lambda_1)D''_{nn}(\lambda_1) = 2D'_{nn}(\lambda_1). \end{cases}$$

It was assumed in writing the identities (32) that at least one of the first minors of $D(\lambda_1)$ that is not zero is in the first $n - 1$ rows of $D(\lambda_1)$. Therefore not all the $D_{nj}(\lambda_1)$ of equations (47) are zero. Then it follows from equations (48) that not all the $D'_{nj}(\lambda_1)$ are zero. Since $\lambda = \lambda_1$ is only a triple root of the equation $D(\lambda) = 0$, not all the $D''_{nj}(\lambda_1)$ are zero, a result that follows also from equations (49).

Upon comparing equations (44) with equations (47), it is seen that a solution of the former set of equations is

$$(50) \quad \begin{cases} A_1^{(0)} = C_1 D_{n1}(\lambda_1), \\ \cdot \quad \cdot \quad \cdot \quad \cdot \quad \cdot \quad \cdot \\ A_n^{(0)} = C_1 D_{nn}(\lambda_1), \end{cases}$$

where C_1 is an arbitrary constant.

After substituting the expressions for the $A_i^{(0)}$ from equations (50) into the right members of equations (45) and comparing the results with equations (48), it is found that the solution of equations (45) involving C_1 is

$$(51) \quad \begin{cases} A_1^{(1)} = 2C_1 D'_{n1}(\lambda_1), \\ \cdot \quad \cdot \quad \cdot \quad \cdot \quad \cdot \\ A_n^{(1)} = 2C_1 D'_{nn}(\lambda_1). \end{cases}$$

Since the left members of equations (45) are of the same form as the left members of equations (44), there is another solution of equations (45) of the form of equations (50) with C_1 replaced by a second arbitrary constant C_2. This solution gives rise to a second solution of the differential equations, but it will not be necessary to carry it along because, after the solution $x_i = C_1 P_i(t)e^{\lambda_1 t}$ has been obtained, the two other solutions of the group are

$$(52) \quad \begin{cases} x_1 = C_2 P_1{}'(t)\, e^{\lambda_1 t}, \\ \cdot \quad \cdot \quad \cdot \quad \cdot \quad \cdot \quad \cdot \\ x_n = C_2 P_n{}'(t)\, e^{\lambda_1 t}; \end{cases}$$

$$(53) \quad \begin{cases} x_1 = C_3 P_1{}''(t)\, e^{\lambda_1 t}, \\ \cdot \quad \cdot \quad \cdot \quad \cdot \quad \cdot \\ x_n = C_3 P_n{}''(t)\, e^{\lambda_1 t}. \end{cases}$$

The solution of equations (46) can now be obtained by substituting the expressions for the $A_i{}^{(1)}$ from equations (51) into their right members and comparing the results with equations (49). The solution is seen to be

$$(54) \quad \begin{cases} A_1{}^{(2)} = C_1 D_{n1}''(\lambda_1), \\ \cdot \quad \cdot \quad \cdot \quad \cdot \quad \cdot \\ A_n{}^{(2)} = C_1 D_{nn}''(\lambda_1). \end{cases}$$

Upon substituting the expressions for the $A_i{}^{(0)}$, $A_i{}^{(1)}$, and $A_i{}^{(2)}$ into equations (43) and referring to equations (27), the solution in question is found to be

$$(55) \quad \begin{cases} x_1 = C_1 P_1(t)e^{\lambda_1 t} = C_1[D_{n1}'' + 2D_{n1}'t + D_{n1}t^2]e^{\lambda_1 t}, \\ \cdot \quad \cdot \quad \cdot \quad \cdot \quad \cdot \quad \cdot \quad \cdot \quad \cdot \quad \cdot \quad \cdot \quad \cdot \\ x_n = C_1 P_n(t)e^{\lambda_1 t} = C_1[D_{nn}'' + 2D_{nn}'t + D_{nn}t^2]e^{\lambda_1 t}. \end{cases}$$

The two other solutions associated with λ_1 are

$$(56) \quad \begin{cases} x_1 = C_2 P_1{}'(t)e^{\lambda_1 t} = C_2[D_{n1}' + D_{n1}t]e^{\lambda_1 t}, \\ \cdot \quad \cdot \quad \cdot \quad \cdot \quad \cdot \quad \cdot \quad \cdot \quad \cdot \\ x_n = C_2 P_n{}'(t)e^{\lambda_1 t} = C_2[D_{nn}' + D_{nn}t]e^{\lambda_1 t}; \end{cases}$$

$$(57) \quad \begin{cases} x_1 = C_3 P_1{}''(t)e^{\lambda_1 t} = C_3 D_{n1}e^{\lambda_1 t}, \\ \cdot \quad \cdot \quad \cdot \quad \cdot \quad \cdot \quad \cdot \quad \cdot \\ x_n = C_3 P_n{}''(t)e^{\lambda_1 t} = C_3 D_{nn}e^{\lambda_1 t}. \end{cases}$$

It can be shown by the methods heretofore used in Art. 145

that the solutions (55), (56), and (57), together with those depending upon the simple roots λ_4, $\cdots$, λ_n of the equation $D(\lambda) = 0$, constitute a fundamental set.

Case III. All first minors of $D(\lambda)$ contain the factor $\lambda - \lambda_1$, but not $(\lambda - \lambda_1)^2$; one second minor of $D(\lambda_1)$ is not zero.

Since not all the second minors of $D(\lambda_1)$ are zero, there are two purely exponential solutions, analogous to those obtained in Art. 144, Case I. For notation, let them be

$$(58) \quad x_i = C_1\eta_{i1}e^{\lambda_1 t}, \qquad x_i = C_2\eta_{i2}e^{\lambda_1 t} \qquad (i = 1, \cdots, n),$$

where C_1 and C_2 are arbitrary constants, and where the η_{i1} and the η_{i2} are second minors of the determinant $D(\lambda_1)$.

The third solution is similar to that obtained in Art. 144, Case II. That is, it is of the form

$$(59) \quad x_i = C_3P_i(t)e^{\lambda_1 t} = [A_i^{(0)}t + A_i^{(1)}]e^{\lambda_1 t} \qquad (i = 1, \cdots, n).$$

The conditions that these expressions shall be a solution of the differential equations (1) are the equations (30) and (31). If equations (30) and (31) are compared with equations (47) and (48) respectively, the values found for the $A_i^{(0)}$ and the $A_i^{(1)}$ are $A_i^{(0)} = 0$, $A_i^{(1)} = D'_{ni}(\lambda_1)$. It follows from equations (59) that the corresponding solution is composed of purely exponential functions; therefore this solution is a linear function of the two solutions given by equations (58), which are the only two linearly independent purely exponential solutions.

If equations (30) and (31) are compared, however, with equations (48) and (49) and use is made of the fact that the $D_{ni}(\lambda_1)$ are zero, the expressions for the $A_i^{(0)}$ and the $A_i^{(1)}$ are found to be

$$(60) \quad \begin{cases} A_i^{(0)} = 2C_3D'_{ni}(\lambda_1) & (i = 1, \cdots, n), \\ A_i^{(1)} = C_3D''_{ni}(\lambda_1), \end{cases}$$

the factor 2 being introduced to avoid fractional coefficients in the solution. The corresponding solution is

$$(61) \quad \begin{cases} x_1 = C_3[D''_{n1}(\lambda_1) + 2D'_{n1}(\lambda_1)t]e^{\lambda_1 t}, \\ \cdot \quad \cdot \quad \cdot \quad \cdot \quad \cdot \quad \cdot \quad \cdot \quad \cdot \\ x_n = C_3[D''_{nn}(\lambda_1) + 2D'_{nn}(\lambda_1)t]e^{\lambda_1 t}. \end{cases}$$

That the solutions (58) and (61), together with those associated with the simple roots λ_4, $\cdots$, λ_n of the equation $D(\lambda) = 0$, constitute a fundamental set can be readily proved by the method used in Art. 145.

147. Outline of the General Case. It has been found in the special cases that have been treated in the preceding pages that the characteristics of the solutions depend upon the multiplicities of the roots λ_j of the characteristic equation $D(\lambda) = 0$ and upon the properties of the minors of $D(\lambda_j)$. The results obtained in the special cases furnish suggestions for treating the general case in which the equation $D(\lambda) = 0$ has roots of any multiplicities, necessarily not exceeding n, and in which the determinant $D(\lambda_j)$ has any possible properties.

The characteristics of the solutions associated with the root λ_j of the equation $D(\lambda) = 0$ depend only upon the properties of the determinant $D(\lambda_j)$ and not upon any other roots of the equation $D(\lambda) = 0$. Consequently the solutions associated with each root of the characteristic equation $D(\lambda) = 0$ can be obtained without reference to the others, and it is sufficient, therefore, to treat the problem for the root $\lambda = \lambda_j$.

It will be shown that the general characteristics of the solutions associated with the root λ_j depend only upon the highest powers of $\lambda - \lambda_j$ that are contained as factors in all the minors of each order of the determinant $D(\lambda)$. Since the general properties of the solutions do not depend upon which particular minors of a given order contain the lowest powers of $\lambda - \lambda_j$, the notations need not specify the particular minors in terms of which the coefficients of the solutions can be expressed. In order to simplify the notations as much as possible, they will be made to carry explicitly only those properties of the determinant $D(\lambda)$ that are essential to the discussion.

Suppose λ_j is a root of the characteristic equation $D(\lambda) = 0$ of order n_j. Since all the subsequent discussion pertains to this root, the subscript j may be omitted from the notations for the determinant and its minors. Let δ_{im} represent an mth minor, of order $n - m$, of the determinant $D(\lambda)$. This notation does not, of course, completely specify which mth minor of $D(\lambda)$ is under consideration. Suppose all δ_{im} contain $(\lambda - \lambda_j)^{\nu_m}$ as a factor, but that they do not all contain any higher power of $\lambda - \lambda_j$ as a factor. Suppose, also, that $\nu_p = 0$ and that $\nu_m \gtreqless 1$ if $m < p$. It follows that $p \leqq n_j$.

It will be shown that the differential equations have p linearly independent solutions associated with the root λ_j which are simple exponentials of the type $e^{\lambda_j t}$, and that the coefficients of these solutions can be expressed in terms of pth minors of the determinant $D(\lambda_j)$.

It will be shown that, besides the purely exponential solutions, there are also $\nu_{m-1} - \nu_m - 1$ other solutions associated with the root λ_j for each value of m from 1 to p which are of the type $P_i(t)e^{\lambda_j t}$, where the $P_i(t)$ are polynomials in t, and that the coefficients of these solutions are expressible in terms of derivatives with respect to λ_j of mth minors of the determinant $D(\lambda_j)$.

Since

$$(62) \qquad p + \sum_{m=1}^{p} (\nu_{m-1} - \nu_m - 1) = n_j \qquad (\nu_0 = n_j),$$

it follows that there are n_j solutions associated with the root λ_j; and, since $\sum n_j = n$, there are n solutions of the differential equations (1). It will be shown finally that the mth minors in terms of which the coefficients are expressed can be so chosen that the solutions form a fundamental set.

The purely exponential solutions can also be obtained from the solutions of the form $P_i(t)e^{\lambda_j t}$ by taking derivatives of the $P_i(t)$ with respect to t, as was explained in connection with equations (52) and (53). In fact, it is preferable to obtain them in this manner. There is one such solution for each value of m from 1 to p, and consequently there are p of them.

148. The Purely Exponential Solutions.

In spite of the fact that it will be shown to be advantageous to obtain the purely exponential solutions from those of the form $P_i(t)e^{\lambda_j t}$, it is desirable to give them brief separate consideration.

According to present hypotheses, $D(\lambda)$ and all its minors of orders $n - 1$, $n - 2$, $\cdots$, $n - p + 1$ are zero for $\lambda = \lambda_j$, while there is at least one minor of order $n - p$ that is not zero. Therefore, for $\lambda = \lambda_j$, equations (3) have p linearly independent solutions which can be written

$$(63) \qquad \begin{cases} A_1 = C_1 \delta_{11p} + \cdots + C_p \delta_{1pp}, \\ \cdot \quad \cdot \quad \cdot \quad \cdot \quad \cdot \quad \cdot \quad \cdot \quad \cdot \\ A_n = C_1 \delta_{n1p} + \cdots + C_p \delta_{npp}, \end{cases}$$

where C_1, $\cdots$, C_p are arbitrary constants. If C_1, $\cdots$, C_p are identified with p of the A_i, for example $A_{n-p+1}, \cdots, A_n$, the equations (63) take the form

$$(64) \quad \begin{cases} A_1 = C_1\delta_{11p} + \cdots + C_p\delta_{1pp}, \\ \cdots \cdots \cdots \cdots \cdots \cdots \\ A_{n-p} = C_1\delta_{n-11p} + \cdots + C_p\delta_{n-ppp}, \\ A_{n-p+1} = C_1 + 0 + \cdots + 0, \\ \cdots \cdots \cdots \cdots \cdots \cdots \\ A_n = 0 + 0 + \cdots + C_p. \end{cases}$$

The p sets of coefficients in the right members of these equations are obviously linearly independent.

The solutions of equations (1), corresponding to the coefficients A_i defined by equations (63), are

$$(65) \quad \begin{cases} x_1 = C_1\delta_{11p}e^{\lambda_j t} + \cdots + C_p\delta_{1pp}e^{\lambda_j t}, \\ \cdots \cdots \cdots \cdots \cdots \cdots \\ x_n = C_1\delta_{n1p}e^{\lambda_j t} + \cdots + C_p\delta_{npp}e^{\lambda_j t}. \end{cases}$$

The coefficients δ_{ikp} are functions of λ_j. Since the solutions (63) are linearly independent, there are no values of $C_1, \cdots, C_p$, not all zero, such that the x_i are all zero for any finite value of t.

149. Solutions Whose Coefficients Are Expressible in Terms of the Derivatives with Respect to λ_j of mth Minors of $D(\lambda_j)$. It will be shown that the solution, depending upon the mth minors of $D(\lambda_j)$, which involves polynomials of the highest degree in t has the form

$$(66) \quad \begin{cases} x_i = C_{p+1}P_i(t)\,e^{\lambda_j t} \quad (i = 1, \cdots, n), \\ C_{p+1}P_i(t) = A_i^{(0)}t^\omega + A_i^{(1)}t^{\omega-1} + \cdots + A_i^{(\omega-1)}t + A_i^{(\omega)}, \\ \omega = \nu_{m-1} - \nu_m - 1, \end{cases}$$

the coefficient C_{p+1} being an arbitrary constant. The $A_i^{(k)}$ will be shown to be expressible in terms of derivatives with respect to λ_j of mth minors of $D(\lambda_j)$.

The conditions that the right members of the first set of equations (66) shall constitute a solution of equations (1) are identities of the form of (28). The derivatives of these identities with respect to t are also identities. Therefore there exist the ω other solutions

$$(67) \quad x_i = C_{p+q+1}P_i^{(q)}(t)e^{\lambda_j t} \quad (i = 1, \cdots, n; q = 1, \cdots, \omega),$$

where the C_{p+q+1} are arbitrary constants, and where the $P_i^{(q)}(t)$

are qth derivatives with respect to t of the $P_i(t)$. When $q = \omega$, the solution is a pure exponential and is included in the solutions (65) either as one of those solutions or as a linear combination of them, for equations (65) define the totality of independent exponential solutions associated with λ_j.

On substituting the expressions for the x_i from equations (66) into equations (1) and equating corresponding coefficients, necessary and sufficient conditions that these expressions for the x_i shall be a solution of equations (1) are found to be

$$(68) \quad \begin{cases} (a_{ii} - \lambda_j)A_i{}^{(0)} + \sum_{k=1}^{n} a_{ik}A_k{}^{(0)} = 0 \quad (i = 1, \cdots, n; \; k \neq i), \\ (a_{ii} - \lambda_j)A_i{}^{(l)} + \sum_{k=1}^{n} a_{ik}A_k{}^{(l)} = (\omega - l + 1)A_i{}^{(l-1)} \\ \hspace{6cm} (l = 1, \cdots, \omega). \end{cases}$$

The problem is to solve these equations for the coefficients $A_k{}^{(0)}$ and $A_k{}^{(l)}$ for $l = 1, \cdots, \omega$.

According to the hypotheses that have been made, all mth minors of the determinant $D(\lambda)$ contain $(\lambda - \lambda_j)^{\nu_m}$ as a factor, but there is at least one mth minor of $D(\lambda)$ that does not contain any higher power of $\lambda - \lambda_j$ as a factor. The order of such an mth minor is $n - m$. Suppose an mth minor that does not contain $(\lambda - \lambda_j)^{\nu_m+1}$ as a factor is made up of elements common to the rows $i_1, \cdots, i_{n-m}$ and to the columns $j_1, \cdots, j_{n-m}$. This mth minor is included in $(m - 1)$st minors (of order $n - m + 1$) which depend upon the elements of an additional row i, and, of course, upon those of an additional column j. Suppose the additional column j is kept fixed while i takes all values from 1 to n. Now let the $(m - 1)$st minors under consideration, which are of order $n - m + 1$, be expanded in terms of the mth minors from the rows $i_1, \cdots, i_{n-m}$. These minors are first minors of the $(m - 1)$st minors of $D(\lambda)$ that are being expanded, and they are of order $n - m$. The results of the expansions are

$$(69) \quad \begin{cases} (a_{ii} - \lambda)\delta_{im} + \sum_{k=1}^{n} a_{ik}\delta_{km} \underset{\lambda}{\equiv} 0 \quad (i = i_1, \cdots, i_{n-m}; \; k \neq i), \\ (a_{ii} - \lambda)\delta_{im} + \sum_{k=1}^{n} a_{ik}\delta_{km} \underset{\lambda}{\equiv} \delta_{im-1} \quad (i \neq i_1, \cdots, i_{n-m}; \; k \neq i), \end{cases}$$

where the δ_{im} and the δ_{km} are mth minors of $D(\lambda)$ from the rows $i_1, \cdots, i_{n-m}$ and from the columns $j_1, \cdots, j_{n-m}, j$ of $D(\lambda)$ that occur in the $(m - 1)$st minors under consideration; and where the δ_{im-1} also are $(m - 1)$st minors of $D(\lambda)$, containing elements from the rows $i_1, \cdots, i_{n-m}, i$ and from the columns $j_1, \cdots, j_{n-m}, j$. It follows from the notation that δ_{km} is the co-factor of some element, in the column k, of $\delta_{i\,m-1}$.

Since $(m - 1)$st minors of order $n - m + 1$ are now being expanded, there are only $n - m + 1$ terms in the expansions. The notations (69), however, provide for n terms, but it is to be understood that all those are identically zero that do not depend exclusively upon the elements of the columns of the $(m - 1)$st minor that is expanded.

If λ were replaced by λ_j, the identities (69) would be of the same form as equations (68), which the $A_i^{(k)}$ must satisfy. But since all mth minors δ_{im} of $D(\lambda)$ contain $(\lambda - \lambda_j)^{\nu m}$ as a factor, the left members of the identities (69) are identically zero for $\lambda = \lambda_j$. Consequently, before replacing λ by λ_j, derivatives with respect to λ of the identities (69) will be taken. A similar situation was presented in Case III, Art. 146. Since the δ_{im} all contain $(\lambda - \lambda_j)^{\nu m}$ as a factor, the left members of $(\nu_m - 1)$st derivatives of the identities (69) are all zero for $\lambda = \lambda_j$. Consequently the equations will be considered for derivatives of order ν_m and higher.

In order that the equations derived from the identities (69) shall be useful in solving equations (68), their right members must involve only the same arguments as their left members, as is the case with equations (68). Consequently, only those derivatives of the identities (69) will give useful equations for which the derivatives of the $\delta_{i\,m-1}$ are zero for $\lambda = \lambda_j$. Since all the $\delta_{i\,m-1}$ carry $(\lambda - \lambda_j)^{\nu_{m-1}}$ as a factor, all of their derivatives of order less than ν_{m-1} vanish for $\lambda = \lambda_j$, but the derivatives of higher order do not vanish in the case of all $\delta_{i\,m-1}$.

On taking successive derivatives with respect to λ_j of the identities (69) and replacing λ by λ_j in the results, it is found that

$$(70) \begin{cases} (a_{ii} - \lambda_j)\delta_{im}^{(\nu m)} + \sum_{k=1}^{n} a_{ik}\delta_{km}^{(\nu m)} = \nu_m \delta_{im}^{(\nu m-1)} = 0 \\ \qquad\qquad\qquad\qquad (i = 1, \cdots, n; \; k \neq i), \\[2mm] (a_{ii} - \lambda_j)\delta_{im}^{(\nu m+l)} + \sum_{k=1}^{n} a_{ik}\delta_{km}^{(\nu m+l)} = (\nu_m + l)\delta_{im}^{(\nu m+l-1)} \\ \qquad\qquad\qquad\qquad (i = 1, \cdots, n; \; l = 1, \cdots, \omega), \end{cases}$$

where $\delta_{im}^{(\nu_m+l)}$ is the $(\nu_m + l)$th derivative of δ_{im} with respect to λ, for $\lambda = \lambda_j$. These $\omega + 1$ sets of equations are known to be satisfied because they are derived from identities in λ by assigning λ the special value λ_j. Moreover, not all the $\delta_{im}^{(\nu_m)}$ are zero, for there is at least one $\delta_{im}^{(\nu_m)}$ in the $\delta_{i\,m-1}$ chosen that does not contain $\lambda - \lambda_j$ as a factor to a degree higher than ν_m. It follows, too, from equations (70), considered for $l = 1, \cdots, \omega$ sequentially, that not all the $\delta_k^{(\nu_m+l)}$ are zero for any value of l from 1 to ω.

On comparing equations (68) with equations (70), it is found that a solution of the former set is

$$(71) \quad \begin{cases} A_i^{(0)} = c_1 \delta_{im}^{(\nu_m)} \qquad (i = 1, \cdots, n), \\ A_i^{(l)} = c_1 \dfrac{\omega \cdots (\omega - l + 1)}{(\nu_m + 1) \cdots (\nu_m + l)} \delta_{im}^{(\nu_m+l)} \quad (l = 1, \cdots, \omega), \end{cases}$$

where c_1 is an arbitrary constant. Since not all the $\delta_{im}^{(\nu_m+l)}$ $(i = 1, \cdots, n)$ are zero for any value of l from zero to ω, not all the $A_i^{(l)}$ are zero for any value of l from zero to ω.

The solution takes a more convenient form if a new arbitrary constant C_{p+1} is defined in terms of c_1 by the equation

$$(72) \qquad\qquad C_{p+1} = \omega!\, \nu_m!\, c_1.$$

With this definition of C_{p+1}, it follows from equations (66) and (71) that the solution in question is

$$(73) \quad \begin{cases} x_i = C_{p+1} \left[\dfrac{\delta_{im}^{(\nu_m+\omega)}}{(\nu_m + \omega)!} + \dfrac{\delta_{im}^{(\nu_m+\omega-1)}}{1!(\nu_m + \omega - 1)!} t \right. \\ \left. \qquad\qquad\qquad + \cdots + \dfrac{\delta_{im}^{(\nu_m)}}{\omega!\, \nu_m!} t^\omega \right] e^{\lambda_j t}, \\ \omega = \nu_{m-1} - \nu_m - 1. \end{cases}$$

The remaining solutions of this group are found from equations (67) and (73) to be explicitly

$$(74) \quad x_i = C_{p+q+1} \left[\dfrac{\delta_{im}^{(\nu_m+\omega-q)}}{(\nu_m + \omega - q)!} + \cdots + \dfrac{\delta_{im}^{(\nu_m)}}{(\omega - q)!\, \nu_m!} t^{\omega-q} \right] e^{\lambda_j t},$$
$$(q = 1, \cdots, \omega),$$

the purely exponential solution for $q = \omega$ being included in those given in equations (65).

A corresponding group of solutions can be obtained for each

value of m from 1 to p inclusive. As was seen in Art. 147, all these solutions, together with those given in equations (65), make up the n_j solutions associated with the root λ_j, of order n_j, of the equation $D(\lambda) = 0$.

In the foregoing discussion, the hypothesis has been that at least one of the δ_{im} of the identities (69) from which equations (70) were derived contains $(\lambda - \lambda_j)^{\nu_m}$ as a factor, but no higher power of $\lambda - \lambda_j$. Now suppose that an attempt is made to express solutions similarly in terms of δ_{im} which all contain $(\lambda - \lambda_j)^{\nu_m+r}$ as a factor, where $0 < r < \omega$. In this case equations (70) are simply identities for $l = 0, \cdots, r - 1$. For $l = r$, the left members of the equations are not all zero, but the right members are zero. For $l = r + 1, \cdots, \omega$ neither all the left members nor all the right members are zero. Consequently, on comparing equations (68) with these equations, it is found that

$$\begin{cases} A_i{}^{(0)} = \cdots = A_i{}^{(r-1)} = 0, \\ A_i{}^{(r)} = c_1\delta_{im}{}^{(\nu_m+r)}, \\ A_i{}^{(r+l)} = c_1 \dfrac{(\omega - r) \cdots (\omega - r - l + 1)}{(\nu_m + r + 1) \cdots (\nu_m + r + l)} \, \delta_{im}{}^{(\nu_m+r+l)} \\ \hspace{5cm} (l = 1, \cdots, \omega - r). \end{cases}$$

These values of the $A_i{}^{(r+l)}$ determine a solution corresponding to that given by equations (73), but the highest power of t in the polynomial coefficients is $\omega - r$. Therefore the solutions corresponding to those given by equations (73) and (74) are $\omega - r + 1$ in number, leaving undetermined r of those whose coefficients are expressible in terms of derivatives with respect to λ_j of mth minors of the determinant $D(\lambda_j)$. In general, these solutions are not identical with those given by equations (74) for $q = r, \cdots, \omega$, but they are linear homogeneous functions of such solutions. Hence, in determining a fundamental set of solutions, it is necessary to start with an mth minor of $D(\lambda)$ that contains $\lambda - \lambda_j$ as a factor to the power ν_m, and not to a higher power.

150. Transformation of the Determinant $D(\lambda)$.
In the identities (69), the δ_{im} are mth minors of the determinant $D(\lambda)$ made out of the elements of its rows $i_1, \cdots, i_{n-m}$ and its columns $j_1, \cdots, j_{n-m}, j$. There are, therefore, $n - m + 1$ of these mth minors at least one of which contains $(\lambda - \lambda_j)^{\nu_m}$ as a factor,

but no higher power of $\lambda - \lambda_j$. All other mth minors provided for by the notation are, by definition, zero.

Now suppose the kth row of $D(\lambda)$ is added to one of the rows $i_1, \cdots, i_{n-m}$, say i_1, and consider the $n - m + 1$ mth minors of the transformed determinant made up of the elements of the rows $i_1, \cdots, i_{n-m}$ and the columns $j_1, \cdots, j_{n-m}, j$. Each of the mth minors of the transformed determinant is the sum of the corresponding mth minor of the original determinant and an mth minor in which the elements of the row i_1 are replaced by those of the row k. If the added minors are all zero, the solution determined from the transformed determinant is identical with that determined from the original determinant. If at least one of the added minors contains $(\lambda - \lambda_j)^{\nu_m}$, but no higher power of $\lambda - \lambda_j$, as a factor, a set of $\omega + 1$ solutions of the differential equations can be expressed similarly in terms of mth minors from the rows $i_2, \cdots, i_{n-m}, k$ and the columns $j_1, \cdots, j_{n-m}, j$. Since the sum of any two solutions is a solution, the sum of these solutions and those from the rows $i_1, \cdots, i_{n-m}$ of the original determinant are solutions. They are, in fact, the solutions obtained from the rows $i_1, \cdots, i_{n-m}$ and the columns $j_1, \cdots, j_{n-m}, j$ of the transformed determinant. That is, the transformed determinant in either case can be used for the determination of the solutions. If at least one of the added minors contains $(\lambda - \lambda_j)^{\nu_{m+r}}$ as a factor, a set of $\omega - r + 1$ solutions of the differential equations can be expressed in terms of these mth minors, and, as before, the sum of these solutions and those from the rows $i_1, \cdots, i_{n-m}$ of the original determinant are a solution.

Now suppose that, instead of adding the row k of the determinant $D(\lambda)$ to the row i_1, the elements of the row k are multiplied by a polynomial $\phi(\lambda)$ and are added to the corresponding elements of the row i_1. The question is whether mth minors from the rows $i_1, \cdots, i_{n-m}$ of the transformed determinant $D_1(\lambda)$ can be used for the determination of a group of $\omega + 1$ solutions. Each of the δ_{im} of the identities (69) from the transformed determinant is the sum of one from the rows $i_1, \cdots, i_{n-m}$ of the original determinant and of $\phi(\lambda)$ times one from the rows $i_2, \cdots, i_{n-m}, k$ of the original determinant. Since the identities (69) are linear in the δ_{im}, each of the two parts of the δ_{im} may be considered separately.

Consider the part of the δ_{im} from the rows $i_2, \cdots, i_{n-m}, k$ and carrying the factor $\phi(\lambda)$. For this part, the identities (69) may be written in the form

$$\phi(\lambda)F(\lambda) \underset{\lambda}{\equiv} 0 \text{ or } \delta_{i, m-1},$$

where $F(\lambda)$ carries $(\lambda - \lambda_j)^{\nu_m+r}$ $(r \gtreqless 0)$ as a factor. All derivatives of $F(\lambda)$ of order less than $\nu_m + r$ are zero for $\lambda = \lambda_j$, while at least one term of the $(\nu_m + r)$th derivative of $F(\lambda)$ is not zero. The $(\nu_m + r)$th derivative of the identity is

$$\phi^{(\nu_m+r)}(\lambda)F(\lambda) + a_1\phi^{(\nu_m+r-1)}(\lambda)F^{(1)}(\lambda) + \cdots + \phi(\lambda)F^{(\nu_m+r)}(\lambda),$$

where $a_1, \cdots$ are the binomial coefficients. Hence all terms of this sum except the last vanish for $\lambda = \lambda_j$, and consequently the equations corresponding to the first set of equations (70) are satisfied in this case. All terms of the next derivatives are zero for $\lambda = \lambda_j$, except the last two; namely,

$$\phi^{(1)}(\lambda_j)F^{(\nu_m+r)}(\lambda_j) + \phi(\lambda_j)F^{(\nu_m+r+1)}(\lambda).$$

Since $F^{(\nu_m+r)}(\lambda_j) = 0$, as has already been shown, the $F^{(\nu_m+r+1)}(\lambda_j)$ satisfy equations corresponding to the second set of equations (70). The same result holds for all succeeding derivatives up to the $(\nu_m + \omega)$. Consequently the minors in the identities (69) can be multiplied by $\phi(\lambda)$ without destroying their usefulness in deriving equations for determining solutions. Therefore the determinant $D(\lambda)$ can be used for determining solutions after it has been transformed by multiplying any row by the polynomial $\phi(\lambda)$ and adding the product to any other row.

The number of solutions defined in Art. 149 depends upon the highest powers of $\lambda - \lambda_j$ contained in all minors of various orders. It is important to note that the transformation of the determinant $D(\lambda)$ does not change the highest common factors of its minors of the various orders. Let the determinant obtained by adding to the elements of the i_1th row the products of the polynomial $\phi(\lambda)$ and the corresponding elements of the kth row be denoted by $D_1(\lambda)$. It follows that all mth minors of $D_1(\lambda)$ from the rows $i_1, \cdots, i_{n-m}$ are mth minors of $D(\lambda)$ from the rows $i_1, \cdots, i_{n-m}$, plus $\phi(\lambda)$ times mth minors of $D(\lambda)$ from the rows $i_2, \cdots, i_{n-m}, k$. And, conversely, all mth minors of $D(\lambda)$ from the rows $i_1, \cdots, i_{n-m}$ are mth minors of $D_1(\lambda)$ from the rows $i_1, \cdots, i_{n-m}$, minus $\phi(\lambda)$ times mth minors of $D_1(\lambda)$ from the rows $i_2, \cdots, i_{n-m}, k$. It follows that the mth minors of $D_1(\lambda)$ have the highest common factors of the mth minors of $D(\lambda)$, and that the mth minors of $D(\lambda)$ have the highest common factors of the mth minors of $D_1(\lambda)$. That is, the mth minors of $D(\lambda)$ and of $D_1(\lambda)$ have the same highest common factors.

Now consider the simplification of the determinant $D(\lambda)$ by making successive transformations of the type that have been discussed. If all the elements in any column except that in the main diagonal, say $a_{ii} - \lambda$, are zero, the $n - 1$ differential equations, omitting the ith, are independent of the ith and can be treated separately. After omitting such equations, at least one row of $D(\lambda)$ can be multiplied by such a polynomial in λ that when it is added to the first row its first element will be a constant distinct from zero. If the first row is then multiplied successively by suitable constants, and if the products are subtracted sequentially from the remaining $n - 1$ rows, all the elements in the first column except the first will be reduced to zero. Let the resulting determinant be written in the form

$$(75) \qquad D(\lambda) = \begin{vmatrix} f_{11}^{(1)}, & f_{12}^{(1)}, & \cdots, & f_{1n}^{(1)} \\ 0 & , f_{22}^{(1)}, & \cdots, & f_{2n}^{(1)} \\ \cdot & \cdot & & \cdot \\ \cdot & \cdot & & \cdot \\ \cdot & \cdot & & \cdot \\ 0 & , f_{n2}^{(1)}, & \cdots, & f_{nn}^{(1)} \end{vmatrix},$$

where $f_{11}^{(1)}$ is independent of λ and is distinct from zero. The remaining $f_{1j}^{(1)}$ in the first row are linear or quadratic functions of λ. If the first element of the first column has been reduced to a number independent of λ by multiplying the kth row by λ/a_k and subtracting the product from the first, then $f_{1k}^{(1)}$ is a quadratic function of λ at the most, and all the remaining $f_{1j}^{(1)}$ except $f_{11}^{(1)}$ are linear functions of λ at the most. It follows that all the elements in the kth column are quadratic in λ, and that the elements in all the remainder of the $n - 1$ columns are linear in λ. The degree of the determinant in λ has not been changed by this transformation. Moreover, as has been pointed out, the solutions of the differential equations can be determined from the determinant (75), as well as from the original form of $D(\lambda)$.

Now consider the elements $f_{22}^{(1)}, \cdots, f_{n2}^{(1)}$ of the second column. If they are linear functions of λ and do not contain a common factor, such a linear combination of the rows 2, $\cdots$, n can be substituted for the second row that $f_{22}^{(1)}$ will be replaced by a constant independent of λ and distinct from zero. Then, on multiplying the resulting second row by suitable factors linear in λ and substituting the products sequentially from rows 3, $\cdots$, n, all the elements in the second column below the main diagonal will be zero. All the corresponding elements in the remaining $n - 3$ columns will be quadratic in λ, except those in the k column, which will be of the third degree in λ.

If $k = 2$ so that $f_{22}^{(1)}, \cdots, f_{n2}^{(1)}$ of equation (75) are quadratic functions of λ not having a common factor, a corresponding reduction can be made. Linear combinations with coefficients independent of λ can first be made to remove the quadratic terms from all the elements $f_{22}^{(1)}, \cdots, f_{n2}^{(1)}$ except one, and then the term of the first degree in λ can be removed from $f_{22}^{(1)}$. Even if there are only two rows, the second and the third, the reduction can be made. First, the second-degree term of one of the rows is removed by taking a linear combination of the two with coefficients independent of λ. Then the one that is linear in λ is multiplied by a constant times λ and added to the other to remove its term of the second degree in λ. The elements $f_{22}^{(1)}, f_{32}^{(1)}, \cdots$ of the second column are now linear in λ, and $f_{22}^{(1)}$ can be reduced to a constant independent of λ and distinct from zero. It may be noted that a corresponding reduction can be made whatever may be the degrees of the elements, provided they do not all contain a common factor, and whatever may be the number of rows. Let the determinant after this step in the reduction be written

$$(76) \qquad D(\lambda) = \begin{vmatrix} f_{11}^{(1)}, & f_{12}^{(1)}, & f_{13}^{(1)}, & \cdots, & f_{1n}^{(1)} \\ 0 & , f_{22}^{(2)}, & f_{23}^{(2)}, & \cdots, & f_{2n}^{(2)} \\ 0 & , 0 & , f_{33}^{(2)}, & \cdots, & f_{3n}^{(2)} \\ \cdot & \cdot & \cdot & & \\ \cdot & \cdot & \cdot & & \\ \cdot & \cdot & \cdot & & \\ 0 & , 0 & , f_{n3}^{(2)}, & \cdots, & f_{nn}^{(2)} \end{vmatrix}$$

An examination of the steps necessary to reduce the form of

the determinant (75) to the form (76) shows that in both cases the elements in rows 3, $\cdots$, n are second or third-degree functions of λ. After the form (76) has been obtained, the third column is reduced similarly unless the elements $f_{33}{}^{(2)}$, $\cdots$, $f_{n3}{}^{(2)}$ have a common factor. In fact, the process is to be continued until either the nth column is reached or the elements of the column in question from the principal diagonal downward do have a common factor.

Suppose that when the qth column is reached in the reduction of the determinant, all the elements in this column from the principal diagonal downward have the common factor $(\lambda - \lambda_{j_1})^{m_1}$ $\cdots (\lambda - \lambda_{j_k})^{m_k}$. In general, only one such factor will appear at a time, and it will occur to the first degree. Fasten the attention on any one of the factors that does occur, say $(\lambda - \lambda_j)^{m_j}$. Then examine the elements in each of the columns $q + 1$ to n from the row q downward to the row n. There are now two cases to be considered: (a) not all the elements under consideration in at least one of the columns $q + 1$ to n contain $(\lambda - \lambda_j)^{m_j}$ as a factor; or (b) all the elements in the columns $q + 1$ to n and in the rows q to n do contain $(\lambda - \lambda_j)^{m_j}$ as a factor.

Case (a). Consider first the effect of interchanging the dependent variables x_i and x_j in the differential equations (1). In the determinant $D(\lambda)$ the rows i and j are interchanged and the columns i and j also are interchanged. As has been pointed out, an interchange of rows of $D(\lambda)$ does not modify the application of the method of Art. 149 for determining the solutions of the differential equations. Consequently, only the interchange of columns need be considered. The converse proposition is, if two columns i and j of $D(\lambda)$ are interchanged, the original problem is restored by interchanging x_i and x_j in the solutions of the differential equations.

Now, in Case (a), at least one of the elements in one of the columns $q + 1$ to n either does not contain $\lambda - \lambda_j$ as a factor or contains it to a degree lower than m_j. Suppose the elements of the rth column of $D(\lambda)$ contain $\lambda - \lambda_j$ as a factor to the lowest degree, say m_q. Then interchange the rth column with the qth column and make a corresponding interchange of x_r with x_q in the solutions of the differential equations. After the interchange, all the elements in the rows q to n of the columns

$q + 1$ to n contain $\lambda - \lambda_j$ as a factor to as high degree as it is contained in the qth column. The problem has been reduced, therefore, to Case (b).

Case (b). All the elements in the columns q to n of $D(\lambda)$ and in the rows q to n do contain $(\lambda - \lambda_j)^{m_q}$ as a factor, and the elements in the qth column contain no higher power of $\lambda - \lambda_j$. If the element $f_{qq}{}^{(q-1)}$ does not contain any other factor except a constant independent of λ, it can be multiplied successively by such factors, which will be either constants or polynomials in λ, that when the respective products are subtracted from the rows $q + 1$ to n, the elements in the qth column below the principal diagonal will all be zero.

Suppose the element $f_{qq}{}^{(q-1)}$ contains other factors in λ besides $(\lambda - \lambda_j)^{m_q}$. If there is any other element in the qth column below the principal diagonal that does contain λ only in the factor $(\lambda - \lambda_j)^{m_q}$, then its row is interchanged with the qth row and the problem is reduced to that which has just been considered in the preceding paragraph.

Now suppose all the elements in the qth column from the principal diagonal downward contain other factors in λ besides $(\lambda - \lambda_j)^{m_q}$. Consider any two of them, say $f_{qq}{}^{(q-1)}$ and $f_{sq}{}^{(q-1)}$, and suppose

$$\begin{cases} f_{qq}{}^{(q-1)} = (\lambda - \lambda_j)^{m_q} f_q(\lambda), \\ f_{sq}{}^{(q-1)} = (\lambda - \lambda_j)^{m_q} f_s(\lambda). \end{cases}$$

If one or each of these two functions contains factors that are not common to the other, such a linear combination of the two elements can be formed that its highest degree in λ will be less than that of the higher of the two original elements. By repeated applications of this process, which is strictly analogous to that used in the reduction of $f_{22}{}^{(1)}$, $\cdots$, $f_{n2}{}^{(1)}$, the elements in the qth column can be reduced to constants times the same function of λ, and this function will contain $(\lambda - \lambda_j)^{m_q}$ as a factor. Then all the elements in the qth column below the principal diagonal can be reduced to zero.

The process is to be continued to subsequent columns until the nth is reached. Since all elements from the rows q to n and columns $q + 1$ to n contained $(\lambda - \lambda_j)^{m_q}$ before the reduction of the qth column, and since the reduction of the qth column did not alter this property of the elements, the $(q + 1)$st column will contain $(\lambda - \lambda_j)^{m_q}$ at least as a factor. Hence the final reduced determinant can be written in the form

(77) $$D(\lambda) = \begin{vmatrix} f_{11}^{(1)}, & f_{12}^{(1)}, & f_{13}^{(1)}, & \cdots, & f_{1n}^{(1)} \\ 0, & f_{22}^{(2)}, & f_{23}^{(2)}, & \cdots, & f_{2n}^{(2)} \\ 0, & 0, & f_{33}^{(3)}, & \cdots, & f_{3n}^{(3)} \\ \cdot & \cdot & \cdot & & \cdot \\ \cdot & \cdot & \cdot & & \cdot \\ \cdot & \cdot & \cdot & & \cdot \\ 0, & 0, & 0, & \cdots, & f_{nn}^{(n)} \end{vmatrix}.$$

The reduction of the determinant $D(\lambda)$ to the form (77) has been guided by the occurrence of the factor $\lambda - \lambda_j$ in its elements at various stages of the process. Each element of the principal diagonal contains $\lambda - \lambda_j$ as a factor to a degree less than, or at the most equal to, the degree to which it occurs as a factor in the remaining elements of the row. The same relationship may not exist with respect to other factors of the elements, but a corresponding reduction can be made for each factor. In fact, it is in general necessary to make a corresponding reduction for each of the roots of the equation $D(\lambda) = 0$. Moreover, each $f_{ii}^{(i)}$ contains $\lambda - \lambda_j$ to a degree less than, or at the most equal to, the degree to which it is contained in $f_{i+1,\,i+1}^{(i+1)}$.

It follows from the form of equation (77) that finally

$$D(\lambda) = f_{11}^{(1)} \cdots f_{nn}^{(n)}.$$

Therefore the roots of the equation $D(\lambda) = 0$ are the roots of the n equations $f_{ii}^{(i)} = 0$ $(i = 1, \cdots, n)$. That is, unless all the factors of this product except the last are independent of λ, the determinant has been at least partially factored.

It follows from the properties of the right member of equation (77) that the highest power ν_1 of $\lambda - \lambda_j$ contained in all first minors of the determinant $D(\lambda)$ is the sum of the powers of $\lambda - \lambda_j$ contained in the principal diagonal elements $f_{11}^{(1)}, \cdots,$ $f_{n-1,\,n-1}^{(n-1)}$; and the highest power ν_m of $\lambda - \lambda_j$ contained in all mth minors of the determinant $D(\lambda)$ is the sum of the powers of $\lambda - \lambda_j$ contained in $f_{11}^{(1)}, \cdots, f_{n-m,\,n-m}^{(n-m)}$. If there is a pth minor of the determinant $D(\lambda)$ that does not contain $\lambda - \lambda_j$ as a factor, then the elements $f_{11}^{(1)}, \cdots, f_{n-p,\,n-p}^{(n-p)}$ do not contain $\lambda - \lambda_j$ as a factor. If the pth minors of the determinant are not all zero for each of the roots of the equation $D(\lambda) = 0$, then each of the elements $f_{11}{}^{(1)}$, $\cdots$, $f_{n-p,\,n-p}^{(n-)}$ is independent of λ and is distinct from zero. If the roots of the equation $D(\lambda) = 0$ are simple or if at least one first minor of the determinant $D(\lambda)$ is distinct from zero for each of the roots of the equation $D(\lambda) = 0$, then each of the elements $f_{11}{}^{(1)}$, $\cdots$, $f_{n-1,\,n-1}^{(n-1)}$ is independent of λ and distinct from zero, and $f_{n,\,n}^{(n)}$ is a polynomial in λ of degree n. Since the mth minors of the determinant $D(\lambda)$ all contain $(\lambda - \lambda_j)^{\nu_m}$ as a factor, but no higher power of $\lambda - \lambda_j$, and since $\nu_p = 0$, it follows from $D(\lambda)$ given in equation (77) and the factor properties of the $f_{ii}{}^{(i)}$ that $\nu_{p-2} \geqq 2\nu_{p-1}$, $\nu_{p-3} \geqq 3\nu_{p-1}$, $\cdots$, $\nu_1 \geqq (p-1)\nu_{p-1}$, $n_j \geqq p\nu_{p-1}$.

In Art. 146, Case III, it was assumed (a) that the equation $D(\lambda) = 0$ has the triple root $\lambda = \lambda_1$; (b) that all first minors of the determinant $D(\lambda)$ contain $\lambda - \lambda_1$ as a factor, but not $(\lambda - \lambda_1)^2$ as a factor; and (c) that at least one second minor of the determinant $D(\lambda)$ is distinct from zero for $\lambda = \lambda_1$. It might be supposed that there is a fourth case for the triple root $\lambda = \lambda_1$, in which all first minors of the determinant $D(\lambda)$ contain $(\lambda - \lambda_1)^2$ as a factor, while at least one second minor is distinct from zero for $\lambda = \lambda_1$. If this were possible, the value of p would be 2 and ν_{p-1} would also be 2 while $n_j = 3$. Therefore the relation $n_j \geqq p\nu_{p-1}$ would not be satisfied, and hence the case is impossible. That is, the cases treated in Art. 146 exhaust the possibilities for triple roots of the equation $D(\lambda) = 0$. There are, of course, corresponding limitations on the possibilities when the equation $D(\lambda) = 0$ has roots of higher orders of multiplicity; but the fact is of no practical importance when the solutions are determined by the general theory, for it does not involve the enumeration and treatment of special cases..

The form given in equation (77) for the determinant $D(\lambda)$ is not only convenient for determining the roots of the equation $D(\lambda) = 0$, but also it reduces the determination of the solutions associated with λ_j to routine calculations. To get the solutions whose coefficients are expressible in terms of derivatives with respect to λ_j of mth minors of $D(\lambda)$, take the minor made up of the first $n - m$ rows and the first $n - m$ columns of the reduced determinant (77). It will contain $\lambda - \lambda_j$ to the power ν_m as a factor. Construct a matrix having n rows and $n - m + 1$ columns by bordering this mth minor on the right by the first

$n - m$ elements of the $(n - m + 1)$st column of the determinant (77), and by adding the remaining rows from the same columns. There are, in the first $n - m$ rows of this matrix, $n - m + 1$ determinants of order $n - m$, each of which contains $(\lambda - \lambda_j)^{\nu_m}$ as a factor, and at least one of which contains no higher power of $\lambda - \lambda_j$. These are the δ_{im} of equations (71), and in this case $i = 1, \cdots, n - m + 1$ (allowance being made for any permutations of columns that may have occurred in reducing the determinant $D(\lambda)$ to the form (77), and δ_{im} is identically zero, by definition, for $i = n - m + 2, \cdots, n$. These minors are particularly easy to construct because of the zeros below the principal diagonal. The superscripts on the δ_{im} which appear in equations (73) and (74) indicate derivatives of the δ_{im} with respect to λ for $\lambda = \lambda_j$, and these derivatives of the minors of the determinant (77) must of course be formed. Equations (73) and (74) give the solutions whose coefficients are expressible in terms of derivatives with respect to λ_j of mth minors of the determinant $D(\lambda_j)$.

One might be tempted to reduce the determinant (77) to its principal diagonal by multiplying each of its columns sequentially by suitable factors and subtracting the products from all the columns to the right. The roots of the equation $D(\lambda) = 0$ and the powers of $\lambda - \lambda_j$ contained in all minors of $D(\lambda)$ of each order would be identical with those given by the form (77). But the solutions could not be determined from this form of the determinant, because if two columns of the determinant $D(\lambda)$ are added and made to replace one of them, or if any column is replaced by a linear combination of columns, the resulting determinant does not correspond to taking the variables $x_1, \cdots, x_n$ in any order or to replacing one of them by a linear function of all of them. In fact, with this form of the determinant, in general all the δ_{im} except one either would be identically zero or would carry $\lambda - \lambda_j$ as a factor to a power higher than ν_m. Consequently only one of the x_i of equations (73) and (74) would be not identically zero. Obviously equations (1), except in very special cases, cannot be satisfied by all the x_i except one identically zero, and that one not identically zero.

151. Illustrative Example. The considerations involved in the foregoing discussions are so numerous that it is desirable to illustrate the principal ones by a numerical example.

Consider the fourth-order system of differential equations

$$(78) \quad \begin{cases} \dfrac{dx_1}{dt} = + \ x_1 - \tfrac{1}{4}x_2 + \tfrac{1}{2}x_3 + \tfrac{3}{4}x_4, \\[2mm] \dfrac{dx_2}{dt} = - \tfrac{1}{8}x_1 + \ x_2 - \tfrac{3}{8}x_3 - \tfrac{1}{2}x_4, \\[2mm] \dfrac{dx_3}{dt} = + \tfrac{1}{2}x_1 + \tfrac{3}{4}x_2 + \ x_3 - \tfrac{1}{4}x_4, \\[2mm] \dfrac{dx_4}{dt} = - \tfrac{3}{8}x_1 - \tfrac{1}{2}x_2 - \tfrac{1}{8}x_3 + x_4. \end{cases}$$

The characteristic equation associated with these differential equations is

$$(79) \quad D(\lambda) = \begin{vmatrix} 1 - \lambda, & -\tfrac{1}{4}, & +\tfrac{1}{2}, & +\tfrac{3}{4} \\ -\tfrac{1}{8}, & 1 - \lambda, & -\tfrac{3}{8}, & -\tfrac{1}{2} \\ +\tfrac{1}{2}, & +\tfrac{3}{4}, & 1 - \lambda, & -\tfrac{1}{4} \\ -\tfrac{3}{8}, & -\tfrac{1}{2}, & -\tfrac{1}{8}, & 1 - \lambda \end{vmatrix} = 0.$$

Equations (78) will first be treated without reducing the determinant $D(\lambda)$ by the method of Art. 150. It is found by direct expansion of the right member of equation (79) that $D(\lambda) = (\lambda - 1)^4$. Therefore $\lambda = 1$ is a quadruple root of the equation $D(\lambda) = 0$.

There are sixteen first minors of $D(\lambda)$, each of the third order, to be developed. It is found that all of these minors, except those that are co-factors of the elements of the principal diagonal, contain $(\lambda - 1)^2$ as a factor. The co-factors of the elements of the principal diagonal contain $(\lambda - 1)^3$ as a factor. The second minor in the upper left-hand corner of $D(\lambda)$ does not contain $\lambda - 1$ as a factor. Hence it is not necessary to examine all the other of the thirty-six second minors.

Now refer to Art. 149 and let $m = 1$. It follows that there are two solutions whose coefficients are expressible in terms of derivatives with respect to λ of first minors of $D(\lambda)$ for $\lambda = 1$. Since the first minors contain $(\lambda - 1)^2$ as a factor, the second and third derivatives are to be taken to form the equations corresponding to equations (70). As the first minor containing $(\lambda - 1)^2$ as a factor to be used in writing the identities corresponding to (69), choose the minor from the first three rows and the last three columns of $D(\lambda)$, equation (79). In this case the minor of order $m - 1$ is the determinant $D(\lambda)$ itself. Let the co-factors of the elements of the last row of the determinant be designated by $D_{41}, \cdots, D_{44}$ respectively. Then, on referring to the determinant (79), it is seen that the identities (69) are in this case

$$(80) \quad \begin{cases} + (1 - \lambda)D_{41} - \tfrac{1}{4}D_{42} + \tfrac{1}{2}D_{43} + \tfrac{3}{4}D_{44} \underset{\lambda}{\equiv} 0, \\ - \tfrac{1}{8}D_{41} + (1 - \lambda)D_{42} - \tfrac{3}{8}D_{43} - \tfrac{1}{2}D_{44} \underset{\lambda}{\equiv} 0, \\ + \tfrac{1}{2}D_{41} + \tfrac{3}{4}D_{42} + (1 - \lambda)D_{43} - \tfrac{1}{4}D_{44} \underset{\lambda}{\equiv} 0, \\ - \tfrac{3}{8}D_{41} - \tfrac{1}{2}D_{42} - \tfrac{1}{8}D_{43} + (1 - \lambda)D_{44} \underset{\lambda}{\equiv} D. \end{cases}$$

The coefficients of the two solutions in question are obtained from the second and third derivatives of these identities for $\lambda = \lambda_i = 1$, which correspond to equations (70). It is found from the determinant (79) that

$$\begin{cases} D_{41} = + \tfrac{3}{4}(\lambda - 1)^2, & D_{43} = - \tfrac{1}{4}(\lambda - 1)^2, \\ D_{42} = - \tfrac{1}{2}(\lambda - 1)^2, & D_{44} = + (\lambda - 1)^3. \end{cases}$$

Since the solution in this case has the form

$$(81) \quad \begin{cases} x_1 = C_1[A_1^{(0)}t + A_1^{(1)}]e^t, \\ \cdot \quad \cdot \quad \cdot \quad \cdot \quad \cdot \quad \cdot \quad \cdot \\ x_4 = C_1[A_4^{(0)}t + A_4^{(1)}]e^t, \end{cases}$$

it is found, on referring to equations (71) and (72), in which $m = 1, \nu_m = 2, \omega = 1, n = 4$, and the δ_{im} are the D_{4i} respectively, that the coefficients of the solution are

$$(82) \quad \begin{cases} A_1^{(0)} = D_{41}''(1) = + \tfrac{3}{2}, & A_1^{(1)} = \tfrac{1}{3}D_{41}'''(1) = 0, \\ A_2^{(0)} = D_{42}''(1) = - 1, & A_2^{(1)} = \tfrac{1}{3}D_{42}'''(1) = 0, \\ A_3^{(0)} = D_{43}''(1) = - \tfrac{1}{2}, & A_3^{(1)} = \tfrac{1}{3}D_{43}'''(1) = 0, \\ A_4^{(0)} = D_{44}''(1) = 0; & A_4^{(1)} = \tfrac{1}{3}D_{44}'''(1) = 2. \end{cases}$$

Therefore the solution (81) is found to be explicitly

$$(83) \quad \begin{cases} x_1 = C_1[+ \tfrac{3}{2}t + 0]e^t, \\ x_2 = C_1[- t + 0]e^t, \\ x_3 = C_1[- \tfrac{1}{2}t + 0]e^t, \\ x_4 = C_1[0 + 2]e^t. \end{cases}$$

The associated solution corresponding to equations (74) is

$$(84) \quad \begin{cases} x_1 = + \tfrac{3}{2} C_2 e^t, \\ x_2 = - C_2 e^t, \\ x_3 = - \tfrac{1}{2} C_2 e^t, \\ x_4 = 0. \end{cases}$$

Now let $m = 2$. Since the second minors of $D(\lambda)$ do not all contain $\lambda - 1$ as a factor while all first minors contain $(\lambda - 1)^2$ as a factor, there are two solutions whose coefficients are expressible in terms of second minors of $D(\lambda)$ and their first derivatives with respect to λ, for $\lambda = 1$. The second minor in the upper right-hand corner of $D(\lambda)$ is not zero for $\lambda = 1$, and, consequently, it can be made to serve as a basis for writing the identities corresponding to (69). Let it be bordered on the left by the second column of $D(\lambda)$. Then there results the matrix

$$M = \begin{Vmatrix} & -\tfrac{1}{4}, & +\tfrac{1}{2}, & +\tfrac{3}{4} \\ 1 - \lambda, & -\tfrac{3}{8}, & -\tfrac{1}{2} \\ +\tfrac{3}{4}, & 1 - \lambda, & -\tfrac{1}{4} \\ -\tfrac{1}{2}, & -\tfrac{1}{8}, & 1 - \lambda \end{Vmatrix},$$

which is to be developed in terms of second-order minors from the first two rows. Let these minors obtained by omitting the columns sequentially be represented by δ_{32}, δ_{33}, and δ_{34} respectively, the notation corresponding to that for developing the upper right-hand third-order determinant of $D(\lambda)$. With this notation, the identities corresponding to (69) become

$$(85) \quad \begin{cases} -\tfrac{1}{4}\delta_{32} + \tfrac{1}{2}\delta_{33} + \tfrac{3}{4}\delta_{34} \underset{\lambda}{\equiv} 0, \\ (1 - \lambda)\delta_{32} - \tfrac{3}{8}\delta_{33} - \tfrac{1}{2}\delta_{34} \underset{\lambda}{\equiv} 0, \\ \tfrac{3}{4}\delta_{32} + (1 - \lambda)\delta_{33} - \tfrac{1}{4}\delta_{34} \underset{\lambda}{\equiv} D_{41}, \\ -\tfrac{1}{2}\delta_{32} - \tfrac{1}{8}\delta_{33} + (1 - \lambda)\delta_{34} \underset{\lambda}{\equiv} D_{31}, \end{cases}$$

where

$$(86) \quad \begin{cases} \delta_{32} = \tfrac{1}{32}, \\ \delta_{33} = -\tfrac{3}{4}\lambda + \tfrac{5}{8}, \\ \delta_{34} = \tfrac{1}{2}\lambda - \tfrac{13}{32}, \end{cases}$$

and δ_{31}, by definition, is identically zero. In this case, $m = 2$,

$\nu_m = 0$, $\omega = 1$, and hence the solutions also have the form (81). Therefore, on referring to equations (70), (71), (85), and (86), and on changing the $A_i{}^{(0)}$ to $B_i{}^{(0)}$ and the $A_i{}^{(1)}$ to $B_i{}^{(1)}$ in order to keep the notations distinct for the two groups of solutions, it is found that

$$(87) \quad \begin{cases} B_1{}^{(0)} = \delta_{31}(1) = 0, & B_1{}^{(1)} = \delta_{31}'(1) = 0, \\ B_2{}^{(0)} = \delta_{32}(1) = +\tfrac{1}{32}, & B_2{}^{(1)} = \delta_{32}'(1) = 0, \\ B_3{}^{(0)} = \delta_{33}(1) = -\tfrac{1}{8}, & B_3{}^{(1)} = \delta_{33}'(1) = -\tfrac{3}{4}, \\ B_4{}^{(0)} = \delta_{34}(1) = +\tfrac{3}{32}; & B_4{}^{(1)} = \delta_{34}'(1) = +\tfrac{1}{2}. \end{cases}$$

Therefore this solution is explicitly

$$(88) \quad \begin{cases} x_1 = C_3[0 + 0]e^t, \\ x_2 = C_3[\tfrac{1}{32}t + 0]e^t, \\ x_3 = C_3[-\tfrac{1}{8}t - \tfrac{3}{4}]e^t, \\ x_4 = C_3[\tfrac{3}{32}t + \tfrac{1}{2}]e^t. \end{cases}$$

The associated solution corresponding to equations (74) is

$$(89) \quad \begin{cases} x_1 = 0, \\ x_2 = \tfrac{1}{32}C_4 e^t, \\ x_3 = -\tfrac{1}{8}C_4 e^t, \\ x_4 = \tfrac{3}{32}C_4 e^t. \end{cases}$$

The solutions (83), (84), (88), and (89) constitute a fundamental set, for their determinant at $t = 0$ reduces to $-9/128$.

It should not be assumed that a fundamental set of solutions will necessarily be obtained whatever minors, containing the proper factors, are chosen as a basis for determining the solutions. For example, if instead of taking a second minor from the upper right-hand corner of the determinant $D(\lambda)$, the second minor from the upper left-hand corner, which is also distinct from zero for $\lambda = 1$, had been chosen, the solutions obtained similarly and corresponding to those given in equations (88) and (89) would have been

$$(90) \quad \begin{cases} x_1 = C_3[+\tfrac{3}{32}t + \tfrac{1}{2}]e^t, & x_1 = +\tfrac{3}{32}C_4 e^t, \\ x_2 = C_3[-\tfrac{1}{16}t - \tfrac{3}{8}]e^t, & x_2 = -\tfrac{1}{16}C_4 e^t, \\ x_3 = C_3[-\tfrac{1}{32}t + 0]e^t, & x_3 = -\tfrac{1}{32}C_4 e^t, \\ x_4 = 0; & x_4 = 0. \end{cases}$$

Solutions (83), (84), and (90) do not constitute a fundamental set, for their determinant at $t = 0$ is zero. On the other hand, solutions (88), (89), and (90), all of which have been determined by the same process from second minors, do constitute a fundamental set, for their determinant at $t = 0$ is $-9/32^3$. This possibility of obtaining all the solutions of a set of differential equations from the minors of highest order that do not vanish for $\lambda = \lambda_j$ is exceptional. In general, in applying the method it is necessary to follow the steps of Art. 149 and to use minors of all the various orders that contain powers of $\lambda - \lambda_j$ as common factors. The exceptional property in this problem is due in part to the fact that each of the groups of solutions consists of two solutions.

Now consider the determination of the solutions of equations (78) from the reduced form of the determinant $D(\lambda)$, corresponding to that given in equation (77). It is found from equation (79) that the reduced form of $D(\lambda)$ is

$$(91) \quad D(\lambda) = \begin{vmatrix} 1, & 6(\lambda-1)+1, & -8\lambda(\lambda-1)+1, & -10(\lambda-1)+1 \\ 0, & 1 & , -12(\lambda-1)-2 , & -16(\lambda-1)-3 \\ 0, & 0 & , -32(\lambda-1)^2 , & -32(\lambda-1)^2 \\ 0, & 0 & , 0 , & 32(\lambda-1)^2 \end{vmatrix}.$$

There are two first minors in this determinant which contain $(\lambda - 1)^2$ as a factor, one involving elements from the third column and the other involving elements from the fourth column. If the determinant $D(\lambda)$ were of the fifth degree in λ so that the element at the lower right-hand corner would carry $(\lambda - 1)^3$ as a factor, there would be only one first minor carrying $(\lambda - 1)^2$ as a factor. Inasmuch as there are two first minors that may be used in determining two of the solutions, the one that will require the minimum of computation should be chosen. The first minor obtained by deleting the third row and the third column has more zero elements than the one obtained by deleting the fourth row and the fourth column, and it is therefore preferable. The third-order minors that involve the elements of the first, second, and fourth rows are co-factors of the elements of the third row and may be represented by $D_{31}, \cdots, D_{34}$. Then it is found from equation (91) that

$$(92) \quad \begin{cases} D_{31} = -32(\lambda-1)^2[3 + 16(\lambda-1) + 64(\lambda-1)^2], \\ D_{32} = +64(\lambda-1)^2[1 + 6(\lambda-1)], \\ D_{33} = +32(\lambda-1)^2, \\ D_{43} = 0. \end{cases}$$

Since $n = 4$, $m = 1$, $\omega = 2$, $\nu_m = 2$, it at once follows from equations (71) that

$$\begin{cases} A_1^{(0)} = D_{31}''(1) = -192, & A_1^{(1)} = \tfrac{1}{3}D_{31}'''(1) = -1024, \\ A_2^{(0)} = D_{32}''(1) = +128, & A_2^{(1)} = \tfrac{1}{3}D_{32}'''(1) = +768, \\ A_3^{(0)} = D_{33}''(1) = +64, & A_3^{(1)} = \tfrac{1}{3}D_{33}'''(1) = 0, \\ A_4^{(0)} = D_{43}''(1) = 0; & A_4^{(1)} = \tfrac{1}{3}D_{43}'''(1) = 0. \end{cases}$$

Hence the solutions corresponding to equations (73) and (74), when the factor 64 is absorbed in the arbitrary constants C_1 and C_2, are

$$(93) \quad \begin{cases} x_1 = C_1[-3t - 16]e^t, & x_1 = -3C_2 e^t, \\ x_2 = C_1[+2t + 12]e^t, & x_2 = +2C_2 e^t, \\ x_3 = C_1[+t + 0]e^t, & x_3 = +C_2 e^t, \\ x_4 = 0; & x_4 = 0. \end{cases}$$

In this particular problem the other two solutions can be determined from the other first minor of the determinant (91) that has $(\lambda - 1)^2$ as a factor, or their coefficients can be expressed in terms of second minors. The second minor in the upper left-hand corner is not zero for $\lambda = 1$, and hence it may be used for determining the remaining solutions. Since the first two elements in the fourth column are linear in λ, it is simpler to use the fourth column to border the second minor than it would be to use the third column. On letting the co-factors of the elements in the third row of the determinant consisting of the first three rows of the determinant (91) and the first two and fourth columns be represented by δ_{3i}, it is found that

$$(94) \quad \begin{cases} \delta_{31} = -96(\lambda - 1)^2 - 24(\lambda - 1) - 4, \\ \delta_{32} = +16(\lambda - 1) + 3, \\ \delta_{33} = 0 \text{ (by definition)}, \\ \delta_{34} = 1. \end{cases}$$

Consequently, since $n = 4$, $m = 2$, $\nu_m = 0$, it follows from equations (71) that

$$\begin{cases} B_1^{(0)} = \delta_{31}(1) = -4, & B_1^{(1)} = \delta_{31}'(1) = -24, \\ B_2^{(0)} = \delta_{32}(1) = +3, & B_2^{(1)} = \delta_{32}'(1) = +16, \\ B_3^{(0)} = \delta_{33}(1) = 0, & B_3^{(1)} = \delta_{33}'(1) = 0, \\ B_4^{(0)} = \delta_{34}(1) = 1; & B_4^{(1)} = \delta_{34}'(1) = 0. \end{cases}$$

The corresponding solutions of this group are explicitly

$$(95) \quad \begin{cases} x_1 = C_3[-4t - 24]e^t, & x_1 = -4C_4 e^t, \\ x_2 = C_3[+3t + 16]e^t, & x_2 = +3C_4 e^t, \\ x_3 = 0, & x_3 = 0, \\ x_4 = C_3[t + 0]e^t; & x_4 = +C_4 e^t. \end{cases}$$

The solutions (93) and (95) constitute a fundamental set, for their determinant at $t = 0$ is -32. The solutions (90) and (93) differ from each other only by a constant factor, but the solutions (88) and (89) have no superficial resemblance to the solutions (95). Nevertheless, the four solutions (88), (89), and (90) are equivalent to the solutions (93) and (95), because each of the groups constitutes a fundamental set.

152. The Solutions in the General Case Constitute a Fundamental Set. It will be shown that the processes which have been described define n solutions that constitute a fundamental set, at least if certain simple precautions are taken in choosing, for each λ_j, the minors of successive orders for determining the solutions of the several groups.

The general method of proof that a set of solutions constitutes a fundamental set was explained in a simple case in Art. 145. It consists in assuming that the solutions do not constitute a fundamental set, from which it follows that equations (7) can be satisfied with the B_i not all zero. Then it is shown from this same assumption and from the properties of the solutions that the B_i must all be zero. Hence the assumption that the solutions do not form a fundamental set is false. Essentially the same proof can be made in the general case.

The group of solutions (73) and (74) can be written briefly in the form

$$(96) \quad \begin{cases} x_i = P_i(t) = Q_i(t) e^{\lambda_j t} & (i = 1, \cdots, n), \\ x_i = P_{iq}(t) = Q_i^{(q)}(t) e^{\lambda_j t} & (i = 1, \cdots, n; q = 1, \cdots, \omega), \end{cases}$$

where $Q_i^{(q)}(t)$ is the qth derivative of the polynomial $Q_i(t)$ with respect to t. The solution for $q = \omega$ is a pure exponential, for $Q_i(t)$ is of degree ω in t. There are, in general, other groups of solutions associated with λ_j whose coefficients are expressible in terms of derivatives with respect to λ_j of minors of $D(\lambda_j)$ of other orders. There are also one or more groups of solutions associated with each of the other roots of the equation $D(\lambda) = 0$.

If the solutions (96), together with the other groups of solutions associated with λ_j and with those associated with the other roots of the equation $D(\lambda) = 0$, do not constitute a fundamental set, then n constants $B_1, \cdots, B_n$, not all of which are zero, exist such that

$$B_1 P_i(0) + \cdots + B_{\omega+1} P_{i\omega}(0) + \cdots = 0 \qquad (i = 1, \cdots, n).$$

Corresponding to these values of the B_i, there exists the solution

$$x_i = B_1 P_i(t) + \cdots + B_{\omega+1} P_{i\omega}(t) + \cdots \underset{t}{\equiv} 0.$$

The pth of these identities and its successive derivatives with respect to t give the identities

$$(97) \qquad \begin{cases} B_1 P_p + \cdots + B_\omega P_{p\omega} + \cdots \underset{t}{\equiv} 0, \\ B_1 P_p{}^{(1)} + \cdots + B_\omega P_{p\omega}{}^{(1)} + \cdots \underset{t}{\equiv} 0, \\ \cdot \quad \cdot \quad \cdot \quad \cdot \quad \cdot \quad \cdot \quad \cdot \quad \cdot \quad \cdot \quad \cdot \\ B_1 P_p{}^{(k)} + \cdots + B_\omega P_{p\omega}{}^{(k)} + \cdots \underset{t}{\equiv} 0. \end{cases}$$

Suppose $1 + k$ equals the number of the polynomials $P_p, \cdots, P_{p\omega}$ which are not identically zero. Then, if the B_i are not all zero, the determinant

$$(98) \qquad V = K \begin{vmatrix} P_p, & P_{p1}, & \cdots, & P_{p\omega}, & \cdots \\ P_p{}^{(1)}, & P_{p1}{}^{(1)}, & \cdots, & P_{p\omega}{}^{(1)}, & \cdots \\ \cdot & & & & \\ \cdot & & & & \\ \cdot & & & & \\ P_p{}^{(k)}, & P_{p1}{}^{(k)}, & \cdots, & P_{p\omega}{}^{(k)}, & \cdots \end{vmatrix}$$

must be identically zero in t, where K is a constant that is not zero.

The determinant (98) can be greatly simplified. In the first place, it follows from the first of equations (96) that

$$\begin{cases} P_p{}^{(1)} = (\lambda_j Q_p + Q_p{}^{(1)}) e^{\lambda_j t}, \\ P_p{}^{(2)} = (\lambda_j{}^2 Q_p + 2\lambda_j Q_p{}^{(1)} + Q_p{}^{(2)}) e^{\lambda_j t}, \\ \cdot \quad \cdot \quad \cdot \quad \cdot \quad \cdot \quad \cdot \quad \cdot \quad \cdot \quad \cdot \quad \cdot \\ P_p{}^{(k)} = \left(\lambda_j{}^k Q_p + \frac{k}{1} \lambda_j{}^{k-1} Q_p{}^{(1)} + \frac{k}{1} \cdot \frac{k-1}{2} \lambda_j{}^{k-2} Q_p{}^{(2)} + \cdots + Q_p{}^{(k)} \right) e^{\lambda_j t}, \\ P_{pq}{}^{(k)} = \left(\lambda_j{}^k Q_p{}^{(q)} + \frac{k}{1} \lambda_j{}^{k-1} Q_p{}^{(q+1)} + \cdots + Q_p{}^{(k+q)} \right) e^{\lambda_j t}, \end{cases}$$

the numerical multipliers being the binomial coefficients.

Then it follows from the second set of equations (96) that $P_{pq} = Q_p{}^{(q)}e^{\lambda_j t}$. The polynomial Q_p is of degree ω in t. The coefficient of t^ω, by equations (73), is the ν_mth derivative with respect to λ_j of mth minors of $D(\lambda_j)$. It easily follows from these properties and from equations (73) and (74) that the determinant of the coefficients of the identities (97), at $t = 0$, reduces to

$$(99) \quad V_0 = K_1 \begin{vmatrix} 0, & 0 & , \cdots, & 0 & , & 1 & , \cdots \\ 0, & 0 & , \cdots, & 1 & , & \lambda_j & , \cdots \\ \cdot & \cdot & & \cdot & & \cdot & \\ \cdot & \cdot & & \cdot & & \cdot & \\ \cdot & \cdot & & \cdot & & \cdot & \\ 0, & (\omega-1)! & , \cdots, & (\omega-1)\lambda_j{}^{\omega-2}, & \lambda_j{}^{\omega-1}, & \cdots \\ \omega!, & \omega!\lambda_j & , \cdots, & \omega\lambda_j{}^{\omega-1} & , & \lambda_j{}^{\omega} & , \cdots \\ \cdot & \cdot & & \cdot & & \cdot & \\ \cdot & \cdot & & \cdot & & \cdot & \\ \cdot & \cdot & & \cdot & & \cdot & \end{vmatrix},$$

where K_1 is a constant that is not zero. Each of the columns written, with the exception of the last one, is the derivative with respect to λ_j of the one immediately to the right of it.

Let $\Lambda(\lambda)$ represent the determinant V_0 when the elements of its first column are replaced by 1, λ, λ^2, $\cdots$ respectively. It follows that

$$\left[\frac{d^\omega \Lambda}{d\lambda^\omega} \right]_{\lambda = \lambda_j} = V_0.$$

Moreover, the factors of the equation $\Lambda(\lambda) = 0$ are $(\lambda - \lambda_j)^\omega$, $(\lambda - \lambda_{j_1})^{q_1}$, $\cdots$, $(\lambda - \lambda_{j_r})^{q_r}$, where λ_{j_1}, $\cdots$, λ_{j_r} are those of the remaining roots of the equation $D(\lambda) = 0$ that occur in the determinant V, and where q_1, $\cdots$, q_r are the numbers of columns of V_0 in which they occur respectively. The degree of $\Lambda(\lambda)$ in λ is $\omega + q_1 + \cdots + q_r$. Consequently, all the roots of the equation $\Lambda(\lambda) = 0$ being accounted for, it follows that the ωth derivative of $\Lambda(\lambda)$ for $\lambda = \lambda_j$ is not zero. That is, V_0 is not zero. Consequently the identities (97) can be satisfied only if all the B_i are zero. That is, the solutions constitute a fundamental set.

In the foregoing discussion it has been tacitly assumed that the only solutions involved in the identities (97) associated with the root λ_j are the group whose coefficients are expressible in terms of derivatives with respect to λ_j of mth minors of the determinant $D(\lambda_j)$ by equations (73) and (74). Only under this hypothesis has the conclusion been proved. It will now be shown that, whatever other groups of solutions are associated with λ_j, if the solutions have been properly determined and if p has been suitably chosen, the conclusion also follows.

Suppose the determinant $D(\lambda)$ has been reduced to the form given in equation (77) before the solutions associated with the root λ_j are determined. Consider first the solutions whose coefficients are expressible in terms of derivatives with respect to λ_j of first minors of $D(\lambda_j)$. To obtain these solutions, use as the basic first minor the one which is made up of the first $n-1$ rows and the first $n-1$ columns of the determinant $D(\lambda)$. This first minor has $(\lambda - \lambda_j)^{r_1}$ as a factor and no higher power of $\lambda - \lambda_j$, and consequently it always can be used. In general, first minors involving the element $f_{nn}^{(n)}$ may not be used, for they involve $\lambda - \lambda_j$ to a power higher than r_1. In the group of solutions whose coefficients depend upon first minors of $D(\lambda_j)$, part of the dependent variables $x_1, \cdots, x_n$ may be identically zero or they may all be distinct from zero. The variable x_n (allowance being made for possible permutation of columns), however, is always distinct from zero, for its co-factor carries $(\lambda - \lambda_j)^{r_1}$ as a factor.

Now consider the solutions associated with λ_j whose coefficients are expressible in terms of derivatives with respect to λ_j of second minors of $D(\lambda_j)$. Use as the basic determinant for these solutions the one which consists of the first $n-2$ rows and the first $n-2$ columns of the form of $D(\lambda)$ given by equation (77). This minor can always be used, for, by its construction, it carries $(\lambda - \lambda_j)^{r_2}$ as a factor, and no higher power of $\lambda - \lambda_j$. Border it on the right by the $(n-1)$st column of $D(\lambda)$. Then, in this group of solutions, the variables $x_1, \cdots, x_{n-2}$ will be identically zero or not, depending upon the minors which define them, x_{n-1} will always be distinct from zero, and x_n will always be identically zero. Similarly, in the case of solutions expressible in terms of third minors, x_{n-2} will always be distinct from zero, while x_{n-1} and x_n will always be identically zero. The method of choice is to be followed for all succeeding minors in terms of which the coefficients solutions may be expressed.

Let $x_i = F_i^{(m)} e^{\lambda_j t}$ be the solution whose coefficients are expressible in terms of derivatives with respect to λ_j of mth minors of $D(\lambda_j)$ and whose degree in t is the highest. Then it follows from the foregoing discussions that the groups of solutions associated with the root λ_j have the properties indicated in the following table:

$$
(100) \quad
\begin{cases}
\begin{array}{cccc}
& \text{1st Minors} & \text{2d Minors} & \text{3d Minors} \\
x_1 = & F_1^{(1)}e^{\lambda_j t}, & F_1^{(2)}e^{\lambda_j t}, & F_1^{(3)}e^{\lambda_j t}, & \cdots, \\
\cdot & \cdot\;\cdot\;\cdot\;\cdot & \cdot\;\cdot\;\cdot\;\cdot & \cdot\;\cdot\;\cdot\;\cdot \\
x_{n-2} = & F_{n-2}^{(1)}e^{\lambda_j t}, & F_{n-2}^{(2)}e^{\lambda_j t}, & F_{n-2}^{(3)}e^{\lambda_j t}, & \cdots, \\
x_{n-1} = & F_{n-1}^{(1)}e^{\lambda_i t}, & F_{n-1}^{(2)}e^{\lambda_j t}, & 0, & \cdots, \\
x_n = & F_n^{(1)}e^{\lambda_j t}, & 0, & 0, & \cdots,
\end{array}
\end{cases}
$$

where the last function appearing in each column is distinct from zero. Changes in the notation for the subscripts on the x_i must be made, of course, if permutations of the columns of the determinant $D(\lambda)$ are required in order to reduce it to the form given in equation (77).

It follows from the table of solutions (100) that there is not a linear relation among the solutions associated with the root λ_j of the equation $D(\lambda) = 0$. This property is not due to the fact that the determinant $D(\lambda)$ was reduced to the form (77), for in the process of the reduction the highest common power of $\lambda - \lambda_j$ contained in the mth minors that can be made out of any $n - m$ columns was not altered. Therefore the same property pertains to the solutions obtained from the original form of the determinant $D(\lambda)$. The form (77) of the determinant $D(\lambda)$ makes the property evident. The solutions associated with other roots of the equation $D(\lambda) = 0$ also have the same property. Therefore the determinant V_0, equation (99), is not zero, even if it depends upon more than one group of solutions associated with the root λ_j. In fact, if p is first taken equal to n, only solutions whose coefficients are expressible in terms of derivatives with respect to λ_j of first minors of $D(\lambda_j)$ will be present. It will follow that the corresponding B_i will be proved to be zero. Then if p is taken equal to $n - 1$, another set of B_i will be proved to be zero, and so on through all the solutions associated with the root λ_j. Simultaneously, the B_i attached to the solutions associated with the other roots of the equation $D(\lambda) = 0$ will all be proved to be zero. Hence the solutions obtained by using the minors from the upper left-hand corner of $D(\lambda_j)$, in the form (77), as basic constitute a fundamental set.

XV. QUESTIONS AND PROBLEMS

1. Solve the differential equation

$$\frac{d^2x}{dt^2} + k\frac{dx}{dt} + c^2x = 0,$$

subject to the initial conditions $x(0) = a$, $x'(0) = a'$. Determine the properties of the solutions as functions of t in each of the three cases $k^2 \gtreqless 4c^2$.

2. Find a fundamental set of solutions of the differential equations

$$\begin{cases} \dfrac{dx_1}{dt} = +\dfrac{5}{2}x_1 - \dfrac{1}{2}x_2 - x_3 + 0, \\[2mm] \dfrac{dx_2}{dt} = -\dfrac{1}{2}x_1 + \dfrac{5}{2}x_2 + 0 - x_4, \\[2mm] \dfrac{dx_3}{dt} = -x_1 + 0 + \dfrac{5}{2}x_3 - \dfrac{1}{2}x_4, \\[2mm] \dfrac{dx_4}{dt} = 0 - x_2 - \dfrac{1}{2}x_3 + \dfrac{5}{2}x_4. \end{cases}$$

Find a fundamental set of solutions also after reducing the determinant $D(\lambda)$ to the form (77).

3. Find a fundamental set of solutions of the differential equations

$$\begin{cases} \dfrac{dx_1}{dt} = -x_1 + \dfrac{1}{6}x_2 + \dfrac{1}{2}x_3 + \dfrac{1}{3}x_4, \\[2mm] \dfrac{dx_2}{dt} = -\dfrac{36}{7}x_1 + \dfrac{16}{7}x_2 + \dfrac{3}{7}x_3 + \dfrac{10}{7}x_4, \\[2mm] \dfrac{dx_3}{dt} = -\dfrac{52}{7}x_1 + \dfrac{4}{21}x_2 + \dfrac{23}{7}x_3 + \dfrac{20}{21}x_4, \\[2mm] \dfrac{dx_4}{dt} = -\dfrac{36}{7}x_1 + \dfrac{9}{7}x_2 + \dfrac{3}{7}x_3 + \dfrac{17}{7}x_4. \end{cases}$$

4. Reduce equation (12) to an equivalent system of n differential equations, each of the first order, and prove that $D(\lambda)$, of equation (14), is the characteristic determinant of the system.

5. Reduce the determinant corresponding to that of equation (19) when $\lambda = \lambda_1$ is a triple root, $\lambda = \lambda_2$ is a triple root, and $\lambda = \lambda_3$ is a double root of the equation $D(\lambda) = 0$.

6. Prove in detail that the η_{i1}, of equations (24), are not simply proportional to the η_{i2}.

7. Prove by comparing equations (30) and (31) with equations (33) and (34) respectively that the former have the general solution

$$A_i{}^{(0)} = C_1 D_{ni}(\lambda_1), \qquad A_i{}^{(1)} = C_1 D_{ni}'(\lambda_1) + C_2 D_{ni}(\lambda_1),$$

where C_1 and C_2 are arbitrary constants. Note that therefore $x_i = C_2 D_{ni}(\lambda_1)e^{\lambda_1 t}$ is a solution of equations (1), agreeing with equations (38).

8. Prove that if $x_i = F_i(t)$ is a solution of equations (1), the function $x_i = F_i'(t)$, where the accent indicates the derivative with respect to t, is also a solution of equations (1). Verify the results in Problems 2 and 3.

Why are not these solutions as important in obtaining a fundamental set of solutions as those given by $x_i = P_i^{(k)}(t)e^{\lambda_j t}$ $(k = 1, 2, \cdots)$, where $P_i^{(k)}(t)$ is the kth derivative of $P_i(t)$ with respect to t?

9. Work out the details of the proof that the solutions given by equations (55), (56), and (57), together with those associated with the simple roots $\lambda_4, \cdots, \lambda_n$ of the equation $D(\lambda) = 0$, constitute a fundamental set.

10. Prove in detail that the solutions of the differential equations in Case III, Art. 146, constitute a fundamental set.

11. Verify, by comparing equations (68) with equations (70) for $l = 1$, $\cdots$, ω, that equations (71) are solutions of the former sets. Equations (70) have also ω other independent solutions. Derive them and prove that the corresponding solutions of the differential equations are those derived otherwise and given in equations (74).

12. Write the determinant $D(\lambda)$ for the differential equations of Problem 2. Then reduce it by successive steps to the form given in equation (77). Derive the solutions from the original determinant and also from it at the successive stages in its reduction.

13. Verify the fact that if the determinant $D(\lambda)$, of Problem 2, is transformed by adding two of its columns, the reduced form does not lead to solutions of the differential equations.

14. By the aid of $D(\lambda)$ in the form given by equation (77), list the cases that can exist when $\lambda = \lambda_1$ is a quadruple root of the equation $D(\lambda) = 0$ and $\lambda_5, \cdots, \lambda_n$ are simple roots. Indicate the types of all the solutions in each case.

15. Prove that if the differential equations (1) have a solution

$$x_i = [A_i^{(0)}t^\omega + A_i^{(1)}t^{\omega-1} + \cdots + A_i^{(\omega)}]e^{\lambda_j t},$$

where not all the $A_i^{(0)}$ $(i = 1, \cdots, n)$ are zero, then not all the $A_i^{(k)}$ for each $k = 1, \cdots, \omega$ are zero.

16. Solve the differential equations (78) by using various first and second minors of the determinant (79) as the basis for determining the solutions. Find in what cases the solutions constitute a fundamental set. Compare the results with the instructions given near the close of Art. 152 for obtaining a fundamental set of solutions.

17. Prove that if any first minor of $D(\lambda)$ carries $(\lambda - \lambda_j)^{\nu_1}$ as a factor, where ν_1 is the highest power of $\lambda - \lambda_j$ common to all first minors of $D(\lambda)$, then there is a second minor of $D(\lambda)$ interior to this first minor that carries $(\lambda - \lambda_j)^{\nu_2}$ as a factor, where ν_2 is the highest power of $\lambda - \lambda_j$ common to all second minors of $D(\lambda)$; prove, similarly, that there is a third minor interior to this second minor that carries $(\lambda - \lambda_j)^{\nu_3}$ as a factor, where ν_3 is the highest power of $\lambda - \lambda_j$ common to all third minors; and so on for minors of succeeding orders. Prove that if these minors are taken as the basis for determining the successive groups of solutions, the solutions so obtained constitute a fundamental set.

18. Reduce the determinant $D(\lambda)$ for the differential equation (12) to the form given in equation (77).

HISTORICAL SKETCH

Many of the processes used in obtaining the solutions of differential equations had their origin with Euler, and this is true with respect to linear differential equations having constant coefficients. Euler, however, treated only very simple cases. His successors, Laplace, Lagrange, and Gauss, considered more general problems, but only those for which the roots of the characteristic equation $D(\lambda) = 0$ are simple. Lagrange made a notable application of the use of a system of linear differential equations in his treatment of the so-called secular variations of certain elements of the orbits of the planets. (See Art. 156.)

In the interval of about seventy years between Lagrange and Weierstrass, various symbolic methods were developed for solving a simple linear differential equation of the nth order. As was shown in Art. 142, the single nth order equation is simpler than the general nth order system of n equations, each of the first order, because it corresponds to the simplest case in which the equation $D(\lambda) = 0$ has multiple roots. Weierstrass gave the first complete treatment of the general system of differential equations (1). His method consisted in replacing one of the dependent variables x_i, say x_1, by such a linear homogeneous function of the x_i, say y_1, having constant coefficients, that in the transformed problem in the dependent variables y_1, x_2, $\cdots$, x_n the new variable y_1 satisfies the differential equation $y_1' = \lambda_1 y_1$, where λ_1 is a root of the equation $D(\lambda) = 0$. If λ_1 is a multiple root, a second variable y_2 is similarly defined in terms of x_2, $\cdots$, x_n in such a way that it satisfies the differential equation $y_2' = \lambda_1 y_2 + c_2 y_1$, where c_2 may be zero. If λ_1 is a simple root, the new variable y_2 satisfies the differential equation $y_2' = \lambda_2 y_2$. If λ_1 is an n_1-fold root, there are n_1 equations in the new variables having the form

$$
\begin{cases}
\dfrac{dy_1}{dt} = \lambda_1 y_1, \\[2mm]
\dfrac{dy_2}{dt} = \lambda_1 y_2 + c_2 y_1, \\[2mm]
\cdots \cdots \cdots \cdots \cdots \\[2mm]
\dfrac{dy_{n_1}}{dt} = \lambda_1 y_{n_1} + c_{n_1} y_{n_1-1},
\end{cases}
$$

and similar groups of differential equations for each of the other roots of the equation $D(\lambda) = 0$.

Although the method of Weierstrass has all generality, it is indirect and very tedious in application. Similar treatments of the problem were given by Weber (*Lehrbuch der Algebra*, Vol. 2, pp. 41–42) and by Frobenius (*Mathematische Annalen*, Vol. 86, pp. 42–72 and 146–209).

Thomé treated the problem (*Mathematische Annalen*, Vol. 131, pp. 8–24, and Vol. 133, pp. 1–17) by differentiating one of equations

(1), say the first one, $n - 1$ times and eliminating $x_2', \cdots, x_n'$ at each step by means of the last $n - 1$ of equations (1). The result is n equations that are linear in $x_1, x_2, \cdots, x_n$, and the derivatives of x_1 from the first to the nth. The variables $x_2, \cdots, x_n$ can be eliminated and will give a resulting equation in x_1 and its derivatives from the first to the nth that is not identically zero provided a certain determinant is distinct from zero. If this determinant is zero, the resulting system involves non-homogeneous differential equations. Although the method of Thomé has some advantages over the methods of his predecessors, it also is indirect and tedious in application.

As was pointed out in the Art. 144, the method developed in this chapter is that of Nyswander (*American Journal of Mathematics*, Vol. 47, pp. 257–276.) It has all desirable directness and simplicity. In fact, in practice it requires only a small part of the labor of the earlier methods. The work of Nyswander has been somewhat simplified here by deriving the group of equations (74) from the derivatives with respect to t of the polynomial coefficients of $e^{\lambda_j t}$ in the solution (73), instead of deriving them by obtaining the general solutions of equations (68) from a comparison with equations (70). Moreover, it has been completed here in an essential point by reducing the determinant $D(\lambda)$ to the form (77), and by applying this form of $D(\lambda)$ in Art. 152 to define a procedure that invariably will lead to a fundamental set of solutions.

CHAPTER XVI

APPLICATIONS OF LINEAR DIFFERENTIAL EQUATIONS

153. Problems Depending upon Linear Differential Equations with Constant Coefficients. Not only are many physical problems expressible in terms of linear differential equations with constant coefficients, but these problems are of the most diverse character. Among the simplest of them are those in which there are harmonic oscillations such as are produced by a tuning fork. In all cases in which the restoring forces obey Hooke's law and in which the frictional terms are proportional to the first power of the velocity, the associated differential equations are linear.

It is true that in many cases the linear equations are not exact expressions of the physical conditions, but are sufficiently approximate for practical purposes. For example, the differential equation satisfied by a simple pendulum swinging freely in a vacuum is

$$\frac{d^2\theta}{dt^2} = - \kappa^2 \sin \theta.$$

This equation is often simplified by replacing $\sin \theta$ by θ, which reduces the equation to the linear form. When the oscillation is through only a few degrees, the error committed by this approximation is not serious, and the results obtained closely resemble those given by the exact equation.

Among other problems expressible in terms of linear differential equations, at least approximately, are that of the tides in the oceans, that of the variations in the earth's axis of rotation (the so-called variation of latitude), and even that of the stability of the planetary system.

In Art. 133 the equations for variations were set up. As was there explained, they define small variations from some special solution of the problem defined by the general differential equations which are satisfied in the problem under all conditions.

295

When the variations are from a solution in which the dependent variables are constant, the differential equations for the variations have constant coefficients; when the variations are from a periodic solution, the differential equations for the variations have periodic coefficients; when the variations are from some other type of solution, the differential equations for the variations have corresponding other properties. Most physical problems expressible in terms of linear differential equations with constant coefficients may be regarded as variations from some especially simple particular solution. For example, the tuning fork oscillates around the particular state in which it is at rest, and the pendulum oscillates about a state of hanging at rest. If the equations for the variations are only approximate, the complete system can be solved by the method of Art. 138.

One of the historically interesting problems is that of the stability of the solar system. In this theory it is shown (Art. 156) under certain assumptions that the planetary orbits oscillate about their present positions.

A recent important problem is that of determining the stability of an airplane in flight. When an airplane is disturbed by internal or external forces from a condition of uniform horizontal straight-line flight, its motion will vary from this steady state in accordance with equations (23), of Art. 133. If the roots λ_j of the equation $D(\lambda) = 0$ do not have positive real parts, the motion is stable; otherwise it is unstable. The coefficients of the differential equations upon which the λ_j depend in this problem are the moments of inertia and the other constants of the airplane, all of which can be determined from physical measurements when the airplane is at rest.

By far the most important and the most extensively developed application of linear differential equations with constant coefficients is in the field of electrical circuits. The problems connected with telephone and telegraph circuits, electrical amplification, electrical filters, and radio hook-ups have given rise to such a great variety of special mathematical devices that they constitute a domain that is almost distinct from the general theory, to which attention must be largely limited here.

154. Certain Differential Equations of Dynamical Origin.

In dynamical problems having potential functions that do not involve the velocities, the differential equations of motion are

$$(1) \qquad \frac{d^2 x_i}{dt^2} = \frac{\partial V}{\partial x_i} \qquad (i = 1, \cdots, n).$$

The corresponding equations for the variations from any solutions of equations (1) are (Art. 133)

$$(2) \qquad \begin{cases} \dfrac{d\xi_i}{dt} = \eta_i \qquad (i = 1, \cdots, n), \\[2mm] \dfrac{d\eta_i}{dt} = \dfrac{\partial^2 V}{\partial x_i \partial x_1} \xi_1 + \cdots + \dfrac{\partial^2 V}{\partial x_i \partial x_n} \xi_n. \end{cases}$$

Suppose all the coefficients of equations (2) are constants. Then it follows from Chapter XV that a fundamental set of solutions of these equations can be written in the form

$$(3) \qquad \begin{cases} \xi_i = p_{i,1} e^{\lambda_1 t}, \; \cdots, \; p_{i,2n} e^{\lambda_{2n} t} \qquad (i = 1, \cdots, n), \\[1mm] \eta_i = q_{i,1} e^{\lambda_1 t}, \; \cdots, \; q_{i,2n} e^{\lambda_{2n} t}, \end{cases}$$

where the functions in each column are a solution, and where the p_{ij} and the q_{ij} are constants or polynomials in t.

Since in the notation of Art. 139 the a_{ii} are all zero, it follows from Art. 131 that the determinant of the fundamental set is

$$(4) \qquad \Delta(t) \underset{t}{\equiv} \begin{vmatrix} p_{1,1}(0), & \cdots, & p_{1,2n}(0) \\ \cdot & & \cdot \\ \cdot & & \cdot \\ \cdot & & \cdot \\ q_{n,1}(0), & \cdots, & q_{n,2n}(0) \end{vmatrix} e^{\sum\limits_{j=1}^{2n} \lambda_j t}, \qquad \sum_{j=1}^{2n} \lambda_j = 0$$

Equation (4) would be satisfied if the λ_j were equal numerically and opposite in sign in pairs. It will be shown that they have this property. It follows from Art. 139 that the characteristic equation for equations (2) is

$$D(\lambda) = \begin{vmatrix} -\lambda, & \cdots, & 0, & 1, & \cdots, & 0 \\ \cdot & & \cdot & \cdot & & \cdot \\ \cdot & & \cdot & \cdot & & \cdot \\ \cdot & & \cdot & \cdot & & \cdot \\ 0, & \cdots, & -\lambda, & 0, & \cdots, & 1 \\ a_{11}, & \cdots, & a_{1n}, & -\lambda, & \cdots, & 0 \\ \cdot & & \cdot & \cdot & & \cdot \\ \cdot & & \cdot & \cdot & & \cdot \\ \cdot & & \cdot & \cdot & & \cdot \\ a_{n1}, & \cdots, & a_{nn}, & 0, & \cdots, & -\lambda \end{vmatrix},$$

where the coefficients a_{ij} are defined by the equations

$$a_{ij} = \frac{\partial^2 V}{\partial x_i \partial x_j}.$$

On multiplying the first n rows of $D(\lambda)$ by λ and adding them to the last n rows respectively, the determinant reduces to

$$(5) \qquad D(\lambda) = \begin{vmatrix} a_{11} - \lambda^2, & \cdots, & a_{1n} \\ \cdot & & \cdot \\ \cdot & & \cdot \\ \cdot & & \cdot \\ a_{n1}, & \cdots, & a_{nn} - \lambda^2 \end{vmatrix},$$

which is a function of λ^2. Therefore if λ_j is a root of the equation $D(\lambda) = 0$, then $-\lambda_j$ is also a root. If the a_{ij} are real and if there is a complex root $\alpha + \beta\sqrt{-1}$, then there are other roots $\alpha - \beta\sqrt{-1}$, $-\alpha + \beta\sqrt{-1}$, and $-\alpha - \beta\sqrt{-1}$. Hence the solutions are not stable unless all the λ_j are pure imaginaries.

155. Case in Which the Determinant $D(\lambda)$ Is Symmetric. If the coefficients of the differential equations are real and if $a_{ij} = a_{ji}$, the roots of the equation $D(\lambda) = 0$ are all real. This conclusion will be established by an indirect proof.

Suppose the root λ_j is the complex number $\alpha_j + \beta_j\sqrt{-1}$, where the α_j and β_j are real. Then there exist n constants $A_1, \cdots, A_n$, not all of which are zero, such that the equations

$$(6) \quad \begin{cases} (a_{11} - \alpha_j - \beta_j\sqrt{-1})A_1 + a_{12}A_2 + \cdots + a_{1n}A_n = 0, \\ \cdot \quad \cdot \quad \cdot \quad \cdot \quad \cdot \quad \cdot \quad \cdot \quad \cdot \quad \cdot \quad \cdot \quad \cdot \quad \cdot \\ a_{n1}A_1 + a_{n2}A_2 + \cdots + (a_{nn} - \alpha_j - \beta_j\sqrt{-1})A_n = 0 \end{cases}$$

are all satisfied. These equations can be written in the form

$$(7) \quad \begin{cases} a_{11}A_1 + \cdots + a_{1n}A_n = (\alpha_j + \beta_j\sqrt{-1})A_1, \\ \cdot \quad \cdot \quad \cdot \quad \cdot \quad \cdot \quad \cdot \quad \cdot \quad \cdot \quad \cdot \\ a_{n1}A_1 + \cdots + a_{nn}A_n = (\alpha_j + \beta_j\sqrt{-1})A_n. \end{cases}$$

The constants $A_1, \cdots, A_n$ may be complex number. Suppose $A_i = B_i + C_i\sqrt{-1}$, where B_i and C_i are real. Then, since the a_{ij} are real, equations (7) give, on equating their real and imaginary parts separately to zero, the equations

$$(8) \quad \begin{cases} a_{11}B_1 + \cdots + a_{1n}B_n - \alpha_jB_1 + \beta_jC_1 = 0, \\ \cdot \quad \cdot \quad \cdot \quad \cdot \quad \cdot \quad \cdot \quad \cdot \quad \cdot \quad \cdot \\ a_{n1}B_1 + \cdots + a_{nn}B_n - \alpha_jB_n + \beta_jC_n = 0; \end{cases}$$

$$(9) \quad \begin{cases} a_{11}C_1 + \cdots + a_{1n}C_n - \alpha_j C_1 - \beta_j B_1 = 0, \\ \cdot \quad \cdot \quad \cdot \quad \cdot \quad \cdot \quad \cdot \quad \cdot \quad \cdot \quad \cdot \quad \cdot \\ a_{n1}C_1 + \cdots + a_{nn}C_n - \alpha_j C_n - \beta_j B_n = 0. \end{cases}$$

On multiplying equations (8) by $C_1, \cdots, C_n$ respectively and adding, and equations (9) by $B_1, \cdots, B_n$ respectively and adding, the results are found to be

$$(10) \quad \begin{cases} (a_{11}B_1 + \cdots + a_{1n}B_n)C_1 + \cdots + (a_{n1}B_1 + \cdots + a_{nn}B_n)C_n \\ \qquad = \alpha_j(B_1 C_1 + \cdots + B_n C_n) - \beta_j(C_1^2 + \cdots + C_n^2), \\ (a_{11}C_1 + \cdots + a_{1n}C_n)B_1 + \cdots + (a_{n1}C_1 + \cdots + a_{nn}C_n)B_n \\ \qquad = \alpha_j(B_1 C_1 + \cdots + B_n C_n) + \beta_j(B_1^2 + \cdots + B_n^2). \end{cases}$$

Since, when $a_{ij} = a_{ji}$, there is the identity

$$\sum_{i=1}^n (a_{i1}B_1 + \cdots + a_{in}B_n)C_i = \sum_{i=1}^n (a_{i1}C_1 + \cdots + a_{in}C_n)B_i,$$

it follows from equations (10) that $\beta_j = 0$. Therefore, in this case, the roots of the equation $D(\lambda) = 0$ are all real.

156. The Stability Equations for the Planetary Orbits. If a planet were revolving about the sun subject only to the sun's attraction, its orbit would be an ellipse whose six elements would be constants. The mutual attractions of the planets produce variations from the purely elliptical motion. If the elements of the orbits are taken as variables, after the manner developed by Lagrange, it is found that these variables can be expanded as power series in the planetary masses, which are small parameters in the problem.* The method of solution is that of Arts. 23–26.

Now consider the equations for the terms of the solutions that are of the first degree in the masses. The right members of the equations which define the first-order variations in the major axes of the orbits contain only terms that are trigonometric functions of t. Therefore the first-order terms in the major axes have only trigonometric variations from their values at t_0. If the periods of the trigonometric terms are commensurable, the variations are periodic. But the right members of the differential equations for the first-order terms in the masses of the other elements of the planetary orbits contain terms that

* Moulton, *Introduction to Celestial Mechanics*, pp. 420–425.

are independent of t. Therefore it follows from Art. 24 that the solutions contain terms that are constants multiplied by t. These are the so-called "secular terms."

Lagrange's treatment of the problem was as follows. He regarded the major axes as constants and in the equations for the other elements he ignored all except their secular terms. He also ignored the equations that define the longitudes of the planets at a fixed epoch, for this element has no part in defining the geometric characteristics of the orbits. With these limitations and approximations, after a suitable transformation of variables he obtained the differential equations in the form *

$$(11) \quad \begin{cases} \dfrac{dx_1}{dt} = + a_{11}y_1 + \cdots + a_{1n}y_n, \\ \phantom{\dfrac{dx_1}{dt}} \cdot \quad \cdot \quad \cdot \quad \cdot \quad \cdot \quad \cdot \quad \cdot \\ \dfrac{dx_n}{dt} = + a_{n1}y_1 + \cdots + a_{nn}y_n; \\ \dfrac{dy_1}{dt} = - a_{11}x_1 - \cdots - a_{1n}x_n, \\ \phantom{\dfrac{dy_1}{dt}} \cdot \quad \cdot \quad \cdot \quad \cdot \quad \cdot \quad \cdot \quad \cdot \\ \dfrac{dy_n}{dt} = - a_{n1}x_1 - \cdots - a_{nn}x_n, \end{cases}$$

where the a_{ij} are real constants and $a_{ij} = a_{ji}$. Since

$$e^{\lambda t} = \cosh \lambda t + \sinh \lambda t$$
$$= \cos \sqrt{-1}\lambda t - \sqrt{-1} \sin \sqrt{-1}\lambda t,$$

where λ is any constant, real, imaginary or complex, the solutions in all cases can be expressed in terms of hyperbolic functions or trigonometric functions (the arguments of which may be not real) as well as in terms of exponentials. In general, however, it is much simpler to use exponentials in obtaining the solutions than it is to use hyperbolic or trigonometric functions.

To obtain the solutions of equations (11), assume that they can be expressed in the form

$$(12) \quad \begin{cases} x_i = A_i \sin \lambda t, \\ y_i = B_i \cos \lambda t, \end{cases}$$

where λ, the A_i, and the B_i are undetermined constants. In general, such an assumption would not lead to solutions, but

* Tisserand, *Mécanique Céleste*, Vol. I, Chap. 26.

the special properties of equations (11) imply the relations between the x_i and the y_i respectively given in equations (12).

On substituting the expressions for the x_i and the y_i from equations (12) into equations (11) and equating coefficients of corresponding functions of t, it is found that the equations

(13)
$$\begin{cases} - \lambda A_1 + a_{11}B_1 + \cdots + a_{1n}B_n = 0, \\ \qquad \cdots \qquad \cdots \qquad \cdots \\ - \lambda A_n + a_{n1}B_1 + \cdots + a_{nn}B_n = 0; \\ - a_{11}A_1 - \cdots - a_{1n}A_n + \lambda B_1 = 0, \\ \qquad \cdots \qquad \cdots \qquad \cdots \\ - a_{n1}A_1 - \cdots - a_{nn}A_n + \lambda B_n = 0 \end{cases}$$

must be satisfied in order that equations (12) shall be a solution of equations (11). A necessary and sufficient condition that equations (13) can be satisfied by A_i and B_i that are not all zero is the equation

(14) $\quad D(\lambda) = \begin{vmatrix} - \lambda, & \cdots, & 0, & a_{11}, & \cdots, & a_{1n} \\ & & & \cdot & & \cdot \\ & & & \cdot & & \cdot \\ 0, & \cdots, & - \lambda, & a_{n1}, & \cdots, & a_{nn} \\ - a_{11}, & \cdots, & - a_{1n}, & \lambda, & \cdots, & 0 \\ & & & \cdot & & \cdot \\ & & & \cdot & & \cdot \\ - a_{n1}, & \cdots, & - a_{nn}, & 0, & \cdots, & \lambda \end{vmatrix} = 0.$

On changing the signs of the elements in the n last rows, this equation becomes symmetric and of the form of that treated in Art. 155. Hence the λ_j are all real and the right members of equations (12) are trigonometric. If the solutions were expressed in terms of exponentials, all the corresponding λ_j would be pure imaginaries.

Laplace proved by deriving an integral of equations (11) that the x_i and the y_i do not increase with t beyond very narrow limits. On multiplying the first n equations by $x_1, \cdots, x_n$ respectively, and the last n equations by $y_1, \cdots, y_n$ respectively, and adding these products, the sum is a complete derivative whose integral is

(15) $\quad x_1^2 + \cdots + x_n^2 + y_1^2 + \cdots + y_n^2 = \text{constant} = c.$

Therefore no x_i^2 or y_i^2 can exceed the positive constant c that is determined by the initial conditions.

It follows from the fact that the whole discussion pertains only to terms of the first order in the planetary masses in the solutions for the elements as power series in the masses, and from the further limitations and assumptions that were made in arriving at equations (11), that the conclusion that the elements of the planetary orbits undergo only trigonometric oscillations is far from being rigorously established. Yet the results have real physical significance, and they mean that the planetary orbits depart slowly from their present general values, if, indeed, they undergo large variations at all.

157. Non-homogeneous Differential Equations. In physical applications, particularly in the field of electrical networks, non-homogeneous differential equations arise much more frequently than homogeneous systems. The general system of non-homogeneous linear differential equations with constant coefficients can be written in the form

$$
(16) \quad
\begin{cases}
\dfrac{dx_1}{dt} - [a_{11}x_1 + \cdots + a_{1n}x_n] = \theta_1(t), \\
\cdot \quad \cdot \quad \cdot \quad \cdot \quad \cdot \quad \cdot \quad \cdot \quad \cdot \quad \cdot \quad \cdot \quad \cdot \\
\dfrac{dx_n}{dt} - [a_{n1}x_1 + \cdots + a_{nn}x_n] = \theta_n(t),
\end{cases}
$$

where $\theta_1(t), \cdots, \theta_n(t)$ are known functions of t. In most physical problems, the $\theta_i(t)$ are either simple periodic functions or sums of periodic functions that are expressible in terms of sines and cosines. For present purposes it will be sufficient to assume that the $\theta_i(t)$ are continuous functions of t for all values of t for which solutions are desired.

Let the fundamental set of solutions for the corresponding differential equations when $\theta_1(t), \cdots, \theta_n(t)$ are all identically zero be

$$
(17) \quad
\begin{cases}
x_1 = p_{11} e^{\lambda_1 t}, \quad \cdots, \quad p_{1n} e^{\lambda_n t}, \\
\cdot \quad \cdot \quad \cdot \quad \cdot \quad \cdot \quad \cdot \quad \cdot \quad \cdot \\
x_n = p_{n1} e^{\lambda_1 t}, \quad \cdots, \quad p_{nn} e^{\lambda_n t},
\end{cases}
$$

where the p_{ij} are constants or polynomials in t, and where the functions in each column constitute a solution.

Now transform equations (16) from the dependent variables

$x_1, \cdots, x_n$ to the variables $y_1, \cdots, y_n$ by the equations (Art. 38)

$$(18) \quad \begin{cases} x_1 = p_{11} e^{\lambda_1 t} y_1 + \cdots + p_{1n} e^{\lambda_n t} y_n, \\ \cdot \quad \cdot \quad \cdot \quad \cdot \quad \cdot \quad \cdot \quad \cdot \quad \cdot \\ x_n = p_{n1} e^{\lambda_1 t} y_1 + \cdots + p_{nn} e^{\lambda_n t} y_n. \end{cases}$$

On substituting these expressions for the x_i into equations (16) and making use of the facts that the columns in the right members of equations (17) identically satisfy the left members of equations (16) set equal to zero, it is found that the y_i satisfy the equations

$$(19) \quad \begin{cases} p_{11} e^{\lambda_1 t} \dfrac{dy_1}{dt} + \cdots + p_{1n} e^{\lambda_n t} \dfrac{dy_n}{dt} = \theta_1(t), \\ \cdot \quad \cdot \quad \cdot \quad \cdot \quad \cdot \quad \cdot \quad \cdot \quad \cdot \quad \cdot \quad \cdot \\ p_{n1} e^{\lambda_1 t} \dfrac{dy_1}{dt} + \cdots + p_{nn} e^{\lambda_n t} \dfrac{dy_n}{dt} = \theta_n(t). \end{cases}$$

The determinant of the fundamental set of solutions is (Art. 131)

$$\Delta = \Delta_0 e^{\int \sum\limits_{i=1}^{n} \theta_{ii} dt} = \Delta_0 e^{\sum\limits_{i=1}^{n} a_{ii} t}.$$

It follows from the form of equations (16) that $a_{11} + \cdots + a_{nn} = \lambda_1 + \cdots + \lambda_n$ is the negative of the coefficient of λ^{n-1} in the expansion of the determinant $D(\lambda)$. Therefore the determinant of the coefficients of the left members of equations (19) is

$$\Delta = \begin{vmatrix} p_{11}, & \cdots, & p_{1n} \\ \cdot & & \cdot \\ \cdot & & \cdot \\ \cdot & & \cdot \\ p_{n1}, & \cdots, & p_{nn} \end{vmatrix} e^{(\lambda_1 + \cdots + \lambda_n)t} = \Delta_0 e^{(\lambda_1 + \cdots + \lambda_n)t}.$$

Hence the solution of equations (19) for the dy_i/dt is

$$(20) \quad \begin{cases} \dfrac{dy_1}{dt} = \begin{vmatrix} \theta_1, & p_{12}, & \cdots, & p_{1n} \\ \cdot & \cdot & & \cdot \\ \cdot & \cdot & & \cdot \\ \cdot & \cdot & & \cdot \\ \theta_n, & p_{n2}, & \cdots, & p_{nn} \end{vmatrix} \dfrac{e^{-\lambda_1 t}}{\Delta_0} = \sum\limits_{j=1}^{n} P_{1j} \theta_j(t) e^{-\lambda_1 t}, \\ \cdot \quad \cdot \quad \cdot \quad \cdot \quad \cdot \quad \cdot \quad \cdot \quad \cdot \quad \cdot \quad \cdot \quad \cdot \\ \dfrac{dy_n}{dt} = \begin{vmatrix} p_{11}, & \cdots, & p_{1\,n-1}, & \theta_1 \\ \cdot & & \cdot & \cdot \\ \cdot & & \cdot & \cdot \\ \cdot & & \cdot & \cdot \\ p_{n1}, & \cdots, & p_{n\,n-1}, & \theta_n \end{vmatrix} \dfrac{e^{-\lambda_n t}}{\Delta_0} = \sum\limits_{j=1}^{n} P_{nj} \theta_j(t) e^{-\lambda_n t}, \end{cases}$$

where the P_{ij} are constants or polynomials in t.

Since the $\theta_j(t)$ are by hypothesis continuous functions of t, equations (20) are quadratures whose integrals exist and can be written

$$(21) \quad \begin{cases} y_1 = \int_0^t \sum_{j=1}^n P_{1j}\theta_j(t)e^{-\lambda_1 t}\,dt + c_1 = F_1(t) + c_1, \\ \cdot \quad \cdot \quad \cdot \quad \cdot \quad \cdot \quad \cdot \quad \cdot \quad \cdot \quad \cdot \quad \cdot \\ y_n = \int_0^t \sum_{j=1}^n P_{nj}\theta_j(t)e^{-\lambda_n t}\,dt + c_n = F_n(t) + c_n, \end{cases}$$

where $c_1, \cdots, c_n$ are arbitrary constants. On substituting these expressions for the y_i into equations (18), the final solutions are found to be

$$(22) \quad \begin{cases} x_1 = c_1 p_{11} e^{\lambda_1 t} + \cdots + c_n p_{1n} e^{\lambda_n t} + \Phi_1(t), \\ \cdot \quad \cdot \quad \cdot \quad \cdot \quad \cdot \quad \cdot \quad \cdot \quad \cdot \quad \cdot \\ x_n = c_1 p_{n1} e^{\lambda_1 t} + \cdots + c_n p_{nn} e^{\lambda_n t} + \Phi_n(t), \end{cases}$$

where

$$(23) \quad \begin{cases} \Phi_1(t) = p_{11} e^{\lambda_1 t}F_1 + \cdots + p_{1n} e^{\lambda_n t}F_n, \\ \cdot \quad \cdot \quad \cdot \quad \cdot \quad \cdot \quad \cdot \quad \cdot \quad \cdot \\ \Phi_n(t) = p_{n1} e^{\lambda_1 t}F_1 + \cdots + p_{nn} e^{\lambda_n t}F_n. \end{cases}$$

In elementary differential equations theory, particularly in the case of one equation, the part of the solution that is multiplied by the arbitrary constants $c_1, \cdots, c_n$ is often called "the complementary function," and the part that is independent of these constants, namely, $\Phi_1(t), \cdots, \Phi_n(t)$, is called the "particular integral." There appears to be nothing to recommend this terminology in the general theory. In the theory of electrical circuits the parts of the solution multiplied by $c_1, \cdots, c_n$ are called "transients," because in those problems the λ_j contain a negative real part due to electrical resistance and, therefore, these terms decrease numerically as t increases. The terms represented by $\Phi_1(t), \cdots, \Phi_n(t)$ are called the "steady state" terms, because they define the state of the circuit after the "transients" have become inappreciable. As will be shown in Art. 158, these terms are in general similar in character to the $\theta_i(t)$ which, in electrical circuits, usually represent continuously applied periodic voltages.

In this discussion the $\Phi_i(t)$ have been proved to exist and have been determined by using the solutions of the homogeneous parts of the differential equations. In many cases, however, the $\Phi_i(t)$ can be determined more directly. For example, consider the differential equation

$$(24) \qquad \frac{d^2x}{dt^2} + a^2x = c \cos \omega t.$$

It is clear that the $\Phi(t)$ belonging to this equation is a constant times $\cos \omega t$, for the second derivative of $\cos \omega t$ is $-\omega^2 \cos \omega t$ and the left member is the same function of t as the right. On setting $x = A \cos \omega t$ and determining A by the condition that equation (24) shall be identically satisfied, it is found that $A = c/(a^2 - \omega^2)$ unless $\omega = \pm a$. Suppose $\omega = a$. Since the right member of equation (24) is an even function of t, $\Phi(t)$ must be an even function of t. On trying the form $x = At \sin \omega t$, it is found that equation (24) is identically satisfied if $A = c/2\omega$.

If, however, there is a frictional resistance and the differential equation has the form

$$\frac{d^2x}{dt^2} + b \frac{dx}{dt} + a^2x = c \cos \omega t,$$

then the function $\Phi(t)$ has terms in both $\cos \omega t$ and $\sin \omega t$. The value of $\Phi(t)$ can be determined by assuming the form

$$x = A \cos \omega t + B \sin \omega t,$$

substituting it in the differential equation, and imposing the condition that the result shall be an identity. The special development of the theory of electrical circuits consists to a considerable extent in devices for obtaining the $\Phi_i(t)$ without determining the remainder of the solution. Yet the so-called "transients" are a part of the solution and may not be neglected in a complete theory.

158. Application to a Simple Electric Circuit. The differential equation for a simple electric circuit having an inductance L, a resistance r, and a capacity $C = 1/\gamma$ in series, and to which there is applied a periodic electromotive force $E \cos \omega t$, is

$$(25) \qquad L \frac{d^2x}{dt^2} + r \frac{dx}{dt} + \gamma x = E \cos \omega t,$$

where x represents the quantity of electricity and dx/dt the electric current. This is also the differential equation for such an oscillating physical system as a tuning fork vibrating in a resisting medium and acted upon by a periodic force.

The differential equation (25) is equivalent to the two equations

$$(26) \quad \begin{cases} \dfrac{dx_1}{dt} - x_2 = 0, \\ \dfrac{dx_2}{dt} + \dfrac{\gamma}{L} x_1 + \dfrac{r}{L} x_2 = \dfrac{E}{L} \cos \omega t, \end{cases}$$

in which $x_1 = x$ and $x_2 = dx/dt$. The solutions of the homogeneous parts of equations (26) corresponding to equations (18) are (except when $r^2 = 4\gamma L$)

$$(27) \quad \begin{cases} x_1 = \quad e^{\lambda_1 t} \quad , \quad e^{\lambda_2 t}, \\ x_2 = \lambda_1 e^{\lambda_1 t} \quad , \quad \lambda_2 e^{\lambda_2 t}, \end{cases}$$

where

$$(28) \quad \begin{cases} \lambda_1 = \dfrac{-r + \sqrt{r^2 - 4\gamma L}}{2L}, \\ \lambda_2 = \dfrac{-r - \sqrt{r^2 - 4\gamma L}}{2L}. \end{cases}$$

It follows from equations (26) that in this problem the equations corresponding to equations (20) are

$$\begin{cases} \dfrac{dy_1}{dt} = \dfrac{E}{L(\lambda_1 - \lambda_2)} \cos \omega t \, e^{-\lambda_1 t}, \\ \dfrac{dy_2}{dt} = \dfrac{-E}{L(\lambda_1 - \lambda_2)} \cos \omega t \, e^{-\lambda_2 t}. \end{cases}$$

Then, since

$$\int \cos \omega t \, e^{-\lambda t} \, dt = \frac{-\lambda}{\lambda^2 + \omega^2} \cos \omega t \, e^{-\lambda t} + \frac{\omega}{\lambda^2 + \omega^2} \sin \omega t \, e^{-\lambda t},$$

it follows that the equations corresponding to equations (22) are

$$(29) \quad \begin{cases} x_1 = c_1 e^{\lambda_1 t} + c_2 e^{\lambda_2 t} \\ \quad + \dfrac{E}{(\gamma - \omega^2 L)^2 + \omega^2 r^2} [(\gamma - \omega^2 L) \cos \omega t + \omega r \sin \omega t], \\ x_2 = c_1 \lambda_1 e^{\lambda_1 t} + c_2 \lambda_2 e^{\lambda_2 t} \\ \quad - \dfrac{E\omega}{(\gamma - \omega^2 L)^2 + \omega^2 r^2} [(\gamma - \omega^2 L) \sin \omega t - \omega r \cos \omega t]. \end{cases}$$

In most practical problems the systems start from rest, or

with the initial conditions $x_1(0) = x_2(0) = 0$. It follows from equations (29) that for these initial conditions the constants c_1 and c_2 have the values

$$(30) \quad \begin{cases} c_1 = \dfrac{-E}{2[(\gamma - \omega^2 L)^2 + \omega^2 r^2]} \left[\dfrac{r(\gamma + \omega^2 L)}{\sqrt{r^2 - 4\gamma L}} + (\gamma - \omega^2 L) \right], \\ c_2 = \dfrac{+E}{2[(\gamma - \omega^2 L)^2 + \omega^2 r^2]} \left[\dfrac{r(\gamma + \omega^2 L)}{\sqrt{r^2 - 4\gamma L}} - (\gamma - \omega^2 L) \right]. \end{cases}$$

This completes the solution of the problem. It is desirable, however, to inquire into the properties of the solution, particularly in certain special cases.

The Transient Terms. If $r^2 - 4\gamma L > 0$, both λ_1 and λ_2 are real and negative. In this case the first two terms in the right members of equations (29) decrease numerically as t increases, and they approach zero as a limit as t becomes infinite. The terms become inappreciable, in comparison with the last terms of equations (29), for some finite value of t depending upon the values of r, γ, and L. For this reason, as has been remarked, the exponential terms are called "transients." When r^2 is large compared to $4\gamma L$, it follows from equations (28) that the exponential terms are approximately

$$\begin{cases} e^{\lambda_1 t} = e^{-(\gamma/r)t}, \\ e^{\lambda_2 t} = e^{-(r/L)t}, \end{cases}$$

the first of which decreases rapidly if γ/r is large, and the second of which decreases rapidly if r/L is large. These conditions would be satisfied if, for example, $\gamma = 10r$ and $r = 1600L$. Such relationships are satisfied in an electric circuit if the inductance L is small compared to the resistance and the reciprocal of the capacity, and in a mechanical system if the moving mass is small compared to the resistance and the restoring force.

If $r^2 = 4\gamma L$, the solutions corresponding to those given in equations (27) are

$$(31) \quad \begin{cases} x_1 = + \quad e^{-(r/2L)t} \qquad , \qquad t e^{-(r/2L)t}, \\ x_2 = -\dfrac{r}{2L} e^{-(r/2L)t} \qquad , \quad -\dfrac{r}{2L} t e^{-(r/2L)t} + e^{-(r/2L)t}. \end{cases}$$

In this case also the transient terms approach zero as t becomes infinite, for the exponential decreases with increasing t for all values of t, and the term t times the exponential decreases with increasing t for all values of t greater than $2L/r$. In this case the coefficients c_1 and c_2 corresponding to the initial conditions $x_1(0) = x_2(0) = 0$ are

$$(32) \quad \begin{cases} c_1 = -\dfrac{E(\gamma - \omega^2 L)}{(\gamma + \omega^2 L)^2}, \\[2mm] c_2 = \dfrac{-E\sqrt{\gamma/L}}{\gamma + \omega^2 L}. \end{cases}$$

If $r^2 < 4\gamma L$, the exponential terms in equations (29) can be put in the form

$$(33) \quad \begin{cases} e^{\lambda_1 t} = e^{-(r/2L)t}\left[\cos\dfrac{\sqrt{4\gamma L - r^2}}{2L}t + \sqrt{-1}\sin\dfrac{\sqrt{4\gamma L - r^2}}{2L}t\right], \\[3mm] e^{\lambda_2 t} = e^{-(r/2L)t}\left[\cos\dfrac{\sqrt{4\gamma L - r^2}}{2L}t - \sqrt{-1}\sin\dfrac{\sqrt{4\gamma L - r^2}}{2L}t\right], \end{cases}$$

from which it follows that in this case, too, the exponential terms approach zero as a limit as t becomes infinite. Equations (30) give the values of c_1 and c_2 corresponding to the initial conditions $x_1(0) = x_2(0) = 0$.

It follows from equations (29), (30), and (33) that in the limiting case $r = 0$ the solution reduces to

$$(34) \quad \begin{cases} x_1 = \dfrac{-E}{\gamma - \omega^2 L}\cos\sqrt{\dfrac{\gamma}{L}}\,t + \dfrac{E}{\gamma - \omega^2 L}\cos\omega t, \\[3mm] x_2 = \dfrac{E\sqrt{\dfrac{\gamma}{L}}}{\gamma - \omega^2 L}\sin\sqrt{\dfrac{\gamma}{L}}\,t - \dfrac{E\omega}{\gamma - \omega^2 L}\sin\omega t. \end{cases}$$

In this case the exponential terms are purely periodic and do not approach zero as t becomes infinite; that is, in the case in which there is no resistance (friction in a mechanical system), the so-called transient terms are not transients.

Phase Displacements. In practice, an electrical circuit or a mechanism is acted upon by an input voltage or force and delivers a corresponding output. The input is represented by the right member of equation (25); the output, in this simple problem, by the last two terms in the right members of equations (29). In practice there are usually several input terms and corresponding output terms. In general, it is highly desirable that the output be a faithful reproduction of the input, both in relative amplitudes and in phase relationships.

In this discussion the transient terms will be omitted from consideration. On defining an angle θ by the equations

$$(35) \quad \begin{cases} \sin\theta = \dfrac{\omega r}{\sqrt{(\gamma - \omega^2 L)^2 + \omega^2 r^2}}, \\[3ex] \cos\theta = \dfrac{\gamma - \omega^2 L}{\sqrt{(\gamma - \omega^2 L)^2 + \omega^2 r^2}}, \end{cases}$$

the steady-state terms of equations (29) can be written in the form

$$(36) \quad \begin{cases} x_1 = \dfrac{E}{\sqrt{(\gamma - \omega^2 L)^2 + \omega^2 r^2}} \cos(\omega t - \theta), \\[3ex] x_2 = \dfrac{-E\omega}{\sqrt{(\gamma - \omega^2 L)^2 + \omega^2 r^2}} \sin(\omega t - \theta). \end{cases}$$

The angle θ is the phase displacement of the output as compared with the input.

It follows from equations (35) that the phase displacement of the steady-state part of the output depends upon the period $2\pi/\omega$ of the input. Hence if there are inputs of several periods having certain phase relationships, the outputs have different phase relationships. For example, if the input is into a telephone circuit or an electrical amplifier of sound oscillations, the output is subject to different phase displacements of the various frequencies. For very high frequencies the phase displacement is nearly π, the limit of θ being π for ω infinite. With decreasing ω^2 the angle θ decreases until $\omega^2 L = \gamma + r\sqrt{\gamma/L}$; then θ increases until $\omega^2 L = \gamma - r\sqrt{\gamma/L}$; then θ decreases again and becomes $\pi/2$ for $\omega^2 L = \gamma$; and then θ decreases still further and vanishes for $\omega = 0$. In more extensive networks, such as are required in practice, the different parts can often be so designed as to minimize the phase displacements, particularly over some restricted range of frequencies that it is desired to transmit.

Amplitude Distortions. Not only is it important to reproduce the input of various frequencies with small relative phase displacements, but it is equally important to reproduce the various frequencies with the same relationships among their amplitudes (intensities) that they have in the input. For example, if the amplitude relationships were not closely preserved in the electrical reproduction of music, the quality of the music might be entirely changed by the alterations in the relative intensities of tones of various pitches.

The coefficients of the trigonometric terms in equations (36) are the amplitudes which measure the intensity of the output. It is noted that the amplitudes depend upon the period $2\pi/\omega$ of the input, as well as upon its amplitude E. Consider the expression for x_2, equation (36), which represents current in an electrical circuit and velocity in a mechanical system. At the limit $\omega = 0$, the solution is $x_1 = E/\gamma$, $x_2 = 0$. Since

$$\frac{\partial}{\partial \omega}\frac{\omega}{\sqrt{(\gamma - \omega^2 L)^2 + \omega^2 r^2}} = \frac{\gamma^2 - \omega^4 L^2}{[(\gamma - \omega^2 L)^2 + \omega^2 r^2]^{3/2}},$$

the amplitude of x_2 increases as ω increases from zero until it attains its maximum E/r at $\omega^2 = \gamma/L$, after which it decreases to its minimum $E/\sqrt{L^2 + r^2}$ at ω infinite. (The variable x_1 has its maximum for $\omega^2 = \gamma/L - r^2/2L^2$.) If r is small relative to γ and L, the maximum of the amplitude may be very great compared to values of the amplitude for other values of ω.

Distortion Due to the Transient Terms. The complete output consists of both the transient and the steady-state terms. Suppose the transient terms are of the quasi-periodic form given in equations (33). Since $x_1(0) = x_2(0) = 0$, the phases of the transient terms initially differ from those of the steady-state terms by 180°. Since the periods of the two classes of terms are in general different, the phases will steadily undergo a shift with respect to each other until they coincide at a certain value of t. Then the amplitudes of the variations in x_1 and x_2 will be relatively very large until further changes in relative phases alter the condition. In the meantime the amplitudes of the transient terms steadily decrease as a consequence of the exponential factor in equations (33). When r is small and the periods of the transient and the steady-state terms are nearly equal, the output has beats (maxima) whose period depends upon the periods of the two classes of terms. Let the periods be represented by P_T and P_S respectively. Express the ratio P_T/P_S in the form of a continued fraction. Let the first of its convergents, which approximately equals P_T/P_S, be $N_1/N_2 = n_1/n_2$, where n_1 and n_2 are relatively prime integers. Then there will be beats in the period $N_1n_2 = N_2n_1$.

The Quasi-Resonance Period. A phenomenon known as resonance will be discussed in Art. 159. It cannot arise in the problem under discussion, but from the physical point of view it is approached for the value of ω for which the amplitude of the solution is a maximum. For $\omega^2 = \gamma/L$, the solution (36) becomes

$$(37) \quad \begin{cases} x_1 = + \dfrac{E}{\omega r} \cos (\omega t - \tfrac{1}{2}\pi), \\ x_2 = - \dfrac{E}{r} \sin (\omega t - \tfrac{1}{2}\pi). \end{cases}$$

The smaller r the greater the maximum of the amplitude, and since for $\omega^2 = \gamma/L$

$$\frac{\partial}{\partial \omega^2} \frac{\omega}{\sqrt{(\gamma - \omega^2 L)^2 + \omega^2 r^2}} = - \frac{4L^2}{r^3},$$

the smaller r the sharper the maximum. If the differential equation (25) contained many terms in its right member differing in the values of ω, the solution would have corresponding terms, and the amplitude of the one for which $\omega^2 = \gamma/L$ would be much greater than the amplitudes of the other terms, particularly if r were small. That is, the output of the quasi-resonance period would be greatly over-emphasized in comparison with that of the other periods.

The Radio Carrier Wave. The present theory is sufficient to illustrate the principle of the radio carrier wave. Suppose ω, corresponding to quasi-resonance, is so large that the frequency is far above the frequencies of the audible range. Suppose the input consists of waves of many frequencies including that of quasi-resonance. The output will be small for all frequencies except those which are at or near the quasi-resonance frequencies. Now suppose the output is transformed into sound waves. They will be inaudible because those corresponding to quasi-resonance are above the audible range and the remainder are much too feeble (have too small amplitudes). It follows from equations (37) that the output is proportional to the amplitude E of the input. Suppose E is varied with the frequencies of audible sound waves, far below the radio frequencies associated with ω. Then, when the output is transformed into sound waves, the ear will perceive the variations in atmospheric pressure corresponding to the variations in E.

Multiple telephony over a single circuit depends upon similar principles. Each end is equipped with sending and receiving devices connected in multiple, and a pair at each end has a quasi-resonance frequency different from that of the others. Then, when the amplitude E of one of the inputs is modulated by sound waves, it is received at the output end by the receiver tuned to the frequency of its particular carrier wave, and it is inaudible through the receivers that are tuned to the frequencies of other carrier waves. It should be kept in mind that the mathematical problem that has been discussed does not cover the complexities of the physical problems to which references have been made; it only illustrates the principles that apply in more difficult problems.

Besides the several practical applications that have been mentioned and many others, including the important subject of filters, many questions of a purely scientific nature depend on the same principles. For example, some of the numerous frequencies of the tide-raising forces of the sun and of the moon may have the quasi-resonance relationship to some of the free oscillation periods of the ocean or of such land-locked bodies of water as Hudson's Bay. In the much more difficult problem of the mutual interactions of the planets similar principles are involved, and on them rests the explanation of the vacant spaces in the planetoid system and the gaps in Saturn's ring system. The selective absorption of light by gases, giving rise to dark-line spectra, depends upon another application of essentially similar principles. Indeed, the absorption of radiant energy by living organisms probably is a quasi-resonance phenomenon.

159. Non-homogeneous Equations When $D(\lambda) = 0$ Has Simple Roots and the $\theta_i(t)$ Are Trigonometric. When the roots of the equation $D(\lambda) = 0$ are all simple, the p_{ij} of equations (17) and the P_{ij} of equations (20) are all constants. It is assumed that the $\theta_i(t)$ are sums of sines and cosines of the argument $\omega_j t$.

If the ω_j are commensurable, the $\theta_i(t)$ are periodic; otherwise they are not periodic, but they are composed of terms that are individually periodic.

It will be sufficient to consider the terms in the $\theta_i(t)$ of a single period, because the terms of every period, with an exception which will be noted, give rise to similar terms in the solution. Instead of using the trigonometric forms $\cos \omega t$ and $\sin \omega t$, it is more convenient to use exponentials. Since ω may be positive or negative, it is sufficient to treat the case in which

$$(38) \qquad \theta_i(t) = c_i e^{\omega \sqrt{-1} t}.$$

The first problem is to determine the properties of the $F_i(t)$ in the right members of equations (21). Suppose first that $\lambda_j^2 + \omega^2 \neq 0$ for $j = 1, \cdots, n$. Then, since

$$\int e^{\omega \sqrt{-1} t} e^{-\lambda_j t} dt = \frac{-1}{\lambda_j - \omega \sqrt{-1}} e^{\omega \sqrt{-1} t} e^{-\lambda_j t},$$

it follows from equations (21) and (23) that, so far as they depend upon the period $2\pi/\omega$, the $\Phi_i(t)$ have the form

$$(39) \qquad \Phi_i(t) = A_i \sin \omega t + B_i \cos \omega t.$$

Suppose now that $\lambda_j = \omega \sqrt{-1}$. Then, since

$$\int (e^{\omega \sqrt{-1} t} + e^{-\omega \sqrt{-1} t}) e^{-\lambda_j t} dt = t - \frac{1}{\lambda_j + \omega \sqrt{-1}} e^{-\omega \sqrt{-1} t} e^{-\lambda_j t},$$

it follows from equations (21) and (23) that in this case the functions $\Phi_i(t)$ have the form

$$(40) \quad \Phi_i(t) = A_i^{(0)} \sin \omega t + B_i^{(0)} \cos \omega t$$
$$+ t[A_i^{(1)} \sin \omega t + B_i^{(1)} \cos \omega t].$$

The amplitudes of the last terms in the right members increase with t without limit.   These are pure resonance terms as distinguished from the quasi-resonance terms of the preceding article.

160. Case in Which $D(\lambda) = 0$ Has a Double Root $\lambda = \lambda_1$. When the equation $D(\lambda) = 0$ has a double root, the homogeneous parts of the differential equations present two cases which were treated in Art. 144.   In Case I, the two solutions associated with the root λ_1 are both pure exponentials and the solutions have the forms given in equations (39) or equations (40), according as the resonance relationship is satisfied or not. In Case II, the p_{i1} and the p_{i2} of equations (17) have the form

$$(41) \quad \begin{cases} p_{i1} = [D_{ni}'(\lambda_1) + t D_{ni}(\lambda_1)], \\ p_{i2} = D_{ni}(\lambda_1), \end{cases}$$

where the $D_{ni}(\lambda_1)$ are first minors of the determinant $D(\lambda_1)$, and $D_{ni}'(\lambda_1)$ is the derivative of $D_{ni}(\lambda_1)$ with respect to λ_1.

Suppose no two of λ_1, λ_3, $\cdots$, λ_n are equal. Then the p_{i3}, $\cdots$, p_{in} are constants which will be represented by c_{i3}, $\cdots$, c_{in} respectively. With these notations equations (20) become

$$(42) \quad \begin{cases} \dfrac{dy_1}{dt} = \dfrac{e^{-\lambda_1 t}}{\Delta_0} \begin{vmatrix} \theta_1, & D_{n1}, & c_{13}, & \cdots, & c_{1n} \\ \cdot & \cdot & \cdot & & \cdot \\ \cdot & \cdot & \cdot & & \cdot \\ \cdot & \cdot & \cdot & & \cdot \\ \theta_n, & D_{nn}, & c_{n3}, & \cdots, & c_{nn} \end{vmatrix}, \\[4em] \dfrac{dy_2}{dt} = \dfrac{e^{-\lambda_1 t}}{\Delta_0} \begin{vmatrix} D_{n1}' + t D_{n1}, & \theta_1, & c_{13}, & \cdots, & c_{1n} \\ \cdot & & & & \cdot \\ \cdot & & & & \cdot \\ D_{nn}' + t D_{nn}, & \theta_n, & c_{n3}, & \cdots, & c_{nn} \end{vmatrix}, \\[4em] \dfrac{dy_j}{dt} = \dfrac{e^{-\lambda_j t}}{\Delta_0} \begin{vmatrix} D_{n1}', & D_{n1}, & \cdots, & \theta_1, & \cdots, & c_{1n} \\ \cdot & \cdot & & \cdot & & \cdot \\ \cdot & \cdot & & \cdot & & \cdot \\ D_{nn}', & D_{nn}, & \cdots, & \theta_n, & \cdots, & c_{nn} \end{vmatrix} \quad (j = 3, \cdots, n). \end{cases}$$

Therefore the P_{3j}, $\cdots$, P_{nj} of equations (20) are constants; and it follows from the first two of equations (42) that

$$(43) \qquad P_{2j} = P_{2j}^{(1)} - t P_{1j},$$

where the P_{1j} and the $P_{2j}^{(1)}$ are constants.

Suppose $\lambda_j^2 + \omega^2 \neq 0$ for $j = 1, \cdots, n$. Then since

$$(44) \quad \begin{cases} \displaystyle\int e^{\omega\sqrt{-1}\,t}\, e^{-\lambda_1 t}\, dt = \dfrac{-1}{\lambda_1 - \omega\sqrt{-1}}\, e^{\omega\sqrt{-1}\,t}\, e^{-\lambda_1 t}, \\[1.5em] \displaystyle\int t\, e^{\omega\sqrt{-1}\,t}\, e^{-\lambda_1 t}\, dt = \dfrac{-t}{\lambda_1 - \omega\sqrt{-1}}\, e^{\omega\sqrt{-1}\,t}\, e^{-\lambda_1 t} \\[1.5em] \qquad\qquad\qquad\qquad - \dfrac{1}{(\lambda_1 - \omega\sqrt{-1})^2}\, e^{\omega\sqrt{-1}\,t}\, e^{-\lambda_1 t}, \end{cases}$$

it follows from equations (20), (21), and (43) that the $F_i(t)$ are of the form

$$(45) \begin{cases} F_1(t) = -\sum_{j=1}^{n} \frac{P_{1j}c_j}{\lambda_1 - \omega\sqrt{-1}} e^{\omega\sqrt{-1}t} e^{-\lambda_1 t}, \\ F_2(t) = -\sum_{j=1}^{n} \frac{(P_{2j}^{(1)} - tP_{1j})c_j}{\lambda_1 - \omega\sqrt{-1}} e^{\omega\sqrt{-1}t} e^{-\lambda_1 t} \\ \qquad\qquad + \sum_{j=1}^{n} \frac{P_{1j}c_j}{(\lambda_1 - \omega\sqrt{-1})^2} e^{\omega\sqrt{-1}t} e^{-\lambda_1 t}, \\ F_k(t) = -\sum_{j=1}^{n} \frac{P_{kj}c_j}{\lambda_k - \omega\sqrt{-1}} e^{\omega\sqrt{-1}t} e^{-\lambda_k t} \quad (k = 3, \cdots, n). \end{cases}$$

Consequently, it follows from equations (23) and (41) that the terms containing t as a factor cancel, and that the $\Phi_i(t)$ in this case also have the form of equations (39). That is, in spite of the fact that the coefficients of one solution of the homogeneous part of the differential equations carry a term in t to the first degree, the steady-state terms are purely trigonometric.

Suppose $\lambda_j = \omega\sqrt{-1}$; then the $F_i(t)$ associated with λ_j are of the same form as when λ_1 is a simple root of the equation $D(\lambda) = 0$, and the $\Phi_i(t)$ have the same form as equations (40).

Now suppose $\lambda_1 = \omega\sqrt{-1}$. In this case the right members of equations (44) become t and $\frac{1}{2}t^2$ respectively. Therefore it follows from equations (20), (21), and (43) that

$$(46) \begin{cases} F_1(t) = \sum_{j=1}^{n} P_{1j}c_j t, \\ F_2(t) = \sum_{j=1}^{n} P_{2j}^{(1)} c_j t - \frac{1}{2}\sum_{j=1}^{n} P_{1j}c_j t^2, \\ F_k(t) = -\sum_{j=1}^{n} \frac{P_{kj}c_j}{\lambda_k - \omega\sqrt{-1}} e^{\omega\sqrt{-1}t} e^{-\lambda_k t} \quad (k = 3, \cdots, n). \end{cases}$$

Then it follows from equations (23) and (41) that the part of the solution contained in the $\Phi_i(t)$ is of the form

$$(47) \begin{cases} \Phi_i(t) = [A_i^{(0)} \sin \omega t + B_i^{(0)} \cos \omega t] \\ \qquad + t[A_i^{(1)} \sin \omega t + B_i^{(1)} \cos \omega t] \\ \qquad\qquad + t^2[A_i^{(2)} \sin \omega t + B_i^{(2)} \cos \omega t]. \end{cases}$$

That is, if the equation $D(\lambda) = 0$ has a double root $\lambda = \lambda_1$ and the solutions of the homogeneous part of the differential equations belong to Case II, Art. 144, and if $\lambda_1 \neq \omega\sqrt{-1}$, $\lambda_j \neq \omega\sqrt{-1}$ ($j = 3, \cdots, n$), then the $\Phi_i(t)$ are linear functions of $\sin \omega t$ and $\cos \omega t$; if $\lambda_j = \omega\sqrt{-1}$, the $\Phi_i(t)$ contain terms linear in $\sin \omega t$ and $\cos \omega t$ and other similar terms with t in their coefficients; and if $\lambda_1 = \omega\sqrt{-1}$, the $\Phi_i(t)$ contain, in addition, terms of the type $t^2 \sin \omega t$ and $t^2 \cos \omega t$. In this case the resonance is more marked than in the case where the equation $D(\lambda) = 0$ does not have a double root.

If the equation $D(\lambda) = 0$ has roots of higher order of multiplicity, there are corresponding additional cases which can be treated by methods analogous to those that have been used in the case of a double root $\lambda = \lambda_1$.

XVI. QUESTIONS AND PROBLEMS

1. After referring to Art. 155, find whether any general conclusion respecting the roots of the equation $D(\lambda) = 0$ can be inferred if the determinant $D(\lambda)$ is skew symmetric.

2. After referring to Art. 156, discuss the problem of finding the solutions of the differential equations

$$\frac{dx_1}{dt} = a_{11}x_1 + a_{12}x_2, \qquad \frac{dx_2}{dt} = a_{21}x_1 + a_{22}x_2,$$

by assuming that they can be expressed in the form

$$\begin{cases} x_1 = A_1 \sin \lambda t + B_1 \cos \lambda t, \\ x_2 = A_2 \sin \lambda t + B_2 \cos \lambda t. \end{cases}$$

Why is the method of Art. 156 convenient?

3. Formulate general properties of the $\theta_i(t)$ for which the method given in Art. 157 is valid.

4. Prove directly from the properties of the solutions given in equations (73) and (74), of Chapter XV, that the determinant of the $p_{ij}(t)$ of Art. 157 is a constant.

5. Assume that $r^2 - 4\gamma L$ is negative. Substitute c_1 and c_2 from equations (30) into equations (29). Transform the transient terms so as to place in evidence the phase displacement. Compare both the phases and the amplitudes with the steady-state terms given in equations (36). Examine the special case of quasi-resonance.

6. Treat the problems of Arts. 159 and 160 when the $\theta_i(t)$ are polynomials in t of degree k.

7. Treat the problems of Arts. 159 and 160, using the $\theta_i(t)$ in the trigonometrical form.

8. Treat the problem when the characteristic equation $D(\lambda) = 0$ has a triple root $\lambda = \lambda_1$ and a solution whose coefficients are polynomials in t of the second degree, and when the $\theta_i(t)$ are periodic with the period $2\pi/\omega$.

CHAPTER XVII

LINEAR DIFFERENTIAL EQUATIONS WITH PERIODIC COEFFICIENTS

161. The Homogeneous System. The homogeneous system on which the problem depends will be written in the form

$$
(1) \quad
\begin{cases}
\dfrac{dx_1}{dt} = \theta_{11}(t)x_1 + \cdots + \theta_{1n}(t)x_n, \\
\;\cdot\quad\cdot\quad\cdot\quad\cdot\quad\cdot\quad\cdot\quad\cdot \\
\dfrac{dx_n}{dt} = \theta_{n1}(t)x_1 + \cdots + \theta_{nn}(t)x_n,
\end{cases}
$$

where the $\theta_{ij}(t)$ are periodic functions of t. It can be assumed without loss of generality that the period of the $\theta_{ij}(t)$ is 2π. In practical problems the $\theta_{ij}(t)$ are usually Fourier series that converge uniformly for all finite values of t. Although somewhat milder restrictions would suffice for present purposes, it will be assumed that the $\theta_{ij}(t)$ have this property.

Since the property that the $\theta_{ij}(t)$ converge uniformly with respect to t for all finite values of t implies their continuity in t, it follows from Chapter XI that the solutions of equations (1) for any finite initial conditions can be obtained for any finite range on t by the method of successive integrations. The general solution has the form

$$
(2) \quad
\begin{cases}
x_1 = a_1\phi_{11}(t) + \cdots + a_n\phi_{1n}(t), \\
\;\cdot\quad\cdot\quad\cdot\quad\cdot\quad\cdot\quad\cdot\quad\cdot \\
x_n = a_1\phi_{n1}(t) + \cdots + a_n\phi_{nn}(t),
\end{cases}
$$

where $a_1, \cdots, a_n$ are arbitrary constants and the $\phi_{ij}(t)$ constitute a fundamental set. The $\phi_{ij}(t)$ are continuous functions of t. In general, the initial conditions will be so chosen that $\phi_{ij}(0) = 0$ if $j \neq i$ and $\phi_{ii}(0) = 1$; that is, $x_i(0) = a_i$.

As was pointed out in Art. 133, the equations for the variations from a periodic solution are of the type of equations (1). A

317

particular case of such a system, consisting of the single equation

$$(3) \qquad \frac{d^2x}{dt^2} + \theta(t)x = 0,$$

was first completely treated by G. W. Hill * in his work on the motion of the moon. In spite of the fact that the differential equation (3) appears to be very simple, most formidable difficulties were encountered in getting its solution. In his method, Hill made use of an infinite system of homogeneous linear equations and he obtained the roots of an infinite determinant, analogous to $D(\lambda)$, involving an arbitrary parameter λ.

Systems of linear differential equations having periodic coefficients may also arise in connection with electrical networks. Suppose, for example, that in such a simple problem as that discussed in Art. 158 the capacity C is varied periodically by a periodic relative displacement of the elements of the condenser in the circuit. Then the coefficient of the last term is periodic, and the differential equation is included in equations (1).

162. A Simple Problem of the First Order. As preliminary to the treatment of the general case and in order to throw light on the nature of the solutions, consider the simple problem

$$(4) \qquad \frac{dx}{dt} = \theta(t)x,$$

where $\theta(t)$ is periodic in t with the period 2π. Its solution is

$$(5) \qquad x = a\, e^{\int_0^t \theta(t)\, dt},$$

where a is the initial value of x. Suppose, for simplicity in writing the equations, that $\theta(t)$ is an even function of t and that its Fourier development is

$$(6) \qquad \theta(t) = c_0 + c_1 \cos t + 2c_2 \cos 2t + \cdots.$$

Then equation (5) becomes

$$(7) \qquad x = ae^{(c_0 t + c_1 \sin t + c_2 \sin 2t \cdots)} = a\, y(t)\, e^{c_0 t},$$

where $y(t)$ is periodic in t with the period 2π. The function $y(t)$ can be developed as a Fourier series in t. The solution (7)

* *Collected Works*, Vol. 1, pp. 243–270.

differs from that of a differential equation having constant coefficients only in that the coefficient $y(t)$ is a periodic function of t instead of a constant.

163. The Fundamental Equation. Let it be assumed provisionally that in the general case a solution of equations (1) exists, having the form of the right member of equation (7). In order to get the coefficient of t in the exponentials explicitly in the equations, make the transformation

$$(8) \qquad x_i = e^{\alpha t} y_i \qquad (i = 1, \cdots, n),$$

where α is an undetermined constant. Equations (1) become as a consequence of this transformation

$$(9) \qquad \begin{cases} \dfrac{dy_1}{dt} + \alpha y_1 = \theta_{11} y_1 + \cdots + \theta_{1n} y_n, \\[4pt] \cdot \quad \cdot \quad \cdot \quad \cdot \quad \cdot \quad \cdot \quad \cdot \quad \cdot \\[4pt] \dfrac{dy_n}{dt} + \alpha y_n = \theta_{n1} y_1 + \cdots + \theta_{nn} y_n. \end{cases}$$

It follows from equations (2) and (8) that any solution of equations (9) can be written in the form

$$(10) \qquad \begin{cases} y_1 = e^{-\alpha t}[\phi_{11} A_1 + \cdots + \phi_{1n} A_n], \\[4pt] \cdot \quad \cdot \quad \cdot \quad \cdot \quad \cdot \quad \cdot \quad \cdot \quad \cdot \\[4pt] y_n = e^{-\alpha t}[\phi_{n1} A_1 + \cdots + \phi_{nn} A_n], \end{cases}$$

where $A_1, \cdots, A_n$ are suitably determined constants.

The question now is whether it is possible to determine the constant α and the constants $A_1, \cdots, A_n$ in such a manner that the y_i shall be periodic with the period 2π. Since the coefficients of the differential equations (9) are periodic with the period 2π, it follows that sufficient conditions for the periodicity of the y_i (with the period 2π) are $y_i(2\pi) = y_i(0)$ $(i = 1, \cdots, n)$. These conditions become as a consequence of equations (10) and the initial conditions $\phi_{ij}(0) = 0$, $\phi_{ii}(0) = 1$

$$(11) \qquad \begin{cases} [\phi_{11}(2\pi) - e^{2\pi\alpha}]A_1 + \phi_{12}(2\pi)A_2 + \cdots + \phi_{1n}(2\pi)A_n = 0, \\[4pt] \cdot \quad \cdot \quad \cdot \quad \cdot \quad \cdot \quad \cdot \quad \cdot \quad \cdot \\[4pt] \phi_{n1}(2\pi)A_1 + \phi_{n2}(2\pi)A_2 + \cdots + [\phi_{nn}(2\pi) - e^{2\pi\alpha}]A_n = 0. \end{cases}$$

In order that these equations shall have a solution for the A_i in which not all the A_i are zero, the determinant of the coefficients of the A_i must be zero; or, on putting $s = e^{2\pi\alpha}$ and omitting the argument 2π in the ϕ_{ij},

$$(12) \qquad \Delta(s) = \begin{vmatrix} \phi_{11} - s, & \cdots, & \phi_{1n} \\ \cdot & & \cdot \\ \cdot & & \cdot \\ \cdot & & \cdot \\ \phi_{n1}, & \cdots, & \phi_{nn} - s \end{vmatrix} = 0.$$

This is an equation of the nth degree in s; the term in its expansion which is independent of s is distinct from zero because the determinant of the ϕ_{ij}, a fundamental set of solutions, is distinct from zero. Therefore none of the n roots of equation (12) is either zero or infinite.

Equation (12) is *the fundamental equation* of the differential equations (1) for the period 2π. Since

$$(13) \qquad s = e^{2\pi\alpha},$$

it follows that corresponding to each value of s there are infinitely many values of α which differ only by imaginary integers. If α_0 is one value of α that satisfies equation (13), then $\alpha_0 \pm j\sqrt{-1}$, where j is any integer, also satisfies the same equation. Since the y_i are periodic, it is obvious from equations (8) that adding $j\sqrt{-1}$ to α_0 does not change the periodic property of the y_i.

164. Solutions When the Roots of the Fundamental Equation Are Simple. If s_j is a simple root of equation (12), there is at least one first minor of the determinant $\Delta(s_j)$ that is distinct from zero. In this case equations (11) uniquely determine the ratios of the A_i, from which it follows that the A_i can be expressed in the form

$$(14) \qquad A_i = \Delta_i^{(p)}(s_j)C_j,$$

where the $\Delta_i^{(p)}$ are first minors of Δ from the rows $1, \cdots, p-1$, $p + 1, \cdots, n$, and at least one of which is not zero. The factor C_j is an arbitrary constant. When α_j and these values of the A_i are substituted into equations (10), the y_i are uniquely determined, except for the constant factor C_j, and are periodic, for the conditions for their periodicity have been satisfied. It follows from the properties of the θ_{ij} that the right members of (10) can be expanded as Fourier series whose coefficients can be determined by the usual integrals. The process defines a solution for each of the n roots of equation (12). These n solutions constitute a fundamental set. The proof of this fact is indirect and similar to that employed in Art. 141.

If the solutions do not constitute a fundamental set, then n constants $B_1, \cdots, B_n$, not all of which are zero, exist such that

$$\begin{cases} x_{11}(0)B_1 + \cdots + x_{1n}(0)B_n = 0, \\ \cdot \quad \cdot \quad \cdot \quad \cdot \quad \cdot \quad \cdot \quad \cdot \quad \cdot \quad \cdot \\ x_{n1}(0)B_1 + \cdots + x_{nn}(0)B_n = 0. \end{cases}$$

These B_i define initial conditions for which the x_i are identically zero in t, whence the identities

$$(15) \qquad x_{i1}(t)B_1 + \cdots + x_{in}(t)B_n \underset{t}{\equiv} 0 \qquad (i = 1, \cdots, n).$$

Consider the kth of these identities and replace t successively by $t + 2\pi$, $t + 4\pi$, $\cdots$. It follows from equations (8) for $\alpha = \alpha_j$ that $x_i(t + 2\pi) = s_j x_i(t)$. Therefore the kth identity gives rise to the identities

$$(16) \qquad \begin{cases} x_{k1}B_1 + \cdots + x_{kn}B_n \underset{t}{\equiv} 0, \\ x_{k1}s_1B_1 + \cdots + x_{kn}s_nB_n \underset{t}{\equiv} 0, \\ x_{k1}s_1{}^2B_1 + \cdots + x_{kn}s_n{}^2B_n \underset{t}{\equiv} 0, \\ \cdot \quad \cdot \quad \cdot \quad \cdot \quad \cdot \quad \cdot \quad \cdot \quad \cdot \quad \cdot \end{cases}$$

Suppose p of the x_{ki} in these equations are not identically zero, and consider p of the equations. It follows, as in Art. 141, that the corresponding B_i must be zero. The discussion is completed precisely as in Art. 141.

165. Solutions When the Fundamental Equation Has a Double Root. There are two possible cases when the equation $\Delta(s) = 0$ has a double root $s = s_1$. In one, all the first minors of the determinant $\Delta(s_1)$ are zero; in the other, not all the first minors of $\Delta(s_1)$ are zero.

Case I. In this case equations (11) can be solved for A_1, $\cdots, A_n$ in terms of two arbitrary constants C_1 and C_2, and the solutions have the form

$$(17) \qquad \begin{cases} A_1 = \eta_{11}(s_1)C_1 + \eta_{12}(s_1)C_2, \\ \cdot \quad \cdot \quad \cdot \quad \cdot \quad \cdot \quad \cdot \quad \cdot \\ A_n = \eta_{n1}(s_1)C_1 + \eta_{n2}(s_1)C_2. \end{cases}$$

At least one of the η_{i1} and one of the η_{i2} are distinct from zero, and the two sets of coefficients are linearly independent.

On substituting the expressions for the A_i from equations (17) into equations (10), two sets of the y_i are obtained that are linearly independent. When these values of the y_i are substituted into equations (8), the two solutions of the differential equations that are associated with the root $s_1 = e^{2\pi\alpha_1}$ of equation (12) are obtained. If the other roots of equation (12) are simple, the corresponding solutions can be determined separately by the steps used in Art. 164. It can be shown by the method outlined in Art. 164 that the n solutions obtained constitute a fundamental set.

Case II. Since there is at least one first minor of the determinant $\Delta(s_1)$ that is distinct from zero, only one solution associated with the root s_1 can be determined by the method heretofore used. Let this solution be represented by $x_i = y_i^{(0)} e^{\alpha_1 t}$. Then let the question be raised whether there exists a second solution of equations (1) associated with the root s_1 of the form

$$(18) \qquad x_i = [y_i^{(0)} t + y_i^{(1)}] e^{\alpha_1 t} \qquad (i = 1, \cdots, n),$$

where the $y_i^{(0)}$ and the $y_i^{(1)}$ are functions of t that are periodic with the period 2π, and where α_1 is a constant.

On transforming equations (1) from the x_i to the $y_i^{(0)}$ and the $y_i^{(1)}$ by equations (18), it is found that

$$(19) \quad \begin{cases} t\left[\dfrac{dy_i^{(0)}}{dt} + \alpha_1 y_i^{(0)}\right] + \left[\dfrac{dy_i^{(1)}}{dt} + \alpha_1 y_i^{(1)} + y_i^{(0)}\right] \\ \qquad = t\left[\theta_{i1} y_1^{(0)} + \cdots + \theta_{in} y_n^{(0)}\right] \\ \qquad\qquad + \left[\theta_{i1} y_1^{(1)} + \cdots + \theta_{in} y_n^{(1)}\right]. \end{cases}$$

Each of these equations, which becomes an identity in t for the solutions, can be written briefly in the form

$$t F_0(t) + F_1(t) \equiv 0,$$

where $F_0(t)$ and $F_1(t)$ are both periodic in t with the period 2π. Since $F_0(t)$ and $F_1(t)$ are periodic, the identity

$$(t + 2\pi) F_0(t) + F_1(t) \equiv 0$$

is also satisfied; and it follows from the two identities that $F_0(t) \equiv 0$, $F_1(t) \equiv 0$.

On applying these results to equations (19), it is found that the $y_i^{(0)}$ and the $y_i^{(1)}$ satisfy the differential equations

$$(20) \quad \begin{cases} \dfrac{dy_i^{(0)}}{dt} + \alpha_1 y_i^{(0)} = \theta_{i1} y_1^{(0)} + \cdots + \theta_{in} y_n^{(0)} \quad (i = 1, \cdots, n), \\[2mm] \dfrac{dy_i^{(1)}}{dt} + \alpha_1 y_i^{(1)} = \theta_{i1} y_1^{(1)} + \cdots + \theta_{in} y_n^{(1)} - y_i^{(0)}. \end{cases}$$

The first of these sets of equations is identical in form with equations (9); the second set is the same except for the additive terms $- y_i^{(0)}$, which are known functions of t after the first set of equations has been solved. That is, the second set is not homogeneous.

It follows from the form of the differential equations (20) that sufficient conditions that the $y_i^{(0)}$ and the $y_i^{(1)}$ shall be periodic functions of t with the period 2π are

$$(21) \quad \begin{cases} y_i^{(0)}(2\pi) = y_i^{(0)}(0) \quad (i = 1, \cdots, n), \\[1mm] y_i^{(1)}(2\pi) = y_i^{(1)}(0). \end{cases}$$

Since $y_i^{(0)} = x_i^{(0)} e^{-\alpha_1 t}$, the first set of (21) lead to equations of the form of (11). It follows from equations (18) that

$$(22) \qquad y_i^{(1)} = - t y_i^{(0)} + x_i e^{-\alpha_1 t},$$

from which the second set of equations (21) can be formed by expressing the x_i in terms of the ϕ_{ij} by equations (2) and making use of the fact that $\phi_{ij}(0) = 0$ $(j \neq i)$ and $\phi_{ii}(0) = 1$. On representing $\phi_{ij}(2\pi)$ simply by ϕ_{ij} and noting the fact that $y_i^{(0)}(0) = x_i^{(0)}(0) = A_i^{(0)}$, the detailed expressions for equations (21) are found to be

$$(23) \quad \begin{cases} (\phi_{11} - e^{2\pi\alpha_1}) A_1^{(0)} + \cdots + \phi_{1n} A_n^{(0)} = 0, \\ \quad \cdot \quad \cdot \quad \cdot \quad \cdot \quad \cdot \quad \cdot \quad \cdot \quad \cdot \\ \phi_{n1} A_1^{(0)} + \cdots + (\phi_{nn} - e^{2\pi\alpha_1}) A_n^{(0)} = 0; \end{cases}$$

$$(24) \quad \begin{cases} (\phi_{11} - e^{2\pi\alpha_1}) A_1^{(1)} + \cdots + \phi_{1n} A_n^{(1)} = 2\pi e^{2\pi\alpha_1} A_1^{(0)}, \\ \quad \cdot \quad \cdot \quad \cdot \quad \cdot \quad \cdot \quad \cdot \quad \cdot \quad \cdot \\ \phi_{n1} A_1^{(1)} + \cdots + (\phi_{nn} - e^{2\pi\alpha_1}) A_n^{(1)} = 2\pi e^{2\pi\alpha_1} A_n^{(0)}. \end{cases}$$

The problem is to solve equations (23) and (24) for the $A_i^{(0)}$ and the $A_i^{(1)}$ respectively. Equations (23) can be solved for the $A_i^{(0)}$ by equations of the form of (14). To lay a foundation for obtaining the solutions of equations (24), consider the determinant (12) with s replaced by $e^{2\pi\alpha}$. Suppose, to fix the notation, that a first minor of this determinant from the first $n - 1$ rows is distinct from zero for $\alpha = \alpha_1$. Let the co-factors of the elements in the nth row be represented by $\Delta_{n1}, \cdots, \Delta_{nn}$ respectively. Then the expansions of the determinant give the following identities in α:

$$(25) \begin{cases} (\phi_{11} - e^{2\pi\alpha})\Delta_{n1}(\alpha) + \cdots + \phi_{1n}\Delta_{nn}(\alpha) \underset{\alpha}{\equiv} 0, \\ \cdot \quad \cdot \quad \cdot \quad \cdot \quad \cdot \quad \cdot \quad \cdot \quad \cdot \quad \cdot \quad \cdot \quad \cdot \quad \cdot \\ \phi_{n-1,1}\Delta_{n1}(\alpha) + \cdots + \phi_{n-1,n}\Delta_{nn}(\alpha) \underset{\alpha}{\equiv} 0, \\ \phi_{n,1}\Delta_{n1}(\alpha) + \cdots + (\phi_{nn} - e^{2\pi\alpha})\Delta_{nn}(\alpha) \underset{\alpha}{\equiv} \Delta(e^{2\pi\alpha}). \end{cases}$$

The ϕ_{ij} in the identities (25) are the values of the $\phi_{ij}(t)$ at $t = 2\pi$, and they are independent of α. The minors $\Delta_{n1}(\alpha)$, $\cdots, \Delta_{nn}(\alpha)$ involve α through its occurrence in the exponential $e^{2\pi\alpha}$. Since $s = s_1$ is a double root of the equation $\Delta(s) = 0$, and since $s_1 = e^{2\pi\alpha_1}$, it follows that $\Delta(e^{2\pi\alpha})$ and the derivative of $\Delta(e^{2\pi\alpha})$ with respect to α are both zero for $\alpha = \alpha_1$. Therefore the identities (25) and their first derivatives with respect to α give, for $\alpha = \alpha_1$, the two sets of equations

$$(26) \begin{cases} (\phi_{11} - e^{2\pi\alpha_1})\Delta_{n1} + \cdots + \phi_{1n}\Delta_{nn} = 0, \\ \cdot \quad \cdot \quad \cdot \quad \cdot \quad \cdot \quad \cdot \quad \cdot \quad \cdot \quad \cdot \\ \phi_{n1}\Delta_{n1} + \cdots + (\phi_{nn} - e^{2\pi\alpha_1})\Delta_{nn} = 0; \end{cases}$$

$$(27) \begin{cases} (\phi_{11} - e^{2\pi\alpha_1})\Delta_{n1}' + \cdots + \phi_{1n}\Delta_{nn}' = 2\pi e^{2\pi\alpha_1}\Delta_{n1}, \\ \cdot \quad \cdot \quad \cdot \quad \cdot \quad \cdot \quad \cdot \quad \cdot \quad \cdot \quad \cdot \\ \phi_{n1}\Delta_{n1}' + \cdots + (\phi_{nn} - e^{2\pi\alpha_1})\Delta_{nn}' = 2\pi e^{2\pi\alpha_1}\Delta_{nn}, \end{cases}$$

where the argument in the Δ_{ni} is α_1 and where the Δ_{ni}' are the derivatives of the $\Delta_{ni}(\alpha)$ with respect to α for $\alpha = \alpha_1$.

Equations (26) and (27) are satisfied because they were derived from identities in α for $\alpha = \alpha_1$; equations (23) and (24) are to be solved for the $A_i^{(0)}$ and the $A_i^{(1)}$, if possible. Since the left members of equations (23) and (24) have the same coefficients as the left members of equations (26) and (27), and since the right members of equations (24) and (27) are similarly related to the left members of equations (23) and (26)` respectively, it follows that solutions of equations (23) and (24) are

$$(28) \begin{cases} A_1^{(0)} = \Delta_{n1}, \quad A_1^{(1)} = \Delta_{n1}'; \\ \cdot \quad \cdot \quad \cdot \quad \cdot \quad \cdot \quad \cdot \quad \cdot \\ A_n^{(0)} = \Delta_{nn}; \quad A_n^{(1)} = \Delta_{nn}'. \end{cases}$$

Consequently it follows from equations (2), (8), and (22) that

$$(29) \quad \begin{cases} y_1^{(0)} = [\phi_{11}(t)A_1^{(0)} + \cdots + \phi_{1n}(t)A_n^{(0)}]e^{-\alpha_1 t}, \\ \phantom{y_1^{(0)} = } \cdot \quad \cdot \quad \cdot \quad \cdot \quad \cdot \quad \cdot \quad \cdot \quad \cdot \quad \cdot \quad \cdot \\ y_n^{(0)} = [\phi_{n1}(t)A_1^{(0)} + \cdots + \phi_{nn}(t)A_n^{(0)}]e^{-\alpha_1 t}; \end{cases}$$

$$(30) \quad \begin{cases} y_1^{(1)} = -ty_1^{(0)} + [\phi_{11}(t)A_1^{(1)} + \cdots + \phi_{1n}(t)A_n^{(1)}]e^{-\alpha_1 t}, \\ \phantom{y_1^{(1)} = } \cdot \quad \cdot \quad \cdot \quad \cdot \quad \cdot \quad \cdot \quad \cdot \quad \cdot \quad \cdot \quad \cdot \\ y_n^{(1)} = -ty_n^{(0)} + [\phi_{n1}(t)A_1^{(1)} + \cdots + \phi_{nn}(t)A_n^{(1)}]e^{-\alpha_1 t}. \end{cases}$$

In the applications it might be desirable to have the $y_i^{(0)}$ and the $y_i^{(1)}$ developed as Fourier series. With the notation

$$(31) \quad \begin{cases} y_i^{(0)} = \tfrac{1}{2}a_0^{(i)} + a_1^{(i)} \cos t + a_2^{(i)} \cos 2t + \cdots \\ \phantom{y_i^{(0)} = } + b_1^{(i)} \sin t + b_2^{(i)} \sin 2t + \cdots, \end{cases}$$

the coefficients $a_j^{(i)}$ and $b_j^{(i)}$ are given by the equations

$$(32) \quad \begin{cases} a_j^{(i)} = \dfrac{1}{2\pi} \displaystyle\int_0^{2\pi} y_i^{(0)} \cos jt \, dt, \\ b_j^{(i)} = \dfrac{1}{2\pi} \displaystyle\int_0^{2\pi} y_i^{(0)} \sin jt \, dt; \end{cases}$$

and there are similar equations for the coefficients of the Fourier expansions of the $y_i^{(1)}$. There are, of course, the solutions associated with the roots $s_3, \cdots, s_n$ of the equation $\Delta(s) = 0$ which can be obtained by the method of Art. 164, after which the coefficients of the Fourier development of the corresponding y_i can be determined by equations of the form of (32).

The fact that the solutions determined by the foregoing processes constitute a fundamental set can be established by the method used in Art. 164, with slight modifications similar to those introduced in Art. 145.

Now compare the steps used in this article with those taken in Art. 144 in discussing the corresponding problem for differential equations with constant coefficients. The characteristic equation in the problem with constant coefficients corresponds to the fundamental equation in the problem with periodic coefficients. The two cases in each problem correspond to identical properties of the respective determinants. The solutions in Case I are found by the same steps.

In Case II there is also a complete correspondence. In the

problem with constant coefficients, the solutions have the form given in equations (29), Art. 144, with the $A_i{}^{(0)}$ and the $A_i{}^{(1)}$ constants; in the problem with periodic coefficients, the solutions have the form given in equations (18), with the $y_i{}^{(0)}$ and the $y_i{}^{(1)}$ periodic. In the former problem, the conditions that the forms shall be a solution give rise to equations (30) and (31); in the latter problem, the conditions that the forms shall be a solution and that the $y_i{}^{(0)}$ and the $y_i{}^{(1)}$ shall be periodic give rise to the corresponding equations (23) and (24). In preparing to solve these respective sets of equations, the start is the identities (32) built out of $D(\lambda)$ in the former problem, and the corresponding identities (25) built out of $\Delta(e^{2\pi\alpha})$ in the latter problem. The former identities lead to equations (33) and (34) of Chapter XV; by exactly the same method the latter identities lead to equations (26) and (27) of this chapter. The principal difference is that the a_{ij} of the determinant $D(\lambda)$ are constants of the differential equations, while the $\phi_{ij}(2\pi)$ of the determinant $\Delta(e^{2\pi\alpha})$ are the elements at $t = 2\pi$ of a fundamental set of solutions that must be computed.

166. The General Case of Multiple Roots of $\Delta(e^{2\pi\alpha}) = 0$. The general case is closely parallel to that for differential equations with constant coefficients, $\Delta(e^{2\pi\alpha})$ in the latter playing the rôle $D(\lambda)$ in the former.

Suppose the equation $\Delta(e^{2\pi\alpha}) = 0$ has the root α to the multiplicity n_1. Suppose, further, that all its $(m-1)$st and mth minors contain $(\alpha - \alpha_1)^{\nu_{m-1}}$ and $(\alpha - \alpha_1)^{\nu_m}$ respectively as a factor at the most. Let $\omega = \nu_{m-1} - \nu_m - 1$. Then assume

$$(33) \quad x_i = \left[\frac{1}{\omega!} y_i{}^{(0)} t^\omega + \frac{1}{(\omega-1)!} y_i{}^{(1)} t^{\omega-1} + \cdots \right.$$
$$\left. + y_i{}^{(\omega-1)} t + y_i{}^{(\omega)} \right] e^{\alpha t}.$$

On substituting these expressions for the x_i into equations (1), it is found that the $y_i{}^{(i)}$ must satisfy the differential equations

$$(34) \quad \sum_{j=0}^{\omega} \frac{t^j}{j!} \left[\frac{dy_i{}^{(\omega-i)}}{dt} + \alpha_1 y_i{}^{(\omega-i)} + y_i{}^{(\omega-j-1)} \right]$$
$$= \sum_{j=0}^{\omega} \frac{t^j}{j!} \left[\theta_{i1} y_1{}^{(\omega-i)} + \cdots + \theta_{in} y_n{}^{(\omega-i)} \right],$$

where $y_i{}^{(\omega-i-1)} \equiv 0$ for $j = \omega$.

Since in the solutions these equations are identities, it follows that if the $y_i^{(\omega-j)}$ are periodic with the same period, they satisfy the equations

$$(35) \quad \begin{cases} \dfrac{dy_i^{(0)}}{dt} + \alpha_1 y_i^{(0)} = \theta_{i1} y_1^{(0)} + \cdots + \theta_{in} y_n^{(0)} \quad (i = 1, \cdots, n), \\[2ex] \dfrac{dy_i^{(j)}}{dt} + \alpha_1 y_i^{(j)} = \theta_{i1} y_1^{(j)} + \cdots + \theta_{in} y_n^{(j)} - y_i^{(j-1)} \\[1ex] \hspace{10em} (j = 1, \cdots, \omega). \end{cases}$$

The first set of these equations is homogeneous; the remainder are non-homogeneous. It follows from their form that sufficient conditions that the $y_i^{(j)}$ shall all be periodic with the period 2π are $y_i^{(j)}(2\pi) - y_i^{(j)}(0) = 0$, $i = 1, \cdots, n$, $j = 0, \cdots, \omega$.

Consider a new set of equations obtained by differentiating the coefficient of $e^{\alpha_1 t}$ in the right members of equations (33) with respect to t so far as t appears to the powers ω, $\omega - 1$, $\cdots$; that is, in the differentiation the $y_i^{(j)}$ are regarded as constants. These new equations have the same form as equations (33), and the conditions that they shall constitute a solution of equations (1) are identities of the form of equations (34). These identities are satisfied by virtue of equations (35). Therefore if the functions defined by the ω sets of equations (33) constitute solutions of equations (1), then the equations

$$(36) \quad x_i = \left[\frac{1}{j!} y_i^{(0)} t^j + \cdots + y_i^{(j)} \right] e^{\alpha_1 t} \quad (j = 0, \cdots, \omega)$$

also define solutions. It follows from these equations solved for the $y_i^{(j)}$ sequentially in the order $j = 0, \cdots, \omega$ that the $y_i^{(j)}$ are expressible in terms of solutions x_i by the equations

$$(37) \quad \begin{cases} y_i^{(0)} = x_i^{(0)} e^{-\alpha_1 t}, \\[1.5ex] y_i^{(1)} = -\dfrac{t}{1} y_i^{(0)} + x_i^{(1)} e^{-\alpha_1 t}, \\[1.5ex] y_i^{(2)} = -\dfrac{t^2}{2!} y_i^{(0)} - \dfrac{t}{1} y_i^{(1)} + x_i^{(2)} e^{-\alpha_1 t}, \\[1ex] \cdots \cdots \cdots \cdots \cdots \cdots \cdots \cdots \\[1ex] y_i^{(\omega)} = -\dfrac{t^\omega}{\omega!} y_i^{(0)} - \cdots - \dfrac{t}{1} y_i^{(\omega-1)} + x_i^{(\omega)} e^{-\alpha_1 t}. \end{cases}$$

The superscripts on the x_i distinguish the various solutions.

It follows from equations (10) that $y_i{}^{(j)}(0) = A_i{}^{(j)}$. Therefore it follows from equations (37) and equations (10) that the periodicity conditions $y_i{}^{(j)}(2\pi) - y_i{}^{(j)}(0) = 0$ become

$$(38) \begin{cases} \phi_{i1}A_1{}^{(0)} + \cdots + \phi_{in}A_n{}^{(0)} - e^{2\pi\alpha_1}A_i{}^{(0)} = 0 \quad (i = 1, \cdots, n), \\[2mm] \phi_{i1}A_1{}^{(1)} + \cdots + \phi_{in}A_n{}^{(1)} - e^{2\pi\alpha_1}A_i{}^{(1)} = \dfrac{2\pi}{1} e^{2\pi\alpha_1}A_i{}^{(0)}, \\[2mm] \phi_{i1}A_1{}^{(2)} + \cdots + \phi_{in}A_n{}^{(2)} - e^{2\pi\alpha_1}A_i{}^{(2)} \\[2mm] \qquad = e^{2\pi\alpha_1}\left[\dfrac{2\pi}{1} A_i{}^{(1)} + \dfrac{(2\pi)^2}{2!} A_i{}^{(0)} \right], \\[2mm] \cdots\cdots\cdots\cdots\cdots\cdots\cdots\cdots\cdots\cdots\cdots \\[2mm] \phi_{i1}A_1{}^{(\omega)} + \cdots + \phi_{in}A_n{}^{(\omega)} - e^{2\pi\alpha_1}A_i{}^{(\omega)} \\[2mm] \qquad = e^{2\pi\alpha_1}\left[\dfrac{2\pi}{1} A_i{}^{(\omega-1)} + \cdots + \dfrac{(2\pi)^\omega}{\omega!} A_i{}^{(0)} \right]. \end{cases}$$

The problem is to show that these equations can be satisfied by a suitable determination of the $A_i{}^{(j)}$, not all of which are zero, for every value of j from zero to ω.

By hypothesis, there is at least one mth minor of the determinant $\Delta(e^{2\pi\alpha})$ which does not contain $(\alpha - \alpha_1)^{\nu_m+1}$ as a factor. Choose such a minor, which will be of order $n - m$ and made up from the elements common to the rows $i_1, \cdots, i_{n-m}$ and to the columns $j_1, \cdots, j_{n-m}$. As was noted in Art. 149, such an mth minor is imbedded in an $(m - 1)$st minor depending on an additional row i and an additional column j. Then, keeping j fixed, expand the $(m - 1)$st minors corresponding to all values of i from 1 to n in terms of the mth minors from the rows $i_1, \cdots, i_{n-m}$. Let the mth minors be represented by δ_{im}, and the $(m - 1)$st minors by $\delta_{i, m-1}$. The expansions are

$$(39) \begin{cases} \phi_{i1}\delta_{1m} + \cdots + \phi_{in}\delta_{nm} - e^{2\pi\alpha}\delta_{im} \underset{\alpha}{\equiv} 0 \quad (i = i_1, \cdots, i_{n-m}), \\[2mm] \phi_{i1}\delta_{1m} + \cdots + \phi_{in}\delta_{nm} - e^{2\pi\alpha}\delta_{im} \underset{\alpha}{\equiv} \delta_{i, m-1} \\[2mm] \qquad\qquad\qquad\qquad\qquad\qquad\qquad (i \neq i_1, \cdots, i_{n-m}). \end{cases}$$

It follows from the hypotheses respecting the mth minors that all derivatives of the δ_{im} with respect to α up to the $(\nu_m - 1)$st inclusive are zero for $\alpha = \alpha_1$, but that there is at least one δ_{im} whose ν_mth derivative with respect to α does not vanish for $\alpha = \alpha_1$. Similarly, all $(\nu_{m-1} - 1)$st derivatives of the $\delta_{i, m-1}$ are zero for $\alpha = \alpha_1$. Hence, if the pth derivative of δ_{im} for $\alpha = \alpha_1$

is represented by $\delta_{im}{}^{(p)}$, the successive derivatives with respect to α of the identities (39) for $\alpha = \alpha_1$ give the equations

$$(40)\quad\begin{cases}\displaystyle\sum_{j=1}^{n} \phi_{ij}\delta_{jm}{}^{(\nu_m)} - e^{2\pi\alpha_1}\delta_{im}{}^{(\nu_m)} = e^{2\pi\alpha_1}\left[\frac{2\pi\nu_m}{1}\delta_{im}{}^{(\nu_m-1)}\right.\\[2mm]\qquad\left.+\frac{\nu_m}{1}\frac{(\nu_m-1)}{2}(2\pi)^2\delta_{im}{}^{(\nu_m-2)} + \cdots + (2\pi)^{\nu_m}\delta_{im}\right],\\[4mm]\displaystyle\sum_{j=1}^{n}\phi_{ij}\delta_{jm}{}^{(\nu_m+l)} - e^{2\pi\alpha_1}\delta_{im}{}^{(\nu_m+l)}\\[2mm]\qquad = e^{2\pi\alpha_1}\left[2\pi\frac{(\nu_m+l)}{1}\delta_{im}{}^{(\nu_m+l-1)} + \cdots + (2\pi)^{\nu_m+l}\delta_{im}\right],\end{cases}$$

where the numerical multipliers in the right members are the binomial coefficients, beginning with the second, for the powers ν_m and $\nu_m + l$ respectively. The index l takes integral values from 1 to $\omega = \nu_{m-1} - \nu_m - 1$. Since all derivatives with respect to α of the $\delta_{i,\,m-1}$ of order less than ν_{m-1} are zero, the right members of equations (40) do not involve derivatives of the $\delta_{i,\,m-1}$. Since all derivatives with respect to α of the δ_{im} of order less than ν_m are zero, equations (40) give explicitly

$$(41)\quad\begin{cases}\phi_{i1}\delta_{1m}{}^{(\nu_m)} + \cdots + \phi_{in}\delta_{nm}{}^{(\nu_m)} - e^{2\pi\alpha_1}\delta_{im}{}^{(\nu_m)} = 0\\[2mm]\qquad\qquad\qquad\qquad\qquad\qquad (i = 1, \cdots, n),\\[3mm]\phi_{i1}\delta_{1m}{}^{(\nu_m+1)} + \cdots + \phi_{in}\delta_{nm}{}^{(\nu_m+1)} - e^{2\pi\alpha_1}\delta_{im}{}^{(\nu_m+1)}\\[2mm]\qquad\qquad\qquad = e^{2\pi\alpha_1}\frac{(\nu_m+1)}{1}2\pi\delta_{im}{}^{(\nu_m)},\\[3mm]\phi_{i1}\delta_{im}{}^{(\nu_m+2)} + \cdots + \phi_{in}\delta_{nm}{}^{(\nu_m+2)} - e^{2\pi\alpha_1}\delta_{im}{}^{(\nu_m+2)}\\[2mm]\qquad = e^{2\pi\alpha_1}\left[\frac{(\nu_m+2)}{1}2\pi\delta_{im}{}^{(\nu_m+1)}\right.\\[2mm]\qquad\qquad\left.+\frac{(\nu_m+2)}{1}\frac{(\nu_m+1)}{2}(2\pi)^2\delta_{im}{}^{(\nu_m)}\right],\\[2mm]\cdots\cdots\cdots\cdots\cdots\cdots\cdots\cdots\cdots\cdots\\[1mm]\phi_{i1}\delta_{im}{}^{(\nu_m+\omega)} + \cdots + \phi_{in}\delta_{nm}{}^{(\nu_m+\omega)} - e^{2\pi\alpha_1}\delta_{im}{}^{(\nu_m+\omega)}\\[2mm]\qquad = e^{2\pi\alpha_1}\left[\frac{(\nu_m+\omega)}{1}2\pi\delta_{im}{}^{(\nu_m+\omega-1)}\right.\\[2mm]\qquad\qquad+\frac{(\nu_m+\omega)}{1}\frac{(\nu_m+\omega-1)}{2}(2\pi)^2\delta_{im}{}^{(\nu_m+\omega-2)}\\[2mm]\qquad\qquad\qquad\left.+\cdots + (2\pi)^{\omega}\delta_{im}{}^{(\nu_m)}\right].\end{cases}$$

Since equations (41) have been derived from identities in α for the special value α_1, they are satisfied; equations (38) are to be satisfied, if possible. On comparing equations (38) with equations (41), it is found that solutions of the former are

$$(42) \quad \begin{cases} A_i{}^{(0)} = \delta_{im}{}^{(\nu_m)}, \\[2mm] A_i{}^{(1)} = \dfrac{\delta_{im}{}^{(\nu_m+1)}}{\nu_m + 1}, \\[2mm] \cdots \cdots \cdots \cdots \\[2mm] A_i{}^{(\omega)} = \dfrac{\delta_{im}{}^{(\nu_m+\omega)}}{(\nu_m + 1) \cdots (\nu_m + \omega)}. \end{cases}$$

Since the $\delta_{im}{}^{(\nu_m)}$ are not all zero, it follows sequentially from equations (41) that not all $\delta_{im}{}^{(\nu_m+l)}$ are zero for any value of l from 1 to ω. Consequently, not all the $A_i{}^{(l)}$ $(i = 1, \cdots, n)$ are zero for any value of l from 0 to ω.

When the $A_i{}^{(l)}$ are substituted into equations (10) sequentially for $l = 0, 1, \cdots, \omega$, the corresponding $y_i{}^{(0)}, y_i{}^{(1)}, \cdots, y_i{}^{(\omega)}$ are given. Then the coefficients of their expansions into Fourier series are given by equations of the form of equations (32). The $\omega + 1$ solutions associated with the root α_1 whose coefficients are expressible in terms of derivatives with respect to α_1 of mth minors of the determinant $\Delta(e^{2\pi\alpha_1})$ are determined. It follows, precisely as in Art. 147, that the process under discussion gives n_1 solutions associated with the root α_1, and altogether n solutions. The only remaining problem is to prove that the n solutions constitute a fundamental set.

In Art. 150 the determinant $D(\lambda)$ was reduced to a normal form in which all the elements on one side of its principal diagonal are zero. The determinant at each stage of its transformation and in its final form could be used for the determination of the solutions. It was easily proved that the solutions obtained from the determinant in its final form constitute a fundamental set, for the solutions associated with each root of the characteristic equation are obviously independent, because each contains a non-zero term that corresponds to zero terms for all the other solutions belonging to the root λ_j; and the groups of solutions associated with the various roots are shown to be linearly independent by the general method used in the case of simple roots.

The determinant $\Delta(e^{2\pi\alpha})$ defined by equation (12) can be transformed by precisely the method used in Art. 150 to transform the determinant $D(\lambda)$. At every stage of the transformation it can be used for determining the solutions associated with the root upon which the details of the transformation depend. In the final form certain of the A_i are shown to be zero, precisely as in Art. 152. Then it follows from equations (10) and the initial values of the ϕ_{ij} that the corresponding values of the y_i are zero at $t = 0$. Hence, as in Art. 152, the determinant of the solutions at $t = 0$ is distinct from zero, and consequently it is distinct from zero for all finite values of t. That is, the solutions constitute a fundamental set.

It has been observed that in important respects this problem is analogous to that in which the differential equations have constant coefficients. The problem of determining the character of the solutions in which the $\theta_{ij}(t)$ are not periodic, but are analytic in t and have a singular point at $t = t_0$ around which they are uniform, can be similarly treated. It will, however, not be taken up in this work.

167. The Problem When the $\theta_{ij}(t)$ Are Expansible as Power Series in a Parameter. In the general problem that has been treated in the preceding articles of this chapter, it has been necessary to compute the $\phi_{ij}(t)$ of a fundamental set for $0 \leqq t \leqq 2\pi$ in order to obtain the solutions. In the problem now to be taken up the coefficients of the solution are directly expressible in terms of the constants of the differential equations.

Suppose the $\theta_{ij}(t)$ are expansible as power series in μ of the form

$$(43) \qquad \theta_{ij}(t) = a_{ij} + \sum_{k=1}^{\infty} \theta_{ij}^{(k)}(t)\mu^k,$$

where the a_{ij} are constants and where the right members of the differential equations converge for $0 \leqq t \leqq 2\pi$ provided $|\mu| < \rho$. Moreover, since the θ_{ij} are periodic for $|\mu| < \rho$, it follows that each $\theta_{ij}^{(k)}(t)$ is separately periodic.

When the θ_{ij} have the form given in equations (43), the differential equations (1) take the form

$$(44) \qquad \frac{dx_i}{dt} = \sum_{j=1}^{n} \left[a_{ij} + \sum_{k=1}^{\infty} \theta_{ij}^{(k)} \mu^k \right] x_j \qquad (i = 1, \cdots, n).$$

The solutions of these equations can be expressed by the method of Chapter III as power series of the form

$$(45) \qquad x_i = x_i{}^{(0)} + \sum_{k=1}^{\infty} x_i{}^{(k)}\mu^k \qquad (i = 1, \cdots, n),$$

where, by Art. 29, the right members converge for $0 \leqq t \leqq 2\pi$ provided $|\mu| < \rho$.

The differential equations satisfied by the $x_i{}^{(0)}$ are

$$(46) \qquad \frac{dx_i{}^{(0)}}{dt} = \sum_{j=1}^{n} a_{ij} x_j{}^{(0)} \qquad (i = 1, \cdots, n),$$

which are of the type of those treated in Chapter XV. It will be convenient to represent the parameter λ of the general theory by $\alpha^{(0)}$ in this problem. Then the characteristic equation of the system (46) is

$$(47) \qquad D(\alpha^{(0)}) = \begin{vmatrix} a_{11} - \alpha^{(0)}, & \cdots, & a_{1n} \\ & \cdot & \\ & \cdot & \\ & \cdot & \\ a_{n1} & , \cdots, & a_{nn} - \alpha^{(0)} \end{vmatrix} = 0,$$

which has n roots $\alpha_1{}^{(0)}, \cdots, \alpha_n{}^{(0)}$. Let the solution of equations (44) that corresponds to the root $\alpha_j{}^{(0)}$ of equation (47) be denoted by x_{ij}. Then the general solutions become

$$(48) \qquad x_i = \sum_{j=1}^{n} \left[p_{ij} e^{\alpha_j{}^{(0)} t} + \sum_{k=1}^{\infty} x_{ij}{}^{(k)}\mu^k \right] A_j,$$

where the A_j are constants, and where the p_{ij} are constants or polynomials in t, depending upon the properties of the determinant $D(\alpha^{(0)})$. The initial conditions for the x_i will be so chosen that the determinant of the p_{ij} is 1 for $t = 0$ and that the $x_{ij}{}^{(k)}(0) = 0$, the latter conditions meaning simply that the initial values of the x_i are independent of μ.

When the dependent variables are changed from the x_i to the y_i by the transformation $x_i = e^{\alpha t} y_i$, the differential equations become

$$(49) \qquad \frac{dy_i}{dt} + \alpha y_i = \sum_{j=1}^{n} \left[a_{ij} + \sum_{k=1}^{\infty} \theta_{ij}{}^{(k)}\mu^k \right] y_j \qquad (i = 1, \cdots, n).$$

Therefore sufficient conditions that the y_i shall be periodic with the period 2π are $y_i(2\pi) - y_i(0) = 0$. When the $\alpha_j{}^{(0)}$ are distinct, the $p_{ij} = c_{ij}$ (constants), and the conditions for the periodicity of the y_i become explicitly

$$(50) \quad \sum_{j=1}^{n} e^{2\alpha_j{}^{(0)}\pi} \left[c_{ij}(1 - e^{2(\alpha - \alpha_j{}^{(0)})\pi}) + e^{-2\alpha_j{}^{(0)}\pi} \sum_{k=1}^{\infty} x_{ij}{}^{(k)}(2\pi)\mu^k \right] A_j = 0.$$

A necessary and sufficient condition that these equations may be satisfied by A_j, not all of which are zero, is the determinant equation

$$(51) \quad \Delta = \left\| \left[c_{ij}(1 - e^{2(\alpha - \alpha_j{}^{(0)})\pi}) + e^{-2\alpha_j{}^{(0)}\pi} \sum_{k=1}^{\infty} x_{ij}{}^{(k)}(2\pi)\mu^k \right] \right\| = 0,$$

where only the general element common to the row i and the column j is written.

When equation (47) has multiple roots, the equations corresponding to equations (50) and (51) may take different forms. Suppose, for example, that $\alpha_2{}^{(0)} = \alpha_1{}^{(0)}$ and that the p_{i1} and the p_{i2} of equations (48) have the forms

$$(52) \quad \begin{cases} p_{i1} = c_{i1}, \\ p_{i2} = c_{i2} + t\, c_{i1}; \end{cases}$$

then the equations corresponding to equations (48) are

$$(53) \quad \begin{cases} x_i = \left[c_{i1} e^{\alpha_1{}^{(0)}t} + \sum_{k=1}^{\infty} x_{i1}{}^{(k)}\mu^k \right] A_1 \\ \qquad + \left[(c_{i2} + t\, c_{i1})e^{\alpha_1{}^{(0)}} + \sum_{k=1}^{\infty} x_{i2}{}^{(k)}\mu^k \right] A_2 \\ \qquad + \sum_{j=3}^{n} \left[c_{ij} e^{\alpha_j{}^{(0)}t} + \sum_{k=1}^{\infty} x_{ij}{}^{(k)}\mu^k \right] A_j. \end{cases}$$

The determinant corresponding to the determinant (51) is in this case

$$(54) \quad \begin{cases} \Delta = \left\| \left[c_{i1}(1 - e^{2(\alpha - \alpha_1{}^{(0)})\pi}) + e^{-2\alpha_1{}^{(0)}\pi} \sum_{k=1}^{\infty} x_{i1}{}^{(k)}(2\pi)\mu^k \right], \\ \qquad \left[c_{i2}(1 - e^{2(\alpha - \alpha_1{}^{(0)})\pi}) + 2\pi c_{i1} \right. \\ \qquad\qquad \left. + e^{-2\alpha_1{}^{(0)}\pi} \sum_{k=1}^{\infty} x_{i2}{}^{(k)}(2\pi)\mu^k \right] \right\| = 0, \end{cases}$$

where the elements in the columns $3, \cdots n$, are of the same form as those in equation (51).

If equation (47) has roots of higher order of multiplicity, the conditions that the y_i shall be periodic can be formed in a similar manner from the results of Chapter XV.

168. Solutions When the $\alpha_j^{(0)}$ Are Distinct and No Two of Them Differ by an Imaginary Integer. The part of the determinant Δ, equation (51), which is independent of μ is in this case

$$(55) \qquad \Delta_0 = \left| c_{ij}(1 - e^{2(\alpha - \alpha_j^{(0)})\pi}) \right| = \prod_{j=1}^{n} (1 - e^{2(\alpha - \alpha_j^{(0)})\pi}),$$

since the determinant of the c_{ij} equals unity. In order to get the solutions of equation (51), let

$$(56) \quad \begin{cases} \alpha = \alpha_k^{(0)} + \beta_k, \quad \text{whence} \\ \Delta = \Delta_0 + \mu F_k(\beta_k; \mu) \\ \quad = (1 - e^{2\beta_k \pi}) \prod_{j=1}^{n} (1 - e^{2(\alpha_k^{(0)} - \alpha_j^{(0)} + \beta_k)\pi}) \\ \qquad\qquad\qquad + \mu F_k(\beta_k; \mu) = 0 \qquad (j \neq k), \end{cases}$$

where $F_k(\beta_k; \mu)$ is a power series in β_k and μ, converging if $|\mu| < \rho$ and $|\beta_k|$ is finite.

Since, by hypothesis, no $\alpha_k^{(0)} - \alpha_j^{(0)}$ is an imaginary integer, the expansion of the first term in the right member of this equation contains a term of the first degree in β_k alone and no term independent of both β_k and μ. Therefore it follows from Art. 46 that the equation can be solved uniquely for β_k as a power series in μ of the form

$$(57) \qquad\qquad \beta_k = \mu P_k(\mu),$$

where the series $P_k(\mu)$ converges if $|\mu|$ is sufficiently small. On substituting this expression for β_k into the first of equations (56) and the resulting expression for α into equations (50), n linear homogeneous relations among the A_i are obtained. The determinant of the coefficients of these equations is zero, but for sufficiently small values of $|\mu|$ there is at least one first minor which is not zero, because the roots of equation (56) are simple when $\mu = 0$. Therefore in this case equations (50) uniquely define the ratios of the A_i as power series in μ which converge if $|\mu|$ is sufficiently small. On substituting these expressions for the A_i into equations (48), the x_i are determined as power series in μ. Since $x_i = e^{\alpha t} y_i$ and both α and the x_i have been shown to be expansible as power series in μ, the solution may be written in the form

$$(58) \qquad x_{ik} = e^{\alpha_k t} \sum_{\nu=0}^{\infty} y_{ik}^{(\nu)} \mu^{\nu} C_k,$$

where C_k is an arbitrary constant. There is a similar solution for each value of k from 1 to n.

169. Solutions When No Two $\alpha_i^{(0)}$ Are Equal and When $\alpha_2^{(0)} - \alpha_1^{(0)}$ Is an Imaginary Integer. In the present case, the equation (51) takes the form

$$(59) \quad (1 - e^{2\beta_1 \pi})^2 \prod_{j=3}^{n} (1 - e^{2(\alpha_1^{(0)} - \alpha_j^{(0)} + \beta_1)\pi}) \\ + \beta_1 \mu F_1(\beta_1; \mu) + \mu^2 F_2(\beta_1; \mu) = 0,$$

corresponding to the second of equations (56). When the first term of equation (59) is expanded as a power series in β_1, it is found that the terms independent of μ contain β_1^2 as a factor. If there were a similar congruence among the roots $\alpha_1^{(0)}, \cdots, \alpha_p^{(0)}$, then the terms independent of μ would contain β_1^p as a factor.

The expansion of the left member of equation (59) gives rise to an equation of the form

$$(60) \qquad \beta_1^2 + \gamma_{11} \beta_1 \mu + \gamma_{02} \mu^2 + \cdots = 0,$$

where $\gamma_{11}, \gamma_{02}, \cdots$ are constants. The quadratic terms in β_1 and μ can be factored, giving

$$(\beta_1 - b_1 \mu)(\beta_1 - b_2 \mu) + \cdots = 0.$$

If b_1 and b_2 are distinct, as will in general be the case, the solutions of this equation (Art. 53) have the form

$$(61) \qquad \begin{cases} \beta_{11} = b_1 \mu + \mu^2 P_1(\mu), \\ \beta_{12} = b_2 \mu + \mu^2 P_2(\mu), \end{cases}$$

where $P_1(\mu)$ and $P_2(\mu)$ are power series in μ. Hence in this case α_1 and the y_{i1} are expansible as power series in μ.

If γ_{02} were zero, at least one of the solutions would start with a degree greater than the first in μ. A great variety of possibilities exists, as was shown in Art. 54, but the solutions have the form of equations (61) except when the coefficients satisfy special conditions.

170. Solutions When $\alpha_2^{(0)} = \alpha_1^{(0)}$. There are two cases, in the first of which the solutions for $\mu = 0$ are both pure exponentials, and in the second of which the coefficients of the exponentials are given in equations (52). If no two $\alpha_j^{(0)}$ differ by an imaginary integer, it follows from equation (51) that in the first case the value of Δ for $\mu = 0$ is

$$(62) \qquad \Delta_0 = (1 - e^{2(\alpha - \alpha_1^{(0)})\pi})^2 \prod_{j=3}^{n} (1 - e^{2(\alpha - \alpha_j^{(0)})\pi}),$$

since the determinant of the c_{ij} is unity.

After substituting $\alpha = \alpha_1^{(0)} + \beta_1$ into equation (62) and expanding the result as a power series in β_1, it is found that the term of lowest degree in β_1 alone is $4\pi^2\beta_1^2$. It also follows from equation (51) that the term of lowest degree in μ in the expansion of the determinant Δ as a power series in β_1 and μ is at least of the second degree, and that there is no term in $\beta_1\mu$. Therefore it follows from Art. 52 that in this case the solutions of the equation $\Delta(\beta_1; \mu) = 0$ for β_1 in general have the form

$$(63) \qquad \begin{cases} \beta_{11} = + \mu P_1(\mu), \\ \beta_{12} = - \mu P_2(\mu). \end{cases}$$

Therefore, in the two solutions associated with the root $\alpha_1^{(0)}$, both α and the y_i are expansible as power series in μ.

In the second case, in which the solutions have the form given in equations (53) and in which the determinant Δ has the form given in equation (54), it follows from the form of the first two columns of Δ that β_1^2 is a factor of the terms of the expansion that are independent of μ. On the other hand, it follows from the presence of the terms $2\pi c_{i1}$ in the second column of the determinant that, in general, there is a term of the first degree in μ alone. Consequently, the solutions in this case, which is the general case in which the equation $\Delta_0(e^{2\pi\alpha}) = 0$ has a double root $\alpha = \alpha_1$, are of the form

$$(64) \qquad \begin{cases} \beta_{11} = + \mu^{1/2}P_1(+ \mu^{1/2}), \\ \beta_{12} = - \mu^{1/2}P_1(- \mu^{1/2}), \end{cases}$$

where $P_1(+ \mu^{1/2})$ contains a term independent of μ. As in the preceding cases, there are sub-cases in which the coefficients of the determinant $\Delta(\alpha; \mu)$ satisfy special conditions.

Suppose the solutions of the equation $\Delta(\alpha, \mu) = 0$ are $\alpha_{11} = \alpha_1{}^{(0)} + \beta_{11}$, $\alpha_{12} = \alpha_1{}^{(0)} + \beta_{12}$, where β_{11} and β_{12} are given in equations (64). In general, the two values of α are unequal and, consequently, at least one first minor of the determinant Δ is distinct from zero for $\alpha = \alpha_{11}$ and $\alpha = \alpha_{12}$. Therefore equations (50) define the ratios of the A_i as power series in $\mu^{1/2}$, and, consequently, the corresponding solutions have the form

$$(65) \qquad \begin{cases} x_{i1} = e^{\alpha t}y_{i1}, \\ \alpha = \alpha_1{}^{(0)} + \alpha_1{}^{(1)}\mu^{1/2} + \cdots, \\ y_{i1} = y_{i1}{}^{(0)} + y_{i1}{}^{(1)}\mu^{1/2} + \cdots. \end{cases}$$

There is still another case in which $\alpha_2{}^{(0)} = \alpha_1{}^{(0)}$; namely, that in which $\beta_{11} \equiv \beta_{12}$. In this case the equation $\Delta(\alpha; \mu) = 0$ has a double solution

$$(66) \qquad\qquad \alpha_1 = \alpha_1{}^{(0)} + \mu P(\mu).$$

There is the corresponding solution $x_{i1} = e^{\alpha_1 t}y_{i1}$, where α_1 and the y_{i1} are expansible as power series in μ. It follows from Art. 165 that the second solution associated with α_1 has the form given in equations (18). It follows from equations (20) that the y_{i2} of the second solution satisfy the equations

$$(67) \qquad \frac{dy_{i2}}{dt} + \alpha_1 y_{i2} = \sum_{j=1}^{n} \theta_{ij}(t)y_{i2} - y_{i1},$$

where α_1 is a known function of μ, and where the y_{i1} are known functions of t, given in the first solutions. Hence these equations can be solved by the method of successive integrations.

There are many other possible cases, depending upon combinations of multiple roots of various orders and congruences mod $\sqrt{-1}$ among the roots. The discussions that have been given indicate the method of procedure necessary for the treatment of any particular case.

171. Direct Construction of the Solutions When the $\alpha_i{}^{(0)}$ Are Distinct and No Two Differ by an Imaginary Integer. Although the preceding discussions provide methods, in each case, for the construction of the solutions, they were given primarily for the purpose of establishing the properties of the solutions in the respective cases. As was remarked in Art. 167, when the $\theta_{ij}(t)$ are expansible as power series in a parameter μ with constant values for $\mu = 0$, the solutions can be constructed directly from the differential equations.

It was shown in Art. 168 that in this case the y_{ik} are expansible as power series in μ that converge for $0 \leqq t \leqq 2\pi$ if $|\mu|$ is sufficiently small. Therefore it follows from the periodicity property of the y_{ik} that

$$(68) \qquad \sum_{j=0}^{\infty} y_{ik}{}^{(j)}(t)\mu^j \underset{\mu,\, t}{\equiv} \sum_{j=0}^{\infty} y_{ik}{}^{(j)}(2\pi + t)\mu^j.$$

Therefore each $y_{ik}{}^{(j)}$ is separately periodic with the period 2π.

The initial values of the y_{ik} are determined only up to an arbitrary factor. For simplicity in the later work, this factor will be so determined that $y_{1k}(0) = c_{1k}$, provided c_{1k} is not zero, whatever value μ may have. Therefore the initial values of the $y_{1k}{}^{(j)}$ are

$$(69) \qquad \begin{cases} y_{1k}{}^{(0)}(0) = c_{1k}, \\ y_{1k}{}^{(\nu)}(0) = 0 \qquad (\nu = 1, 2, \cdots). \end{cases}$$

If c_{1k} is zero, a corresponding choice is made for some c_{pk} which is not zero. Such a choice is always possible because $c_{1k}, \cdots, c_{nk}$ are not all zero.

In the case under discussion, the solutions have the form

$$(70) \qquad \begin{cases} \alpha_k = \alpha_k{}^{(0)} + \alpha_k{}^{(1)}\mu + \cdots, \\ y_{ik} = y_{ik}{}^{(0)} + y_{ik}{}^{(1)}\mu + \cdots. \end{cases}$$

On substituting these expressions into equations (49) and equating coefficients of corresponding powers of μ, in accordance with the method of Chapter III, an infinite series of sets of differential equations is obtained which can be solved sequentially.

Terms Independent of μ. The terms of the solution independent of μ are defined by the differential equations

$$(71) \quad \frac{dy_{ik}{}^{(0)}}{dt} + \alpha_k{}^{(0)}y_{ik}{}^{(0)} - [a_{i1}y_{1k}{}^{(0)} + \cdots + a_{in}y_{nk}{}^{(0)}] = 0,$$

the general solution of which is

$$(72) \quad y_{ik}{}^{(0)} = c_{i1} e^{(\alpha_1{}^{(0)} - \alpha_k{}^{(0)})t}\eta_{1k}{}^{(0)} + \cdots + c_{in} e^{(\alpha_n{}^{(0)} - \alpha_k{}^{(0)})t}\eta_{nk}{}^{(0)},$$

where $\eta_{1k}{}^{(0)}, \cdots, \eta_{nk}{}^{(0)}$ are arbitrary constants.

Since the $y_{ik}^{(0)}$ are periodic with the period 2π, and since, by hypothesis, no two of the $\alpha_j^{(0)}$ differ by an imaginary integer, it follows that every $\eta_{ik}^{(0)}$ must be set equal to zero except $\eta_{kk}^{(0)}$. Then it follows from the first of equations (69) that $\eta_{kk}^{(0)} = 1$. Hence the part of the solution that is independent of μ is

$$(73) \qquad \begin{cases} y_{1k}^{(0)} = c_{1k}, \\ \cdot \quad \cdot \quad \cdot \quad \cdot \\ y_{nk}^{(0)} = c_{nk}. \end{cases}$$

Coefficients of μ. The differential equations that determine the coefficients of the terms of the first degree in μ are

$$(74) \quad \frac{dy_{ik}^{(1)}}{dt} + \alpha_k^{(0)} y_{ik}^{(1)} - \sum_{j=1}^{n} a_{ij} y_{jk}^{(1)} = -\alpha_k^{(1)} y_{ik}^{(0)} + \sum_{j=1}^{n} \theta_{ij}^{(1)} y_{jk}^{(0)}.$$

The homogeneous parts of these equations for the $y_{ik}^{(1)}$ have the same form as equations (71). Therefore their general solution is

$$(75) \qquad y_{ik}^{(1)} = \sum_{j=1}^{n} c_{ij} e^{(\alpha_j^{(0)} - \alpha_k^{(0)})t} \eta_{jk}^{(1)},$$

where the $\eta_{jk}^{(1)}$ are undetermined constants and the c_{ij} are the same as in equations (72).

On using the method of Art. 157 to solve the non-homogeneous system (74), it is found that

$$(76) \qquad \sum_{j=1}^{n} c_{ij} e^{(\alpha_j^{(0)} - \alpha_k^{(0)})t} \frac{d\eta_{jk}^{(1)}}{dt} = -\alpha_k^{(1)} c_{ik} + \sum_{j=1}^{n} \theta_{ij}^{(1)} c_{jk}.$$

The determinant of the coefficients of the derivatives in the left members of these equations is

$$(77) \qquad \Delta = e^{\sum_{j=1}^{n} (\alpha_j^{(0)} - \alpha_k^{(0)})t},$$

for the determinant of the c_{ij} is unity. Since Δ is not zero for any finite value of t, the solution of equations (76) is

$$(78) \qquad \frac{d\eta_{jk}^{(1)}}{dt} = e^{-(\alpha_j^{(0)} - \alpha_k^{(0)})t} \Delta_{jk}^{(1)},$$

where the $\Delta_{jk}^{(1)}$ are periodic functions of t with the period 2π.

The solutions of equations (78) for $j \neq k$ have the form

$$(79) \qquad \eta_{jk}^{(1)} = e^{-(\alpha_j^{(0)} - \alpha_k^{(0)})t} P_{jk}^{(1)} + B_{jk}^{(1)} \qquad (j \neq k),$$

where the $P_{jk}^{(1)}$ are periodic functions of t, with the period 2π, and the $B_{jk}^{(1)}$ are undetermined constants. For the case $j = k$, equation (78) becomes

$$(80) \qquad \frac{d\eta_{kk}^{(1)}}{dt} = \Delta_{kk}^{(1)} = -\alpha_k^{(1)} + \delta_{kk}^{(1)},$$

where $\delta_{kk}^{(1)}$ is periodic in t with the period 2π. Let

$$\delta_{kk}^{(1)} = d_k^{(1)} + Q_k^{(1)},$$

where $d_k^{(1)}$ is a known constant and $Q_k^{(1)}$ is a function whose Fourier development contains no constant term. Since the $y_{ik}^{(1)}$ of equations (75) are periodic in t, the $\eta_{ik}^{(1)}$ must contain no term of the first degree in t. These conditions are satisfied in the $\eta_{ik}^{(1)}$ defined in equations (79); in order that $\eta_{kk}^{(1)}$, defined by equation (80), shall not have a term in t, the undetermined constant $\alpha_k^{(1)}$ must have the value

$$(81) \qquad \alpha_k^{(1)} = d_k^{(1)}.$$

Then $\eta_{kk}^{(1)} = P_{kk}^{(1)} + B_{kk}^{(1)}$, where $P_{kk}^{(1)}$ is periodic in t with the period 2π and $B_{kk}^{(1)}$ is an undetermined constant. Hence the general solution of equations (74) is found as a consequence of equations (75), (79), and this value of $\eta_{kk}^{(1)}$ to be

$$(82) \qquad y_{ik}^{(1)} = \sum_{j=1}^{n} c_{ij} e^{(\alpha_j^{(0)} - \alpha_k^{(0)})t} B_{jk}^{(1)} + \sum_{j=1}^{n} c_{ij} P_{jk}^{(1)}(t).$$

In order that the $y_{ik}^{(1)}$ shall be periodic, all the $B_{jk}^{(1)}$ except $B_{kk}^{(1)}$ must be zero. Since by the second of equations (69) the value of $y_{1k}^{(\nu)}(0)$ is zero, it follows from equation (82), for $i = 1$, that

$$B_{kk}^{(1)} = -\frac{1}{c_{1k}} \sum_{j=1}^{n} c_{1j} P_{jk}^{(1)}(0).$$

Therefore the solution satisfying all the conditions is

$$(83) \qquad y_{ik}^{(1)} = \sum_{j=1}^{n} \left[c_{ij} P_{jk}^{(1)}(t) - \frac{c_{ik}}{c_{1k}} c_{1j} P_{jk}^{(1)}(0) \right].$$

The General Terms. It remains to be shown that the coefficients of higher powers of μ in the solutions can be determined similarly. Suppose $\alpha_k^{(1)}, \cdots, \alpha_k^{(m-1)}$ and the $y_{ik}^{(1)}, \cdots, y_{ik}^{(m-1)}$

have been uniquely determined so that the $y_{ik}^{(p)}$ are periodic in t with the period 2π, and also so that $y_{1k}^{(p)}(0) = 0$ for $p = 1, \cdots, m - 1$.

The differential equations which define the $y_{ik}^{(m)}$ are

$$(84) \quad \begin{cases} \dfrac{dy_{ik}^{(m)}}{dt} + \alpha_k^{(0)} y_{ik}^{(m)} - \sum_{j=1}^{n} a_{ij} y_{jk}^{(m)} = -\alpha_k^{(m)} y_{ik}^{(0)} + \sum_{j=1}^{n} \theta_{ij}^{(m)} y_{jk}^{(0)} \\ \qquad\qquad + \sum_{p=1}^{m-1} \left[-\alpha_k^{(p)} y_{ik}^{(m-p)} + \sum_{j=1}^{n} \theta_{ij}^{(p)} y_{jk}^{(m-p)} \right]. \end{cases}$$

These equations are of the same form as equations (74), except for the additive periodic terms on the right. Consequently, there are equations corresponding to equations (76) which differ from the latter only in having the superscript m instead of 1 in the left members and other functions of t in the right members. The remaining equations down to (83) inclusive differ only in the superscript and in the $\Delta_{jk}^{(m)}$ and the $P_{jk}^{(m)}$. Hence the process can be continued as far as may be desired.

172. Direct Construction of the Solutions When No Two of the $\alpha_i^{(0)}$ Are Equal and When $\alpha_2^{(0)} - \alpha_1^{(0)}$ Is an Imaginary Integer. The solutions associated with the roots $\alpha_3^{(0)}, \cdots, \alpha_n^{(0)}$ can be determined by the method of Art. 171. It was shown in Art. 169 that, in general, in this case $\alpha_1^{(0)}$ and the y_{i1} are expansible as power series in μ. It will be assumed that the case under consideration has these properties rather than special ones of some exceptional case.

Terms Independent of μ. In all cases in which α and the y_i are power series in μ, the differential equations (71) define the terms that are independent of μ. The general solutions of these differential equations are given by equations (72). In the present case the periodicity properties of the $y_{i1}^{(0)}$ imply $\eta_{31}^{(0)} = \cdots = \eta_{n1}^{(0)} = 0$. The constant $\eta_{11}^{(0)}$ can be eliminated by the condition $y_{11}^{(0)}(0) = c_{11}$. On imposing these conditions and making use of the fact that $\alpha_2^{(0)} - \alpha_1^{(0)}$ is an imaginary integer, the terms of the solution that are independent of μ are found to be

$$(85) \quad y_{i1}^{(0)} = \left(1 - \frac{c_{12}}{c_{11}} \eta_{21}^{(0)} \right) c_{i1} + c_{i2}\, e^{(\alpha_2^{(0)} - \alpha_1^{(0)})t} \eta_{21}^{(0)},$$

where $\eta_{21}^{(0)}$ is a constant as yet undetermined.

Coefficients of μ. The differential equations satisfied by the $y_{i1}^{(1)}$ are the same as equations (74) with the index k replaced by 1. On proceeding with the solution precisely as in Art. 171, the equations corresponding to equations (76) are found to be at this step

$$(86) \quad \sum_{j=1}^{n} c_{ij} e^{(\alpha_j^{(0)} - \alpha_1^{(0)})t} \frac{d\eta_{j1}^{(1)}}{dt} = - \alpha_1^{(1)} y_{i1}^{(0)} + \sum_{j=1}^{n} \theta_{ij}^{(1)} y_{j1}^{(0)}.$$

On substituting the expressions for the $y_{i1}^{(0)}$ from equations (85) into equations (86) and solving the latter for the derivatives of the $\eta_{j1}^{(1)}$, it is found that

$$(87) \quad \begin{cases} \dfrac{d\eta_{11}^{(1)}}{dt} = - \alpha_1^{(1)}\left(1 - \dfrac{c_{12}}{c_{11}} \eta_{21}^{(0)}\right) + \Delta_{11}^{(1)}(t)\eta_{21}^{(0)} + D_{11}^{(1)}(t), \\[2mm] \dfrac{d\eta_{21}^{(1)}}{dt} = - \alpha_1^{(1)}\eta_{21}^{(0)} + \Delta_{21}^{(1)}(t)\eta_{21}^{(0)} + D_{21}^{(1)}(t), \\[2mm] \dfrac{d\eta_{j1}^{(1)}}{dt} = e^{-(\alpha_j^{(0)} - \alpha_1^{(0)})t}\Delta_{j1}^{(1)}(t) \qquad (j = 3, \cdots, n), \end{cases}$$

where the $\Delta_{j1}^{(1)}$ and the $D_{j1}^{(1)}$ are periodic functions of t with the period 2π, depending upon the $\theta_{ij}^{(1)}$ and $e^{(\alpha_2^{(0)} - \alpha_1^{(0)})t}$. In the first two of equations (87), the undetermined constants $\alpha_1^{(1)}$ and $\eta_{21}^{(0)}$ enter only as they are exhibited explicitly.

Equations (87) are to be integrated and the resulting expressions are to be substituted into the equations corresponding to equations (75). In order that the results shall be periodic, the right members of the first two of equations (87) must contain no constant terms, and the additive constants associated with the last $n - 2$ equations must be zero. These conditions are explicitly

$$(88) \quad \begin{cases} - \alpha_1^{(1)}\left(1 - \dfrac{c_{12}}{c_{11}} \eta_{21}^{(0)}\right) + \eta_{21}^{(0)} b_{11}^{(1)} + d_{11}^{(1)} = 0, \\[2mm] - \alpha_1^{(1)}\eta_{21}^{(0)} + \eta_{21}^{(0)} b_{21}^{(1)} + d_{21}^{(1)} = 0, \\[2mm] B_{j1}^{(1)} = 0 \qquad (j = 3, \cdots, n), \end{cases}$$

where $b_{11}^{(1)}$, $b_{21}^{(1)}$, $d_{11}^{(1)}$, and $d_{21}^{(1)}$ are the constant terms in the Fourier developments of the functions $\Delta_{11}^{(1)}$, $\Delta_{21}^{(1)}$, $D_{11}^{(1)}$, and $D_{21}^{(1)}$ respectively.

On eliminating $\eta_{21}{}^{(0)}$ between the first two of equations (88), the equation which $\alpha_1{}^{(1)}$ must satisfy is found to be

$$(89) \quad (\alpha_1{}^{(1)})^2 - \left[d_{11}{}^{(1)} + b_{21}{}^{(1)} + \frac{c_{12}}{c_{11}} d_{21}{}^{(1)} \right] \alpha_1{}^{(1)}$$
$$+ \left[b_{21}{}^{(1)} d_{11}{}^{(1)} - b_{11}{}^{(1)} d_{21}{}^{(1)} \right] = 0.$$

In case the discriminant of this quadratic equation is not zero (which is the general case under discussion), equation (89) determines two distinct values of $\alpha_1{}^{(1)}$.

On taking one of the roots of equation (89) and the corresponding value of $\eta_{21}{}^{(0)}$ from either of the first two of equations (88), and on imposing the initial condition $y_{11}{}^{(1)}(0) = 0$, the final solution corresponding to that given by equations (83) in the preceding case is found to be

$$(90) \quad y_{i1}{}^{(1)} = B_{21}{}^{(1)} \left[-\frac{c_{12}}{c_{11}} c_{i1} + c_{i2} e^{(\alpha_2{}^{(0)} - \alpha_1{}^{(0)})t} \right]$$
$$+ \sum_{j=1}^{n} \left[c_{ij} P_{j1}{}^{(1)}(t) - \frac{c_{1j}}{c_{11}} c_{i1} P_{j1}{}^{(1)}(0) \right],$$

where $B_{21}{}^{(1)}$ is a constant as yet undetermined, and where the $P_{j1}{}^{(1)}(t)$ are known periodic functions of t with the period 2π.

Coefficients of μ^2. The coefficients of μ^2 are defined by the differential equations

$$(91) \quad \frac{dy_{i1}{}^{(2)}}{dt} + \alpha_1{}^{(0)} y_{i1}{}^{(2)} - \sum_{j=1}^{n} a_{ij} y_{j1}{}^{(2)} = -\alpha_1{}^{(2)} y_{i1}{}^{(0)} - \alpha_1{}^{(1)} y_{i1}{}^{(1)}$$
$$+ \sum_{j=1}^{n} (\theta_{ij}{}^{(2)} y_{j1}{}^{(0)} + \theta_{ij}{}^{(1)} y_{j1}{}^{(1)}).$$

On proceeding as in determining the coefficients of μ, the equations corresponding to equations (87) are found to be

$$(92) \quad \begin{cases} \dfrac{d\eta_{11}{}^{(2)}}{dt} = -\alpha_1{}^{(2)} \left(1 - \dfrac{c_{12}}{c_{11}} \eta_{21}{}^{(0)} \right) + \dfrac{c_{12}}{c_{11}} \alpha_1{}^{(1)} B_{21}{}^{(1)} \\ \qquad\qquad\qquad + B_{21}{}^{(1)} \Delta_{11}{}^{(1)}(t) + D_{11}{}^{(2)}(t), \\[2mm] \dfrac{d\eta_{21}{}^{(2)}}{dt} = -\alpha_1{}^{(2)} \eta_{21}{}^{(0)} - \alpha_1{}^{(1)} B_{21}{}^{(1)} \\ \qquad\qquad\qquad + B_{21}{}^{(1)} \Delta_{21}{}^{(1)}(t) + D_{21}{}^{(2)}(t), \\[2mm] \dfrac{d\eta_{j1}{}^{(2)}}{dt} = e^{-(\alpha_j{}^{(0)} - \alpha_1{}^{(0)})t} \Delta_{j1}{}^{(2)}(t) \qquad (j = 3, \cdots, n). \end{cases}$$

The undetermined constants $\alpha_1{}^{(2)}$ and $B_{21}{}^{(1)}$ enter in the first two equations only so far as they are exhibited explicitly, and the functions $\Delta_{11}{}^{(1)}(t)$ and $\Delta_{21}{}^{(1)}(t)$ are the same as those in the right members of equations (87).

In order that equations (92) shall lead to periodic values of the $y_{i1}{}^{(2)}$, the undetermined constants $\alpha_1{}^{(2)}$ and $B_{21}{}^{(1)}$ must satisfy the conditions

$$(93) \quad \begin{cases} -\alpha_1{}^{(2)}\left(1 - \dfrac{c_{12}}{c_{11}}\eta_{21}{}^{(0)}\right) + \dfrac{c_{12}}{c_{11}}\alpha_1{}^{(1)}B_{21}{}^{(1)} \\ \qquad\qquad\qquad\qquad + b_{11}{}^{(1)}B_{21}{}^{(1)} + d_{11}{}^{(2)} = 0, \\ -\alpha_1{}^{(2)}\eta_{21}{}^{(0)} - \alpha_1{}^{(1)}B_{21}{}^{(1)} + b_{21}{}^{(1)}B_{21}{}^{(1)} + d_{21}{}^{(2)} = 0, \\ B_{j1}{}^{(2)} = 0 \qquad (j = 3, \cdots, n). \end{cases}$$

The first two of equations (93) are linear in the undetermined constants $\alpha_1{}^{(2)}$ and $B_{21}{}^{(1)}$, and they define these constants uniquely provided the determinant of their coefficients is not zero. This determinant is

$$\delta = - \begin{vmatrix} 1 - \dfrac{c_{12}}{c_{11}}\eta_{21}{}^{(0)}, & b_{11}{}^{(1)} + \dfrac{c_{12}}{c_{11}}\alpha_1{}^{(1)} \\ \eta_{21}{}^{(0)}, & b_{21}{}^{(1)} - \alpha_1{}^{(1)} \end{vmatrix} = -b_{21}{}^{(1)} + \alpha_1{}^{(1)}$$
$$+ \left[b_{11}{}^{(1)} + \dfrac{c_{12}}{c_{11}}b_{21}{}^{(1)}\right]\eta_{21}{}^{(0)}.$$

On eliminating $\eta_{21}{}^{(0)}$ and $\alpha_1{}^{(1)}$ by means of equations (88) and reducing, it is found that

$$\delta = \pm \sqrt{D},$$

where D is the discriminant of equation (89), which was assumed to be distinct from zero. Hence equations (93) uniquely define $\alpha_1{}^{(2)}$ and $B_{21}{}^{(1)}$. With these values of $\alpha_1{}^{(2)}$ and $B_{21}{}^{(1)}$, equations (92) are integrated and the solution is obtained as in preceding cases. After the conditions $y_{11}{}^{(2)}(0) = 0$ and $B_{j1}{}^{(2)} = 0$ for $j = 3, \cdots, n$ have been imposed, the final solution at this step is found to be

$$(94) \quad y_{i1}{}^{(2)} = B_{21}{}^{(2)}\left[-\dfrac{c_{12}}{c_{11}}c_{i1} + c_{i2}\,e^{(\alpha_2{}^{(0)} - \alpha_1{}^{(0)})t}\right]$$
$$+ \sum_{j=1}^{n}\left[c_{ij}P_{j1}{}^{(2)}(t) - \dfrac{c_{1j}}{c_{11}}c_{i1}P_{j1}{}^{(2)}(0)\right],$$

where $B_{21}^{(2)}$ is a constant that remains undetermined until the next step.

The next and all succeeding steps are the same as the one just completed except for changes in the superscripts. In this way a solution is obtained for each of the roots of equation (89).

173. Direct Construction of the Solutions When $\alpha_2^{(0)} = \alpha_1^{(0)}$. Suppose there are no equalities or congruences among the $\alpha_j^{(0)}$ except $\alpha_2^{(0)} = \alpha_1^{(0)}$. In this case α_1 and the y_{i1} are expansible as power series in $\mu^{1/2}$ (Art. 170), which may be written

$$(95) \quad \begin{cases} \alpha_1 = \alpha_1^{(0)} + \alpha_1^{(1)}\mu^{1/2} + \cdots, \\ y_{i1} = y_{i1}^{(0)} + y_{i1}^{(1)}\mu^{1/2} + \cdots \quad (i = 1, \cdots, n). \end{cases}$$

The second solution associated with the double root is obtained from this one by changing the sign of $\mu^{1/2}$.

Terms independent of μ. The terms in the solution that are independent of μ are defined by equations (71) for $k = 1$. The general solution of these equations in this case is

$$(96) \quad y_{i1}^{(0)} = c_{i1}\eta_{11}^{(0)} + (c_{i2} + tc_{i1})\eta_{21}^{(0)} + \sum_{j=3}^{n} c_{ij} e^{(\alpha_j^{(0)} - \alpha_1^{(0)})t}\eta_{j1}^{(0)}.$$

In order that the $y_{i1}^{(0)}$ shall be periodic in t with the period 2π and $y_{11}^{(0)}(0) = c_{11}$, the conditions $\eta_{21}^{(0)} = \cdots = \eta_{n1}^{(0)} = 0$ must be satisfied. The solution of equations (96) then reduces to

$$(97) \quad y_{i1}^{(0)} = c_{i1} \quad (i = 1, \cdots, n).$$

Coefficients of $\mu^{1/2}$. The differential equations that define the coefficients of $\mu^{1/2}$ are found from equations (49) and (95) to be

$$(98) \quad \frac{dy_{i1}^{(1)}}{dt} + \alpha_1^{(0)}y_{i1}^{(1)} - \sum_{j=1}^{n} a_{ij}y_{j1}^{(1)} = -\alpha_1^{(1)}y_{i1}^{(0)} = -\alpha_1^{(1)}c_{i1}.$$

The general solution of the homogeneous parts of these equations is the same as equations (96), except the superscript on the y_{i1} and the η_{j1} is 1 instead of zero. On imposing the conditions that these forms shall satisfy equations (98), it is found that the $\eta_{i1}^{(1)}$ must satisfy the equations

$$(99) \quad c_{i1}\frac{d\eta_{11}^{(1)}}{dt} + (c_{i2} + tc_{i1})\frac{d\eta_{21}^{(1)}}{dt} + \sum_{j=3}^{n} c_{ij} e^{(\alpha_j^{(0)} - \alpha_1^{(0)})t}\frac{d\eta_{j1}^{(1)}}{dt}$$
$$= -\alpha_1^{(1)}c_{i1}.$$

On solving these equations for the derivatives, it is found that

$$\begin{cases} \dfrac{d\eta_{11}{}^{(1)}}{dt} = -\ \alpha_1{}^{(1)}, \\[2ex] \dfrac{d\eta_{j1}{}^{(1)}}{dt} = 0 \qquad (j = 2, \cdots, n). \end{cases}$$

Therefore it follows that

$$\begin{cases} \eta_{11}{}^{(1)} = -\ \alpha_1{}^{(1)}t + B_{11}{}^{(1)}, \\[1.5ex] \eta_{j1}{}^{(1)} = B_{j1}{}^{(1)} \qquad (j = 2, \cdots, n). \end{cases}$$

On substituting these expressions into the equations corresponding to equations (96), it is found that

$$(100) \qquad y_{i1}{}^{(1)} = (B_{11}{}^{(1)} - \alpha_1{}^{(1)}t)c_{i1} + B_{21}{}^{(1)}(c_{i2} + t\,c_{i1})$$
$$+ \sum_{j=3}^{n} B_{j1}{}^{(1)} c_{ij}\, e^{(\alpha_j{}^{(0)} - \alpha_1{}^{(0)})t}.$$

In order that the right members of equations (100) shall be periodic in t and that $y_{11}{}^{(1)}(0) = 0$, the $B_{j1}{}^{(1)}$ must satisfy the equations

$$\begin{cases} B_{21}{}^{(1)} = \alpha_1{}^{(1)}, \\[1.5ex] B_{11}{}^{(1)}c_{11} + B_{21}{}^{(1)}c_{12} = 0, \\[1.5ex] B_{j1}{}^{(1)} = 0 \qquad (j = 3, \cdots, n). \end{cases}$$

With these values of the constants, the solution at this stage, satisfying all the conditions, is

$$(101) \qquad y_{i1}{}^{(1)} = \left(-\,\frac{c_{12}}{c_{11}}\,c_{i1} + c_{i2} \right) \alpha_1{}^{(1)},$$

where the constant $\alpha_1{}^{(1)}$ is as yet undetermined. Not all the coefficients of $\alpha_1{}^{(1)}$ are zero, for then the determinant of the c_{ij} would be zero instead of unity.

Coefficients of μ. The coefficients of μ satisfy the differential equations

$$(102) \qquad \frac{dy_{i1}{}^{(2)}}{dt} + \alpha_1{}^{(0)}y_{i1}{}^{(2)} - \sum_{j=1}^{n} a_{ij}y_{j1}{}^{(2)}$$
$$= -\ \alpha_1{}^{(2)}y_{i1}{}^{(0)} - \alpha_1{}^{(1)}y_{i1}{}^{(1)} + \sum_{j=1}^{n} \theta_{ij}{}^{(1)}y_{j1}{}^{(1)}.$$

The equations corresponding to equations (99) are in this case

$$c_{i1}\frac{d\eta_{11}{}^{(2)}}{dt} + (c_{i2} + tc_{i1})\frac{d\eta_{21}{}^{(2)}}{dt} + \sum_{j=3}^{n} c_{ij}\, e^{(\alpha_j{}^{(0)} - \alpha_1{}^{(0)})t}\frac{d\eta_{j1}{}^{(2)}}{dt}$$

$$= -\alpha_1{}^{(2)}c_{i1} + \left(\frac{c_{12}}{c_{11}}c_{i1} - c_{i2}\right)(\alpha_1{}^{(1)})^2 + \sum_{j=1}^{n}\theta_{ij}{}^{(1)}y_{j1}{}^{(1)}.$$

The solution of these equations for the derivatives is

$$(103)\quad \begin{cases} \dfrac{d\eta_{11}{}^{(2)}}{dt} = -\alpha_1{}^{(2)} + \left(t + \dfrac{c_{12}}{c_{11}}\right)(\alpha_1{}^{(1)})^2 \\ \qquad\qquad\qquad\qquad\qquad + t\Delta_{11}{}^{(2)}(t) + D_{11}{}^{(2)}(t), \\[2mm] \dfrac{d\eta_{21}{}^{(2)}}{dt} = -(\alpha_1{}^{(1)})^2 - \Delta_{11}{}^{(2)}(t), \\[2mm] \dfrac{d\eta_{j1}{}^{(2)}}{dt} = e^{-(\alpha_j{}^{(0)} - \alpha_1{}^{(0)})t}\Delta_{j1}{}^{(2)}(t) \qquad (j = 3, \cdots, n), \end{cases}$$

where $D_{11}{}^{(2)}$ and the $\Delta_{j1}{}^{(2)}$ are known functions of t.

The first of equations (103) gives rise to integrals of the type

$$a_p \int t\,\frac{\sin}{\cos}\,pt\,dt = \mp\frac{a_p t}{p}\,\frac{\cos}{\sin}\,pt + \frac{a_p}{p^2}\,\frac{\sin}{\cos}\,pt,$$

and the second equation gives rise to the corresponding integrals

$$-a_p \int \frac{\sin}{\cos}\,pt\,dt = \pm\frac{a_p}{p}\,\frac{\cos}{\sin}\,pt.$$

When these results are substituted into the equations corresponding to equations (96), the terms of the type $t \cos pt$ and $t \sin pt$ cancel each other. Hence, at this step the general solution of equations (102) is

$$(104)\quad \begin{cases} y_{i1}{}^{(2)} = B_{11}{}^{(2)}c_{i1} + B_{21}{}^{(2)}(c_{i2} + tc_{i1}) + \sum_{j=3}^{n} B_{j1}{}^{(2)}e^{(\alpha_j{}^{(0)} - \alpha_1{}^{(0)})t} \\ \qquad + \left[\left(-\alpha_1{}^{(2)} + \dfrac{c_{i2}}{c_{11}}(\alpha_1{}^{(1)})^2 + d_{11}{}^{(2)}\right)t \right. \\ \qquad\qquad \left. + \dfrac{1}{2}\left\{(\alpha_1{}^{(1)})^2 + b_{11}{}^{(2)}\right\}t^2 + P_{11}{}^{(2)}(t)\right]c_{i1} \\ \qquad - \left[\left\{(\alpha_1{}^{(1)})^2 + b_{11}{}^{(2)}\right\}t - P_{21}{}^{(2)}(t)\right]c_{i2} + \sum_{j=3}^{n} c_{ij}P_{j1}{}^{(2)}(t), \end{cases}$$

where the $P_{j1}{}^{(2)}$ are known periodic functions of t, and where $b_{11}{}^{(2)}$ and $d_{11}{}^{(2)}$ are the constant terms in the Fourier developments of $\Delta_{11}{}^{(2)}(t)$ and $D_{11}{}^{(2)}(t)$ respectively. In order that equations (104) shall satisfy the condition $y_{11}{}^{(2)}(0) = 0$ and have the periodicity property, the constants $\alpha_1{}^{(1)}$ and the $B_{j1}{}^{(2)}$ must satisfy the equations

$$(105) \quad \begin{cases} \alpha_1{}^{(1)} = \pm \sqrt{-b_{11}{}^{(2)}}, \\[2mm] B_2{}^{(2)} = \alpha_1{}^{(2)} + \dfrac{c_{12}}{c_{11}} b_{11}{}^{(2)} - d_{11}{}^{(2)}, \\[2mm] B_{11}{}^{(2)} c_{11} + B_{21}{}^{(2)} c_{12} + \sum_{j=1}^{n} P_{j1}{}^{(2)}(0) = 0, \\[2mm] B_{j1}{}^{(2)} = 0 \qquad (j = 3, \cdots, n), \end{cases}$$

where $\alpha_1{}^{(2)}$ remains as yet undetermined. The solution becomes

$$(106) \qquad y_{i1}{}^{(2)} = \left(-\frac{c_{12}}{c_{11}} c_{i1} + c_{i2} \right) \alpha_1{}^{(2)} + \Phi_{i1}{}^{(2)}(t),$$

where the $\Phi_{i1}{}^{(2)}$ are known periodic functions of t.

After making a choice of sign in the first of equations (105), if $b_{11}{}^{(2)}$ is not zero, the process becomes unique. The constant $\alpha_1{}^{(2)}$ is determined uniquely by the periodicity conditions for the $y_{i1}{}^{(3)}$. All succeeding steps are similar. The solutions associated with the roots $\alpha_3{}^{(0)}, \cdots, \alpha_n{}^{(0)}$ are determined by the method of Art. 171.

The cases that have been treated illustrate the methods that apply, with suitable variations in the details, to any case that it may be desired to treat. The processes give explicit formulas for the solutions in all cases in which the θ_{ij} are expansible as power series in μ, with the $\theta_{ij}{}^{(0)}$ constants.

Non-homogeneous Equations

174. Case in Which the α_j Are Distinct and the Right Members Are Periodic. Let the differential equations be written in the form

$$(107) \qquad \frac{dx_i}{dt} - \sum_{j=1}^{n} \theta_{ij} x_j = \theta_i \qquad (i = 1, \cdots, n),$$

where the θ_{ij} and the θ_i are periodic functions of t with the period 2π. For all the θ_i identically zero, the general solution of the equations (107) is

$$(108) \qquad x_i = \sum_{j=1}^{n} e^{\alpha_i t} y_{ij}\, \overline{\eta_j} \qquad (i = 1, \cdots, n),$$

where $s_j = e^{2\pi\alpha_j}$ are the roots of the characteristic equation (12), the y_{ij} are periodic functions of t with the period 2π, and the η_j are arbitrary constants.

On applying the method of varying the η_j so that the forms given in equations (108) shall satisfy equations (107), the equations that the η_j must satisfy are found to be

$$(109) \qquad \sum_{j=1}^{n} e^{\alpha_j t} y_{ij} \frac{d\eta_j}{dt} = \theta_i \qquad (i = 1, \cdots, n).$$

Since the determinant of the coefficients of the derivatives is the determinant of a fundamental set of solutions, it is not zero for any finite value of t. Therefore the solution of these linear equations for the derivatives is

$$(110) \qquad \frac{d\eta_j}{dt} = \frac{D_j}{D} e^{-\alpha_j t} \qquad (j = 1, \cdots, n),$$

where D is the determinant of the coefficients in equations (109), and where D_j denotes the determinant D with its jth column replaced by the θ_i. The quotient D_j/D is a periodic function of t in the interval $0 \leqq t \leqq 2\pi$ which can be expanded as a Fourier series of the form

$$(111) \qquad \frac{D_j}{D} = a_0^{(j)} + \sum_{m=1}^{\infty} \left[a_m^{(j)} \cos mt + b_m^{(j)} \sin mt \right].$$

Therefore if $\alpha_j^2 + m^2 \neq 0$ $(j = 1, \cdots, n; m = 1, 2, \cdots)$, the integrals of the right members of equations (110) are

$$\int \frac{D_j}{D} e^{-\alpha_j t} dt = -\frac{a_0^{(j)}}{\alpha_j} e^{-\alpha_j t}$$
$$- \sum_{m=1}^{\infty} \left[\frac{\alpha_j a_m^{(j)} + m b_m^{(j)}}{\alpha_j^2 + m^2} \cos mt - \frac{m a_m^{(j)} - \alpha_j b_m^{(j)}}{\alpha_j^2 + m^2} \sin mt \right] e^{-\alpha_j t}.$$

Hence

$$(112) \qquad \eta_j = P_j(t) e^{-\alpha_j t} + B_j,$$

where the $P_j(t)$ are periodic functions of t with the period 2π and the B_j are arbitrary constants. On substituting these expressions for the η_j into equations (108), the final solution is found to be in this case

$$(113) \qquad x_i = \sum_{j=1}^{n} e^{\alpha_j t} y_{ij} B_j + \sum_{j=1}^{n} y_{ij} P_j(t),$$

the last terms of which are periodic in t with the period 2π.

Now suppose $\alpha_l = k\sqrt{-1}$, where k is an integer. Then there occurs the integral

$$\int [a_k \cos kt + b_k \sin kt] e^{-k\sqrt{-1}t} dt = \tfrac{1}{2}[a_k - b_k\sqrt{-1}]t$$
$$+ \frac{1}{4k}[a_k\sqrt{-1} - b_k][\cos 2kt - \sqrt{-1} \sin 2kt].$$

Therefore the expression corresponding to equation (113) becomes in this case

$$(114) \quad x_i = \sum_{j=1}^{n} e^{\alpha_j t} y_{ij} B_j + \sum_{j=1}^{n} y_{ij} P_j(t) + \tfrac{1}{2}[a_k - b_k\sqrt{-1}] t y_{il} e^{\alpha_l t}.$$

Since α_l is an imaginary integer, the last term of this solution is t times a periodic function of t. This case is the counterpart of that of simple resonance in the problem in which the differential equations have constant coefficients.

175. Case in Which $\alpha_2 = \alpha_1$ and the θ_i Are Periodic. If the homogeneous part of the problem belongs to Case I of Art. 165, the complete solutions have the properties of those developed in Art. 174. If the homogeneous part of the problem belongs to Case II, of Art. 165, the general solution for the homogeneous terms of equations (107) is

$$(115) \quad x_i = e^{\alpha_1 t} y_{i1}\eta_1 + e^{\alpha_1 t}(y_{i2} + ty_{i1})\eta_2 + \sum_{j=3}^{n} e^{\alpha_j t} y_{ij}\eta_j.$$

In this case the equations corresponding to equations (109) are

$$(116) \quad e^{\alpha_1 t} y_{i1} \frac{d\eta_1}{dt} + e^{\alpha_1 t}(y_{i2} + ty_{i1}) \frac{d\eta_2}{dt} + \sum_{j=3}^{n} e^{\alpha_j t} y_{ij} \frac{d\eta_j}{dt} = \theta_i.$$

The solution of these equations for the derivatives of the η_i with respect to t is found to be

$$(117) \quad \begin{cases} \dfrac{d\eta_1}{dt} = e^{-\alpha_1 t} P_1(t) - e^{-\alpha_1 t} t P_2(t), \\[2mm] \dfrac{d\eta_2}{dt} = e^{-\alpha_1 t} P_2(t), \\[2mm] \dfrac{d\eta_j}{dt} = e^{-\alpha_j t} P_j(t) \qquad (j = 3, \cdots, n), \end{cases}$$

where the $P_i(t)$ are periodic functions of t with the period 2π.

Suppose that $\alpha_j{}^2 + m^2 \neq 0$ for $j = 1, \cdots, n$; $m = 1, 2, \cdots$. Then the integrals of equations (117) are

$$(118) \quad \begin{cases} \eta_1 = e^{-\alpha_1 t} Q_1(t) + e^{-\alpha_1 t} t\, Q_2(t) + B_1, \\ \eta_2 = e^{-\alpha_1 t} Q_2(t) + B_2, \\ \eta_j = e^{-\alpha_j t} Q_j(t) + B_j \qquad (j = 3, \cdots, n) \end{cases}$$

where the $Q_j(t)$ are periodic functions of t with the period 2π.

On substituting the expressions for the η_i from equations (118) into equations (115), the solution of equations (107) is found to be in this case

$$(119) \quad x_i = e^{\alpha_1 t} y_{i1} B_1 + e^{\alpha_1 t}(y_{i2} + t y_{i1}) B_2 \\ + \sum_{j=3}^{n} e^{\alpha_j t} y_{ij} B_j + \sum_{j=1}^{n} y_{ij} Q_j(t),$$

where the B_j are arbitrary constants. It is an interesting fact that in the part of the solution not involving the B_j (the steady-state terms) the terms containing t as a factor cancel one another.

If one α_j $(j = 3, \cdots, n)$ is an imaginary integer, the problem is simply a combination of that treated in Art. 174 and that treated so far in this article.

The case in which $\alpha_2 = \alpha_1 = m\sqrt{-1}$ does not differ essentially from that in which $\alpha_2 = \alpha_1 = 0$. When $\alpha_2 = \alpha_1 = 0$, the equations corresponding to equations (117) are

$$(120) \quad \begin{cases} \dfrac{d\eta_1}{dt} = P_1(t) - t P_2(t), \\[2mm] \dfrac{d\eta_2}{dt} = P_2(t), \\[2mm] \dfrac{d\eta_j}{dt} = e^{-\alpha_j t} P_j(t) \qquad (j = 3, \cdots, n). \end{cases}$$

Since the $P_j(t)$ are periodic in t with the period 2π, they can be written in the form of the right members of equations (111). Therefore the integrals of equations (120) are

$$(121) \quad \begin{cases} \eta_1 = Q_1(t) + a_0{}^{(1)} t - \tfrac{1}{2} a_0{}^{(2)} t^2 - t\, Q_2(t), \\ \eta_2 = Q_2(t) + a_0{}^{(2)} t, \\ \eta_j = e^{-\alpha_j t} Q_j(t) \qquad (j = 3, \cdots, n), \end{cases}$$

where $Q_1(t), \cdots, Q_n(t)$ are periodic functions of t.

On substituting the expressions for the η_i from equations (121) into equations (115), the solution of equations (107) is found to be in this case

$$(122) \quad \begin{cases} x_i = y_{i1}B_1 + (y_{i2} + ty_{i1})B_2 + \sum_{j=3}^{n} e^{\alpha_j t}y_{ij}B_j \\ \qquad + [a_0^{(1)}t + \tfrac{1}{2}a_0^{(2)}t^2]y_{i1} + a_0^{(2)}ty_{i2} + \sum_{j=3}^{n} y_{ij}Q_j(t). \end{cases}$$

In the right member of these equations there are terms containing t^2 in their coefficients.

The problems that have been treated include those that are most important for practical purposes, and they illustrate how any problem in this domain can be solved.

XVII. QUESTIONS AND PROBLEMS

1. Solve the differential equation $\dfrac{dx}{dt} - \theta_1(t)x = \theta(t)$, where $\theta_1(t)$ is periodic with the period 2π, and (a), $\theta(t)$ is constant; (b), $\theta(t)$ is periodic with the period 2π; (c), $\theta(t)$ is periodic with the period P, which is incommensurable with 2π.

2. Analyze the possible cases when equation (12) has a triple root and determine the general properties of the solution in each case.

3. Prove in detail that the solutions defined in Case II, Art. 165, constitute a fundamental set.

4. Find the properties of the solution of the equation

$$\frac{d^2x}{dt^2} + \theta(t)x = 0,$$

without reducing the equation to an equivalent set of two equations. Construct the solution to terms of the third degree inclusive in μ when

$$\theta = a^2 + \tfrac{1}{2}\cos t\,\mu + \tfrac{1}{4}(1 + \cos 2t)\mu^2 + \tfrac{1}{8}(\cos t + \cos 3t)\mu^3 + \cdots.$$

5. Verify equations (38) and (41).

6. Discuss the problem in which the $\theta_{ij}(t)$ are expansible as power series in a parameter μ and in which the terms independent of μ are all zero.

7. In what other ways can the ϕ_{ij} of equations (2) be determined besides by using the method of successive integrations? Are there any additional ways in which the ϕ_{ij} could be determined for equations (44)?

8. Discuss the problem of Art. 174 when the θ_i are polynomials in t. What differences are there in the solutions if the θ_i are periodic, with a period incommensurable with 2π?

9. Discuss the problem of Art. 175 when the θ_i are polynomials in t.

10. Discuss the problems of Art. 174 and Art. 175 when the θ_i are real exponentials e^{ct}.

HISTORICAL SKETCH

The theory of homogeneous linear differential equations with periodic coefficients had its origin in 1877, when Dr. G. W. Hill, of Washington, published privately a remarkably original and important memoir on the motion of the moon's perigee. He first determined, by a very skillful discussion, a periodic solution of the differential equations for the motion of the moon that approximates the actual motion of the moon in its orbit. He then wrote out the equations for variations from this orbit, which led him to a fourth-order system of linear differential equations with periodic coefficients. Since the original differential equations did not involve the time explicitly, Hill derived one solution of the equations for variation essentially by the method of Art. 134. An energy integral is known for the original differential equations, which enabled him to derive an integral of the equations for variations by the method of Art. 136. The solution and the integral enabled him to reduce his fourth-order system to a single linear differential equation of the second order.

Hill's treatment of this differential equation led to the introduction of infinite determinants into mathematics. On translating his methods into the notations of this chapter, he first expressed the function y, where $x = e^{\alpha t}y$ is the solution, as an infinite Laurent series in z, where $z = e^{\sqrt{-1}\,t}$, with undetermined coefficients. He also expressed the periodic coefficients of the equations as Laurent series in z, with known coefficients. Then he substituted the Laurent series for $x = e^{\alpha t}y$ into the differential equation and imposed the conditions that the result should be an identity in z. It is easy to see that, on equating to zero the coefficient of each positive and negative power of z, an equation is obtained which is linear and homogeneous in infinitely many undetermined coefficients of the Laurent series for y, and that certain of the coefficients of these linear equations involve the undetermined parameter α to the second degree.

By analogy with the finite homogeneous systems of equations that arise in the case of equations with constant coefficients, Hill set the determinant of the coefficients equal to zero. Without covering the question of the convergence of the infinite determinant, a question that up to that time had not been raised, he set the infinite determinant equal to zero and determined the properties of its infinitely many solutions for α with a skill that will always command the highest admiration. Simple explicit formulas were given for the practical determination of α, and the infinite homogeneous linear equations were then solved for the ratios of their arguments. Hill's paper was republished in *Acta Mathematica*, Vol. 8, pp. 1–36, and in his *Collected Works*, Vol. 2, p. 243.

Following the publication of Hill's memoir, Poincaré took up the question of the convergence of infinite determinants (*Bulletin de la Société de France*, Vol. 14, p. 77), and the subject was continued by von Koch (*Acta Mathematica*, Vol. 15, pp. 53–63; Vol. 16, pp. 217–296; Vol. 18, pp. 337–426).

At about the time of Hill's memoir, Hermite determined the general properties of the solutions of Lamé's equation, which is similar to Hill's, with the coefficient of x a doubly periodic function of t. (*Comptes Rendus*, 1877.) Starting with the results of Hermite, Picard showed [*Comptes Rendus*, 1877; *Journal für Mathematik*, Vol. 90 (1881)] that, in general, a fundamental set of solutions of a linear differential equation of the nth order with doubly periodic coefficients can be expressed as a sum of products of functions of the type $e^{\alpha_i t} y_{ij}$, where the y_{ij} are doubly periodic. In 1883, Floquet published (*Annales de l'École Normale Supérieure*) a complete discussion of the properties of the solutions of a linear differential equation of the nth order having periodic coefficients. The general properties of the solutions having been determined, later writers devoted considerable attention to the problem of discovering practical methods of obtaining them. Among these investigations are those of Lindemann [*Mathematische Annalen*, Vol. 22 (1883), pp. 117–123] and Lindstedt, Bruns, Callandreau, Stieltjes, and Harzer. (*Astronomische Nachrichten* in 1883, 1884, and 1888.) None of these methods is capable of general application, nor is any of them particularly convenient in treating Hill's equation.

A more general discussion of the problem of linear differential equations with periodic coefficients was given by Poincaré in his *Les Méthodes Nouvelles de la Mécanique Céleste*, Vol. 1, Chap. IV. It was treated with greater generality, including important nonhomogeneous cases, by Moulton and MacMillan in *American Journal of Mathematics*, Vol. 33 (1911); and Hill's problem was given a new and exhaustive treatment by Moulton in *Rendiconti Matematico di Palermo*, Vol. 32 (1911). These investigations are included in *Periodic Orbits*, by Moulton and Collaborators, Chapters I and III. The application of the identities (39), corresponding to those introduced by Nyswander for determining the solutions of differential equations with constant coefficients, has not been heretofore published.

The solutions of linear differential equations in the neighborhood of a pole of order one were treated by Nyswander, *American Journal of Mathematics*, Vol. 51 (1929), in harmony with the method suggested at the close of Art. 166 for the general case.

CHAPTER XVIII

DIFFERENTIAL EQUATIONS IN INFINITELY MANY VARIABLES

176. The Differential Equations. In many mathematical theories, such as those of continuity, maxima and minima, algebraic equations, implicit functions, and differential equations, there is an enormous increase in difficulties as one passes from the case of a single variable to two variables. As a rule, the difficulties do not increase greatly as the number of variables increases from two to any finite number. But when the number of variables becomes infinite, entirely new questions of logic at once appear. Even in defining the differential equations for the present problem, questions of convergence come up which were entirely absent in the discussions of the preceding chapters.

The problem that will be treated in this chapter is analogous to that of the analytic case in differential equations with a finite number of dependent variables. The infinite system of differential equations in the infinitely many dependent variables $x_1, x_2, \cdots$ will be written in the form

$$(1) \quad \frac{dx_i}{dt} = f_i(t; x_1, x_2, \cdots) = a_i \sum_{j=1}^{\infty} f_i^{(j)} \qquad (i = 1, 2, \cdots),$$

where the a_i are constants and the $f_i^{(j)}$ are the terms of the f_i respectively which are homogeneous of degree j in the variables $t, x_1, x_2, \cdots$.

Obviously, in order that the right members of the differential equations shall converge, the $f_i^{(j)}$ must have further properties.

Property 1. The x_j are all zero at $t = 0$.

Property 2. Finite positive constants $c_0, c_1, c_2, \cdots; r_0, r_1, r_2, \cdots;$ A and a exist, such that the series

$$(2) \quad s = c_0 t + c_1 x_1 + c_2 x_2 + \cdots$$

converges if $|t| \leqq r_0$, $|x_i| \leqq r_i$ $(i = 1, 2, \cdots)$.

Property 3. The $f_i{}^{(j)}$ are dominated by $Ar_i s^j$; that is, the absolute values of the coefficients of the $f_i{}^{(j)}$ are less than the corresponding coefficients in the series $Ar_i s^j$, where s^j is expressed as a series in t and the x_i by raising the right member of equation (2) to the jth power.

Property 4. The coefficients a_i of equations (1) satisfy the relations $|a_i| < Ar_i a$, where a is a finite constant.

Since the series (2) converges if $|t| \leqq r_0$, $|x_i| \leqq r_i$, it follows that a finite constant M exists, such that

$$(3) \qquad S = c_0 \frac{r_0}{M} + c_1 \frac{r_1}{M} + c_2 \frac{r_2}{M} + \cdots < 1.$$

Consequently, for all values of t and the x_i for which $M|t| \leqq r_0$ and $M|x_i| \leqq r_i$, it follows that

$$(4) \quad |f_i| \leqq Ar_i[a + S + S^2 + \cdots] = Ar_i \left[a + \frac{S}{1 - S} \right].$$

That is, under the conditions that are assumed to be satisfied, not only do the terms of each degree in the right members of equations (1) converge, but the whole right members converge.

The hypotheses satisfied by the right members of the differential equations have been given their particular form in order to include under one analysis as wide a range of cases as possible. If the c_i are bounded from zero, then the series $r_0 + r_1 + \cdots$ converges and the $|x_i|$ converge to zero as i becomes infinite. In this case the series $f_1 + f_2 + \cdots$ converges if $M|t| \leqq r_0$ and $M|x_i| \leqq r_i$.

On the other hand, if the series $c_0 + c_1 + \cdots$ converges, all the conditions that have been imposed can be satisfied also by values of the $|x_i|$ that are bounded from zero. In this case the series $f_1 + f_2 + \cdots$ need not converge.

The right members of equations (1) are of the analytic type, for they are of the form of the limit, as n becomes infinite, of a power series in n variables whose terms are grouped according to their degree.

177. Formal Solution of the Differential Equations. If an analytic solution of the differential equations (1) satisfying the initial conditions $x_i(0) = 0$ exists, it can be written in the form

$$(5) \qquad x_i = a_i{}^{(1)}t + a_i{}^{(2)}t^2 + \cdots \qquad (i = 1, 2, \cdots).$$

On substituting these expressions for the x_i into equations (1), rearranging their right members as power series in t, and equating coefficients of corresponding powers of t, the equations of condition that the $a_i^{(j)}$ must satisfy in order that the series (5) shall be a solution are found to be

$$(6) \quad \begin{cases} a_i^{(1)} = a_i \quad (i = 1, 2, \cdots), \\ 2a_i^{(2)} = \dfrac{\partial f_i^{(1)}}{\partial t} + \displaystyle\sum_{j=1}^{\infty} \dfrac{\partial f_i^{(1)}}{\partial x_j} a_j^{(1)}, \\ \cdot \quad \cdot \quad \cdot \quad \cdot \quad \cdot \quad \cdot \quad \cdot \quad \cdot \quad \cdot \\ na_i^{(n)} = P_i^{(n)}(a_j^{(1)}, \cdots, a_j^{(n-1)}) \quad (j = 1, 2, \cdots), \end{cases}$$

where the $P_i^{(n)}$ are infinite series in the $a_j^{(1)}, \cdots, a_j^{(n-1)}$ ($j = 1, 2, \cdots$) whose coefficients are linear functions of the coefficients of f_i with positive numerical multipliers.

Equations (6) formally determine the $a_i^{(1)}, a_i^{(2)}, \cdots$ sequentially, where in each case $i = 1, 2, \cdots$. It follows that the formal analytic solution is unique. But a proof must be given that the series (5) converge in order to complete the problem.

178. Proof that the Formal Solution Converges. In order to prove the convergence of the series (5), consider the differential equations

$$(7) \qquad \frac{dX_i}{dt} = Ar_i \left[a + \frac{\sigma}{1 - \sigma} \right],$$

where
$$(8) \qquad \sigma = c_0 t + c_1 X_1 + c_2 X_2 + \cdots.$$

It follows from the Property 2 that the right member of equation (8) converges if $|t| \leqq r_0$, $|X_i| \leqq r_i$. Moreover, the right members of equations (7) dominate the right members of equations (1).

Let the formal analytic solution of equations (7), corresponding to equations (5), be written in the notation

$$(9) \qquad X_i = A_i^{(1)}t + A_i^{(2)}t^2 + \cdots \qquad (i = 1, 2, \cdots).$$

The coefficients of the right members of these equations are determined by equations analogous to equations (6). Since the right members of equations (7) dominate the right members of equations (1), it follows that

$$(10) \qquad A_i^{(j)} \geqq |a_i^{(j)}| \qquad (i, j = 1, 2, \cdots).$$

Therefore if the right members of equations (9) converge for all values of t for which $|t| < \rho$, then the right members of equations (5) converge for at least all values of t for which $|t| < \rho$, and they may converge for values of t that do not satisfy this inequality. The problem, therefore, is to prove the convergence of the right members of equations (9) for $|t| < \rho$.

It follows from equations (7) that

$$(11) \qquad \frac{1}{r_1}\frac{dX_1}{dt} = \frac{1}{r_2}\frac{dX_2}{dt} = \cdots = \frac{dX}{dt},$$

where the variable X is defined by the equations (11). In fact,

$$(12) \qquad X_i = r_i X \qquad (i = 1, 2, \cdots).$$

Therefore each of equations (7) reduces to

$$(13) \qquad \frac{dX}{dt} = A\left[a + \frac{c_0 t + CX}{1 - (c_0 t + CX)}\right],$$

where

$$(14) \qquad C = c_1 r_1 + c_2 r_2 + \cdots,$$

which is finite by Property 2.

It follows from Chapter II that the equation (13) has a unique analytic solution of the form of equations (9), which converges if

$$(15) \qquad |t| < \rho,$$

where ρ is a finite positive constant that can easily be determined. Hence the right members of equations (5) converge at least for values of t for which $|t| < \rho$.

179. Analytic Extension of the Solution. The limitation (15) placed on t, in order to insure the convergence of the solution, is in general so restrictive that t and the corresponding x_i of the solution do not attain the boundary defined by $M|t| \leqq r_0$, $M|x_i| \leqq r_i$ within which the right members of equations (1) have the properties on which the proof of the existence of the solution was based. The question arises whether the solution can be continued beyond its original domain in t, defined by the inequality (15), as it can be continued when the number of dependent variables is finite. Of course, each of the series (5) can be extended by analytic continuation, but it may not be assumed without proof that the extended series satisfy the differential equations.

Suppose t_0 is any value of t for which the inequality (15) is satisfied, and let the corresponding values of the x_i be represented by $x_i^{(0)}$. Since the $x_i^{(0)}$ are in the region for which the right members of equations (1) satisfy the Properties 1, $\cdots$, 4, it follows from the inequality (3) that positive numbers S_0 and S exist, such that

$$(16) \quad c_0|t_0| + c_1|x_1^{(0)}| + c_2|x_2^{(0)}| + \cdots = S_0 < S < 1.$$

Now transform from the variables t and x_i to new variables τ and y_i by the equations

$$(17) \quad \begin{cases} t = t_0 + \tau, \\ x_i = x_i^{(0)} + y_i. \end{cases}$$

Then the differential equations (1) become in the new variables

$$(18) \quad \frac{dy_i}{d\tau} = b_i + g_i^{(1)} + g_i^{(2)} + \cdots \qquad (i = 1, 2, \cdots),$$

where $g_i^{(j)}$ is the totality of terms in the ith equation which are of degree j in the variables $\tau, y_1, y_2, \cdots$.

It follows from equations (1) that the explicit expressions for the b_i and the $g_i^{(j)}$ are

$$(19) \quad \begin{cases} b_i = f_i(t; x_1^{(0)}, x_2^{(0)}, \cdots), \\ g_i^{(1)} = \left(\dfrac{\partial f_i}{\partial t}\right)_0 \tau + \left(\dfrac{\partial f_i}{\partial x_1}\right)_0 y_1 + \left(\dfrac{\partial f_i}{\partial x_2}\right)_0 y_2 + \cdots, \\ g_i^{(j)} = \dfrac{1}{j!}\left[\left(\dfrac{\partial f_i}{\partial t}\right)_0 \tau + \left(\dfrac{\partial f_i}{\partial x_1}\right)_0 y_1 + \cdots\right]^j \qquad (j = 2, 3, \cdots), \end{cases}$$

where the indicated power in the right member of the last equation is symbolic with the meaning

$$(20) \quad \left(\frac{\partial f_i}{\partial t}\right)_0^{j_0} \tau^{j_0} \left(\frac{\partial f_i}{\partial x_1}\right)_0^{j_1} x_1^{j_1} \cdots = \left(\frac{\partial^j f_i}{\partial t^{j_0} \partial x_1^{j_1} \cdots}\right)_0 \tau^{j_0} x_1^{j_1} \cdots$$
$$(j = j_0 + j_1 + \cdots).$$

The subscript zero indicates that, in the partial derivatives, t and the x_i are replaced by t_0 and the $x_i^{(0)}$ respectively.

Since the transformation (17) is linear, the $g_i^{(j)}$ depend only upon the $f_i^{(i)}$, $f_i^{(i+1)}$, $\cdots$. Since the $f_i^{(i)}$, $f_i^{(i+1)}$, $\cdots$ are dominated by the $Ar_i s^i$, $Ar_i s^{i+1}$, $\cdots$, it follows that

$$(21) \qquad \left|\frac{\partial^i f_i}{\partial t^{j_0} \partial x_1^{j_1} \cdots}\right|_0 \leqq Ar_i \left[\frac{\partial^i \left(\dfrac{s^i}{1-s}\right)}{\partial t^{j_0} \partial x_1^{j_1} \cdots}\right]_{\substack{|t_0| \\ |x_i^{(0)}|}}.$$

Therefore it follows from equation (16) that

$$\left[\frac{\partial^i \left(\dfrac{s^i}{1-s}\right)}{\partial t^{j_0} \partial x_1^{j_1} \cdots}\right]_{\substack{|t_0| \\ |x_i^{(0)}|}} \leqq j! c_0^{j_0} c_1^{j_1} \cdots \sum_{p=0}^{j} \frac{S_0^p}{(1-S_0)^{p+1}}$$

$$= j! c_0^{j_0} c_1^{j_1} \cdots \left[\frac{(1-S_0)^i + S_0(1-S_0)^{i-1} + \cdots + S_0^i}{(1-S_0)^{i+1}}\right].$$

Since

$$\sum_{p=0}^{j-1} S_0^p (1-S_0)^{i-p} < (1-S_0)[1 + S_0 + \cdots + S_0^{j-1}] = 1 - S_0^j,$$

it follows from the relation (21) that

$$(22) \qquad \frac{1}{j!}\left|\frac{\partial^i f_i}{\partial t^{j_0} \partial x_1^{j_1} \cdots}\right|_0 \leqq \frac{Ar_i c_0^{j_0} c_1^{j_1} c_2^{j_2} \cdots}{(1-S_0)^{i+1}} \qquad (j = j_0 + j_1 \cdots).$$

Therefore, if γ_0, γ_1, γ_2, $\cdots$ are defined by the equations

$$(23) \qquad \begin{cases} \gamma_0 = \dfrac{c_0}{(1-S_0)^2}, \\[2mm] \gamma_i = \dfrac{c_i}{(1-S_0)^2}, \end{cases}$$

and σ is defined by the equation

$$(24) \qquad \sigma = \gamma_0 \tau + \gamma_1 y_1 + \cdots,$$

it follows from the original hypotheses and equations (2) and (3) that if $|\tau| \leqq r_0$, $|y_i| \leqq r_i$, then the right member of equation (24) converges, and that $|\sigma| < 1$ if

$$M|\tau| \leqq r_0(1-S_0)^2, \qquad M|y_i| \leqq r_i(1-S_0)^2.$$

Consequently, in this region the differential equations (18) have the properties on which the existence of the solution of equations (1) was based. That is, it is possible to continue the solution, step by step, as long as the variables remain in the region for which the original hypotheses hold.

180. An Infinite Universe. The physical universe is consti-
tuted of units of various orders of magnitude, such as electrons,
atoms, molecules, etc., and the units of each order are far from
one another in comparison with their linear dimensions. In an
atom, the electrons are far from one another in comparison with
their diameters; in a molecule, the atoms are relatively far apart;
in a satellite system, the satellites are relatively far apart; in
the solar system, the planets are relatively far apart; and in our
galaxy, the stars are relatively far apart.

There is no reason for making the far-reaching assumption
that galaxies are the largest cosmic units. By analogy with
physical systems of lower orders, one is impelled to make the
hypothesis that, just as myriads of stars make up a galaxy,
so myriads of galaxies make up a super-galaxy. Such a cosmic
unit would be a super-galaxy of the first order. Similarly, one
is led to assume, by analogy, that myriads of super-galaxies of
the first order make up a super-galaxy of the second order;
that myriads of super-galaxies of the second order make up a
super-galaxy of the third order; and so on, in an unending
sequence. Similarly, the electrons may be assumed to be composed of sub-electrons of the first order; these sub-electrons of
the first order may be assumed to be composed of sub-electrons
of the second order; and so on, in an unending sequence downward. The essential properties, for this discussion, of each
cosmic unit are that it be composed of a finite number of cosmic
units of the next lower order which are far from one another in
comparison with their linear dimensions.

In its upward reaches, the hypothesis that has been outlined
brings vividly under considerations magnitudes that are vast in
comparison with those of the objects of every-day experience,
and for this reason some minds shrink from it in a sort of terror.
Yet there are no essential difficulties in the conception that are
not involved equally in the notion of infinite time and space,
and in all the limiting processes of mathematics. Many minds,
having strong physical intuitions, find it difficult to conceive of
electrons, because they are very minute in comparison with
the objects of every-day experience, as being highly complicated
systems of smaller units. A generation ago our predecessors had
similar difficulties in conceiving of atoms as composite structures.

Mathematicians, however, know well that there is no such thing as absolute smallness, and that, in the sense of point-set theory, there are as many points in an electron as in a world, and that, logically speaking, the possibilities for intricate structure in an electron are as great as the possibilities for intricate structure in the earth, for example.

Under the hypotheses that have been made, there are denumerably infinitely many cosmic units of every order—infinitely many stars, galaxies, super-galaxies of the first order, etc. The mass of the hypothetical universe is infinite in the sense that the limit of the mass included in a sphere with a given center is infinite as the radius of the sphere becomes infinite. On the other hand, the limit of the mean density of the matter in the sphere approaches zero as the radius of the sphere becomes infinite. There is, moreover, no definite center of gravity of the hypothetical universe, for the formula for the center of gravity becomes indeterminate, nor are there any borders to the universe, though each cosmic unit of every order has boundaries.

181. Differential Equations of Motion for Stars of an Infinite Universe. For simplicity, suppose spherical stars are the smallest cosmic units in an infinite universe of the type that has been described. Let m_1, m_2, $\cdots$ represent the masses of the stars, and suppose $m_i < M$ $(i = 1, 2, \cdots)$, where M is a finite constant. That is, the set of numbers representing the masses of the stars is bounded. This is a reasonable assumption from the physical point of view, for it is thought likely that high temperatures and enormous rates of radiation put superior limits on stellar masses.

Let n_1, n_2, $\cdots$ represent the numbers of the stars in the galaxies g_1, g_2, $\cdots$ respectively, and suppose $n_i < N$ $(i = 1, 2, \cdots)$, where N is a finite constant. That is, the set of numbers representing the numbers of stars in the infinitely many galaxies is bounded. If this assumption were not satisfied, there would be an infinite sequence of galaxies, each containing more stars than its predecessor in the sequence, and unless the masses of the stars decreased *pari passu* with zero as a limit, the limit of the masses of the individual galaxies in the sequence would be infinite. Therefore, unless the mean density of the galaxies in the sequence approached zero as a limit, the volumes of the galaxies in the sequence would approach infinity as a limit. Under the assumptions that have been made, such limits do not exist.

Corresponding assumptions will be made for the super-galaxies of every order; namely, if $N_1^{(k)}, N_2^{(k)}, \cdots$ represent the numbers of super-galaxies of order $k - 1$ in the super-galaxies $G_1^{(k)}, G_2^{(k)}, \cdots$ of order k, then $N_i^{(k)} < N$ $(i, k = 1, 2, \cdots)$. The right member of this inequality might be represented by N_k with the condition that $N_k < N$ $(k = 1, 2, \cdots)$, but no useful increase in generality would be secured.

If the two stars m_i and m_j are members of the same galaxy, let the distance between their centers be represented by $r_{ij}^{(0)}$. If the stars m_i and m_j are not in the same galaxy but are in the same super-galaxy of order one, let the distance between their centers be represented by $r_{ij}^{(1)}$. In general, if the stars m_i and m_j are not in the same super-galaxy of order $k - 1$ but are in the same super-galaxy of order k, let the distance between their centers be represented by $r_{ij}^{(k)}$.

The next step is to assign inferior limits to the distances separating the cosmic units of the various orders. The essential property to be secured is that the constituents of each cosmic unit shall be small in comparison with their distances from one another. It will be simpler for the subsequent developments to impose sufficient hypotheses upon the $r_{ij}^{(k)}$ to secure the desired results directly. Let it be assumed that, at $t = 0$,

$$(25) \quad \begin{cases} R > r_{ij}^{(0)} > r & (i, j = 1, 2, \cdots; j \neq i), \\ C^k R > r_{ij}^{(k)} > C^k r & (k = 1, 2, \cdots), \end{cases}$$

where R and r are finite positive constants and C is a constant greater than unity that is otherwise as yet unrestricted. It is obvious that, where C is large, the distribution of the stars, the galaxies, and the super-galaxies of the various orders satisfies the general conditions that have been imposed.

Let the origin for a system of rectangular coördinates be chosen arbitrarily; for example, at the center of gravity of our galaxy. Suppose the stars are subject to no forces except their mutual attractions according to the Newtonian law of gravitation. Then, if the coördinates of the star m_i are x_i, y_i, and z_i, the differential equations of motion for the infinite system of stars are

$$(26) \begin{cases} \dfrac{d^2 x_i}{dt^2} = -\gamma \sum_{j=1}^{\infty} m_j \dfrac{(x_i - x_j)}{(r_{ij}{}^{(k)})^3} & (i = 1, 2, \cdots; j \neq i), \\[2mm] \dfrac{d^2 y_i}{dt^2} = -\gamma \sum_{j=1}^{\infty} m_j \dfrac{(y_i - y_j)}{(r_{ij}{}^{(k)})^3}, \\[2mm] \dfrac{d^2 z_i}{dt^2} = -\gamma \sum_{j=1}^{\infty} m_j \dfrac{(z_i - z_j)}{(r_{ij}{}^{(k)})^3}, \end{cases}$$

where γ is the gravitational constant. The terms in the right members of these equations might be grouped with respect to the superscript k. In general, the terms for which $k = 0$ are much more important than the remainder, particularly if the constant C is large.

Let the values of x_i, y_i, and z_i at $t = 0$ be represented by $x_i{}^{(0)}$, $y_i{}^{(0)}$, and $z_i{}^{(0)}$ respectively. Then transform to new variables ξ_i, η_i, and ζ_i by the equations

$$(27) \begin{cases} x_i = x_i{}^{(0)} + \xi_i & (i = 1, 2, \cdots), \\ y_i = y_i{}^{(0)} + \eta_i, \\ z_i = z_i{}^{(0)} + \zeta_i. \end{cases}$$

Since, by the inequalities (25), every $r_{ij}{}^{(k)} > r$ for $x_i = x_i{}^{(0)}$, $y_i = y_i{}^{(0)}$, $z_i = z_i{}^{(0)}$, it follows that each term in the right members of equations (26) can be expanded as a power series in the ξ_i, η_i, and ζ_i, which will converge provided the absolute values of these arguments are sufficiently small. The right members, however, are infinite sums of such power series, and the question is whether these infinite sums converge.

Consider first the series obtained from the terms for which $k = 0$. According to the hypothesis made respecting the number of stars in a galaxy, the number of such series is less than N. The coefficients of these series will be the larger the smaller the $r_{ij}{}^{(0)}$ at $t = 0$. By hypothesis, these distances are all greater than r. Consequently, the sum of the finite number of series that are obtained for $k = 0$ is dominated by the sum of N series for which all $r_{ij}{}^{(0)} = r$ at $t = 0$. Let this dominating series for the first group of (26) be represented by $P_i{}^{(0)}(\xi_{j_1}, \eta_{j_2}, \zeta_{j_3})$, where j_1, j_2, and j_3 take N values. That is, in general j_1, j_2, and j_3 take some values for which there are no corresponding equations (26).

Now consider the series derived from the terms involving the $r_{ij}^{(1)}$. According to the hypotheses that have been made, the number of such series is less than N^2. It has also been assumed that every $r_{ij}^{(1)} > Cr$. Suppose the $P_i^{(0)}(\xi_{i_1}, \eta_{i_2}, \zeta_{i_3})$ converge if $|\xi_{i_1}| \leqq \delta$, $|\eta_{i_2}| \leqq \delta$, $|\zeta_{i_3}| \leqq \delta$. Then the series coming from the terms of the right members of equations (26), which depend upon the $r_{ij}^{(1)}$, will also converge when their variables satisfy the same inequalities. It should be observed that the values of j in these terms are entirely distinct from the values of j occurring in the group of terms depending upon the $r_{ij}^{(0)}$. The sum of these $n_1 N_1^{(1)} + n_2 N_2^{(1)} + \cdots$ series will be dominated by N^2 series in each of which $r_{ij}^{(1)}$ at $t = 0$ is replaced by Cr. Let this dominating series be represented by $P_i^{(1)}$. In general, let the corresponding dominating series for the sum of the series depending upon the $r_{ij}^{(k)}$ be represented by $P_i^{(k)}$. The sum of these dominating series for $\xi_{i_1} = \delta$, $\eta_{i_2} = \delta$, $\zeta_{j_.} = \delta$ satisfies the relation

$$(28) \quad \begin{cases} |P_i| = |P_i^{(0)} + P_i^{(1)} + P_i^{(2)} + \cdots | \\ \qquad \leqq |P_i^{(0)}| \left[1 + \dfrac{N}{C^2} + \dfrac{N^2}{C^4} + \cdots \right], \end{cases}$$

which converges if $C^2 > N$, a condition that will be assumed to be satisfied. It will be noted, of course, that if the corresponding inequality were not satisfied for any finite number of values of k, the conclusions would not be essentially modified. When the right members of the equations (28) converge, the expansions of the right members of equations (26) as power series in the ξ_{i_1}, η_{i_2}, and ζ_{i_3} also converge, provided $|\xi_{i_1}| \leqq \delta$, $|\eta_{i_2}| \leqq \delta$, $|\zeta_{i_3}| \leqq \delta$. The differential equations (26), after the transformation of variables (27) and the expansions into power series, can be written in the form

$$(29) \quad \begin{cases} \dfrac{d^2 \xi_i}{dt^2} = f_i(\xi_{i_1}, \eta_{i_2}, \zeta_{i_3}) \quad (j_1, j_2, j_3 = 1, 2, \cdots; i = 1, 2, \cdots), \\ \dfrac{d^2 \eta_i}{dt^2} = g_i(\xi_{i_1}, \eta_{i_2}, \zeta_{i_3}), \\ \dfrac{d^2 \zeta_i}{dt^2} = h_i(\xi_{i_1}, \eta_{i_2}, \zeta_{i_3}). \end{cases}$$

The differential equations of the problem are, therefore, fully defined, their right members being power series in the infinitely many dependent variables; and the power series converge if the absolute values of the variables are less than an assignable positive number δ.

182. The Ten Integrals. The differential equations of motion for any finite number of bodies have ten general integrals: six expressing the fact that the center of gravity of the system moves in a straight line with uniform speed; three expressing the fact the sums of the projections of the moments of momentum of the system on the three planes of reference are constants; and one expressing the constancy of the total energy of the system. As will be shown, all of these integrals exist formally in the infinite case, but they are divergent.

The Center of Gravity Integrals. If the first of equations (26) is multiplied by m_i and the product is summed with respect to i, the result is formally

$$\sum_{i=1}^{\infty} m_i \frac{d^2 x_i}{dt^2} = - \gamma \sum_{i=1}^{\infty} \sum_{j=1}^{\infty} m_i m_j \frac{(x_i - x_j)}{r_{ij}^3} \qquad (j \neq i),$$

the right member of which may be taken to be zero because corresponding to each term in it there is another that is equal to it numerically but opposite in sign. Then the formal integrals of the equation are

$$(30) \quad \begin{cases} \sum_{i=1}^{\infty} m_i \dfrac{dx_i}{dt} = \alpha_1, \\ \sum_{i=1}^{\infty} m_i x_i = \alpha_1 t + \alpha_2, \end{cases}$$

the left members of which diverge unless the limit of the m_i is zero for i infinite, which is a condition that would be wholly unsatisfactory from a physical point of view. This result, together with the corresponding formal integrals for the other coördinates, means that the center of gravity of the infinite system of stars is not defined. That is, there is nothing in the system as a whole that distinguishes any special point. On the other hand, every galaxy g_i and every super-galaxy $G_i^{(k)}$ of order k has separately a center of gravity; but, as a consequence of the attractions of other groups, the center of gravity of such a group of stars would not move in a straight line with uniform speed with respect to general axes of reference.

The Moment of Momentum Integrals. If the first of equations (26) is multiplied by $- m_i y_i$ and the second by $+ m_i x_i$, and if the products are added and summed with respect to i, the result is formally

$$\sum_{i=1}^{\infty} m_i \left[x_i \frac{d^2 y_i}{dt^2} - y_i \frac{d^2 x_i}{dt^2} \right] = -\gamma \sum_{i=1}^{\infty} \sum_{j=1}^{\infty} m_i m_j \frac{[x_i(y_i - y_j) - y_i(x_i - x_j)]}{r_{ij}^3},$$

the right member of which may be taken to be zero, because corresponding to each term in it there is another that is equal to it numerically, but opposite in sign. Then the formal integral of the equation is

$$(31) \qquad \sum_{i=1}^{\infty} m_i \left[x_i \frac{dy_i}{dt} - y_i \frac{dx_i}{dt} \right] = \alpha_3,$$

the left member of which also diverges unless the m_i or the derivatives have the limit zero as i becomes infinite, neither of which is a satisfactory hypothesis. This result, together with the two corresponding formal integrals, means that the infinite system of stars does not define any fundamental plane, like the "invariable plane" in the problem of n bodies.

The Energy Integral. The right members of equations (26) are the derivatives with respect to x_i, y_i, and z_i respectively of the function

$$U = \frac{1}{2} \sum_{i=1}^{\infty} \sum_{j=1}^{\infty} \frac{m_i m_j}{r_{ij}^{(k)}} \qquad (i \neq j).$$

Therefore it is found that

$$2 \sum_{i=1}^{\infty} m_i \left[\frac{dx_i}{dt} \frac{d^2 x_i}{dt^2} + \frac{dy_i}{dt} \frac{d^2 y_i}{dt^2} + \frac{dz_i}{dt} \frac{d^2 z_i}{dt^2} \right] = 2 \frac{dU}{dt},$$

the formal integral of which is

$$(32) \qquad \sum_{i=1}^{\infty} m_i \left[\left(\frac{dx_i}{dt} \right)^2 + \left(\frac{dy_i}{dt} \right)^2 + \left(\frac{dz_i}{dt} \right)^2 \right] = 2U + \alpha_4.$$

Under the hypotheses that have been made, the expression for U converges if $C > N$, but the left member of equation (32) diverges unless the limit of the m_i or of the velocity of m_i is zero for i infinite, neither of which is a satisfactory hypothesis. That is, the potential energy of the system is finite if $C > N$, but the kinetic energy is infinite.

183. Explicit Development of a Dominating Function. Although the differential equations are defined for the motions of stars in an infinite universe of the type considered, the ten integrals corresponding to those that exist for a finite system all diverge. Consequently, it is evident that it may not be assumed without proof that a solution of the differential equations (29) exists. The first step in the proof that a solution exists is that of constructing dominating differential equations.

Since equations (26) are symmetrical in x_i, y_i, and z_i, it will be sufficient to consider the first of them. The right member of the first of equations (29) is a sum of expansions of functions of the type

$$(33) \qquad m_j \frac{(x_i^{(0)} - x_j^{(0)} + \xi_i - \xi_j)}{(r_{ij}^{(k)})^3},$$

the convergence of which depends upon the expansion of

$$(34) \quad \begin{cases} r_{ij}^{(k)} = r_{ij}^{(0,\,0)} \left[1 - \dfrac{2\phi}{(r_{ij}^{(0,\,0)})^2} + \dfrac{\psi^2}{(r_{ij}^{(0,\,0)})^2} \right]^{1/2}, \\ \phi = (x_i^{(0)} - x_j^{(0)})(\xi_i - \xi_j) + (y)(\eta) + (z)(\zeta), \\ \psi^2 = (\xi_i - \xi_j)^2 + (\eta_i - \eta_j)^2 + (\zeta_i - \zeta_j)^2. \end{cases}$$

Consider the expansion of the function (33) for $k = 0$. It follows from the hypotheses $m_i < M$, $R > r_{ij}^{(0)} > r$ and the relations (34) that the expansion of the function (33), and the expansion of the corresponding functions for the second and third of equations (26), as power series in ξ_j, η_j, and ζ_j are all dominated by the expansion of the function

$$(35) \qquad \frac{M}{r^3} \frac{R + (\xi_i + \xi_j + \eta_i + \eta_j + \zeta_i + \zeta_j)}{\left[1 - \dfrac{\xi_i + \xi_j + \eta_i + \eta_j + \zeta_i + \zeta_j}{r} \right]^3}.$$

The expansion of this function, in turn, is dominated by the expansion of the function

$$(36) \quad \frac{MR}{r^3} \left[1 - \frac{\xi_i + \xi_j + \eta_i + \eta_j + \zeta_i + \zeta_j}{r} \right]^{-4}$$

$$\ll \frac{MR}{r^3} \left[1 - \frac{4(\xi_i + \xi_j + \eta_i + \eta_j + \zeta_i + \zeta_j)}{r} \right]^{-1}.$$

By hypothesis, the star m_i is in the galaxy g_1, and the number of stars in g_1 is $n_1 < N$. It will be advantageous in the sequel to have a function analogous to (36) whose expansion dominates the right members of equations (29) for all values of i for which the star m_i is in the galaxy g_1. Such a function is the sum of the functions (36) for which i has the n_1 requisite values; and the sum increased by similar functions for $N - n_1$ arbitrary values of i will also have the property. Since

$$\sum_{i=1}^{n} a_i[1 - p_i]^{-1} \ll A\left[1 - \sum_{i=1}^{n} p_i\right]^{-1},$$

where $\sum_{i=1}^{n} a_i = A$, it follows that a function having all the required properties is

$$(37) \qquad \Phi_{g_1}{}^{(0)} = \frac{MRN}{r^3}\left[1 - 4\sum_{i_0}\frac{(\xi_{i_0} + \eta_{i_0} + \zeta_{i_0})}{r}\right]^{-1},$$

where i_0 take N values including all values for which m_i belongs to the galaxy g_1.

Now consider the power series that come from the expansions of the terms involving the $r_{ij}{}^{(1)}$, where m_i is in the galaxy g_1. For each value of i there are $n_2 + n_3 + \cdots < N^2$ of these terms. It follows from the inequalities (25) that the function corresponding to (35), for a given value of j in $r_{ij}{}^{(1)}$, is

$$\frac{M}{C^3 r^3}\frac{CR + (\xi_i + \xi_j + \eta_i + \eta_j + \zeta_i + \zeta_j)}{\left[1 - \dfrac{\xi_i + \xi_j + \eta_i + \eta_j + \zeta_i + \zeta_j}{Cr}\right]^3},$$

the expansion of which is dominated by the expansion of the function

$$(38) \qquad \frac{MR}{C^2 r^3}\left[1 - \frac{4(\xi_i + \xi_j + \eta_i + \eta_j + \zeta_i + \zeta_j)}{Cr}\right]^{-1}.$$

The expansions of the right members of all of equations (26), so far as they depend upon terms involving the $r_{ij}{}^{(1)}$, are dominated by the sum of the expansions of the functions (38) for all values of j for which the m_j are in $G_1{}^{(1)}$ and not in g_1. Let i_1 take N^2 values, including all the values of i and j in $r_{ij}{}^{(1)}$. Then the function, corresponding to the one defined by equation (37), which dominates the right members of equations (29) for N^2

values of i, including all values for which m_i is in g_1, so far as these expansions depend upon the $r_{ij}^{(1)}$, is found to be

$$(39) \qquad \Phi_{g_1}{}^{(1)} = \frac{MRN^2}{C^2 r^3} \left[1 - 4 \sum_{i_1} \frac{(\xi_{i_1} + \eta_{i_1} + \zeta_{i_1})}{Cr} \right]^{-1}.$$

The process which has been carried out for two steps can evidently be continued. The function corresponding to those defined by equations (37) and (39) which, for all m_i in g_1, dominates the expansions of the right members of equations (26), so far as they depend upon the $r_{ij}^{(k)}$, is

$$(40) \qquad \Phi_{g_1}{}^{(k)} = \frac{MRN^{k+1}}{C^{2k} r^3} \left[1 - 4 \sum_{i_k} \frac{(\xi_{i_k} + \eta_{i_k} + \zeta_{i_k})}{C^k r} \right]^{-1}.$$

The right members of equations (29) for all values of i for which m_i is in g_1 are dominated by the sum with respect to k of the expansions of the functions defined by equations (40). This sum is dominated by

$$(41) \qquad \Phi_{g_1} = \frac{MRN}{r^3 \left(1 - \dfrac{N}{C^2}\right)} \left[1 - 4 \sum_{k=0}^{\infty} \sum_{i_k} \frac{(\xi_{i_k} + \eta_{i_k} + \zeta_{i_k})}{C^k r} \right]^{-1}.$$

There are corresponding functions associated with each of the galaxies g_1, g_2, g_3, $\cdots$ as a starting point for the notation.

It is necessary to pause a moment to consider the convergence of the expansion of the right member of equation (41) as a power series in the ξ_{i_k}, η_{i_k}, and ζ_{i_k}. When $k = 0$, there are N terms in the sum with respect to i_0; when $k = 1$, there are N^2 terms in the sum with respect to i_1; and for $k = k$, there are N^{k+1} terms in the sum with respect to i_k. Consequently, if $\xi_{i_k} = \eta_{i_k} = \zeta_{i_k} = \theta$, equation (41) becomes

$$(42) \quad \begin{cases} \Phi_{g_1}(\theta) = \dfrac{MRN}{r^3 \left(1 - \dfrac{N}{C^2}\right)} \left[1 - 12N \dfrac{\theta}{r} \sum_{p=0}^{\infty} \left(\dfrac{N}{C}\right)^p \right]^{-1} \\[2em] \qquad\quad = \dfrac{MRN}{r^3 \left(1 - \dfrac{N}{C^2}\right)} \left[1 - \dfrac{12N\theta}{r \left(1 - \dfrac{N}{C}\right)} \right]^{-1}. \end{cases}$$

The expansion of the right member of this equation as a power series in θ converges for $N < C$, $|\theta| \leqq |\theta_0|$, if θ_0 is so chosen that the absolute value of the second term in the bracket is less than unity for $\theta = \theta_0$. Consequently, it follows that the expansion of the right members of equation (41) converges if $|\xi_{i_k}| < \theta_0$, $|\eta_{i_k}| < \theta_0$, $|\zeta_{i_k}| < \theta_0$.

184. Convergence of the Formal Solution of the Differential Equations. In order to prove the convergence of the formal solutions of equations (29), consider the dominating differential equations

$$(43) \qquad \frac{d^2X_i}{dt^2} = \frac{d^2Y_i}{dt^2} = \frac{d^2Z_i}{dt^2} = \Phi_{g_p} \qquad (p = 1, 2, \cdots),$$

where, in the notation of equation (41), the Φ_{g_p} are defined by the equation

$$(44) \qquad \Phi_{g_p} = \frac{MRN}{r^3 \left(1 - \dfrac{N}{C^2}\right)} \left[1 - 4 \sum_{k=0}^{\infty} \sum_{i_k} \frac{(X_{i_k} + Y_{i_k} + Z_{i_k})}{C^k r}\right]^{-1}.$$

It follows from the discussion of Art. 177 and from the properties of the Φ_{g_p} ($p = 1, 2, \cdots$) that the formal solution of equations (43) dominates the formal solution of equations (29). Hence it is sufficient to prove the convergence of the formal solution of equations (43).

Since the initial values of the ξ_i, η_i, and ζ_i and of their first derivatives are zero, the initial values of the X_i, Y_i, and Z_i and of their first derivatives will also be zero. The first fact to be noted is that, since the Φ_{g_p} are symmetrical in the X_{i_k}, Y_{i_k}, and Z_{i_k}, the right members of the three equations (43), for each i, are equal whatever values the variables may have. Since they all have the value zero at $t = 0$, they remain equal for all values of t for which a solution may exist. That is,

$$(45) \qquad X_i \underset{t}{\equiv} Y_i \underset{t}{\equiv} Z_i \qquad (i = 1, 2, \cdots).$$

Let W_i represent their common value; then the differential equations (43) may be replaced by the system

$$(46) \qquad \frac{d^2W_i}{dt^2} = \frac{MRN}{r^3 \left(1 - \dfrac{N}{C^2}\right)} \left[1 - 12 \sum_{k=0}^{\infty} \sum_{i_k} \frac{W_{i_k}}{C^k r}\right]^{-1} \qquad (i = 1, 2, \cdots).$$

There is now only one differential equation for each star.

In order to proceed further, it is necessary to use other properties of the differential equations, some of which are not expressed by the notation. When $k = 0$, the values of i correspond to the stars in a single galaxy, say g_1. The number of stars in the galaxy g_1 is $n_1 < N$, but i for this group of equations takes the full N values. That is, the dominating system of equations (43) contains equations for which there are no corresponding equations in the system (29). This circumstance does not interfere with the application of the method of dominating differential equations, as can be readily seen in the simpler problem of a finite number of differential equations. There are not only $3N$ differential equations for each galaxy g_p, but there are differential equations corresponding to N galaxies in each super-galaxy of the first order, and for N super-galaxies of the first order in each super-galaxy of the second order, and so on for all higher orders. Since the coördinates of the stars in the successive larger units enter in different ways in the differential equations, it is evident that in general the dominating differential equations, up to units of any order, contain many more variables and equations than the original problem. This increase in the number of variables has led to very important symmetries.

Now consider equations (46) for a value of i associated with a star in any galaxy, say g_1. In the right member, the sum for $k = 0$ includes symmetrically all the W_i associated with the galaxy g_1. The sum for $k = 1$ includes symmetrically all the W_i associated with all the galaxies (real and fictitious) in the super-galaxy $G_1{}^{(1)}$ of the first order. In general, the sum for $k = k$ includes symmetrically all the W_i associated with the super-galaxy $G_1{}^{(k)}$ of order k. It follows at once from these properties that, for all values of i associated with any particular galaxy g_p, the right members of the corresponding equations of (46) are identical. Since the initial values of the W_i and of their first derivatives are zero, all the W_i associated with each galaxy are equal. Let V_i represent their common value. Then the differential equations (46) can be reduced to

$$(47) \quad \frac{d^2 V_i}{dt^2} = \frac{MRN}{r^3 \left(1 - \dfrac{N}{C^2}\right)} \left[1 - 12N \sum_{k=0}^{\infty} \frac{V_{i_k}}{C^k r}\right]^{-1} \quad (i = 1, 2, \cdots).$$

There is now only one variable V_i associated with each galaxy g_i, whether it is real or fictitious.

Now consider the totality of differential equations (47). Although the right members vary as i varies in the left members, it follows from their symmetries that every equation can be obtained from any one of them by a permutation of the subscripts. Therefore all the V_i are equal, for the formal solution of the equations is unique and the equations become identical if $V_1 = V_2 = \cdots$. If the symmetrical equations are written down in the finite case, the conclusion is obvious. On letting V represent the common value of the V_i, the system of differential equations (47) reduces to

$$(48) \qquad \frac{d^2V}{dt^2} = \frac{MRN}{r^3\left(1 - \dfrac{N}{C^2}\right)}\left[1 - 12\frac{N}{Cr}\frac{V}{1 - \dfrac{N}{C}}\right]^{-1}.$$

The solution of this differential equation as a power series in t converges, provided the absolute value of t is sufficiently small. Therefore the formal solution of equations (29) as power series in t converges provided $|t|$ is sufficiently small.

It follows from the results of Art. 179 that the solution continues to exist for all values of t for which the original differential equations (26) have the properties upon which the demonstration of the existence of the solution rests. These are essentially the inequalities (25) and the relation $C > N$. Therefore, although the infinite system of stars has no defined center of gravity nor defined fundamental planes, yet the individual stars have determinable motions with respect to an arbitrary set of axes, just as they have in a finite system. Although the system is infinite in number of stars and in number of galaxies and of super-galaxies of every order, it occupies infinite space in such a way that the sums of the components of attraction on each star are finite. Since light and gravitation both vary inversely as the square of the distance from the source, the light received by each star is finite. An examination of the known facts respecting the stellar system shows that there is nothing that contradicts any of the assumptions on which this discussion has been based; or that the physical universe is not infinite in some such way as has been postulated in this problem.

XVIII. QUESTIONS AND PROBLEMS

1. Define implicit function equations analogous to the differential equations (1), construct their formal solution, and prove its convergence.

2. Define differential equations, analogous to equations (1), in which the right members have the Lipschitz property, suitably generalized. Define a formal solution by a generalization of the method of successive approximations; prove that the process converges to limit functions; and prove that the limits are a solution.

3. Examine the problem of linear differential equations with constant coefficients in infinitely many variables. Does the characteristic equation necessarily have infinitely many roots? A finite number? If the characteristic equation has infinitely many distinct roots, is it possible to define a fundamental set of solutions?

4. Determine the region within which the solution of equation (13) as a power series in t converges.

5. Why is not the analogue of the discussion of Art. 179 required in case the number of dependent variables is finite?

6. Suppose the physical universe is infinite, upward, in harmony with the hypothesis of Art. 180. Suppose the mean relative velocities of super-galaxies of order $k - 1$ in a super-galaxy of order k exceeds a constant V_0, independent of k. Suppose stars radiate their masses away in space, in the form of energy that loses its property of gravitation, until their masses are reduced to a certain minimum at which they become cold bodies. Suppose their masses and heat energies are from time to time restored by collisions. Will the energy of the infinite universe maintain infinitely many luminous stars for an infinite time?

7. Discuss the reason why both inferior and superior limits are introduced by the inequalities (25). Is it necessary to have such limits for the cosmic units of all orders?

8. Is the problem of the infinite universe solvable if the law of force is not Newtonian gravitation? If there is a non-gravitating resisting medium?

9. Why are there N indices in the dominating function of Art. 183 for the stars of each galaxy?

10. Show from the differential equations

$$\begin{cases} \dfrac{dx_1}{dt} = f(x_1, \cdots, x_n; t), \\[2mm] \dfrac{dx_2}{dt} = f(x_2, \cdots, x_n, x_1; t), \\[2mm] \cdots \cdots \cdots \cdots \cdots \cdots \\[2mm] \dfrac{dx_n}{dt} = f(x_n, x_1, \cdots, x_{n-1}; t), \end{cases}$$

with the initial conditions $x_i(0) = 0$ and with the right members cyclically symmetrical, that $x_1 = \cdots = x_n$. Compare Art. 184.

HISTORICAL SKETCH

It is remarkable that the differential equations in infinitely many variables should have so long escaped the notice of mathematicians. The first discussion of the subject seems to have been by H. von Koch [*Ofversigt of Konliga Akademie Förhandlingar*, Vol. 56 (1899)]. Since this publication has not been available to the author, an account of von Koch's researches cannot be given here.

At the Fourth International Congress of Mathematicians, held at Rome, in 1908, E. H. Moore read a paper that included a discussion of differential equations in the sense of General Analysis (cf. *Introduction to a Form of General Analysis*, by E. H. Moore, New Haven Mathematical Colloquium, 1906). In the work of Moore, a general variable was used in place of the index for systems in denumerably infinite systems of equations. In this respect the methods of Moore were of great generality, but, on the other hand, the dependent variables he employed were limited to a so-called Hilbert space, and they would, consequently, not be suitable for such applications as were made in this chapter. In fact, the methods of Moore and those of this chapter have very little, if anything, in common.

The first part of this chapter was published by the author in *Proceedings of the National Academy of Sciences*, Vol. 1 (1915), pp. 350–354. The latter part of the chapter was worked out at the same time, but was not published. In 1917, J. F. Ritt treated a single differential equation of infinite order (*Transactions of the American Mathematical Society*, Vol. 18, page 27). In 1917, W. L. Hart published a paper (*Transactions of the American Mathematical Society*, Vol. 18, pp. 125–160) in which the functions involved satisfy more general properties than those imposed in this paper. When the results of Hart are suitably specialized, they reduce to those of the first part of this chapter. Since the appearance of Hart's paper, many others have been published that treat the problem from more general points of view, such as that of Moore's *General Analysis*. Among these writers are T. H. Hildebrandt (*Trans. of Am. Math. Soc.*, 1917); G. A. Bliss (*Trans. of Am. Math. Soc.*, 1920); I. A. Barnett (*Am. Jour. of Math.*, 1922 and 1923); W. L. Hart (*Annals of Math.*, 1922). The theory of implicit functions has been similarly generalized: L. Graves (*Trans. of Am. Math. Soc.*, 1927).

APPENDICES

APPENDIX A

DEFINITIONS: (1) Suppose the function $f(x)$ is defined for all values of x in a closed region R, such as $b \leqq x \leqq c$ when x is limited to real values or such as $|x - d| \leqq r$ when x may take complex values. Then the statement that $f(x)$ is a *continuous* function of x at $x = a$ (a in R) means the following: Corresponding to *every* $\epsilon > 0$, there exists a $\delta_{\epsilon, a} > 0$, depending in general upon both ϵ and a, such that, for *every* value of x in R for which $|x - a| < \delta_{\epsilon, a}$, it is true that $|f(x) - f(a)| < \epsilon$.

(2) The function $f(x)$ is continuous in the region R if it is continuous at *every* $x = a$ in R.

(3) The function $f(x)$ is *uniformly* continuous in R if, corresponding to every $\epsilon > 0$, there exists a $\delta_\epsilon > 0$, *independent* of a, such that, for every value of a in R and for every value of x in R for which $|x - a| < \delta_\epsilon$, it is true that $|f(x) - f(a)| < \epsilon$.

It can be proved that if $f(x)$ is continuous at every $x = a$ in a *closed* region R, then it is *uniformly* continuous in R; but if the region R is *open* (such as $b < x < c$ or $|x - d| < r$), the continuity of $f(x)$ at every $x = a$ in R does not imply that $f(x)$ is uniformly continuous in R. For example, $f(x) = 1/(1 - x)$ is not uniformly continuous in the open region $0 \leqq x < 1$.

(4) Suppose $f(x_1, \cdots, x_n)$ is defined for all values of the x_i in a closed region R, such as $b_i \leqq x_i \leqq c_i$ ($i = 1, \cdots, n$) when the x_i are limited to real values or such as $|x_i - d_i| \leqq r_i$ ($i = 1, \cdots, n$) when the x_i may take complex values. Then the statement that $f(x_1, \cdots, x_n)$ is a continuous function of the x_i *separately* at the $x_i = a_i$ in R means that Definition (1) holds for each x_i separately when all the other x_i have the values a_i respectively.

(5) The statement that $f(x_1, \cdots, x_n)$ is a continuous function of the x_i *simultaneously* (usually the word "simultaneously" is omitted) at $x_i = a_i$ (the a_i in R) means the following: Corresponding to every $\epsilon > 0$, there exists a $\delta_{\epsilon, a_1, \cdots, a_n} > 0$ depending in general upon both ϵ and the a_i, such that, for every set of values of the x_i in R for which $|x_i - a_i| < \delta_{\epsilon, a_1, \cdots, a_n}$ ($i = 1, \cdots, n$), it is true that $|f(x_1, \cdots, x_n) - f(a_1, \cdots, a_n)| < \epsilon$.

377

If $f(x_1, \cdots, x_n)$ is a continuous function of the x_i *simultaneously* at the $x_i = a_i$ in R, it is a continuous function of the x_i *separately* at the $x_i = a_i$. The converse, however, is not necessarily true, as is illustrated by the function $f(x_1, x_2) = x_1x_2/(x_1{}^2 + x_2{}^2)$ with $f(0, 0) = 0$ by definition, for $f(x_1, x_2)$ is a continuous function of x_1 and x_2 separately for $x_i = a_i$ (a_i finite), but is not continuous in x_1 and x_2 simultaneously at $x_1 = x_2 = 0$.

THEOREM I: *If $f(x_1, \cdots, x_n; t)$ is defined for every set of values of the x_i and t in a closed region R and is continuous in the x_i simultaneously at every $x_i = a_i$ and t in R uniformly with respect to t in R; and if $f(x_1, \cdots, x_n; t)$ is continuous in t separately at every $x_i = a_i$ and $t = t_0$ in R, then $f(x_1, \cdots, x_n; t)$ is a continuous function of the x_i and t simultaneously at every $x_i = a_i$, $t = t_0$ in R.*

Proof. The first hypothesis is: Corresponding to every $\epsilon > 0$ and to every a_i and t in R, there exists a $\delta_{\epsilon, a_i} > 0$, independent of t, such that, for every set of values of the x_i in R for which $|x_i - a_i| < \delta_{\epsilon, a_i}$, it is true that $|f(x_1, \cdots, x_n; t) - f(a_1, \cdots, a_n; t)| < \frac{1}{2}\epsilon$.

The second hypothesis is: Corresponding to every $\epsilon > 0$ and to every a_i and t_0 in R, there exists a $\delta_{\epsilon, a_i, t_0} > 0$ such that, for every value of t in R for which $|t - t_0| < \delta_{\epsilon, a_i, t_0}$, it is true that $|f(a_1, \cdots, a_n; t) - f(a_1, \cdots, a_n; t_0)| < \frac{1}{2}\epsilon$.

The conclusion is: Corresponding to every $\epsilon > 0$ and to every a_i and t_0 in R, there exists a $\delta_{\epsilon, a_i, t_0} > 0$ such that, for every set of values of the x_i and t in R for which $|x_i - a_i| < \delta_{\epsilon, a_i, t_0}$, $|t - t_0| < \delta_{\epsilon, a_i, t_0}$, it is true that $|f(x_1, \cdots, x_n; t) - f(a_1, \cdots, a_n; t_0)| < \epsilon$. Since

$$|f(x_i; t) - f(a_i; t_0)| \leqq |f(x_i; t) - f(a_i; t)| + |f(a_i; t) - f(a_i; t_0)|,$$

the conclusion immediately follows from the two hypotheses.

Corollary. If the function $f(x_1, \cdots, x_n; t)$ in a closed region R for the x_i and t has any property (such as the Lipschitz property or that of possessing derivatives) which implies continuity simultaneously in the x_i uniformly with respect to t, and if the function is continuous in t separately, then the function is continuous in the x_i and t simultaneously.

THEOREM II: *If $f(x_1, \cdots, x_n)$ is a continuous function of the x_i in any closed region R, such as $a_i \leqq x_i \leqq b_i$ ($i = 1, \cdots, n$) when the x_i are real or $|x_i - a_i| \leqq r_i$ when the x_i are complex, then the function $|f(x_i)|$ has a finite upper bound M in the region R.*

Direct Proof. There is a theorem to the effect that if a function $f(x_i)$ is continuous in the x_i at every set of the $x_i = a_i$ in a *closed* region R, then the function is *uniformly* continuous in the region R. That is, corresponding to every $\epsilon > 0$ and to every a_i in R, there exists a positive number δ_ϵ, depending upon ϵ but independent of the a_i, such that, for every set of values of the x_i in R for which $|x_i - a_i| \leqq \delta_\epsilon$, it is true that $|f(x_i) - f(a_i)| < \epsilon$.

Suppose κ is an integer so chosen that $\kappa\delta_\epsilon \leqq |b_i - a_i|$. Then a bridge can be constructed from the point a_i to any other point x_i in R by κ points $x_i^{(1)}$, $x_i^{(2)}$, $\cdots$, $x_i^{(\kappa)} = x_i$, such that $|x_i^{(j)} - x_i^{(j-1)}| \leqq \delta_\epsilon$. Then, since

(1) $\quad f(x_i) = f(a_i) + [f(x_i^{(1)}) - f(a_i)] + \cdots + [f(x_i^{(\kappa)}) - f(x_i^{(\kappa-1)})],$

it follows that

(2) $\qquad\qquad |f(x_i)| \leqq |f(a_i)| + \kappa\epsilon = M,$

which is finite. This proof applies whether the x_i are real or complex. Therefore the continuous function $|f(x_i)|$ has a finite upper bound M in the closed region R.

Indirect Proof. If $|f(x_i)|$ does not have an upper bound M in R, then, corresponding to every M_j, there are values $x_i^{(j)}$ $(i = 1, \cdots, n)$ of the x_i in R such that $|f(x_i^{(j)})| > M_j$. As $j = 1, 2, \cdots$, let the values of M_j increase without bound, say $M_j = 2^j$. To these M_j there correspond infinite sets $x_i^{(j)}$ of the x_i. Since the region R is closed, each set $x_i^{(j)}$ has an infinite subset $x_i^{(j')}$ which has a limit x_i' in R. It follows from the way the set $x_i^{(j)}$ and its sub-set $x_i^{(j')}$ have been defined, that, for every $x_i^{(j')}$ $(i = 1, \cdots, n)$ of the sub-set $x_i^{(j')}$, it is true that

(3) $\qquad\qquad |f(x_i') - f(x_i^{(j')})| \geqq 2.$

But the continuity property of the hypothesis is that for every ϵ and x_i' and every j' such that $|x_i' - x_i^{(j')}| < \delta_\epsilon$, it is true that $|f(x_i') - f(x_i^{(j')})| < \epsilon$, which contradicts the relations (3) for every value of ϵ less than 2.

If the region R were not closed, the continuity of the function $f(x_i)$ at every point of R would not imply that its absolute value is bounded in R.

Problem 1. Prove that, if a function $f(x)$ is continuous at every $x = a$ in a closed region R, it is uniformly continuous in R.

Problem 2. Prove the theorem: If $f(x_1, \cdots, x_n)$ is defined for every set of values of the x_i in a closed region R; if $f(x_1, \cdots, x_j; a_{j+1}, \cdots, a_n)$ is continuous in $x_1, \cdots, x_j$ simultaneously in R uniformly with respect to $a_{j+1}, \cdots, a_n$ $(j = 1, \cdots, n-1)$ in R; and if $f(a_1, \cdots, a_{n-1}; x_n)$ is continuous in x_n separately at every a_i $(i = 1, \cdots, n-1)$ and $x_n = a_n$ in R; then $f(x_1, \cdots, x_n)$ is continuous in $x_1, \cdots, x_n$ simultaneously at every $x_i = a_i$ $(i = 1, \cdots, n)$ in R.

APPENDIX B

THEOREM: *If the power series*

$$(1) \quad f(x_1, \cdots, x_n) = \sum_{j=0}^{\infty} c_{j_1, \cdots, j_n} (x_1 - a_1)^{j_1} \cdots (x_n - a_n)^{j_n}$$

converges for all values of the x_i for which $|x_i - a_i| < r_i$, *then there exists another power series*

$$(2) \quad F(x_1, \cdots, x_n) = \sum_{j_i=0}^{\infty} C_{j_1, \cdots, j_n} (x_1 - a_1)^{j_1} \cdots (x_n - a_n)^{j_n},$$

which converges for all values of the x_i for which

$$|x_i - a_i| < r_i' < r_i,$$

and the coefficients of which are real and positive and satisfy the inequalities

$$(3) \quad C_{j_1, \cdots, j_n} > |c_{j_1, \cdots, j_n}| \quad (j_1, \cdots, j_n = 0, 1, 2, \cdots).$$

Proof when $n = 1$. On representing the power-series expansion of the function by

$$(4) \qquad f(x) = c_0 + c_1(x - a) + \cdots,$$

it follows from Cauchy's second integral theorem that

$$(5) \qquad c_0 = f(a) = \frac{1}{2\pi \sqrt{-1}} \int_{C'} \frac{f(x)}{x - a} \, dx,$$

where C', the path of integration, is the perimeter of the circle whose center is at a and whose radius is r'. Since the function $f(x)$ and the path of integration are both independent of the parameter a, the derivative of the integral with respect to a is the integral of the derivative of the integrand with respect to a, and so on for successive derivatives. That is,

$$(6) \quad \begin{cases} c_1 = \dfrac{1}{1} f'(a) = \dfrac{1}{2\pi\sqrt{-1}} \displaystyle\int_{C'} \dfrac{f(x)}{(x-a)^2}\,dx, \\[3mm] c_\kappa = \dfrac{1}{\kappa!} f^{(\kappa)}(a) = \dfrac{1}{2\pi\sqrt{-1}} \displaystyle\int_{C'} \dfrac{f(x)}{(x-a)^{\kappa+1}}\,dx \quad (\kappa = 2, 3, \cdots). \end{cases}$$

Let M represent an upper bound to $|f(x)|$ on the perimeter C', and make the transformation

$$(7) \quad \begin{cases} x - a = r'e^{\sqrt{-1}\theta}, \quad \text{whence} \\ |x - a| = r', \\ dx = \sqrt{-1}\, r'e^{\sqrt{-1}\theta}\,d\theta. \end{cases}$$

Therefore it follows from equations (5), (6), and (7) that

$$(8) \quad \begin{cases} |c_0| \leqq \dfrac{1}{2\pi} \displaystyle\int_0^{2\pi} M\,d\theta = M, \\[3mm] |c_\kappa| \leqq \dfrac{1}{2\pi} \displaystyle\int_0^{2\pi} \dfrac{M\,d\theta}{(r')^\kappa} = \dfrac{M}{(r')^\kappa} \quad (\kappa = 1, 2, \cdots). \end{cases}$$

Hence a function having the properties of $F(x)$ is

$$(9) \quad F(x) = M\left[1 + \frac{x-a}{r'} + \left(\frac{x-a}{r'}\right)^2 + \cdots \right],$$

which converges for all values of x for which $|x - a| < r'$.

Proof in the General Case. It follows from successive applications of Cauchy's second integral theorem that

$$(10) \quad \begin{cases} f(a_1, \cdots, a_n) = \dfrac{1}{2\pi\sqrt{-1}} \displaystyle\int_{C'} \dfrac{f(x_1, a_2, \cdots, a_n)}{x_1 - a_1}\,dx_1, \\[3mm] f(x_1, a_2, \cdots, a_n) = \dfrac{1}{2\pi\sqrt{-1}} \displaystyle\int_{C'} \dfrac{f(x_1, x_2, a_3, \cdots, a_n)}{x_2 - a_2}\,dx_2, \\ \cdots \cdots \cdots \cdots \cdots \cdots \cdots \cdots \cdots \\ f(x_1, \cdots, x_{n-1}, a_n) = \dfrac{1}{2\pi\sqrt{-1}} \displaystyle\int_{C'} \dfrac{f(x_1, \cdots, x_n)}{x_n - a_n}\,dx_n. \end{cases}$$

Therefore it follows that the coefficients of the power-series expansion of $f(x_1, \cdots, x_n)$ are defined by the equations

$$(11) \begin{cases} c_{0,\,\cdots,\,0} = f(a_1, \cdots, a_n) \\ \qquad = \dfrac{1}{(2\pi\sqrt{-1})^n} \displaystyle\int_{C_1'} \cdots \int_{C_n'} \dfrac{f(x_i)}{\Pi(x_i - a_i)}\, dx_1 \cdots dx_n, \\ c_{j_1,\,\cdots,\,i_n} = \dfrac{\partial^{i_1 + \cdots + i_n} f(a_1, \cdots, a_n)}{j_1! \cdots j_n!\, \partial a_1^{j_1} \cdots \partial a_n^{i_n}} \\ \qquad = \dfrac{1}{(2\pi\sqrt{-1})^n} \displaystyle\int_{C_1'} \cdots \int_{C_n'} \dfrac{f(x_i)}{\Pi(x_i - a_i)^{i_i+1}}\, dx_1 \cdots dx_n, \end{cases}$$

where

$$\Pi(x_i - a_i)^{i_i+1} = (x_1 - a_1)^{i_1+1} \cdots (x_n - a_n)^{i_n+1}.$$

Now make the transformation $x_i - a_i = r_i' e^{\sqrt{-1}\,\theta}$ and let M represent an upper bound to $|f(x_1, \cdots, x_n)|$ in the closed region $|x_i - a_i| \leqq r_i'$ $(i = 1, \cdots, n)$. Then it follows directly from equations (11) that

$$(12) \begin{cases} |c_{0,\,\cdots,\,0}| \leqq M, \\ |c_{j_1,\,\cdots,\,i_n}| \leqq \dfrac{M}{(r_1')^{j_1} \cdots (r_n')^{i_n}}. \end{cases}$$

Therefore the expansion of the function

$$(13) \quad F(x_1, \cdots, x_n) = \frac{M}{\left(1 - \dfrac{x_1 - a_1}{r_1'}\right) \cdots \left(1 - \dfrac{x_n - a_n}{r_n'}\right)}$$

as a power series in $x_i - a_i$ converges for all values of the x_i for which $|x_i - a_i| < r_i'$ and its coefficients satisfy the inequalities (3).

It is obvious that the power-series expansion of

$$(14) \quad F(x_1, \cdots, x_n) = \frac{M}{1 - \dfrac{(x_1 - a_1) + \cdots + (x_n - a_n)}{r'}}$$

converges if $|x_i - a_i| < r_i'/n$ and dominates the right member of equation (2).

Problem. Prove that the functions in equations (6) are the derivatives with respect to a of those in equation (5).

APPENDIX C

THEOREM (*Weierstrass*): (H_1) *If the series*

(1) $$F(t) = f_1(t) + f_2(t) + \cdots$$

converges uniformly with respect to t for all values of t for which $|t| < R$, *and* (H_2) *if the* $f_j(t)$ *are expansible as power series*

(2) $$f_j(t) = c_j{}^{(0)} + c_j{}^{(1)}t + c_j{}^{(2)}t^2 + \cdots \qquad (j = 1, 2, \cdots),$$

which converge for all values of t for which $|t| \leqq r$, *then* (C_1) *the series*

(3) $$c_n = c_1{}^{(n)} + c_2{}^{(n)} + \cdots \qquad (n = 0, 1, 2, \cdots)$$

converge, (C_2) *the series*

(4) $$\Phi(t) = c_0 + c_1 t + c_2 t^2 + \cdots$$

converges for all values of t for which $|t| < R$, r, *and* (C_3) $\Phi(t) \equiv F(t)$ *in the region* $|t| < R$, r. The hypotheses are (H_1) and (H_2); the conclusions are (C_1), (C_2), and (C_3).

Proof of (C_1). It follows from the hypothesis (H_1), that, corresponding to every $\eta > 0$, there exists an integer κ_η, depending upon η but independent of t, such that, for every $\kappa > \kappa_\eta$ and for all values of t for which $|t| < R$, it is true that

(5) $$|F_{\kappa p}(t)| = |f_\kappa(t) + \cdots + f_{\kappa+p}(t)| < \eta \qquad (p = 1, 2, \cdots).$$

The sum of these $p + 1$ power series equals the power series whose terms are their term-by-term sum for $|t| \leqq r$. Therefore, by Cauchy's second integral theorem, the coefficient of t^n in their sum satisfies the equation

(6) $$c_\kappa{}^{(n)} + \cdots + c_{\kappa+p}{}^{(n)} = \frac{1}{2\pi\sqrt{-1}} \int_{(r)} \frac{F_{\kappa p}(t)}{t^{n+1}} dt$$
$$(n = 0, 1, 2, \cdots).$$

Hence it follows from the inequality (5) that

(7) $$|c_\kappa{}^{(n)} + \cdots + c_{\kappa+p}{}^{(n)}| \leqq \frac{1}{2\pi} \int_{(r)} \frac{|F_{\kappa p}(t)|}{|t^{n+1}|} dt < \frac{\eta}{r^n}$$
$$(n = 0, 1, 2, \cdots; p = 1, 2, \cdots).$$

Since this is a definition of convergence of the series (3), the conclusion (C_1) is established.

Proof of (C_2). The constant c_n can be broken up into the sum of two constants as follows:

(8)
$$\begin{cases} c_n = c_{n\kappa}' + c_{n\kappa}'', \quad \text{where} \\ c_{n\kappa}' = c_1^{(n)} + \cdots + c_{\kappa-1}^{(n)}, \\ c_{n\kappa}'' = \lim_{p=\infty} \left[c_\kappa^{(n)} + \cdots + c_{\kappa+p}^{(n)} \right]. \end{cases}$$

Let two auxiliary functions of t be defined by

(9)
$$\begin{cases} \Phi_\kappa'(t) = c_{0\kappa}' + c_{1\kappa}'t + c_{2\kappa}'t^2 + \cdots, \\ \Phi_\kappa''(t) = c_{0\kappa}'' + c_{1\kappa}''t + c_{2\kappa}''t^2 + \cdots. \end{cases}$$

If the two series (9) converge for $|t| < R, r$, then it follows that

(10) $$c_0 + c_1 t + \cdots \underset{t}{\equiv} \Phi_\kappa'(t) + \Phi_\kappa''(t),$$

because it follows from equations (3) and (8) that, in their common domain of convergence, the left member of equation (10) is the term-by-term sum of the two series in the right member.

In order to prove the convergence of $\Phi_\kappa'(t)$, break it up into the $\kappa - 1$ series

(11)
$$\begin{cases} \Phi_\kappa'(t) = + c_1^{(0)} + c_1^{(1)}t + c_1^{(2)}t^2 + \cdots \\ \qquad\quad + c_2^{(0)} + c_2^{(1)}t + c_2^{(2)}t^2 + \cdots \\ \qquad\quad \cdot\ \cdot\ \cdot\ \cdot\ \cdot\ \cdot\ \cdot\ \cdot \\ \qquad\quad + c_{\kappa-1}^{(0)} + c_{\kappa-1}^{(1)}t + c_{\kappa-1}^{(2)}t^2 + \cdots, \end{cases}$$

one series being written in each line. Since $\Phi_\kappa'(t)$ is a sum of a finite number of power series which converge for $|t| < r$, the series for $\Phi_\kappa'(t)$ converges uniformly if $|t| < r' < r$. That is, corresponding to every $\epsilon > 0$, there exists an integer $n_{\epsilon,\kappa}$, depending on ϵ and κ but independent of t, such that, for every $n > n_{\epsilon,\kappa}$ and for all $|t| < r' < r$, it is true that

(12) $$|c_{n\kappa}' t^n + \cdots + c_{n+p,\,\kappa}' t^{n+p}| < \tfrac{1}{2}\epsilon \qquad (p = 1, 2, \cdots).$$

Now consider the series defining $\Phi_\kappa''(t)$. It follows from the inequality (7) and the last of equations (8) that

(13) $$|c_{n\kappa}''| = \lim_{p=\infty} |c_\kappa^{(n)} + \cdots + c_{\kappa+p}^{(n)}| < \lim_{p=\infty} \frac{\eta}{r^n} = \frac{\eta}{r^n}$$
$$(n = 0, 1, 2, \cdots),$$

provided $\kappa > \kappa_\eta$. Therefore it follows from equations (5), (8), (9), and (13) that, corresponding to every $\epsilon > 0$ and $|t| < R$, it is true that

$$(14) \quad |\Phi_\kappa''(t)| < \eta_\epsilon \left[1 + \frac{|t|}{r} + \frac{|t^2|}{r^2} + \cdots \right] = \frac{\eta_\epsilon}{1 - \frac{|t|}{r}} < \frac{1}{2}\epsilon,$$

provided $\eta_\epsilon < \frac{1}{2}\epsilon \left[1 - \frac{|t|}{r} \right]$ and $\kappa > \kappa_{\eta\epsilon}$. It must be shown that, for every $\epsilon > 0$ and $|t| < R$, r, the inequalities (12) and (14) can be simultaneously satisfied. For every $\epsilon > 0$ and $|t| < R, r$, it is possible to determine $\eta_{\epsilon,t}$ so that the inequality

$$\eta_{\epsilon,t} < \frac{1}{2}\epsilon \left[1 - \frac{|t|}{r} \right]$$

will be satisfied. Then the inequality (14) will be satisfied. For every $\eta_{\epsilon,t} > 0$, it is possible to determine $\kappa(\eta_{\epsilon,t})$ so that, for all $\kappa > \kappa(\eta_{\epsilon,t})$ the inequality (7) will be satisfied. That is, the condition that the inequality (7) shall be satisfied imposes limitations upon κ. But for every $\epsilon > 0$ and $\kappa > 0$, an $n_{\epsilon,\kappa}$ can be determined so that the inequality (12) will be satisfied. That is, for every $\epsilon > 0$, κ and n can be simultaneously determined so that the inequalities (12) and (14) will both be satisfied.

Proof of (C_3). It follows from the definitions of the functions $F(t)$ and $\Phi(t)$ that

$$(15) \quad F(t) - \Phi(t) = [f_1(t) + f_2(t) + \cdots] - [c_0 + c_1 t + c_2 t^2 + \cdots].$$

It follows from equations (2), (8), and (10) that

$$(16) \quad \begin{cases} [f_1(t) + f_2(t) + \cdots] = [f_1(t) + \cdots + f_{\kappa-1}(t)] + \sum_{j=\kappa}^{\infty} f_j(t), \\ [c_0 + c_1 t + \cdots] = [c_{0\kappa}' + c_{1\kappa}' t + \cdots] + \sum_{j=0}^{\infty} c_{j\kappa}'' t^j, \\ [f_1(t) + \cdots + f_{\kappa-1}(t)] = [c_{0\kappa}' + c_{1\kappa}' t + \cdots]. \end{cases}$$

Therefore it follows that

$$(17) \quad F(t) - \Phi(t) = [f_\kappa(t) + \cdots] - [c_{0\kappa}'' + c_{1\kappa}'' t + \cdots].$$

It follows from the inequality (5) that, corresponding to every

$\epsilon > 0$ and $|t| < R$, there exists a κ_ϵ such that, for all $\kappa > \kappa_\epsilon$, it is true that

$$|f_\kappa(t) + f_{\kappa+1}(t) + \cdots| < \tfrac{1}{2}\epsilon.$$

It also follows from equations (9) and the inequality (14) that, if $\eta_{\epsilon,t} < \dfrac{1}{2} \epsilon \left[1 - \dfrac{|t|}{r}\right]$ and $\kappa > \kappa(\eta_{\epsilon,t})$, it is true that

$$|\Phi_\kappa''(t)| = |c_{0\kappa}'' + c_{1\kappa}''t + \cdots| < \tfrac{1}{2}\epsilon.$$

Therefore $|F(t) - \Phi(t)| < \epsilon$ for every $\epsilon > 0$, however small. That is, $F(t) \equiv \Phi(t)$ if $|t| < R, r$.

Problem. Show where the proof breaks down if in (H_1) the condition that the convergence is *uniform* is not satisfied.

APPENDIX D

THEOREM: (H_1) *If* $f_1(t)$, $f_2(t)$, $\cdots$ *are continuous functions of* t *in a common region* R $[T_1 \leqq t \leqq T_2$ *in case* t *is a real variable;* $|t| \leqq r$ *in case* t *is complex* $]$; *and* (H_2) *if the series*

$$(1) \qquad\qquad F(t) = f_1(t) + f_2(t) + \cdots$$

converges uniformly with respect to t *for all values of* t *in* R; *then* $F(t)$ *is a continuous function of* t *in* R.

Proof. Let t_0 be any value of t in R. The condition that the function $F(t)$ shall be a continuous function of t at $t = t_0$ is: Corresponding to every $\epsilon > 0$ and t_0 in R there exists a $\delta_{\epsilon t_0}$, depending upon ϵ and t_0, such that, for every value of t satisfying the inequality $|t - t_0| < \delta_{\epsilon t_0}$, it is true that

$$(2) \qquad\qquad |F(t) - F(t_0)| < \epsilon.$$

This inequality will be established from the hypotheses (H_1) and (H_2).

It follows from equation (1) that

$$(3) \quad F(t) - F(t_0) = F_n(t) - F_n(t_0) + \sum_{j=n+1}^{\infty} f_j(t) - \sum_{j=n+1}^{\infty} f_j(t_0),$$

where

$$(4) \qquad \begin{cases} F_n(t) = f_1(t) + \cdots + f_n(t), \\ F_n(t_0) = f_1(t_0) + \cdots + f_n(t_0). \end{cases}$$

It follows from (H_2) that, corresponding to every $\epsilon > 0$ and t and t_0 in R, there exists an integer n_ϵ, depending upon ϵ but independent of t and t_0, such that, for every integer $n > n_\epsilon$, it is true that

(5)
$$\begin{cases} |f_{n+1}(t) + f_{n+2}(t) + \cdots| < \tfrac{1}{3}\epsilon, \\ |f_{n+1}(t_0) + f_{n+2}(t_0) + \cdots| < \tfrac{1}{3}\epsilon. \end{cases}$$

Since the sum of a finite number of functions that are continuous in a common region is a continuous function, it follows that, corresponding to every $\epsilon > 0$, every finite integer n, and every t_0 in R, there exists a positive number $\delta_{\epsilon t_0 n}$, depending upon ϵ and n and in general upon t_0, such that, for all values of t satisfying $|t - t_0| < \delta_{\epsilon t_0 n}$, it is true that

(6)
$$|F_n(t) - F_n(t_0)| < \tfrac{1}{3}\epsilon.$$

Hence it follows from equation (3) and the inequalities (5) and (6) that the condition for continuity is satisfied, provided

(7)
$$\begin{cases} n > n_\epsilon, \\ |t - t_0| < \delta_{\epsilon t_0 n}. \end{cases}$$

For every $\epsilon > 0$ the first of these inequalities can be satisfied by virtue of the properties of (H_2); and then the second can be satisfied by virtue of the properties (H_1) and (H_2).

Problem 1. Suppose the convergence of the series (1) is not uniform with respect to t. Show where the proof of the theorem fails.

Problem 2. Prove the theorem: If the functions $f_i(t)$ $(i = 1, 2, \cdots)$ are continuous in t in a common region R; and if the sequence of functions $f_1(t)$, $f_2(t)$, $\cdots$ for every value of t in R converges to a limit $F(t)$ uniformly with respect to t; then $F(t)$ is a continuous function of t in R.

APPENDIX E

Theorem: (H_1) *If the series* $F(t) = f_1(t) + f_2(t) + \cdots$ *converges for every value of* t *in a closed region* R; (H_2) *if the derivatives* $f_i'(t)$ *of the* $f_i(t)$ *exist for every value of* t *in* R; *and* (H_3) *if the series* $G(t) = f_1'(t) + f_2'(t) + \cdots$ *converges uniformly with respect to* t *for all values of* t *in* R; *then the derivative* $F'(t)$ *of* $F(t)$ *exists and* $F'(t) = G(t)$ *for every value of* t *in* R.

Proof. It follows from the definition of a derivative that the condition that the theorem shall be true is that, corresponding to every t in R and every $\epsilon > 0$, there shall exist a positive number $\delta_{\epsilon t}$ such that, if $|\Delta t| < \delta_{\epsilon t}$, the inequality

$$(1) \qquad \left| G(t) - \frac{F(t + \Delta t) - F(t)}{\Delta t} \right| < \epsilon$$

shall be satisfied. Hence it is sufficient to prove that, corresponding to every t in R and every $\epsilon > 0$, there exists a $\delta_{\epsilon t} > 0$ such that the inequality (1) will be satisfied when $|\Delta t| < \delta_{\epsilon t}$.

It follows from the notation of the hypotheses (H_1), (H_2), and (H_3) that

$$(2) \qquad \begin{cases} G(t) - \dfrac{F(t + \Delta t) - F(t)}{\Delta t} = F_n'(t) - \dfrac{F_n(t + \Delta t) - F_n(t)}{\Delta t} \\[2mm] \qquad\qquad + \lim_{p = \infty} F_{np}'(t) - \lim_{p = \infty} \dfrac{F_{np}(t + \Delta t) - F_{np}(t)}{\Delta t}, \end{cases}$$

where

$$(3) \qquad \begin{cases} F_n(t) = f_1(t) + \cdots + f_n(t), \\ F_n'(t) = f_1'(t) + \cdots + f_n'(t), \\ F_{np}(t) = f_{n+1}(t) + \cdots + f_{n+p}(t), \\ F_{np}'(t) = f_{n+1}'(t) + \cdots + f_{n+p}'(t). \end{cases}$$

Since $F_{np}(t)$ is a sum of p functions each of which has a derivative with respect to t for all values of t in R, the sum $F_{np}(t)$ has a derivative with respect to t for all values of t in R. Therefore it follows from the mean value theorem that

$$(4) \qquad F_{np}(t + \Delta t) - F_{np}(t) = \Delta t \, F_{np}'(\tau),$$

where $\tau = t + \lambda \Delta t$ and $|\lambda| \leqq 1$. Since, by (H_3), the sum $G(t)$ converges uniformly with respect to t for every t in R, it follows that, corresponding to every $\epsilon > 0$, there exists an integer n_ϵ, depending upon ϵ but *independent* of t, such that, for every $t = \tau$ in R and every $n > n_\epsilon$, it is true that

(5) $$\left| F_{np}'(\tau) \right| < \tfrac{1}{3}\epsilon \qquad (p = 1, 2, \cdots).$$

It also follows from (H_3) that, corresponding to every t in R and every $\epsilon > 0$, there exists an integer n_ϵ, depending upon ϵ but *independent* of t, such that, for every t in R and every $n > n_\epsilon$, it is true that

(6) $$\left| F_{np}'(t) \right| < \tfrac{1}{3}\epsilon \qquad (p = 1, 2, \cdots).$$

Finally, it follows from the notations of equations (3) that

(7) $$\left| F_n'(t) - \frac{F_n(t + \Delta t) - F_n(t)}{\Delta t} \right| \leqq \sum_{j=1}^{n} \left| f_j'(t) - \frac{f_j(t + \Delta t) - f_j(t)}{\Delta t} \right|.$$

It follows from (H_2) that, corresponding to every t in R, every $\epsilon > 0$, and every integer n, there exists a positive number δ_{ent}, depending upon ϵ, n, and t, such that, for every Δt satisfying $|\Delta t| < \delta_{ent}$, it is true that

$$\left| f_j'(t) - \frac{f_j(t + \Delta t) - f_j(t)}{\Delta t} \right| < \frac{\epsilon}{3n} \qquad (j = 1, \cdots, n).$$

When these inequalities are satisfied, it follows from (7) that

(8) $$\left| F_n'(t) - \frac{F_n(t + \Delta t) - F_n(t)}{\Delta t} \right| < \tfrac{1}{3}\epsilon.$$

Hence it follows from equation (2) and the inequalities (5), (6), and (8) that

(9) $$\left| G(t) - \frac{F(t + \Delta t) - F(t)}{\Delta t} \right| < \epsilon,$$

provided

(10) $$\begin{cases} n > n_\epsilon, \\ |\Delta t| < \delta_{ent}. \end{cases}$$

Since these inequalities can be sequentially satisfied, the inequality (1) is established and the theorem is proved.

Problem 1. Show in detail that the proof of the theorem fails if the condition of *uniform* convergence in (H_3) is not satisfied.

Problem 2. Prove the theorem: If the sequence $F_1(t)$, $F_2(t)$, $\cdots$ has the limit $F(t)$ for every t in R; if the derivatives $F_i'(t)$

of the $F(t)$ exist for every t in R; and if the limit $G(t)$ of the sequence $F_1'(t)$, $F_2'(t)$, $\cdots$ exists *uniformly* with respect to t for all values of t in R; then the derivative $F'(t)$ exists and $F'(t) = G(t)$ for all values of t in R.

APPENDIX F

THEOREM: (H_1) *If $f(x, t)$ is a continuous function of x and t at $x = a$ and $t = t_0$, and (H_2) if x is a function of t such that $x(t_0) = a$ and $x(t)$ is continuous at $t = t_0$, then $f(x, t)$ is a continuous function of t at $t = t_0$.*

Proof. The condition that the theorem shall be true is: Corresponding to every $\epsilon > 0$, there exists a δ_ϵ such that, for all values of t satisfying $|t - t_0| < \delta_\epsilon$, it is true that

$$(1) \qquad |f(x, t) - f(a, t_0)| < \epsilon.$$

It follows from (H_1) that, corresponding to every $\epsilon > 0$, there exist $\delta_{1\epsilon} > 0$ and $\delta_{2\epsilon} > 0$ such that, for every x and t satisfying $|x - a| < \delta_{1\epsilon}$, $|t - t_0| < \delta_{2\epsilon}$, it is true that $|f(x, t) - f(a, t_0)| < \epsilon$. It follows from (H_2) that, corresponding to every $\delta_{1\epsilon} > 0$, there exists a $\delta_{3\epsilon}$ such that, for every value of t satisfying $|t - t_0| < \delta_{3\epsilon}$, it is true that $|x(t) - x(t_0)| < \delta_{1\epsilon}$. Consequently for every $\epsilon > 0$, the inequality (1) is satisfied for all values of t such that $|t - t_0| < \delta_{2\epsilon}$, $|t - t_0| < \delta_{3\epsilon}$.

Problem 1. Suppose $f(x; t)$ is a continuous function of x at $x = a$, uniformly with respect to t in a neighborhood including t_0 in its interior, and that it is a continuous function of t at $t = t_0$. Suppose, also, that x is a continuous function of t at $t = t_0$ and that $x(t_0) = a$. Prove that $f[x(t); t]$ is a continuous function of t at $t = t_0$.

Problem 2. Suppose $f[\phi(x); t]$ is a continuous function of ϕ at $\phi = b$; $\phi(x)$ is a continuous function of x at $x = a$ and $\phi(a) = b$; and x is a continuous function of t at $t = t_0$ and $x(t_0) = a$. Prove that $f[\phi(x); t]$ is a continuous function of t at $t = t_0$.

APPENDIX G

THEOREM: *If the function $f(x_1, \cdots, x_n)$ is continuous in the x_i at $x_i = a_i$, and if $x_i^{(\kappa)}$ is an infinite sequence of the x_i such that $\lim_{\kappa=\infty} x_i^{(\kappa)} = a_i$, then $\lim_{\kappa=\infty} f(x_i^{(\kappa)}) = f(\lim_{\kappa=\infty} x_i^{(\kappa)}) = f(a_i)$.*

Proof. It follows from the continuity of $f(x_i)$ at $x_i = a_i$ that, corresponding to every $\epsilon > 0$, there exists a positive number δ_ϵ such that, for all x_i satisfying $|x_i - a_i| < \delta_\epsilon$, it is true that $|f(x_i) - f(a_i)| < \epsilon$. Since $\lim x_i^{(\kappa)} = a_i$, corresponding to every δ_ϵ an integer κ_{δ_ϵ} exists such that, for every integer $\kappa > \kappa_{\delta_\epsilon}$, it is true that $|x_i^{(\kappa)} - a_i| < \delta_\epsilon$. Hence, for every $\epsilon > 0$ it is true that $|f(x_i^{(\kappa)}) - f(a_i)| < \epsilon$ if $\kappa > \kappa_{\delta_\epsilon}$; that is, $\lim_{\kappa=\infty} f(x_i^{(\kappa)}) = f(\lim_{\kappa=\infty} x_i^{(\kappa)}) = f(a_i)$.

APPENDIX H

THEOREM: (H_1) *If $f_1(t), f_2(t), \cdots$ are continuous functions of t in a common region $R\,[T_1 \geqq t \leqq T_2]$; and (H_2) if the series*

$$(1) \qquad F(t) = f_1(t) + f_2(t) + \cdots$$

converges uniformly with respect to t for all values of t in R; then

$$(2) \qquad \int_{T_1}^{t} F(t)dt = \int_{T_1}^{t} f_1(t)dt + \int_{T_1}^{t} f_2(t)dt + \cdots$$

for all values of the upper limit t in R.

Proof. Since the convergence of the right member of equation (1) is uniform in t, it follows (Appendix D) that $F(t)$ is a continuous function of t for all values of t in R, and consequently the integral in the left member of equation (2) exists. Since the $f_i(t)$ are continuous in t, the integrals in the right member of equation (2) also exist. It only remains to prove that the right member converges and that the two members of the equation are equal.

Consider the absolute value of the difference

$$(3) \quad \begin{cases} \left| \int_{T_1}^{t} F(t)dt - \int_{T_1}^{t} F_n(t)dt \right| = \left| \int_{T_1}^{t} [F(t) - F_n(t)]dt \right| \\ = \left| \int_{T_1}^{t} [f_{n+1}(t) + f_{n+2}(t) \cdots]dt \right| \\ \leqq \int_{T_1}^{t} |f_{n+1}(t) + f_{n+2}(t) + \cdots |dt, \end{cases}$$

where

$$(4) \qquad F_n(t) = f_1(t) + \cdots + f_n(t).$$

Since the right member of equation (1) converges uniformly with respect to t for all values of t in R, it follows that, corresponding to every $\epsilon > 0$ and t in R, there exists an integer n_ϵ, depending on ϵ but independent of t, such that, for every integer $n > n_\epsilon$, it is true that

$$(5) \qquad |f_{n+1}(t) + f_{n+2}(t) + \cdots | < \frac{\epsilon}{T_2 - T_1}.$$

When n has a value for which this inequality is satisfied, the absolute value of the right member of equation (3) is less than ϵ for all values of t in R. Therefore, since for every finite value of n it is true that

$$(6) \qquad \int_{T_1}^{t} F_n(t)dt = \int_{T_1}^{t} f_1(t)dt + \cdots + \int_{T_1}^{t} f_n(t)dt,$$

the theorem is established.

Problem. Prove the theorem on which equation (6) rests.

INDEX

393

PARTIAL DIFFERENTIAL EQUATIONS OF MATHEMATICAL PHYSICS

by A. G. Webster

Still one of the most important treatises on partial differential equations in any language, this comprehensive work by one of America's greatest mathematical physicists covers the basic method, theory and application of partial differential equations. There are clear and full chapters on

Fourier series
integral equations
elliptic equations
spherical, cylindrical, ellipsoidal harmonics
Cauchy's method
boundary problems
method of Riemann-Volterra
and many other topics

This is a book complete in itself, developing fully the needed theory and application of every important field.

vibration
elasticity
potential theory
theory of sound
wave propagation
heat conduction
and others

Professor Webster's work is a keystone book in the library of every mature physicist, mathematical physicist, mathematician, and research engineer. It can also serve as an introduction and supplementary text for the student.

Edited by Samuel J. Plimpton. Second corrected edition. 97 illustrations. vii + 440pp. 5⅜ x 8.

S263 Paperbound **$2.00**

ORDINARY DIFFERENTIAL EQUATIONS
by E. L. Ince

The theory of ordinary differential equations in real and complex domains is here clearly explained and analyzed. The author covers not only classical theory, but also main developments of more recent times.

The pure mathematician will find valuable exhaustive sections on existence and nature of solutions, continuous transformation groups, the algebraic theory of linear differential systems, and the solution of differential equations by contour integration. The engineer and physicist will be interested in an especially fine treatment of the equations of Legendre, Bessel, and Mathieu; the transformations of Laplace and Mellin; the conditions for the oscillatory character of solutions of a differential equation; the relation between a linear differential system and an integral equation; the asymptotic development of characteristic numbers and functions; and many other topics.

PARTIAL CONTENTS: **Real Domain.** Elementary methods of integration. Existence and nature of solutions. Continuous transformation-groups. Linear differential equations — theory of, with constant coefficients, solutions of, algebraic theory of. Sturmian theory, its later developments. Boundary problems. **Complex Domain.** Existence theorems. Equations of first order. Non-linear equations of higher order. Solutions, systems, classifications of linear equations. Oscillation theorems.

"Will be welcomed by mathematicians, engineers, and others," MECH. ENGINEERING. " Highly recommended," ELECTRONICS INDUSTRIES. "Deserves the highest praise," BULLETIN, AM. MATH. SOC.

Historical appendix. Bibliography. Index. 18 figures. viii + 558pp. 5⅜ x 8.

S349 Paperbound **\$2.45**

INTRODUCTION TO THE DIFFERENTIAL EQUATIONS OF PHYSICS

by L. Hopf

The first portion of this concise introduction to ordinary and partial differential equations acquaints the reader with equations describing the more important theories of classical physics. It covers the mechanics of particles, potential, heat conduction, energy, electro-dynamics, oscillations, electromagnetic waves and potentials.

The concluding chapters introduce some of the standard ways for solving those differential equations which have been derived: Eigenfunctions, Fourier series and integrals, Green's theorem, particular solutions in coordinates, asymptotic expansions, change of variables, conformal mapping, singularities, and transition to integral equations.

Mathematics is developed in close connection with physical problems, as needed. Elementary physical intuition is skillfully blended with formal mathematics. This volume is specially apt for self-study, since no mathematical background beyond elementary calculus is required of the reader.

"A remarkably good presentation . . . one could hardly be without this book on his shelf for quick reference," YALE BIOPHYSICS REVIEW. "Ideal for the young prospective physicist . . . for the more advanced student who wants a compact compilation," AMERICAN MATHEMATICAL MONTHLY. "The author should be congratulated . . . recommended to future engineers and physicists," ZEITSCHRIFT FUR ANGEWANDTE MATHEMATIK UND PHYSIK.

Translated by Walter Nef. Index. 48 illustrations. v + 154pp. 5⅜ x 8.

Paperbound $1.25

NUMERICAL INTEGRATION OF DIFFERENTIAL EQUATIONS

by A. A. Bennett, W. E. Milne, Harry Bateman

Unabridged republication of an original monograph for the National Research Council. This well-known greatly sought-after volume describes new methods of integration of differential equations developed by three leading mathematicians. It contains much material not readily available in detail elsewhere. Discussions on methods for partial differential equations, transition from difference equations to differential equations, solution of differential equations to non-integral values of a parameter are of special interest to mathematicians, physicists, mathematical physicists.

Partial contents. THE INTERPOLATIONAL POLYNOMIAL, A. A. Bennett. Tabular index, arguments, values, differences. Displacements, divided differences, repeated arguments, derivation of the interpolational polynomial, integral. SUCCESSIVE APPROXIMATIONS, A. A. Bennett. Numerical methods of successive substitutions. Approximate methods in solution of differential equations. STEP-BY-STEP METHODS OF INTEGRATION, W. E. Milne. Differential equations of the 1st order: Taylor's series, methods using ordinates, Runge-Kutta method. Systems of differential equations of the first order. Higher order differential equations. Second order equations in which first derivatives are absent. METHODS FOR PARTIAL DIFFERENTIAL EQUATIONS, Harry Bateman. Transition from solution of difference equations to solution of differential equations. Ritz's method. Least squares method. Extension of solution to nonintegral values of a parameter.

288 footnotes, mostly bibliographic, 285 item classified biblography. 108pp. 5⅜ x 8.

S305 Paperbound $1.35

DOVER BOOKS ON SCIENCE
BOOKS THAT EXPLAIN SCIENCE

CONCERNING THE NATURE OF THINGS, Sir William Bragg. Christmas lectures delivered at the Royal Society by Nobel laureate. Why a spinning ball travels in a curved track; how uranium is transmuted to lead, etc. Partial contents: atoms, gases, liquids, crystals, metals etc. No scientific background needed; wonderful for intelligent high school student. 32pp. of photos, 57 figures. xii + 232pp. 5⅜ x 8. T31 Paperbound **$1.35**

THE NATURE OF LIGHT AND COLOUR IN THE OPEN AIR, M. Minnaert. Why is falling snow sometimes black? What causes mirages, the fata morgana, multiple suns and moons in the sky; how are shadows formed? Prof. Minnaert of the University of Utrecht answers these and similar questions in optics, light, colour, for non-specialists. Particularly valuable to nature, science students, painters, photographers. Translated by H. M. Kremer-Priest, K. Jay. 202 illustrations, including 42 photos. xvi + 362pp. 5⅜ x 8. T196 Paperbound **$1.95**

THE RESTLESS UNIVERSE, Max Born. New enlarged version of this remarkably readable account by a Noble laureate. Moving from subatomic particles to universe, the author explains in very simple terms the latest theories of wave mechanics. Partial contents: air and its relatives, electrons & ions, waves & particles, electronic structure of the atom, nuclear physics. Nearly 600 illustrations, including 7 animated sequences. 325pp. 6 x 9. T412 Paperbound **$2.00**

MATTER & LIGHT, THE NEW PHYSICS, L. de Broglie. Non-technical papers by a Nobel laureate explain electromagnetic theory, relativity, matter, light and radiation, wave mechanics, quantum physics, philosophy of science. Einstein, Planck, Bohr, others explained so easily that no mathematical training is needed for all but 2 of the 21 chapters. Unabridged. Index. 300pp. 5⅜ x 3. T35 Paperbound **$1.75**

THE COMMON SENSE OF THE EXACT SCIENCES, W. K. Clifford. Introduction by James Newman, edited by Karl Pearson. For 70 years this has been a guide to classical scientific and mathematical thought. Explains with unusual clarity basic concepts, such as extension of meaning of symbols, characteristics of surface boundaries, properties of plane figures, vectors, Cartesian method of determining position, etc. Long preface by Bertrand Russell. Bibliography of Clifford. Corrected, 130 diagrams redrawn. 249pp. 5⅜ x 8. T61 Paperbound **$1.60**

THE EVOLUTION OF SCIENTIFIC THOUGHT FROM NEWTON TO EINSTEIN, A. d'Abro. Einstein's special and general theories of relativity, with their historical implications, are analyzed in non-technical terms. Excellent accounts of the contributions of Newton, Riemann, Weyl, Planck, Eddington, Maxwell, Lorentz and others are treated in terms of space and time, equations of electromagnetics, finiteness of the universe, methodology of science. 21 diagrams. 482pp. 5⅜ x 8. T2 Paperbound **$2.00**

WHAT IS SCIENCE, Norman Campbell. This excellent introduction explains scientific method, role of mathematics, types of scientific laws. Contents: 2 aspects of science, science & nature, laws of science, discovery of laws, explanation of laws, measurement & numerical laws, applications of science. 192pp. 5⅜ x 8. S43 Paperbound **$1.25**

THE RISE OF THE NEW PHYSICS, A. d'Abro. A half-million word exposition, formerly titled THE DECLINE OF MECHANISM, for readers not versed in higher mathematics. The only thorough explanation, in everyday language, of the central core of modern mathematical physical theory, treating both classical and modern theoretical physics, and presenting in terms almost anyone can understand the equivalent of 5 years of study of mathematical physics. Scientifically impeccable coverage of mathematical-physical thought from the Newtonian system up through the electronic theories of Dirac and Heisenberg and Fermi's statistics. Combines both history and exposition; provides a broad yet unified and detailed view, with constant comparison of classical and modern views on phenomena and theories. "A must for anyone doing serious study in the physical sciences," JOURNAL OF THE FRANKLIN INSTITUTE. "Extraordinary faculty . . . to explain ideas and theories of theoretical physics in the language of daily life," ISIS. Indexed. 97 illustrations. ix + 982pp. 5⅜ x 8.

T3 Volume 1, Paperbound **$2.00**
T4 Volume 2, Paperbound **$2.00**

A HISTORY OF ASTRONOMY FROM THALES TO KEPLER, J. L. E. Dreyer. (Formerly A HISTORY OF PLANETARY SYSTEMS FROM THALES TO KEPLER.) This is the only work in English to give the complete history of man's cosmological views from prehistoric times to Kepler and Newton. Partial contents: Near Eastern astronomical systems, Early Greeks. Homocentric spheres of Eudoxus, Epicycles. Ptolemaic system, medieval cosmology. Copernicus. Kepler, etc. Revised, foreword by W. H. Stahl. New bibliography. xvii + 430pp. 5⅜ x 8. S79 Paperbound **$1.98**

THE PSYCHOLOGY OF INVENTION IN THE MATHEMATICAL FIELD, J. Hadamard. Where do ideas come from? What role does the unconscious play? Are ideas best developed by mathematical reasoning, word reasoning, visualization? What are the methods used by Einstein, Poincaré, Galton, Riemann. How can these techniques be applied by others? Hadamard, one of the world's leading mathematicians, discusses these and other questions. xiii + 145pp. 5⅜ x 8. T107 Paperbound **$1.25**

SPINNING TOPS AND GYROSCOPIC MOTION, John Perry. Well-known classic of science still unsurpassed for lucid, accurate, delightful exposition. How quasi-rigidity is induced in flexible and fluid bodies by rapid motion; why gyrostat falls, top rises; nature and effect on climatic conditions of earth's precessional movement; effect of internal fluidity on rotating bodies, etc. Appendixes describe practical uses to which gyroscopes have been put in ships, compasses, monorail transportation. 62 figures. 128pp. 5⅜ x 8. T416 Paperbound **$1.00**

A CONCISE HISTORY OF MATHEMATICS, D. Struik. Lucid study of development of mathematical ideas, techniques, from Ancient Near East, Greece, Islamic science, Middle Ages, Renaissance, modern times. Important mathematicians are described in detail. Treatment is not anecdotal, but analytical development of ideas. "Rich in content, thoughtful in interpretation" U. S. QUARTERLY BOOKLIST. Non-technical; no mathematical training needed. Index. 60 illustrations, including Egyptian papyri, Greek mss., portraits of 31 eminent mathematicians. Bibliography. 2nd edition. xix + 299pp. 5⅜ x 8. **S255 Paperbound $1.75**

FOUNDATIONS OF GEOMETRY, Bertrand Russell. Analyzing basic problems in the overlap area between mathematics and philosophy, Nobel laureate Russell examines the nature of geometrical knowledge, the nature of geometry, and the application of geometry to space. It covers the history of non-Euclidean geometry, philosophic interpretations of geometry—especially Kant—projective and metrical geometry. This is most interesting as the solution offered in 1897 by a great mind to a problem still current. New introduction by Prof. Morris Kline of N. Y. University. xii + 201pp. 5⅜ x 8.
S232 Clothbound $3.25
S233 Paperbound $1.60

THE NATURE OF PHYSICAL THEORY, P. W. Bridgman. Here is how modern physics looks to a highly unorthodox physicist—a Nobel laureate. Pointing out many absurdities of science, and demonstrating the inadequacies of various physical theories, Dr. Bridgman weighs and analyzes the contributions of Einstein, Bohr, Newton, Heisenberg, and many others. This is a non-technical consideration of the correlation of science and reality. Index. xi + 138pp. 5⅜ x 8.
S33 Paperbound $1.25

EXPERIMENT AND THEORY IN PHYSICS, Max Born. A Nobel laureate examines the nature and value of the counterclaims of experiment and theory in physics. Synthetic versus analytical scientific advances are analyzed in the work of Einstein, Bohr, Heisenberg, Planck, Eddington, Milne, and others by a fellow participant. 44pp. 5⅜ x 8. **S308 Paperbound 60c**

THE STUDY OF THE HISTORY OF MATHEMATICS & THE STUDY OF THE HISTORY OF SCIENCE, George Sarton. Scientific method & philosophy in 2 scholarly fields. Defines duty of historian of math provides especially useful bibliography with best available biographies of modern mathematicians, editions of their collected works, correspondence. Shows that combination of history & science will aid scholar in understanding science today. Bibliography includes best known treatises on historical methods. 200-item critically evaluated bibliography. Index. 10 illustrations. 2 volumes bound as one. 113pp. + 75pp. 5⅜ x 8. **T240 Paperbound $1.25**

SCIENCE AND METHOD, Henri Poincaré. Procedure of scientific discovery, methodology, experiment, idea-germination—the intellectual processes by which discoveries come into being. Most significant and most interesting aspects of development, application of ideas. Chapters cover selection of facts, chance, mathematical reasoning, mathematics and logic; Whitehead, Russell, Cantor; the new mechanics, etc. 288pp. 5⅜ x 8. **S222 Paperbound $1.25**

SCIENCE AND HYPOTHESIS, Henri Poincaré. Creative psychology in science. How such concepts as number, magnitude, space, force, classical mechanics were developed, and how the modern scientist uses them in his thought. Hypothesis in physics, theories of modern physics. Introduction by Sir James Larmor. "Few mathematicians have had the breadth of vision of Poincaré, and none is his superior in the gift of clear exposition," E. T. Bell. Index. 272pp. 5⅜ x 8.
S221 Paperbound $1.25

FOUNDATIONS OF PHYSICS, R. B. Lindsay & H. Margenau. Excellent bridge between semi-popular works & technical treatises. A discussion of methods of physical description, construction of theory; valuable for physicist with elementary calculus who is interested in ideas that give meaning to data, tools of modern physics. Contents include symbolism, mathematical equations; space & time; foundations of mechanics; probability; physics & continua; electron theory; special & general relativity; quantum mechanics; causality. "Thorough and yet not overdetailed. Unreservedly recommended," NATURE (London). Unabridged, corrected edition. List of recommended readings. 35 illustrations. xi + 537pp. 5⅜ x 8. **S377 Paperbound $2.45**

CLASSICS OF SCIENCE

THE THIRTEEN BOOKS OF EUCLID'S ELEMENTS, edited by **Sir Thomas Heath.** Definitive edition of one of the very greatest classics of Western world. Complete English translation of Heiberg text, together with spurious Book XIV. Detailed 150-page introduction discussing aspects of Greek and medieval mathematics. Euclid, texts, commentators, etc. Paralleling the text is an elaborate critical apparatus analyzing each definition, proposition, postulate, covering textual matters, mathematical analysis, commentators of all times, refutations, supports, extrapolations, etc. This is the full EUCLID. Unabridged reproduction of Cambridge U. 2nd edition. 3 volumes. Total of 995 figures, 1426pp. 5⅜ x 8. **S88,89,90 3 volume set, paperbound $6.00**

OPTICKS, Sir Isaac Newton. In its discussions of light, reflection, color, refraction, theories of wave and corpuscular theories of light, this work is packed with scores of insights and discoveries. In its precise and practical discussion of construction of optical apparatus, contemporary understandings of phenomena it is truly fascinating to modern physicists, astronomers, mathematicians. Foreword by Albert Einstein. Preface by I. B. Cohen of Harvard University. 7 pages of portraits, facsimile pages, letters, etc. cxvi + 414pp. 5⅜ x 8. **S205 Paperbound $2.00**

THE PRINCIPLE OF RELATIVITY, A. Einstein, H. Lorentz, M. Minkowski, H. Weyl. These are the 11 basic papers that founded the general and special theories of relativity, all translated into English. Two papers by Lorentz on the Michelson experiment, electromagnetic phenomena. Minkowski's SPACE & TIME, and Weyl's GRAVITATION & ELECTRICITY. 7 epoch-making papers by Einstein: ELECTROMAGNETICS OF MOVING BODIES, INFLUENCE OF GRAVITATION IN PROPAGATION OF LIGHT, COSMOLOGICAL CONSIDERATIONS, GENERAL THEORY, and 3 others. 7 diagrams. Special notes by A. Sommerfeld. 224pp. 5⅜ x 8. **S81 Paperbound $1.75**

THE ANALYTICAL THEORY OF HEAT, Joseph Fourier. This book, which revolutionized mathematical physics, is listed in the Great Books program, and many other listings of great books. It has been used with profit by generations of mathematicians and physicists who are interested in either heat or in the application of the Fourier integral. Covers cause and reflections of rays of heat, radiant heating, heating of closed spaces, use of trigonometric series in the theory of heat, Fourier integral, etc. Translated by Alexander Freeman. 20 figures. xxii + 466pp. 5⅜ x 8.
S93 Paperbound **$2.00**

THE WORKS OF ARCHIMEDES, edited by **T. L. Heath.** All the known works of the great Greek mathematician are contained in this one volume, including the recently discovered Method of Archimedes. Contains: On Sphere & Cylinder, Measurement of a Circle, Spirals, Concids, Spheroids, etc. This is the definitive edition of the greatest mathematical intellect of the ancient world. 186-page study by Heath discusses Archimides and the history of Greek mathematics. Bibliography. 563pp. 5⅝ x 8.
S9 Paperbound **$2.00**

A PHILOSOPHICAL ESSAY ON PROBABILITIES, Marquis de Laplace. This famous essay explains without recourse to mathematics the principle of probability, and the application of probability to games of chance, natural philosophy, astronomy, many other fields. Translated from the 6th French edition by F. W. Truscott, F. L. Emory, with new introduction for this edition by E. T. Bell. 204pp. 5⅜ x 8.
S166 Paperbound **$1.25**

INVESTIGATIONS ON THE THEORY OF THE BROWNIAN MOVEMENT, Albert Einstein. Reprints from rare European journals. 5 basic papers, including the Elementary Theory of the Brownian Movement, written at the request of Lorentz to provide a simple explanation. Translated by A. D. Cowper. Annotated, edited by R. Fürth. 33pp. of notes elucidate, give history of previous investigations. Author, subject indexes. 62 footnotes. 124pp. 5⅜ x 8.
S304 Paperbound **$1.25**

THE GEOMETRY OF RENÉ DESCARTES. With this book Descartes founded analytical geometry. Original French text, with Descartes' own diagrams, and excellent Smith-Latham translation. Contains Problems the Construction of Which Requires Only Straight Lines and Circles; On the Nature of Curved Lines; On the Construction of Solid or Supersolid Problems. Notes. Diagrams. 258pp. 5⅜ x 8.
S68 Paperbound **$1.50**

DIALOGUES CONCERNING TWO NEW SCIENCES, Galileo Galilei. This classic of experimental science, mechanics, engineering, is as enjoyable as it is important. Based on 30 years' experimentation and characterized by its author as "superior to everything else of mine," it offers a lively exposition of dynamics, elasticity, sound, ballistics, strength of materials, and the scientific method. Translated by H. Grew and A. de Salvio. 126 diagrams. Index. xxi + 288pp. 5⅜ x 8.
S99 Paperbound **$1.65**

TREATISE ON ELECTRICITY AND MAGNETISM, James Clerk Maxwell. For more than 80 years a seemingly inexhaustible source of leads for physicists, mathematicians, engineers. Total of 1082pp. on such topics as Measurement of Quantities, Electrostatics, Elementary Mathematical Theory of Electricity, Electrical Work and Energy in a System of Conductors, General Theorems, Theory of Electrical Images, Electrolysis, Conduction, Polarization, Dielectrics, Resistance, etc. "The greatest mathematical physicist since Newton," Sir James Jeans. 3rd edition. 107 figures, 21 plates. 1082pp. 5⅜ x 8.
S186 Clothbound **$4.95**

PRINCIPLES OF PHYSICAL OPTICS, Ernst Mach. This classical examination of the propagation of light, color, polarization etc. offers a historical and philosophical treatment that has never been surpassed for breadth and easy readability. Contents: Rectilinear propagation of light. Reflection, refraction. Early knowledge of vision. Dioptrics. Composition of light. Theory of color and dispersion. Periodicity. Theory of interference. Polarization. Mathematical representation of properties of light. Propagation of waves, etc. 279 illustrations, 10 portraits. Appendix. Indexes. 324pp. 5⅜ x 8.
S178 Paperbound **$1.75**

THEORY OF ELECTRONS AND ITS APPLICATION TO THE PHENOMENA OF LIGHT AND RADIANT HEAT, H. Lorentz. Lectures delivered at Columbia University by Nobel laureate Lorentz. Unabridged, they form a historical coverage of the theory of free electrons, motion, absorption of heat, Zeeman effect, propagation of light in molecular bodies, inverse Zeeman effect, optical phenomena in moving bodies, etc. 109 pages of notes explain the more advanced sections. Index. 9 figures. 352pp. 5⅜ x 8.
S173 Paperbound **$1.85**

MATTER & MOTION, James Clerk Maxwell. This excellent exposition begins with simple particles and proceeds gradually to physical systems beyond complete analysis: motion, force, properties of centre of mass of material system, work, energy, gravitation, etc. Written with all Maxwell's original insights and clarity! Notes by E. Larmor. 17 diagrams. 178pp. 5⅜ x 8.
S188 Paperbound **$1.25**

AN INTRODUCTION TO THE STUDY OF EXPERIMENTAL MEDICINE, Claude Bernard. 90-year-old classic of medical science, only major work of Bernard available in English, records his efforts to transform physiology into exact science. Principles of scientific research illustrated by specific case histories from his work; roles of chance, error, preliminary false conclusions, in leading eventually to scientific truth; use of hypothesis. Much of modern application of mathematics to biology rests on the foundation set down here. New foreword by Professor I. B. Cohen, Harvard Univ. xxv + 266pp. 5⅜ x 8.
T400 Paperbound **$1.50**

PRINCIPLES OF MECHANICS, Heinrich Hertz. This last work by the great 19th century physicist is not only a classic, but of great interest in the logic of science. Creating a new system of mechanics based upon space, time, and mass, it returns to axiomatic analysis, to understanding of the formal or structural aspects of science, taking into account logic, observation, and a priori elements. Of great historical importance to Poincaré, Carnap, Einstein, Milne. A 20-page introduction by R. S. Cohen, Wesleyan University, analyzes the implications of Hertz's thought and the logic of science. Bibliography. 13-page introduction of Helmholtz. xiii + 274pp. 5⅜ x 8.

S316 Clothbound **$3.50**
S317 Paperbound **$1.75**

ANIMALS IN MOTION, Eadweard Muybridge. Largest, most comprehensive selection of Muybridge's famous action photos of animals, from his ANIMAL LOCOMOTION. 3919 high-speed shots of 34 different animals and birds in 123 different types of action: horses, mules, oxen, pigs, goats, camels, elephants, dogs, cats, guanacos, sloths, lions, tigers, jaguars, raccoons, baboons, deer, elk, gnus, kangaroos, many others, in different actions—walking, running, flying, leaping. Horse alone shown in more than 40 different ways. Photos taken against ruled backgrounds; most actions taken from 3 angles at once: 90°, 60°, rear. Most plates original size. Of considerable interest to scientists as a classic of biology, as a record of actual facts of natural history and physiology. "A really marvellous series of plates," NATURE (London). "A monumental work," Waldemar Kaempffert. Photographed by E. Muybridge. Edited by L. S. Brown, American Museum of Natural History. 74-page introduction on mechanics of motion. 340 pages of plates, 3919 photographs. 416pp. Deluxe binding, paper. (Weight 4½ lbs.) 7⅞ x 10⅝.

T203 Clothbound **$10.00**

THE HUMAN FIGURE IN MOTION, Eadweard Muybridge. This new edition of a great classic in the history of science and photography is the largest selection ever made from the original Muybridge photos of human action: 4789 photographs, illustrating 163 types of motion: walking, running, lifting, etc. in time-exposure sequence photos at speeds up to 1/6000th of a second. Men, women, children, mostly undraped, showing bone and muscle positions against ruled backgrounds, mostly taken at 3 angles at once. Not only was this a great work of photography, acclaimed by contemporary critics as a work of genius, it was also a great 19th century landmark in biological research. Historical introduction by Prof. Robert Taft, U. of Kansas. Plates original size, full detail. Over 500 action strips. 407pp. 7¾ x 10⅝.

T204 Clothbound **$10.00**

ON THE SENSATIONS OF TONE, Hermann Helmholtz. This is an unmatched coordination of such fields as acoustical physics, physiology, experiment, history of music. It covers the entire gamut of musical tone. Partial contents: relation of vibration, resonance, analysis of tones by sympathetic resonance, beats, chords, tonality, consonant chords, discords, progression of parts, etc. 33 appendixes discuss various aspects of sound, physics, acoustics, music, etc. Translated by A. J. Ellis. New introduction by Prof. Henry Margenau of Yale. 68 figures. 43 musical passages analyzed. Over 100 tables. Index. xix + 576pp. 6⅛ x 9¼.

S114 Clothbound **$4.95**

COLLECTED WORKS OF BERNHARD RIEMANN. This important source book is the first to contain the complete text of both 1892 Werke and the 1902 supplement, unabridged. It contains 31 monographs, 3 complete lecture courses, 15 miscellaneous papers, which have been of enormous importance in relativity, topology, theory of complex variables, and other areas of mathematics. Edited by R. Dedekind, H. Weber, M. Noether, W. Wirtinger. German text. English introduction by Hans Lewy. 690pp. 5⅜ x 8. S226 Paperbound **$2.85**

CONTRIBUTIONS TO THE FOUNDING OF THE THEORY OF TRANSFINITE NUMBERS, Georg Cantor. These papers founded a new branch of mathematics. The famous articles of 1895-7 are translated with an 82-page introduction by P. E. B. Jourdain dealing with Cantor, the background of his discoveries, their results, future possibilities. Bibliography. Index. Notes. ix + 211pp. 5⅜ x 8. S45 Paperbound **$1.25**

PRINCIPLES OF PSYCHOLOGY, William James. This is the complete "Long Course," which is not to be confused with abridged editions. It contains all the wonderful descriptions, deep insights that have caused it to be a permanent work in all psychological libraries. Partial contents: functions of the brain, automation theories, mind-stuff theories, relation of mind to other things, consciousness, times, space, thing perception, will, emotions, hypnotism, and dozens of other areas in descriptive psychology. "A permanent classic like Locke's ESSAYS, Hume's TREATISE," John Dewey. "The preeminence of James in American psychology is unquestioned," PERSONALIST. "The American classic in psychology—unequaled in breadth and scope in the entire psychological literature," PSYCHOANALYTICAL QUARTERLY. Index. 94 figures. 2 volumes bound as one. Total of 1408pp.

T381 Vol. 1. Paperbound **$2.00**
T382 Vol. 2. Paperbound **$2.00**

RECREATIONS

SEVEN SCIENCE FICTION NOVELS OF H. G. WELLS. This is the complete text, unabridged, of seven of Wells's greatest novels: War of the Worlds, The Invisible Man, The Island of Dr. Moreau, The Food of the Gods, The First Men in the Moon, In the Days of the Comet, The Time Machine. Still considered by many experts to be the best science-fiction ever written, they will offer amusement and instruction to the scientific-minded reader. 1015pp. 5⅜ x 8.

T264 Clothbound **$3.95**

28 SCIENCE FICTION STORIES OF H. G. WELLS. Unabridged! This enormous omnibus contains 2 full-length novels—Men Like Gods, Star Begotten—plus 26 short stories of space, time, invention, biology, etc. The Crystal Egg, The Country of the Blind, Empire of the Ants, The Man Who Could Work Miracles, Aepyornis Island, A Story of the Days to Come, and 22 others! 915pp. 5⅜ x 8.   T265 Clothbound **$3.95**

FLATLAND, E. A. Abbott. This is a perennially popular science-fiction classic about life in a two-dimensional world, and the impingement of higher dimensions. Political, satiric, humorous, moral overtones. Relativity, the fourth dimension, and other aspects of modern science are explained more clearly than in most texts. 7th edition. New introduction by Banesh Hoffmann. 128pp. 5⅜ x 8.   T1 Paperbound **$1.00**

CRYPTANALYSIS, Helen F. Gaines. (Formerly ELEMENTARY CRYPTANALYSIS.) A standard elementary and intermediate text for serious students. It does not confine itself to old material, but contains much that is not generally known except to experts. Concealment, Transposition, Subsitution ciphers; Vigenere, Kasiski, Playfair, multafid, dozens of other techniques. Appendix with sequence charts, letter frequencies in English, 5 other languages, English word frequencies. Bibliography. 167 codes. New to this edition: solutions to codes. vi + 230pp. 5⅜ x 8⅜.
T97 Paperbound **$1.95**

FADS AND FALLACIES IN THE NAME OF SCIENCE, Martin Gardner. Examines various cults, quack systems, frauds, delusions which at various times have masqueraded as science. Accounts of hollow-earth fanatics like Symmes; Velikovsky and wandering planets; Hoerbiger; Bellamy and the theory of multiple moons; Charles Fort, dowsing, pseudoscientific methods for finding water, ores, oil. Sections on naturopathy, iridiagnosis, zone therapy, food fads, etc. Analytical accounts of Wilhelm Reich and orgone sex energy; L. Ron Hubbard and Dianetics; A. Korzybski and General Semantics; many others. Brought up to date to include Bridey Murphy, others. Not just a collection of anecdotes, but a fair, reasoned appraisal of eccentric theory. Formerly titled IN THE NAME OF SCIENCE. Preface. Index. x + 384pp. 5⅜ x 8.
T394 Paperbound **$1.50**

REINFELD ON THE END GAME IN CHESS, Fred Reinfeld. Analyzes 62 end games by Alekhine, Flohr, Tarrasch, Morphy, Bogolyubov, Capablanca, Vidmar, Rubinstein, Lasker, Reshevsky, other masters. Only first-rate book with extensive coverage of error; of immense aid in pointing out errors you might have made. Centers around transitions from middle play to various types of end play. King & pawn endings, minor piece endings, queen endings, bad bishops, blockage, weak pawns, passed pawns, etc. Formerly titled PRACTICAL END PLAY. 62 figures. vi + 177pp. 5⅜ x 8.   T417 Paperbound **$1.25**

PUZZLE QUIZ AND STUNT FUN, Jerome Meyer. 238 high-priority puzzles, stunts, and tricks—mathematical puzzles like The Clever Carpenter, Atom Bomb, Please Help Alice; mysteries and deductions like The Bridge of Sighs, Dog Logic, Secret Code; observation puzzlers like The American Flag, Playing Cards, Telephone Dial; more than 200 others involving magic squares, tongue twisters, puns, anagrams, word design. Answers included. Revised, enlarged edition of FUN-TO-DO. Over 100 illustrations. 238 puzzles, stunts, tricks. 256pp. 5⅜ x 8.
T337 Paperbound **$1.00**

THE BOOK OF MODERN PUZZLES, G. L. Kaufman. More than 150 word puzzles, logic puzzles. No warmed-over fare but all new material based on same appeals that make crosswords and deduction puzzles popular, but with different principles, techniques. Two-minute teasers, involved word-labyrinths, design and pattern puzzles, puzzles calling for logic and observation, puzzles testing ability to apply general knowledge to peculiar situations, many others. Answers to all problems. 116 illustrations. 192pp. 5⅜ x 8.   T143 Paperbound **$1.00**

101 PUZZLES IN THOUGHT AND LOGIC by C. R. Wylie, Jr. Designed for readers who enjoy the challenge and stimulation of logical puzzles without specialized mathematical or scientific knowledge. These problems are entirely new and range from relatively easy, to brainteasers that will afford hours of subtle entertainment. Detective problems, how to find the lying fisherman, how a blindman can identify color by logic, and many more. Easy-to-understand introduction to the logic of puzzle solving and general scientific method. 128pp. 5⅜ x 8.
T367 Paperbound **$1.00**

MATHEMAGIC, MAGIC PUZZLES, AND GAMES WITH NUMBERS, Royal V. Heath. Over 60 new puzzles and stunts based on properties of numbers. Demonstrates easy techniques for multiplying large numbers mentally, identifying unknown numbers, determining date of any day in any year, dozens of similar useful, entertaining applications of mathematics. Entertainments like The Lost Digit, 3 Acrobats, Psychic Bridge, magic squares, triangles, cubes, circles, other material not easily found elsewhere. Edited by J. S. Meyer. 76 illustrations. 128pp. 5⅜ x 8.
T110 Paperpound **$1.00**

LEARN CHESS FROM THE MASTERS, Fred Reinfeld. Improve your chess, rate your improvement, by playing against Marshall, Znosko-Borovsky, Bronstein, Najdorf, others. Formerly titled CHESS BY YOURSELF, this book contains 10 games in which you move against masters, and grade your moves by an easy system. Games selected for interest, clarity, easy principles; illustrate common openings, both classical and modern. Ratings for 114 extra playing situations that might have arisen. Full annotations. 91 diagrams. viii + 144pp. 5¾ x 8.
T362 Paperbound **$1.00**

THE COMPLETE NONSENSE OF EDWARD LEAR. Original text & illustrations of all Lear's nonsense books: A BOOK OF NONSENSE, NONSENSE SONGS, MORE NONSENSE SONGS, LAUGHABLE LYRICS, NONSENSE SONGS AND STORIES. Only complete edition available at popular price. Old favorites such as The Dong With a Luminous Nose, hundreds of other delightful bits of nonsense for children & adults. 214 different limericks, each illustrated by Lear; 3 different sets of Nonsense Botany; 5 Nonsense Alphabets; many others. 546 illustrations. 320pp. 5⅜ x 8.
T167 Paperbound **$1.00**

CRYPTOGRAPHY, D. Smith. Excellent elementary introduction to enciphering, deciphering secret writing. Explains transposition, substitution ciphers; codes; solutions. Geometrical patterns, route transcription, columnar transposition, other methods. Mixed cipher systems; single-alphabet, polyalphabetical substitution; mechanical devices; Vigenere system, etc. Enciphering Japanese; explanation of Baconian Biliteral cipher frequency tables. More than 150 problems provide practical application. Bibliography. Index. 164pp. 5⅜ x 8.
T247 Paperbound **$1.00**

MATHEMATICAL EXCURSIONS, Helen A. Merrill. Fun, recreation, insights into elementary problem-solving. A mathematical expert guides you along by-paths not generally travelled in elementary math courses—how to divide by inspection, Russian peasant system of multiplication; memory systems for pi; building odd and even magic squares; dyadic systems; facts about 37; square roots by geometry; Tchebichev's machine; drawing five-sided figures; dozens more. Solutions to more difficult ones. 50 illustrations. 145pp. 5⅜ x 8.
T350 Paperbound **$1.00**

MATHEMATICAL RECREATIONS, M. Kraitchik. Some 250 puzzles, problems, demonstrations of recreational mathematics for beginners & advanced mathematicians. Unusual historical problems from Greek, Medieval, Arabic, Hindu sources; modern problems based on "mathematics without numbers," geometry, topology, arithmetic, etc. Pastimes derived from figurative numbers, Mersenne numbers, Fermat numbers; fairy chess; latruncles, reversi, many other topics. Full solutions. Excellent for insights into special fields of math. 181 illustrations. 330pp. 5⅜ x 8.
T163 Paperbound **$1.75**

MATHEMATICAL PUZZLES FOR BEGINNERS AND ENTHUSIASTS, G. Mott-Smith. 188 mathematical puzzles to test mental agility. Inference, interpretation, algebra, dissection of plane figures, geometry, properties of numbers, decimation, permutations, probability, all enter these delightful problems. Puzzles like the Odic Force, How to Draw an Ellipse, Spider's Cousin, more than 180 others. Detailed solutions. Appendix with square roots, triangular numbers, primes, etc. 135 illustrations. 2nd revised edition. 248pp. 5⅜ x 8.
T198 Paperbound **$1.00**

NEW WORD PUZZLES, Gerald L. Kaufman. Contains 100 brand new challenging puzzles based on words and their combinations, never published before in any form. Most are new types invented by the author—for beginners or experts. Chess word puzzles, addle letter anagrams, double word squares, double horizontals, alphagram puzzles, dual acrostigrams, linkogram lapwords—plus 8 other brand new types, all with solutions included. 196 figures. 100 brand new puzzles. vi + 122pp. 5⅜ x 8.
T344 Paperbound **$1.00**

MATHEMATICS, MAGIC AND MYSTERY, Martin Gardner. Card tricks, feats of mental mathematics, stage mind-reading, other "magic" explained as applications of probability, sets, theory of numbers, topology, various branches of mathematics. Creative examination of laws and their application, with sources of new tricks and insights. 115 sections discuss tricks with cards, dice, coins; geometrical vanishing tricks, dozens of others. No sleight of hand needed; mathematics guarantees success. 115 illustrations. xii + 174pp. 5⅜ x 8.
T335 Paperbound **$1.00**

MATHEMATICS ELEMENTARY TO INTERMEDIATE

HOW TO CALCULATE QUICKLY, Henry Sticker. This handy volume offers a tried and true method for helping you in the basic mathematics of daily life—addition, subtraction, multiplication, division, fractions, etc. It is designed to awaken your "number sense" or the ability to see relationships between numbers as whole quantities. It is not a collection of tricks working only on special numbers, but a serious course of over 9,000 problems and their solutions, teaching special techniques not taught in schools: left-to-right multiplication, new fast ways of division, etc. 5 or 10 minutes daily use will double or triple your calculation speed. Excellent for the scientific worker who is at home in higher math, but is not satisfied with his speed and accuracy in lower mathematics. 256pp. 5 x 7¼.
T295 Paperbound **$1.00**

FAMOUS PROBLEMS OF ELEMENTARY GEOMETRY, Felix Klein. Expanded version of the 1894 Easter lectures at Göttingen. 3 problems of classical geometry: squaring circle, trisecting angle, doubling cube, considered with full modern implications: transcendental numbers, pi, etc. Notes by R. Archibald. 16 figures. xi + 92pp. 5⅜ x 8.
T348 Clothbound **$1.50**
T298 Paperbound **$1.00**

HIGHER MATHEMATICS FOR STUDENTS OF CHEMISTRY AND PHYSICS, J. W. Mellor. Not abstract, but practical, building its problems out of familiar laboratory material, this covers differential calculus, coordinate, analytical geometry, functions, integral calculus, infinite series, numerical equations, differential equations, Fourier's theorem, probability, theory of errors, calculus of variations, determinants. "If the reader is not familiar with this book, it will repay him to examine it," CHEM. & ENGINEERING NEWS. 800 problems, 189 figures. Bibliography. xxi + 641pp. 5⅜ x 8.
S193 Paperbound **$2.00**

TRIGONOMETRY REFRESHER FOR TECHNICAL MEN, A. Albert Klaf. 913 detailed questions and answers cover the most important aspects of plane and spherical trigonometry. They will help you to brush up or to clear up difficulties in special areas.—The first portion of this book covers plane trigonometry, including angles, quadrants, trigonometrical functions, graphical representation, interpolation, equations, logarithms, solution of triangle, use of the slide rule and similar topics—188 pages then discuss application of plane trigonometry to special problems in navigation, surveying, elasticity, architecture, and various fields of engineering. Small angles, periodic functions, vectors, polar coordinates, De Moivre's theorem are fully examined—The third section of the book then discusses spherical trigonometry and the solution of spherical triangles, with their applications to terrestrial and astronomical problems. Methods of saving time with numerical calculations, simplification of principal functions of angle, much practical information make this a most useful book—913 questions answered. 1738 problems, answers to odd numbers. 494 figures. 24 pages of useful formulae, functions. Index. x + 629pp. 5⅜ x 8.
T371 Paperbound **$2.00**

CALCULUS REFRESHER FOR TECHNICAL MEN, A. Albert Klaf. This book is unique in English as a refresher for engineers, technicians, students who either wish to brush up their calculus or to clear up uncertainties. It is not an ordinary text, but an examination of most important aspects of integral and differential calculus in terms of the 756 questions most likely to occur to the technical reader. The first part of this book covers simple differential calculus, with constants, variables, functions, increments, derivatives, differentiation, logarithms, curvature of curves, and similar topics—The second part covers fundamental ideas of integration, inspection, substitution, transformation, reduction, areas and volumes, mean value, successive and partial integration, double and triple integration. Practical aspects are stressed rather than theoretical. A 50-page section illustrates the application of calculus to specific problems of civil and nautical engineering, electricity, stress and strain, elasticity, industrial engineering, and similar fields.— 756 questions answered. 566 problems, mostly answered. 36 pages of useful constants, formulae for ready reference. Index. v + 431pp. 5⅜ x 8.
T370 Paperbound **$2.00**

MONOGRAPHS ON TOPICS OF MODERN MATHEMATICS, edited by J. W. A. Young. Advanced mathematics for persons who haven't gone beyond or have forgotten high school algebra. 9 monographs on foundation of geometry, modern pure geometry, non-Euclidean geometry, fundamental propositions of algebra, algebraic equations, functions, calculus, theory of numbers, etc. Each monograph gives proofs of important results, and descriptions of leading methods, to provide wide coverage. New introduction by Prof. M. Kline, N. Y. University. 100 diagrams. xvi + 416pp. 6⅛ x 9¼.
S289 Paperbound **$2.00**

MATHEMATICS: INTERMEDIATE TO ADVANCED

INTRODUCTION TO THE THEORY OF FOURIER'S SERIES AND INTEGRALS, H. S. Carslaw. 3rd revised edition. This excellent introduction is an outgrowth of the author's courses at Cambridge. Historical introduction, rational and irrational numbers, infinite sequences and series, functions of a single variable, definite integral, Fourier series, Fourier integrals, and similar topics. Appendixes discuss practical harmonic analysis, periodogram analysis, Lebesgues theory. Indexes. 84 examples, bibliography. xiii + 368 pp. 5⅜ x 8.
S48 Paperbound **$2.00**

INTRODUCTION TO THE THEORY OF NUMBERS, L. E. Dickson. Thorough, comprehensive approach with adequate coverage of classical literature, an introductory volume beginners can follow. Chapters on divisibility, congruences, quadratic residues & reciprocity, Diophantine equations, etc. Full treatment of binary quadratic forms without usual restriction to integral coefficients. Covers infinitude of primes, least residues, Fermat's theorem, Euler's phi function, Legendre's symbol, Gauss's lemma, automorphs, reduced forms, recent theorems of Thue & Siegel, many more. Much material not readily available elsewhere. 239 problems. Index. 1 figure. viii + 183pp. 5⅜ x 8.
S342 Paperbound **$1.65**

MECHANICS VIA THE CALCULUS, P. W. Norris, W. S. Legge. Covers almost everything from linear motion to vector analysis: equations determining motion, linear methods, compounding of simple harmonic motions, Newton's laws of motion, Hooke's law, the simple pendulum, motion of a particle in 1 plane, centers of gravity, virtual work, friction, kinetic energy of rotating bodies, equilibrium of strings, hydrostatics, sheering stresses, elasticity, etc. 550 problems. 3rd revised edition. xii + 367pp.
S207 Clothbound **$3.95**

NON-EUCLIDEAN GEOMETRY, Roberto Bonola. The standard coverage of non-Euclidean geometry. It examines from both a historical and mathematical point of view the geometries which have arisen from a study of Euclid's 5th postulate upon parallel lines. Also included are complete texts, translated, of Bolyai's THEORY OF ABSOLUTE SPACE, Lobachevsky's THEORY OF PARALLELS. 180 diagrams. 431pp. 5⅜ x 8.
S27 Paperbound **$1.95**

ELEMENTS OF THE THEORY OF REAL FUNCTIONS, J. E. Littlewood. Based on lectures given at Trinity College, Cambridge, this book has proved to be extremely successful in introducing graduate students to the modern theory of functions. It offers a full and concise coverage of classes and cardinal numbers, well-ordered series, other types of series, and elements of the theory of sets of points. 3rd revised edition. vii + 71pp. 5⅜ x 8.
S171 Clothbound **$2.85**
S172 Paperbound **$1.25**

THE CONTINUUM AND OTHER TYPES OF SERIAL ORDER, E. V. Huntington. This famous book gives a systematic elementary account of the modern history of the continuum as a type of serial order. Based on the Cantor-Dedekind ordinal theory, which requires no technical knowledge of higher mathematics, it offers an easily followed analysis of ordered classes, discrete and dense series, continuous series, Cantor's transfinite numbers. 2nd edition. Index. viii + 82pp. 5⅜ x 8.
S129 Clothbound **$2.75**
S130 Paperbound **$1.00**

GEOMETRY OF FOUR DIMENSIONS, H. P. Manning. Unique in English as a clear, concise introduction. Treatment is synthetic, and mostly Euclidean, although in hyperplanes and hyperspheres at infinity, non-Euclidean geometry is used. Historical introduction. Foundations of 4-dimensional geometry. Perpendicularity, simple angles. Angles of planes, higher order. Symmetry, order, motion; hyperpyramids, hypercones, hyperspheres; figures with parallel elements; volume, hypervolume in space; regular polyhedroids. Glossary. 78 figures. ix + 348pp. 5⅜ x 8.
S181 Clothbound **$3.95**
S182 Paperbound **$1.95**

VECTOR AND TENSOR ANALYSIS, G. E. Hay. One of the clearest introductions to this increasingly important subject. Start with simple definitions, finish the book with a sure mastery of oriented Cartesian vectors, Christoffel symbols, solenoidal tensors, and their applications. Complete breakdown of plane, solid, analytical, differential geometry. Separate chapters on application. All fundamental formulae listed & demonstrated. 195 problems, 66 figures. viii + 193pp. 5⅜ x 8.
S109 Paperbound **$1.75**

INTRODUCTION TO THE DIFFERENTIAL EQUATIONS OF PHYSICS, L. Hopf. Especially valuable to the engineer with no math beyond elementary calculus. Emphasizing intuitive rather than formal aspects of concepts, the author covers an extensive territory. Partial contents: Law of causality, energy theorem, damped oscillations, coupling by friction, cylindrical and spherical coordinates, heat source, etc. Index. 48 figures. 160pp. 5⅜ x 8.
S120 Paperbound **$1.25**

INTRODUCTION TO THE THEORY OF GROUPS OF FINITE ORDER, R. Carmichael. Examines fundamental theorems and their application. Beginning with sets, systems, permutations, etc.; it progresses in easy stages through important types of groups: Abelian, prime power, permutation, etc. Except 1 chapter where matrices are desirable, no higher math needed. 783 exercises, problems. Index. xvi + 447pp. 5⅜ x 8.
S299 Clothbound **$3.95**
S300 Paperbound **$2.00**

THEORY OF GROUPS OF FINITE ORDER, W. Burnside. First published some 40 years ago, this is still one of the clearest introductory texts. Partial contents: permutations, groups independent of representation, composition series of a group, isomorphism of a group with itself, Abelian groups, prime power groups, permutation groups, invariants of groups of linear substitution, graphical representation, etc. 45pp. of notes. Indexes. xxiv + 512pp. 5⅜ x 8.
S38 Paperbound **$2.45**

INFINITE SEQUENCES AND SERIES, Konrad Knopp. First publication in any language! Excellent introduction to 2 topics of modern mathematics, designed to give the student background to penetrate farther by himself. Sequences & sets, real & complex numbers, etc. Functions of a real & complex variable. Sequences & series. Infinite series. Convergent power series. Expansion of elementary functions. Numerical evaluation of series. Bibliography. v + 186pp. 5⅜ x 8.
S152 Clothbound **$3.50**
S153 Paperbound **$1.75**

THEORY OF SETS, E. Kamke. Clearest, amplest introduction in English, well suited for independent study. Subdivisions of main theory, such as theory of sets of points, are discussed, but emphasis is on general theory. Partial contents: rudiments of set theory, arbitrary sets and their cardinal numbers, ordered sets and their order types, well-ordered sets and their ordinal numbers. Bibliography. Key to symbols. Index. vii + 144pp. 5⅜ x 8.
S141 Paperbound **$1.35**

ELEMENTS OF NUMBER THEORY, I. M. Vinogradov. Detailed 1st course for persons without advanced mathematics; 95% of this book can be understood by readers who have gone no farther than high school algebra. Partial contents: divisibility theory, important number theoretical functions, congruences, primitive roots and indices, etc. Solutions to both problems and exercises. Tables of primes, indices, etc. Covers almost every essential formula in elementary number theory! 233 problems, 104 exercises. viii + 227pp. 5⅜ x 8.
S259 Paperbound **$1.60**

FIVE VOLUME "THEORY OF FUNCTIONS" SET BY KONRAD KNOPP. This five-volume set, prepared by Konrad Knopp, provides a complete and readily followed account of theory of functions. Proofs are given concisely, yet without sacrifice of completeness or rigor. These volumes are used as texts by such universities as M.I.T., University of Chicago, N. Y. City College, and many others. "Excellent introduction . . . remarkably readable, concise, clear, rigorous," JOURNAL OF THE AMERICAN STATISTICAL ASSOCIATION.

ELEMENTS OF THE THEORY OF FUNCTIONS, Konrad Knopp. This book provides the student with background for further volumes in this set, or texts on a similar level. Partial contents: Foundations, system of complex numbers and the Gaussian plane of numbers, Riemann sphere of numbers, mapping by linear functions, normal forms, the logarithm, the cyclometric functions and binomial series. "Not only for the young student, but also for the student who knows all about what is in it," MATHEMATICAL JOURNAL. Bibliography. Index. 140pp. 5⅜ x 8. S154 Paperbound **$1.35**

THEORY OF FUNCTIONS, PART I., Konrad Knopp. With volume II, this book provides coverage of basic concepts and theorems. Partial contents: numbers and points, functions of a complex variable, integral of a continuous function, Cauchy's integral theorem, Cauchy's integral formulae, series with variable terms, expansion of analytic functions in power series, analytic continuation and complete definition of analytic functions, entire transcendental functions, Laurent expansion, types of singularities. Bibliography. Index. vii + 146pp. 5⅜ x 8. S156 Paperbound **$1.35**

THEORY OF FUNCTIONS, PART II., Konrad Knopp. Application and further development of general theory, special topics. Single valued functions: entire, Weierstrass. Meromorphic functions: Mittag-Leffler. Periodic functions. Multiple-valued functions. Riemann surfaces. Algebraic functions. Analytical configuration, Riemann surface. Bibliography. Index. x + 150pp. 5⅜ x 8.
S157 Paperbound **$1.35**

PROBLEM BOOK IN THE THEORY OF FUNCTIONS, VOLUME 1., Konrad Knopp. Problems in elementary theory, for use with Knopp's THEORY OF FUNCTIONS, or any other text, arranged according to increasing difficulty. Fundamental concepts, sequences of numbers and infinite series, complex variable, integral theorems, development in series, conformal mapping. Answers. viii + 126pp. 5⅜ x 8. S158 Paperbound **$1.35**

PROBLEM BOOK IN THE THEORY OF FUNCTIONS, VOLUME 2, Konrad Knopp. Advanced theory of functions, to be used either with Knopp's THEORY OF FUNCTIONS, or any other comparable text. Singularities, entire & meromorphic functions, periodic, analytic, continuation, multiple-valued functions, Riemann surfaces, conformal mapping. Includes a section of additional elementary problems. "The difficult task of selecting from the immense material of the modern theory of functions the problems just within the reach of the beginner is here masterfully accomplished," AM. MATH. SOC. Answers. 138pp. 5⅜ x 8. S159 Paperbound **$1.35**

SYMBOLIC LOGIC

AN INTRODUCTION TO SYMBOLIC LOGIC, Susanne K. Langer. Probably the clearest book ever written on symbolic logic for the philosopher, general scientist and layman. It will be particularly appreciated by those who have been rebuffed by other introductory works because of insufficient mathematical training. No special knowledge of mathematics is required. Starting with the simplest symbols and conventions, you are led to a remarkable grasp of the Boole-Schroeder and Russell-Whitehead systems clearly and quickly. PARTIAL CONTENTS: Study of forms, Essentials of logical structure, Generalization, Classes, The deductive system of classes, The algebra of logic, Abstraction of interpretation, Calculus of propositions, Assumptions of PRINCIPIA MATHEMATICA, Logistics, Logic of the syllogism, Proofs of theorems. "One of the clearest and simplest introductions to a subject which is very much alive. The style is easy, symbolism is introduced gradually, and the intelligent non-mathematican should have no difficulty in following argument," MATHEMATICS GAZETTE. Revised, expanded second edition. Truth-value tables. 368pp. 5⅜ x 8.
S164 Paperbound **$1.75**

THE ELEMENTS OF MATHEMATICAL LOGIC, Paul Rosenbloom. FIRST PUBLICATION IN ANY LANGUAGE. This book is intended for readers who are mature mathematically, but have no previous training in symbolic logic. It does not limit itself to a single system, but covers the field as a whole. It is a development of lectures given at Lund University, Sweden in 1948. Partial contents: Logic of classes, fundamental theorems, Boolean algebra, logic of propositions, logic of propositional functions, expressive languages, combinatory logics, development of mathematics within an object language, paradoxes, theorems of Post and Goedel, Church's theorem, and similar topics. iv + 214pp. 5⅜ x 8. S277 Paperbound **$1.45**

THE LAWS OF THOUGHT, George Boole. This book founded symbolic logic some hundred years ago. It is the 1st significant attempt to apply logic to all aspects of human endeavour. Partial contents: derivation of laws, signs & laws, interpretations, eliminations, conditions of a perfect method, analysis, Aristotelian logic, probability, and similar topics. xviii + 424pp. 5⅜ x 8.
S28 Paperbound **$2.00**

ELEMENTARY MATHEMATICS FROM AN
ADVANCED STANDPOINT, Felix Klein.

This classic text is an outgrowth of Klein's famous integration and survey course at Göttingen. Using one field of mathematics to interpret, adjust, illuminate another, it covers basic topics in each area, illustrating its discussion with extensive analysis. It is especially valuable in considering areas of modern mathematics. "Makes the reader feel the inspiration of . . . a great mathematician, inspiring teacher . . . with deep insight into the foundations and interrelations," BULLETIN, AMERICAN MATHEMATICAL SOCIETY.

Vol. 1. ARITHMETIC, ALGEBRA, ANALYSIS. Introducing the concept of function immediately, it enlivens abstract discussion with graphical and geometrically perceptual methods. Partial contents: natural numbers, extension of the notion of number, special properties, complex numbers. Real equations with real unknowns, complex quantities. Logarithmic, exponential functions, goniometric functions, infinitesimal calculus. Transcendence of e and pi, theory of assemblages. Index. 125 figures. ix + 247pp. 5⅜ x 8. S150 Paperbound **$1.75**

Vol. 2. GEOMETRY. A comprehensive view which accompanies the space perception inherent in geometry with analytic formulas which facilitate precise formulation. Partial contents: Simplest geometric manifolds: line segment, Grassmann determinant principles, classification of configurations of space, derivative manifolds. Geometric transformations: affine transformations, projective, higher point transformations, theory of the imaginary. Systematic discussion of geometry and its foundations. Indexes. 141 illustrations. ix + 214pp. 5⅜ x 8. S151 Paperbound **$1.75**

MATHEMATICS: ADVANCED

ALMOST PERIODIC FUNCTIONS, A. S. Besicovitch. This unique and important summary by a well-known mathematician covers in detail the two stages of development in Bohr's theory of almost periodic functions: (1) as a generalization of pure periodicity, with results and proofs; (2) the work done by Stepanoff, Wiener, Weyl, and Bohr in generalizing the theory. Bibliography. xi + 180pp. 5⅜ x 8.

S17 Clothbound **$3.50**
S18 Paperbound **$1.75**

LECTURES ON THE ICOSAHEDRON AND THE SOLUTION OF EQUATIONS OF THE FIFTH DEGREE, Felix Klein. The solution of quintics in terms of rotations of a regular icosahedron around its axes of symmetry. A classic & indispensable source for those interested in higher algebra, geometry, crystallography. Considerable explanatory material included. 230 footnotes, mostly bibliographic. 2nd edition, xvi + 289pp. 5⅜ x 8.

S314 Paperbound **$1.85**

LINEAR INTEGRAL EQUATIONS, W. V. Lovitt. Systematic survey of general theory, with some application to differential equations, calculus of variations problems of math, physics. Partial contents: integral equations of 2nd kind by successive substitutions; Fredholm's equation as ratio of 2 integral series in lambda, applications of the Fredholm theory, Hilbert-Schmidt theory of symmetric kernels, application, etc. Neumann, Dirichlet, vibratory problems. Index. ix + 253pp. 5⅜ x 8.

S175 Clothbound **$3.50**
S176 Paperbound **$1.60**

MATHEMATICAL FOUNDATIONS OF STATISTICAL MECHANICS, A. I. Khinchin. Offering a precise and rigorous formulation of problems, this book supplies a thorough and up-to-date exposition. It provides analytical tools needed to replace cumbersome concepts, and furnishes for the first time a logical step-by-step introduction to the subject. Partial contents: geometry & kinematics of the phase space, ergodic problem, reduction to theory of probability, application of central limit problem, ideal monatomic gas, foundation of thermodynamics, dispersion and distributions of sum functions. Key to notations. Index. xiii + 179pp. 5⅜ x 8.

S146 Clothbound **$2.95**
G147 Paperbound **$1.35**

ORDINARY DIFFERENTIAL EQUATIONS, E. L. Ince. A most compendious analysis in real and complex domains. Existence and nature of solutions, continuous transformation groups, solutions in an infinite form, definite integrals, algebraic theory, Sturmian theory, boundary problems, existence theorems, 1st order, higher order, etc. "Deserves the highest praise, a notable addition to mathematical literature," BULLETIN, AM. MATH. SOC. Historical appendix. Bibliography. 18 figures. viii + 558pp. 5⅜ x 8.

S349 Paperbound **$2.55**

TRIGONOMETRICAL SERIES, Antoni Zygmund. Unique in any language on modern advanced level. Contains carefully organized analyses of trigonometric, orthogonal, Fourier systems of functions, with clear adequate descriptions of summability of Fourier series, proximation theory, conjugate series, convergence, divergence of Fourier series. Especially valuable for Russian, Eastern European coverage. Bibliography. 329pp. 5⅜ x 8.

S290 Paperbound **$1.50**

FOUNDATIONS OF POTENTIAL THEORY, O. D. Kellogg. Based on courses given at Harvard this is suitable for both advanced and beginning mathematicians. Proofs are rigorous, and much material not generally available elsewhere is included. Partial contents: forces of gravity, fields of force, divergence theorem, properties of Newtonian potentials at points of free space, potentials as solutions of Laplace's equations, harmonic functions, electrostatics, electric images, logarithmic potential, etc. ix + 384pp. 5⅜ x 8.

S144 Paperbound **$1.98**

LECTURES ON CAUCHY'S PROBLEMS, J. Hadamard. Based on lectures given at Columbia and Rome, this discusses work of Riemann, Kirchhoff, Volterra, and the author's own research on the hyperbolic case in linear partial differential equations. It extends spherical and cylindrical waves to apply to all (normal) hyperbolic equations. Partial contents: Cauchy's problem, fundamental formula, equations with odd number, with even number of independent variables; method of descent. 32 figures. Index. iii + 361pp. 5⅜ x 8.

S105 Paperbound **$1.75**

MATHEMATICAL PHYSICS, STATISTICS

THE MATHEMATICAL THEORY OF ELASTICITY, A. E. H. Love. A wealth of practical illustration combined with thorough discussion of fundamentals—theory, application, special problems and solutions. Partial contents: Analysis of Strain & Stress, Elasticity of Solid Bodies, Isotropic Elastic Solids, Equilibrium of Aeolotropic Elastic Solids, Elasticity of Crystals, Vibration of Spheres, Cylinders, Propagation of Waves in Elastic Solid Media, Torsion, Theory of Continuous Beams, Plates. Rigorous treatment of Volterra's theory of dislocations, 2-dimensional elastic systems, other topics of modern interest. "For years the standard treatise on elasticity," AMERICAN MATHEMATICAL MONTHLY. 4th revised edition. Index. 76 figures. xviii + 643pp. 6⅛ x 9¼.

S174 Paperbound **$2.95**

TABLES OF FUNCTIONS WITH FORMULAE AND CURVES, E. Jahnke & F. Emde. The world's most comprehensive 1-volume English-text collection of tables, formulae, curves of transcendent functions. 4th corrected edition, new 76-page section giving tables, formulae for elementary functions—not in other English editions. Partial contents: sine, cosine, logarithmic integral; factorial function; error integral; theta functions; elliptic integrals, functions; Legendre, Bessel, Riemann, Mathieu, hypergeometric functions, etc. Supplementary books. Bibliography. Indexed. "Out of the way functions for which we know no other source," SCIENTIFIC COMPUTING SERVICE, Ltd. 212 figures. 400pp. 5⅜ x 8.

S133 Paperbound **$2.00**

PRACTICAL ANALYSIS, GRAPHICAL AND NUMERICAL METHODS, F. A. Willers. Translated by R. T. Beyer. Immensely practical handbook for engineers, showing how to interpolate, use various methods of numerical differentiation and integration, determine the roots of a single algebraic equation, system of linear equations, use empirical formulas, integrate differential equations, etc. Hundreds of shortcuts for arriving at numerical solutions. Special section on American calculating machines, by T. W. Simpson. 132 illustrations. 422pp. 5⅜ x 8.　　　　　S273 Paperbound **$2.00**

DICTIONARY OF CONFORMAL REPRESENTATIONS, H. Kober. Laplace's equation in 2 dimensions solved in this unique book developed by the British Admiralty. Scores of geometrical forms & their transformations for electrical engineers, Joukowski aerofoil for aerodynamists, Schwartz-Christoffel transformations for hydrodynamics, transcendental functions. Contents classified accord-ing to analytical functions describing transformation. Twin diagrams show curves of most trans-formations with corresponding regions. Glossary. Topological index. 447 diagrams. 244pp. 6⅛ x 9¼.　　　　　S160 Paperbound **$2.00**

FREQUENCY CURVES AND CORRELATION, W. P. Elderton. 4th revised edition of a standard work covering classical statistics. It is practical in approach, and one of the books most frequently referred to for clear presentation of basic material. Partial contents. Frequency distributions. Method of moment. Pearson's frequency curves. Correlation. Theoretical distributions, spurious correlation. Correlation of characters not quantitatively measurable. Standard errors. Test of goodness of fit. The correlation ratio—contingency. Partial correlation. Corrections for moments, beta and gamma functions, etc. Key to terms, symbols. Bibliography. 25 examples in text. 40 useful tables. 16 figures. xi + 272pp. 5½ x 8½.　　　　　Clothbound **$1.49**

HYDRODYNAMICS, H. Dryden, F. Murnaghan, Harry Bateman. Published by the National Research Council in 1932 this enormous volume offers a complete coverage of classical hydrodynamics. Encyclopedic in quality. Partial contents: physics of fluids, motion, turbulent flow, compressible fluids, motion in 1, 2, 3 dimensions; viscous fluids rotating, laminar motion, resistance of motion through viscous fluid, eddy viscosity, hydraulic flow in channels of various shapes, discharge of gases, flow past obstacles, etc. Bibliography of over 2,900 items. Indexes. 23 figures. 634pp. 5⅜ x 8.　　　　　S303 Paperbound **$2.75**

HYDRODYNAMICS, A STUDY OF LOGIC, FACT, AND SIMILITUDE, Garrett Birkhoff. A stimulating application of pure mathematics to an applied problem. Emphasis is placed upon correlation of theory and deduction with experiment. It examines carefully recently discovered paradoxes, theory of modelling and dimensional analysis, paradox & error in flows and free boundary theory. The author derives the classical theory of virtual mass from homogeneous spaces, and applies group theory to fluid mechanics. Index. Bibliography. 20 figures, 3 plates. xiii + 186pp. 5⅜ x 8.
　　　　　S21 Clothbound **$3.50**
　　　　　S22 Paperbound **$1.85**

HYDRODYNAMICS, Horace Lamb. Internationally famous complete coverage of standard reference work on dynamics of liquids & gases. Fundamental theorems, equations, methods, solutions, background, for classical hydrodynamics. Chapters include Equations of Motion, Integration of Equations in Special Gases, Irrotational Motion, Motion of Liquid in 2 Dimensions, Motion of Solids through Liquid—Dynamical Theory, Vortex Motion, Tidal Waves, Surface Waves, Waves of Expansion, Viscosity, Rotating Masses of Liquids. Excellently planned, arranged; clear, lucid presentation. 6th enlarged, revised edition. Index. Over 900 footnotes, mostly bibliographical. 119 figures. xv + 738pp. 6⅛ x 9¼.　　　　　S256 Paperbound **$2.95**

INTRODUCTION TO RELAXATION METHODS, F. S. Shaw. Fluid mechanics, design of electrical networks, forces in structural frameworks, stress distribution, buckling, etc. Solve linear simul-taneous equations, linear ordinary differential equations, partial differential equations, Eigenvalue problems by relaxation methods. Detailed examples throughout. Special tables for dealing with awkwardly-shaped boundaries. Indexes. 253 diagrams. 72 tables. 400pp. 5⅜ x 8.
　　　　　S244 Paperbound **$2.45**

PARTIAL DIFFERENTIAL EQUATIONS OF MATHEMATICAL PHYSICS, A. G. Webster. A keystone work in the library of every mature physicist, engineer, researcher. Valuable sections on elasticity, compression theory, potential theory, theory of sound, heat conduction, wave propagation, vibration theory. Contents include: deduction of differential equations, vibrations, normal func-tions, Fourier's series, Cauchy's method, boundary problems, method of Riemann-Volterra. Spherical, cylindrical, ellipsoidal harmonics, applications, etc. 97 figures. vii + 440pp. 5⅜ x 8.
　　　　　S263 Paperbound **$1.98**

THE THEORY OF GROUPS AND QUANTUM MECHANICS, H. Weyl. Discussions of Schroedinger's wave equation, de Broglie's waves of a particle, Jordon-Hoelder theorem, Lie's continuous groups of transformations, Pauli exclusion principle, quantization of Maxwell-Dirac field equations, etc. symmetry permutation group, algebra of symmetric transformation, etc. 2nd revised edition. Unitary geometry, quantum theory, groups, application of groups to quantum mechanics, symmetry permutation group, algebra of symmetric transformation, etc. 2nd revised edition. Bibliography. Index. xxii + 422pp. 5⅜ x 8.　　　　　S268 Clothbound **$4.50**
　　　　　S269 Paperbound **$1.95**

PARTIAL DIFFERENTIAL EQUATIONS OF MATHEMATICAL PHYSICS, Harry Bateman. Solution of boundary value problems by means of definite analytical expressions, with wide range of repre-sentative problems, full reference to contemporary literature, and new material by the author. Partial contents: classical equations, integral theorems of Green, Stokes; 2-dimensional problems; conformal representation; equations in 3 variables; polar coordinates; cylindrical, ellipsoidal, paraboloid, toroidal coordinates; non-linear equations, etc. "Must be in the hands of everyone interested in boundary value problems," BULLETIN, AM. MATH. SOC. Indexes. 450 bibliographic footnotes. 175 examples. 29 illustrations. xxii + 552pp. 6 x 9.　　　　　S15 Clothbound **$4.95**

NUMERICAL SOLUTIONS OF DIFFERENTIAL EQUATIONS, H. Levy & E. A. Baggott. Comprehensive collection of methods for solving ordinary differential equations of first and higher order. All must pass 2 requirements: easy to grasp and practical, more rapid than school methods. Partial contents: graphical integration of differential equations, graphical methods for detailed solution. Numerical solution. Simultaneous equations and equations of 2nd and higher orders. "Should be in the hands of all in research in applied mathematics, teaching," NATURE. 21 figures. viii + 238pp. $5\frac{3}{8}$ x 8.
S168 Paperbound **$1.75**

ASYMPTOTIC EXPANSIONS, A. Erdélyi. The only modern work available in English, this is an unabridged reproduction of a monograph prepared for the Office of Naval Research. It discusses various procedures for asymptotic evaluation of integrals containing a large parameter and solutions of ordinary linear differential equations. Bibliography of 71 items. vi + 108pp. $5\frac{3}{8}$ x 8.
S318 Paperbound **$1.35**

THE FOURIER INTEGRAL AND CERTAIN OF ITS APPLICATIONS, Norbert Wiener. The only book-length study of the Fourier integral as link between pure and applied math. An expansion of lectures given at Cambridge. Partial contents: Plancherel's theorem, general Tauberian theorem, special Tauberian theorms, generalized harmonic analysis. Bibliography. viii + 201pp. $5\frac{3}{8}$ x 8.
S272 Clothbound **$3.95**

THE THEORY OF SOUND, Lord Rayleigh. Most vibrating systems likely to be encountered in practice can be tackled successfully by the methods set forth by the great Noble laureate, Lord Rayleigh. Complete coverage of experimental, mathematical aspects of sound theory. Partial contents: Harmonic motions, vibrating systems in general, lateral vibrations of bars, curved plates or shells, applications of Laplace's functions to acoustical problems, fluid friction, plane vortex-sheet, vibrations of solid bodies, etc. This is the first inexpensive edition of this great reference and study work. Bibliography. Historical introduction by R. B. Lindsay. Total of 1040pp. 97 figures. $5\frac{3}{8}$ x 8.
S292, S293, Two volume set, paperbound **$4.00**

ANALYSIS & DESIGN OF EXPERIMENTS, H. B. Mann. Offers a method for grasping the analysis of variance and variance design within a short time. Partial contents: Chi-square distribution and analysis of variance distribution, matrices, quadratic forms, likelihood ratio tests and tests of linear hypotheses, power of analysis, Galois fields, non-orthogonal data, interblock estimates, etc. 15pp. of useful tables. x + 195pp. 5 x $7\frac{3}{8}$.
S180 Paperbound **$1.45**

MATHEMATICAL ANALYSIS OF ELECTRICAL AND OPTICAL WAVE-MOTION, Harry Bateman. Written by one of this century's most distinguished mathematical physicists, this is a practical introduction to those developments of Maxwell's electromagnetic theory which are directly connected with the solution of the partial differential equation of wave motion. Methods of solving wave-equations, polar-cylindrical coordinates, diffraction, transformation of coordinates, homogeneous solutions, electromagnetic fields with moving singularities, etc. Index. 168pp. $5\frac{3}{8}$ x 8.
S14 Paperbound **$1.60**

PHYSICAL PRINCIPLES OF THE QUANTUM THEORY, Werner Heisenberg. A Nobel laureate discusses quantum theory; Heisenberg's own work, Compton, Schroedinger, Wilson, Einstein, many others. Written for physicists, chemists who are not specialists in quantum theory, only elementary formulae are considered in the text; there is a mathematical appendix for specialists. Profound without sacrifice of clarity. Translated by C. Eckart, F. Hoyt. 18 figures. 192pp. $5\frac{3}{8}$ x 8.
S113 Paperbound **$1.25**

FOUNDATIONS OF NUCLEAR PHYSICS, edited by R. T. Beyer. 13 of the most important papers on nuclear physics reproduced in facsimile in the original languages of their authors: the papers most often cited in footnotes, bibliographies. Anderson, Curie, Joliot, Chadwick, Fermi, Lawrence, Cockcroft, Hahn, Yukawa. Unparalleled Bibliography: 122 double-columned pages, over 4,000 articles, books, classified. 57 figures. 288pp. $6\frac{1}{8}$ x $9\frac{1}{4}$.
S19 Paperbound **$1.75**

SELECTED PAPERS ON NOISE AND STOCHASTIC PROCESS, edited by Prof. Nelson Wax, U. of Illinois. 6 basic papers for newcomers in the field, for those whose work involves noise characteristics. Chandrasekhar, Uhlenbeck & Ornstein, Uhlenbeck & Ming, Rice, Doob. Included is Kac's Chauvenet-Prize winning Random Walk. Extensive bibliography lists 200 articles; up through 1953. 21 figures. 337pp. $6\frac{1}{8}$ x $9\frac{1}{4}$.
S262 Paperbound **$2.25**

THERMODYNAMICS, Enrico Fermi. Unabridged reproduction of 1937 edition. Elementary in treatment; remarkable for clarity, organization. Requires no knowledge of advanced math beyond calculus, only familiarity with fundamentals of thermometry, calorimetry. Partial Contents: Thermodynamic systems; First & Second laws of thermodynamics; Entropy; Thermodynamic potentials: phase rule, reversible electric cell; Gaseous reactions: Van't Hoff reaction box, principle of LeChatelier; Thermodynamics of dilute solutions:: osmotic & vapor pressure, boiling & freezing points; Entropy constant. Index. 25 problems. 24 illustrations. x + 160pp. $5\frac{3}{8}$ x 8.
S361 Paperbound **$1.75**

AN INTRODUCTION TO THE STUDY OF STELLAR STRUCTURE, Subrahmanyan Chandrasekhar. Outstanding treatise on stellar dynamics by one of world's greatest astrophysicists. Uses classical & modern math methods to examine relationship between loss of energy, the mass, and radius of stars in a steady state. Discusses thermodynamic laws from Caratheodory's axiomatic standpoint; adiabatic, polytropic laws; work of Ritter, Emden, Kelvin, others; Stroemgren envelopes as starter for theory of gaseous stars; Gibbs statistical mechanics (quantum); degenerate stellar configurations & theory of white dwarfs, etc. "Highest level of scientific merit," BULLETIN, AMER. MATH. SOC. Bibliography. Appendixes. Index. 33 figures. 509pp. $5\frac{3}{8}$ x 8.
S413 Paperbound **$2.75**

APPLIED OPTICS AND OPTICAL DESIGN, A. E. Conrady. Thorough, systematic presentation of physical & mathematical aspects, limited mostly to ''real optics.'' Stresses practical problem of maximum aberration permissible without affecting performance. All ordinary ray tracing methods; complete theory primary aberrations, enough higher aberration to design telescopes, low-powered microscopes, photographic equipment. Covers fundamental equations, extra-axial image points, transverse chromatic aberration, angular magnification, aplanatic optical systems, bending of lenses, oblique pencils, tolerances, secondary spectrum, spherical aberration (angular, longitudinal, transverse, zonal), thin lenses, dozens of similar topics. Index. Tables of functions of N. Over 150 diagrams. x + 518pp. 6⅛ x 9¼.
S366 Paperbound **$2.95**

SPACE-TIME-MATTER, Hermann Weyl. ''The standard treatise on the general theory of relativity,'' (Nature), written by a world-renowned scientists, provides a deep clear discussion of the logical coherence of the general theory, with introduction to all the mathematical tools needed: Maxwell, analytical geometry, non-Euclidean geometry, tensor calculus, etc. Basis is classical space-time, before absorption of relativity. Partial contents: Euclidean space, mathematical form, metrical continuum, relativity of time and space, general theory. 15 diagrams. Bibliography. New preface for this edition. xviii + 330pp. 5⅜ x 8.
S267 Paperbound **$1.75**

RAYLEIGH'S PRINCIPLE AND ITS APPLICATION TO ENGINEERING, G. Temple & W. Bickley. Rayleigh's principle developed to provide upper and lower estimates of true value of fundamental period of a vibrating system, or condition of stability of elastic systems. Illustrative examples; rigorous proofs in special chapters. Partial contents: Energy method of discussing vibrations, stability. Perturbation theory, whirling of uniform shafts. Criteria of elastic stability. Application of energy method. Vibrating system. Proof, accuracy, successive approximations, application of Rayleigh's principle. Synthetic theorems. Numerical, graphical methods. Equilibrium configurations, Ritz's method. Bibliography. Index. 22 figures. ix + 156pp. 5⅜ x8.
S307 Paperbound **$1.50**

PHYSICS, ENGINEERING

THEORY OF VIBRATIONS, N. W. McLachlan. Based on an exceptionally successful graduate course given at Brown University, this discusses linear systems having 1 degree of freedom, forced vibrations of simple linear systems, vibration of flexible strings, transverse vibrations of bars and tubes, transverse vibration of circular plate, sound waves of finite amplitude, etc. Index. 99 diagrams. 160pp. 5⅜ x 8.
S190 Paperbound **$1.35**

WAVE PROPAGATION IN PERIODIC STRUCTURES, L. Brillouin. A general method and application to different problems: pure physics, such as scattering of X-rays of crystals, thermal vibration in crystal lattices, electronic motion in metals; and also problems of electrical engineering. Partial contents: elastic waves in 1-dimensional lattices of point masses. Propagation of waves along 1-dimensional lattices. Energy flow. 2 dimensional, 3 dimensional lattices. Mathieu's equation. Matrices and propagation of waves along an electric line. Continuous electric lines. 131 illustrations. Bibliography. Index. xii + 253pp. 5⅜ x 8.
S34 Paperbound **$1.85**

THE ELECTROMAGNETIC FIELD, Max Mason & Warren Weaver. Used constantly by graduate engineers. Vector methods exclusively: detailed treatment of electrostatics, expansion methods, with tables converting any quantity into absolute electromagnetic, absolute electrostatic, practical units. Discrete charges, ponderable bodies, Maxwell field equations, etc. Introduction. Indexes. 416pp. 5⅜ x 8.
S185 Paperbound **$2.00**

APPLIED HYDRO- AND AEROMECHANICS by L. Prandtl and O. G. Tietjens. Presents, for the most part, methods which will be valuable to engineers. Covers flow in pipes, boundary layers, airfoil theory, entry conditions, turbulent flow in pipes and the boundary layer, determining drag from measurements of pressure and velocity, etc. ''Will be welcomed by all students of aerodynamics,'' NATURE. Unabridged, unaltered. Index. 226 figures. 28 photographic plates illustrating flow patterns. xvi + 311pp. 5⅜ x 8.
S375 Paperbound **$1.85**

FUNDAMENTALS OF HYDRO- AND AEROMECHANICS by L. Prandtl and O. G. Tietjens. The well-known standard work based upon Prandtl's unique insights and including original contributions of Tietjens. Wherever possible, hydrodynamic theory is referred to practical considerations in hydraulics with the view of unifying theory and experience through fundamental laws. Presentation is exceedingly clear and, though primarily physical, proofs are rigorous and use vector analysis to a considerable extent. Translated by L. Rosenhead. 186 figures. Index. xvi + 270pp. 5⅜ x 8.
S374 Paperbound **$1.85**

DYNAMICS OF A SYSTEM OF RIGID BODIES (Advanced Section), E. J. Routh. Revised 6th edition of a classic reference aid. Much of its material remains unique. Partial contents: moving axes, relative motion, oscillations about equilibrium, motion. Motion of a body under no forces, any forces. Nature of motion given by linear equations and conditions of stability. Free, forced vibrations, constants of integration, calculus of finite differences, variations, procession and nutation, motion of the moon, motion of string, chain, membranes. 64 figures. 498pp. 5⅜ x 8.
S229 Paperbound **$2.35**

MECHANICS OF THE GYROSCOPE, THE DYNAMICS OF ROTATION, R. F. Deimel, Professor of Mechanical Engineering at Stevens Institute of Technology. Elementary general treatment of dynamics of rotation, with special application of gyroscopic phenomena. No knowledge of vectors needed. Velocity of a moving curve, acceleration to a point, general equations of motion, gyroscopic horizon, free gyro, motion of discs, the dammed gyro, 103 similar topics. Exercises. 75 figures. 208pp. 5⅜ x 8.
S66 Paperbound **$1.65**

TABLES FOR THE DESIGN OF FACTORIAL EXPERIMENTS, Tosio Kitagawa and Michiwo Mitome.
An invaluable aid for all applied mathematicians, physicists, chemists and biologists, this book contains tables for the design of factorial experiments. It covers Latin squares and cubes, factorial design, fractional replication in factorial design, factorial designs with split-plot confounding, factorial designs confounded in quasi-Latin squares, lattice designs, balanced incomplete block designs, and Youden's squares. New revised corrected edition, with explanatory notes. vii + 253pp. 7⅛ x 10.
S437 Clothbound **$8.00**

NUMERICAL INTEGRATION OF DIFFERENTIAL EQUATIONS, Bennett, Milne & Bateman. Unabridged republication of original monograph prepared for National Research Council. New methods of integration of differential equations developed by 3 leading mathematicians: THE INTERPOLATIONAL POLYNOMIAL and SUCCESSIVE APPROXIMATIONS by A. A. Bennett; STEP-BY-STEP METHODS OF INTEGRATION by W. W. Milne; METHODS FOR PARTIAL DIFFERENTIAL EQUATIONS by H. Bateman. Methods for partial differential equations, transition from difference equations to differential equations, solution of differential equations to non-integral values of a parameter will interest mathematicians and physicists. 288 footnotes, mostly bibliographic; 235-item classified bibliography. 108pp. 5⅜ x 8.
S305 Paperbound **$1.35**

DESIGN AND USE OF INSTRUMENTS AND ACCURATE MECHANISM, T. N. Whitehead. For the instrument designer, engineer; how to combine necessary mathematical abstractions with independent observation of actual facts. Partial contents: instruments & their parts, theory of errors, systematic errors, probability, short period errors, erratic errors, design precision, kinematic semi-kinematic design, stiffness, planning of an instrument, human factor, etc. Index. 85 photos, diagrams. xii + 288pp. 5⅜ x 8.
S270 Paperbound **$1.95**

CHEMISTRY AND PHYSICAL CHEMISTRY

KINETIC THEORY OF LIQUIDS, J. Frenkel. Regarding the kinetic theory of liquids as a generalization and extension of the theory of solid bodies, this volume covers all types of arrangements of solids, thermal displacements of atoms, interstitial atoms and ions, orientational and rotational motion of molecules, and transition between states of matter. Mathematical theory is developed close to the physical subject matter. 216 bibliographical footnotes. 55 figures. xi + 485pp. 5⅜ x 8.
S94 Clothbound **$3.95**
S95 Paperbound **$2.45**

THE PHASE RULE AND ITS APPLICATION, Alexander Findlay. Covering chemical phenomena of 1, 2, 3, 4, and multiple component systems, this "standard work on the subject" (NATURE, London), has been completely revised and brought up to date by A. N. Campbell and N. O. Smith. Brand new material has been added on such matters as binary, tertiary liquid equilibria, solid solutions in ternary systems, quinary systems of salts and water. Completely revised to triangular coordinates in ternary systems, clarified graphic representation, solid models, etc. 9th revised edition. Author, subject indexes. 236 figures. 506 footnotes, mostly bibliographic. xii + 494pp. 5⅜ x 8.
S92 Paperbound **$2.45**

DYNAMICAL THEORY OF GASES, James Jeans. Divided into mathematical and physical chapters for the convenience of those not expert in mathematics, this volume discusses the mathematical theory of gas in a steady state, thermodynamics, Boltzmann and Maxwell, kinetic theory, quantum theory, exponentials, etc. 4th enlarged edition, with new material on quantum theory, quantum dynamics, etc. Indexes. 28 figures. 444pp. 6⅛ x 9¼.
S136 Paperbound **$2.45**

POLAR MOLECULES, Pieter Debye. This work by Nobel laureate Debye offers a complete guide to fundamental electrostatic field relations, polarizability, molecular structure. Partial contents: electric intensity, displacement and force, polarization by orientation, molar polarization and molar refraction, halogen-hydrides, polar liquids, ionic saturation, dielectric constant, etc. Special chapter considers quantum theory. Indexed. 172pp. 5⅜ x 8.
S63 Clothbound **$3.50**
S64 Paperbound **$1.50**

TREATISE ON THERMODYNAMICS, Max Planck. Based on Planck's original papers this offers a uniform point of view for the entire field and has been used as an introduction for students who have studied elementary chemistry, physics, and calculus. Rejecting the earlier approaches of Helmholtz and Maxwell, the author makes no assumptions regarding the nature of heat, but begins with a few empirical facts, and from these deduces new physical and chemical laws. 3rd English edition of this standard text by a Nobel laureate. xvi + 297pp. 5⅜ x 8.
S219 Paperbound **$1.75**

ATOMIC SPECTRA AND ATOMIC STRUCTURE, G. Herzberg. Excellent general survey for chemists, physicists specializing in other fields. Partial contents: simplest line spectra and elements of atomic theory, multiple structure of line spectra and electron spin, building-up principle and periodic system of elements, finer details of atomic spectra, hyperfine structure of spectral lines, some experimental results and applications. Bibliography of 159 items. 80 figures. 20 tables. Index. xiii + 257pp. 5⅜ x 8.
S115 Paperbound **$1.95**

EARTH SCIENCES

THE EVOLUTION OF THE IGNEOUS ROCKS, N. L. Bowen. Invaluable serious introduction applies techniques of physics and chemistry to explain igneous rocks diversity in terms of chemical composition and fractional crystallization. Discusses liquid immiscibility in silicate magmas, crystal sorting, liquid lines of descent, fractional resorption of complex minerals, petrogenesis, etc. Of prime importance to geologists & mining engineers, also to physicists, chemists working with high temperatures and pressures. "Most important," TIMES, London. 3 indexes. 263 bibliographic notes. 82 figures. xviii + 334pp. 5⅜ x 8.
S311 Paperbound **$1.85**

GEOGRAPHICAL ESSAYS, William Morris Davis. Modern geography & geomorphology rests on the fundamental work of this scientist. 26 famous essays presenting most important theories, field researches. Partial contents: Geographical Cycle, Plains of Marine and Subaerial Denudation, The Peneplain, Rivers and Valleys of Pennsylvania, Outline of Cape Cod, Sculpture of Mountains by Glaciers, etc. "Long the leader and guide," ECONOMIC GEOGRAPHY. "Part of the very texture of geography . . . models of clear thought," GEOGRAPHIC REVIEW. Index. 130 figures. vi + 777pp. 5⅜ x 8.   S383 Paperbound **$2.95**

INTERNAL CONSTITUTION OF THE EARTH, edited by **Beno Gutenberg.** Completely revised, brought up-to-date, reset. Prepared for the National Research Council this is a complete & thorough coverage of such topics as earth origins, continent formation, nature & behavior of the earth's core, petrology of the crust, cooling forces in the core, seismic & earthquake material, gravity, elastic constants, strain characteristics and similar topics. "One is filled with admiration . . . a high standard . . . there is no reader who will not learn something from this book," London, Edinburgh, Dublin, Philosophic Magazine. Largest bibliography in print: 1127 classified items. Indexes. Tables of constants. 43 diagrams. 439pp. 6⅛ x 9¼.
                                                                     S414 Paperbound **$2.45**

THE BIRTH AND DEVELOPMENT OF THE GEOLOGICAL SCIENCES, F. D. Adams. Most thorough history of the earth sciences ever written. Geological thought from earliest times to the end of the 19th century, covering over 300 early thinkers & systems: fossils & their explanation, vulcanists vs. neptunists, figured stones & paleontology, generation of stones, dozens of similar topics. 91 illustrations, including medieval, renaissance woodcuts, etc. Index. 632 footnotes, mostly bibliographical. 511pp. 5⅜ x 8.   T5 Paperbound **$2.00**

HYDROLOGY, edited by **Oscar E. Meinzer.** Prepared for the National Research Council. Detailed complete reference library on precipitation, evaporation, snow, snow surveying, glaciers, lakes, infiltration, soil moisture, ground water, runoff, drought, physical changes produced by water, hydrology of limestone terranes, etc. Practical in application, especially valuable for engineers. 24 experts have created "the most up-to-date, most complete treatment of the subject," AM. ASSOC. OF PETROLEUM GEOLOGISTS. Bibliography. Index. 165 illustrations. xi + 712pp. 6⅛ x 9¼   S191 Paperbound **$2.95**

DE RE METALLICA, Georgius Agricola. 400-year old classic translated, annotated by former President Herbert Hoover. The first scientific study of mineralogy and mining, for over 200 years after its appearance in 1556, it was the standard treatise. 12 books, exhaustively annotated, discuss the history of mining, selection of sites, types of deposits, making pits, shafts, ventilating, pumps, crushing machinery; assaying, smelting, refining metals; also salt, alum, nitre, glass making. Definitive edition, with all 289 16th century woodcuts of the original. Bibliographical, historical introductions, bibliography, survey of ancient authors. Indexes. A fascinating book for anyone interested in art, history of science, geology, etc. DELUXE EDITION. 289 illustrations. 672pp. 6¾ x 10¾. Library cloth.   S6 Clothbound **$10.00**

URANIUM PROSPECTING, H. L. Barnes. For immediate practical use, professional geologists considers uranium ores, geological occurrences, field conditions, all aspects of highly profitable occupation. Index. Bibliography. x +117pp. 5⅜ x 8.   T309 Paperbound **$1.00**

BIOLOGICAL SCIENCES

THE BIOLOGY OF THE AMPHIBIA, G. K. Noble, Late Curator of Herpetology at the Am. Mus. of Nat. Hist. Probably the most used text on amphibia, unmatched in comprehensiveness, clarity, detail. 19 chapters plus 85-page supplement cover development; heredity; life history; adaptation; sex, integument, respiratory, circulatory, digestive, muscular, nervous systems; instinct, intelligence habits environment economic value, relationships, classification, etc. "Nothing comparable to it," C. H. Pope, Curator of Amphibia, Chicago Mus. of Nat. Hist. 1047 bibliographic references. 174 illustrations. 600pp. 5⅜ x 8.   S206 Paperbound **$2.98**

THE BIOLOGY OF THE LABORATORY MOUSE, edited by **G. D. Snell.** 1st prepared in 1941 by the staff of the Roscoe B. Jackson Memorial laboratory, this is still the standard treatise on the mouse, assembling an enormous amount of material for which otherwise you would spend hours of research. Embryology, reproduction, histology, spontaneous neoplasms, gene & chromosomes mutations, genetics of spontaneous tumor formation, genetics of tumor formation, inbred, hybrid animals, parasites, infectious diseases, care & recording. Classified bibliography of 1122 items. 172 figures, including 128 photos. ix + 497pp. 6⅛ x 9¼.   S248 Clothbound **$6.00**

BEHAVIOR AND SOCIAL LIFE OF THE HONEYBEE, Ronald Ribbands. Oustanding scientific study; a compendium of practically everything known about social life of the honeybee. Stresses behavior of individual bees in field, hive. Extends von Frisch's experiments on communication among bees. Covers perception of temperature, gravity, distance, vibration; sound production; glands; structural differences; wax production, temperature regulation; recognition communication; drifting, mating behavior, other highly interesting topics. Bibliography of 690 references. Indexes. 127 diagrams, graphs, sections of bee anatomy, fine photographs. 352pp.
                                                                     S410 Clothbound **$4.50**

ELEMENTS OF MATHEMATICAL BIOLOGY, A. J. Lotka. A pioneer classic, the first major attempt to apply modern mathematical techniques on a large scale to phenomena of biology, biochemistry, psychology, ecology, similar life sciences. Partial Contents: Statistical meaning of irreversibility; Evolution as redistribution; Equations of kinetics of evolving systems; Chemical, interspecies equilibrium; parameters of state; Energy transformers of nature, etc. Can be read with profit even by those having no advanced math; unsurpassed as study-reference. Formerly titled ELEMENTS OF PHYSICAL BIOLOGY. 72 figures. xxx + 460pp. 5⅜ x 8.
                                                                     S346 Paperbound **$2.45**

THE ORIGIN OF LIFE, A. I. Oparin. A classic of biology. This is the first modern statement of the theory of gradual evolution of life from nitrocarbon compounds. A brand-new evaluation of Oparin's theory in light of later research, by Dr. S. Margulis, University of Nebraska. xxv + 270pp. 5⅜ x 8.
S213 Paperbound **$1.75**

THE TRAVELS OF WILLIAM BARTRAM, edited by **Mark Van Doren.** This famous source-book of American anthropology, natural history, geography is the record kept by Bartram in the 1770's, on travels through the wilderness of Florida, Georgia, the Carolinas. Containing accurate and beautiful descriptions of Indians, settlers, fauna, flora, it is one of the finest pieces of Americana ever written. Introduction by Mark Van Doren. 13 original illustrations. Index. 448pp. 5⅜ x 8.
T13 Paperbound **$2.00**

A SHORT HISTORY OF ANATOMY AND PHYSIOLOGY FROM THE GREEKS TO HARVEY, Charles Singer. Corrected edition of THE EVOLUTION OF ANATOMY, classic work tracing evolution of anatomy and physiology from prescientific times through Greek & Roman periods, Dark Ages, Renaissance, to age of Harvey and beginning of modern concepts. Centered on individuals, movements, periods that definitely advanced anatomical knowledge: Plato, Diocles, Aristotle, Theophrastus, Herophilus, Erasistratus, the Alexandrians, Galen, Mondino, da Vinci, Linacre, Harvey, others. Special section on Vesalius; Vesalian atlas of nudes, skeletons, muscle tabulae. Index of names. 20 plates, 270 extremely interesting illustrations of ancient, medieval, renaissance, oriental origin. xii + 209pp. 5⅜ x 8.
T389 Paperbound **$1.75**

NEW BOOKS

LES METHODES NOUVELLES DE LA MÉCANIQUE CÉLESTE by H. Poincaré. Complete text (in French) of one of Poincaré's most important works. Revolutionized celestial mechanics: first use of integral invariants, first major application of linear differential equations, study of periodic orbits, lunar motion and Jupiter's satellites, three body problem, and many other important topics. "Started a new era . . . so extremely modern that even today few have mastered his weapons," E. T. Bell. Three volumes; 1282pp. 6⅛ x 9¼.
Vol. 1. S401 Paperbound **$2.75**
Vol. 2. S402 Paperbound **$2.75**
Vol. 3. S403 Paperbound **$2.75**

APPLICATIONS OF TENSOR ANALYSIS by A. J. McConnell. (Formerly, APPLICATIONS OF THE ABSOLUTE DIFFERENTIAL CALCULUS). An excellent text for understanding the application of tensor methods to familiar subjects such as: dynamics, electricity, elasticity, and hydrodynamics. It explains the fundamental ideas and notation of tensor theory, the geometrical treatment of tensor algebra, the theory of differentiation of tensors, and includes a wealth of practice material. Bibliography. Index. 43 illustrations. 685 problems. xii + 381pp.
S373 Paperbound **$1.85**

BRIDGES AND THEIR BUILDERS, David B. Steinman and Sara Ruth Watson. Engineers, historians, and everyone who has ever been fascinated by great spans will find this book an endless source of information and interest. Dr. Steinman, the recent recipient of the Louis Levy Medal, is one of the great bridge architects and engineers of all time, and his analysis of the great bridges of all history is both authoritative and easily followed. Greek and Roman bridges, medieval bridges, oriental bridges, modern works such as the Brooklyn Bridge and the Golden Gate Bridge (and many others) are described in terms of history, constructional principles, artistry, and function. All in all this book is the most comprehensive and accurate semipopular history of bridges in print in English. New greatly revised enlarged edition. 23 photographs, 26 line drawings. Index. xvii + 401pp. 5⅜ x 8.
T431 Paperbound **$1.95**

MATHEMATICS IN ACTION, O. G. Sutton. Excellent middle-level exposition of application of advanced mathematics to the study of the universe. The author demonstrates how mathematics is applied in ballistics, theory of computing machines, waves and wavelike phenomena, theory of fluid flow, meterological problems, statistics, flight, and similar phenomena. No knowledge of advanced mathematics is necessary to follow the author's presentation. Differential equations, Fourier series, group concepts, eigen functions, Planck's constant, airfoil theory and similar topics are explained so clearly in everyday language that almost anyone can derive benefit from reading this book. 2nd edition. Index. 88 figures. viii + 236pp. 5⅜ x 8.
T450 Clothbound **$3.50**

MATHEMATICAL FOUNDATIONS OF INFORMATION THEORY by A. I. Khinchin. For the first time, mathematicians, ~~...~~ mmunications engineers are offered a complete an~~...~~ ield. Entropy as a measure of a finite "scheme,"~~...~~ urces, channels and codes, detailed proofs of bo~~...~~ and any stationary channel with finite memory, a~~...~~ + 120pp. 5⅜ x 8.
S434 Paperbound **$1.35**

Indicate your field of ~~...~~ earth sciences, mathematics, engineering, chemistry ~~...~~ ogy, philosophy, religion history, literature, mat~~...~~ ing, art, graphic arts, etc.

Available at your dealer or write Dover Publications, Inc., 920 Broadway, Department TF1, New York 10, New York.